⊰ THE MASTERY OF READING

Worlds of Adventure
Worlds of People
Worlds to Explore
The World of Endless Horizons
The World of America
The World and Our English Heritage

Worlds of

Not SAMple 4 -school

Adventure

The Mastery of Reading

REVISED AND ENLARGED

Matilda Bailey

Ullin W. Leavell

American Book Company

Worlds of Adventure
REVISED AND ENLARGED

The Mastery of Reading

Matilda Bailey, PROFESSOR OF ENGLISH AT SLIPPERY ROCK STATE TEACHERS COLLEGE, SLIPPERY ROCK, PENNSYLVANIA

Ullin W. Leavell, DIRECTOR, MC GUFFEY READING CLINIC, UNIVERSITY OF VIRGINIA, CHARLOTTESVILLE, VIRGINIA

with the Editorial Advice of

Mary Gould Davis, CHILDREN'S BOOK EDITOR OF *The Saturday Review*

Acknowledgments   The editors of this book wish to express gratitude to all the publishers who have granted permission to use material. In a few cases it has been impossible to trace the copyright owners, but to them—whoever they are—goes sincere appreciation.

To three individuals a very special tribute is due. Miss Bettina Hunter of the Swarthmore (Pennsylvania) Public Library has given generously of her time to every phase of the work—research, testing, and collecting. Mrs. Mabel Howison of Washington, D.C., has been of great assistance in the compilation of the reading helps in the Study Book. Mrs. Dorothy Kendall Bracken, Director of The Reading Clinic of Southern Methodist University, has been invaluable in the preparation of a special reading-skills section in the *Teacher's Guide.*

Special mention should also be made concerning the illustrations in this book. The Artographs combine the reality of the photograph with the imaginative range of drawings in vivid thematic interrelations to the sections of the book. The work has been made possible through the interest and co-operation of Mr. Tom Sinnickson, artist, and Mr. Charles Phelps Cushing, photographer.

The opening color pages and the small scratchboard illustrations are the work of Mr. Scott Maclain.

The photograph on the cover is by Bob and Ira Spring, Free Lance Photographers Guild, Inc.

American Book Company   NEW YORK   CINCINNATI   CHICAGO   ATLANTA   DALLAS   SAN FRANCISCO

Made in U. S. A. McD 17

❧ To You

Worlds of Adventure is the first book of a six-book series called "The Mastery of Reading." You may be sure that worlds of good reading await you.

Certain specific things must be said concerning the series as a whole, but first let us consider *this* book—its aims, its content, its distinguishing contributions.

❧ **Aims.** Two aims have been uppermost in the building of this book and of all the books in the series: (1) pupil interest in the selection of material and (2) development of reading power.

Pupil Interest. Too often books have been made to suit the teacher—not the pupil. A quick glance at the table of contents of this book will show that the girls and boys have been the prime determining factor in the choice of reading material.

Reading Skills. Obviously, interest is of first importance; but obviously, too, interest can never be aroused when pupils are shackled by reading difficulties. We know that the development of reading abilities is a process that continues almost from the cradle to the grave. *Every* pupil can grow in his reading stature if given intelligent direction. For that reason, the development of reading skills has been made a part of the program.

Each chapter in *Worlds of Adventure* concentrates upon one important aspect of reading. However, comprehension, speed, and vocabulary enrichment are considered to be of equal and primary importance. Consequently, while each is developed in a single chapter, each is developed cumulatively throughout the rest of the book. Chapter by chapter, these are the skills which are presented:

1 Comprehension
2 Rate of Reading
3 Vocabulary Development
4 Reading for Specific Details
5 Reading with Correct Enunciation and Pronunciation
6 Recognizing the Author's Organization of Subject Matter
7 Reading to Interpret
8 Reading to Get a Point
9 Reading to Draw Conclusions
10 Reading in Different Ways

There is always the danger that work on the development of reading activities can spoil young people's enjoyment of good reading. On the other hand, there can be no enjoyment at all when serious reading difficulties are present. Work on the reading skills has been woven into the "helps" at the end of the various selections. Consequently, the teacher can use them or ignore them according to the needs of the class and of the individual pupils in the class.

◀◖ SOME SPECIAL HIGHLIGHTS. There are a few additional points that have been touchstones in the building of this book and should be mentioned here.

The Best of the Old and Much of the New. The time chart "Across the Ages" on pages 484 and 485 gives a fair sampling of the distribution of the old and the new. The *cream* of the old is included, but the great majority of the selections come from contemporary juvenile literature.

Favorite Authors—and Good Ones. The list of authors represented in this book reads like a *Who's Who* of favorite authors.

Relation to Other Subject Fields. In the past, boys and girls have often felt no relationship between what they were reading in their literature class and what was going on the rest of the day in their other classes. In *Worlds of Adventure,* the chapter "Portraits of Americans" correlates with American history; the chapter "From Microbes to Atoms" is an extension of general science; "Playing the Game" exemplifies the principles taught in citizenship classes; and "A Treasury of Verse" has an obvious relationship with music.

Helps for Teacher and Pupil. In addition to the reading helps already described, there are motivating introductions, questions for oral discussion and ideas for written communication, memory-teasing tests, annotated bibliographies, biographical sketches, and pertinent footnotes.

Wide Testing. Thousands of boys and girls have had their say in the selection of material for this book. Hundreds and hundreds of teachers and scores of librarians from all over the country have made fine contributions to the project. Very truly, *Worlds of Adventure* and the other books of this series have been compiled by the pupils, teachers, and librarians of America for the boys and girls of America.

◄ CONTENTS

Adventure Bound

Tooth and Claw

Heroes

Fables and Strange Tales

Play-acting

Portraits of Americans

A Treasury of Verse

The Funny Bone

From Microbes to Atoms

Microbes

Playing the Game

Reading can bring you...

Adventures of People

Professor Herbert's eyes got big behind his black-rimmed glasses when he saw Pa's gun.
...STUART

"A man gave his life to let these two people get away."
...PEASE

Then, out of the whirling whiteness, something hit her.
...WILDER

Adventures with Animals

The animal looked as large as a bull as he leaped toward us—his mane flying, fangs bared.

...JOHNSON

The snake was hesitating between anger and surprise.

...DITMARS

One merciless little eye gleamed savagely above me as the elephant drove his tusks into the ground on either side of me, his rolled-up trunk against my chest.

...AKELEY

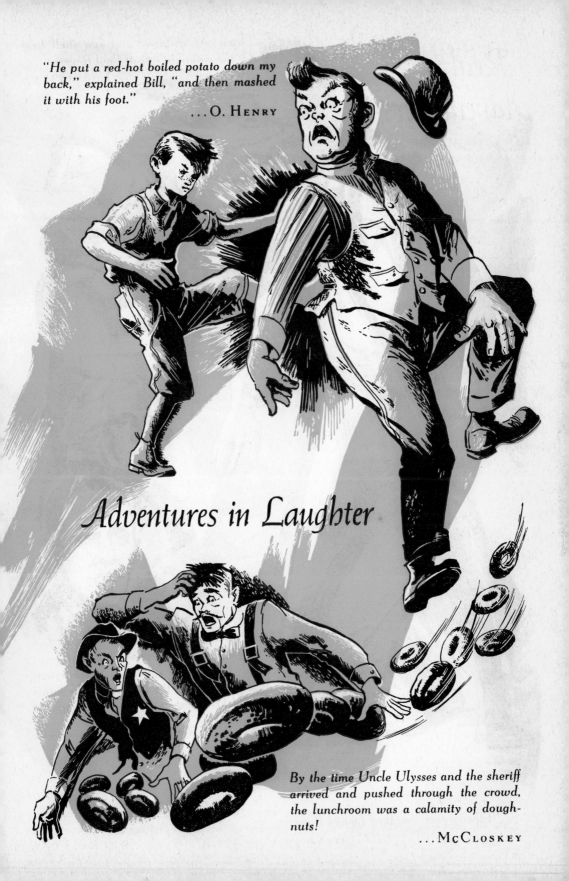

"He put a red-hot boiled potato down my back," explained Bill, "and then mashed it with his foot."

...O. HENRY

Adventures in Laughter

By the time Uncle Ulysses and the sheriff arrived and pushed through the crowd, the lunchroom was a calamity of doughnuts!

...McCloskey

Real Adventurers

Listen, my children, and you shall hear
Of the midnight ride of Paul Revere.
...LONGFELLOW

Andrew Carnegie ... *remarked at his passing, "History will tell of two Washingtons—the white and the black—one the father of his country, the other the leader of his race."*
...FAUSET

"Elbowroom!" laughed Daniel Boone.
...GUITERMAN

When the great day came, all manner of men once more made the attempt; and once more not one of them all could prevail but Arthur.

...MacLeod

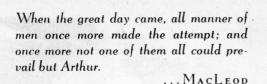

Make-believe Adventurers

Robin Hood is here again; all his merry thieves
Hear a ghostly bugle-note shivering through the leaves.

...Noyes

The American Adventure

Hats off!
The flag is passing by!
...BENNETT

O beautiful for spacious skies,
For amber waves of grain.
...BATES

To the blessed land of Room Enough
beyond the ocean bars,
Where the air is full of sunlight
and the flag is full of stars.
...VAN DYKE

—And all our humming dynamos and our electric light
Go back to what Ben Franklin found, the day he flew his kite.
...BENÉT

The atom, symbol of man's fears today, is likewise the bright star of his highest hopes.

Adventures in Science

We did not believe in knifing sharks, but the final moment had come, when knife and camera were all we had.
...COUSTEAU

... Dolly became, as far as anyone could learn, the only cow that ever belonged to a ball club.

...BRUBAKER

Adventures in Sports

When I was learning to swim, people just swam.

...BENCHLEY

"I'm an iggle," I repeated, "and an iggle never dives. He swoops. Swatch me."

...RECK

I wear the chain I forged in life.
...DICKENS

Dramatic
Adventuring

All right, Captain Hale. Climb up on the
tailboard of the wagon, please. Have you
anything to say before you are hanged as
a spy?

...HENRY AND LYNCH

I saw dawn creep across the sky,
And all the gulls go flying by.
...FIELD

Poetic Adventuring

I think that I shall never see
A poem lovely as a tree.
...KILMER

Adventure
Bound

Split Cherry Tree

Wouldn't you be worried if your father went to school bent on shooting the teacher? Dave's Pa didn't understand schools today and decided it was time for him to have a talk with the teacher. Dave had reason to be worried.

I DON'T mind staying after school," I says to Professor Herbert, "but I'd rather you'd whip me with a switch and let me go home early. Pa will whip me anyway for getting home two hours late."

"You are too big to whip," says Professor Herbert, "and I have to punish you for climbing up in that cherry tree. You boys knew better than that! The other five boys have paid their dollar each. You have been the only one who has not helped pay for the tree. Can't you borrow a dollar?"

"I can't," I says. "I'll have to take the punishment. I wish it would be quicker punishment. I wouldn't mind."

Professor Herbert stood and looked at me. He was a big man. He wore a gray suit of clothes. The suit matched his gray hair.

"You don't know my father," I says to Professor Herbert. "He might be called a little old-fashioned. He makes us mind him until we're twenty-one years old. He believes: 'If you spare the rod you spoil the child.' I'll never be able to make him understand about the cherry tree. I'm

——From *Esquire*, January, 1939. Reprinted by permission of Jesse Stuart and Esquire, Inc.

the first of my people to go to high school."

"You must take the punishment," says Professor Herbert. "You must stay two hours after school today and two hours after school tomorrow. I am allowing you twenty-five cents an hour. That is good money for a high-school student. You can sweep the schoolhouse floor, wash the blackboards, and clean windows. I'll pay the dollar for you."

I couldn't ask Professor Herbert to loan me a dollar. He never offered to loan it to me. I had to stay and help the janitor and work out my fine at a quarter an hour.

I thought as I swept the floor: "What will Pa do to me? What lie can I tell him when I go home? Why did we ever climb that cherry tree and break it down for anyway? Why did we run crazy over the hills away from the crowd? Why did we do all of this? Six of us climbed up in a little cherry tree after one little lizard! Why did the tree split and fall with us? It should have been a stronger tree! Why did Eif Crabtree just happen to be below us plowing and catch us in his cherry tree? Why wasn't he a better man than to charge us six dollars for the tree?"

It was six o'clock when I left the schoolhouse. I had six miles to walk home. It would be after seven when I got home. I had all my work to do when I got home. It took Pa and me both to do the work. Seven cows to milk. Nineteen head of cattle to feed, four mules, twenty-five hogs. Firewood and stovewood to cut and water to draw from the well. He would be doing it when I got home. He would be mad and wondering what was keeping me!

I hurried home. I would run under the dark leafless trees. I would walk fast uphill. I would run down the hill. The ground was freezing. I had to hurry. I had to run. I reached the long ridge that led to our cow pasture. I ran along this ridge. The wind dried the sweat on my face. I ran across the pasture to the house.

I threw down my books in the chipyard. I ran to the barn to spread fodder on the ground for the cattle. I didn't take time to change my clean school clothes for my old work clothes. I ran out to the barn. I saw Pa spreading fodder on the ground to the cattle. That was my job. I ran up to the fence. I says: "Leave that for me, Pa. I'll do it. I'm just a little late."

"I see you are," says Pa. He turned and looked at me. His eyes danced fire. "What in th' world has kept you so? Why ain't you been here to help me with this work? Make a gentleman out'n one boy in th' family and this is what you get! Send you to high school and you get too onery fer th' buzzards to smell!"

I never said anything. I didn't want to tell why I was late from school. Pa stopped scattering the bundles of fodder. He looked at me. He says: "Why are you gettin' in here this time o' night? You tell me or I'll take a hickory withe to you right here on th' spot!"

I says: "I had to stay after school." I couldn't lie to Pa. He'd go to school and find out why I had to stay. If I lied to him it would be too bad for me.

"Why did you haf to stay atter school?" says Pa.

I says: "Our biology class went on a field trip today. Six of us boys broke down a cherry tree. We had to give a dollar apiece to pay for the tree. I didn't have the dollar. Professor Herbert is making me work out my dollar. He gives me twenty-five cents an hour. I had to stay in this afternoon. I'll have to stay in tomorrow afternoon!"

"Are you telling me th' truth?" says Pa.

"I'm telling you the truth," I says. "Go and see for yourself."

"That's just what I'll do in th' mornin'," says Pa. "Jist whose cherry tree did you break down?"

"Eif Crabtree's cherry tree!"

"What was you doin' clear out in Eif Crabtree's place?" says Pa. "He lives four miles from th' County High School. Don't they teach you no books at that high school? Do they jist let you get out and gad over th' hillsides? If that's all they do I'll keep you at home, Dave. I've got work here fer you to do!"

"Pa," I says, "spring is just getting here. We take a subject in school where we have to have bugs, snakes, flowers, lizards, frogs, and plants. It is biology. It was a pretty day today. We went out to find a few of these. Six of us boys saw a lizard at the same time sunning on a cherry tree. We all went up the tree to get it. We broke the tree down. It split at the forks. Eif Crabtree was plowing down below us. He ran up the hill and got our names. The other boys gave their dollar apiece. I didn't have mine. Professor Herbert put mine in for me. I have to work it out at school."

"Poor man's son, huh," says Pa. "I'll attend to that myself in th' mornin'. I'll take keer o' 'im. He ain't from this county nohow. I'll go down there in th' mornin' and see 'im. Lettin' you leave your books and galavant all over th' hills. What kind of a school is it nohow! Didn't do that, my son, when I's a little shaver in school. All fared alike, too."

"Pa, please don't go down there," I says. "Just let me have fifty cents and pay the rest of my fine. I don't want you to go down there! I don't want you to start anything with Professor Herbert!"

"Ashamed of your old Pap, are you, Dave," says Pa, "atter the way I've worked to raise you! Tryin' to send you to school so you can make a better livin' than I've made."

I thought once I'd run through the woods above the barn just as hard as I could go. I thought I'd leave high school and home forever! Pa could not catch me! I'd get away! I couldn't go back to school with him. He'd have a gun and maybe he'd shoot Professor Herbert. It was hard

to tell what he would do. I could tell Pa that school had changed in the hills from the way it was when he was a boy, but he wouldn't understand. I could tell him we studied frogs, birds, snakes, lizards, flowers, insects. But Pa wouldn't understand. If I did run away from home it wouldn't matter to Pa. He would see Professor Herbert anyway. He would think that high school and Professor Herbert had run me away from home. There was no need to run away. I'd just have to stay, finish foddering the cattle and go to school with Pa the next morning.

The moon shone bright in the cold March sky. I finished my work by moonlight. Professor Herbert really didn't know how much work I had to do at home. If he had known he would not have kept me after school. He would have loaned me a dollar to have paid my part on the cherry tree. He had never lived in the hills. He didn't know the way the hill boys had to work so that they could go to school. Now he was teaching in a County High School where all the boys who attended were from hill farms.

After I'd finished doing my work I went to the house and ate my supper. Pa and Mom had eaten. My supper was getting cold. I heard Pa and Mom talking in the front room. Pa was telling Mom about me staying in after school.

"I had to do all th' milkin' tonight, chop th' wood myself. It's too hard on me atter I've turned ground all day. I'm goin' to take a day off tomorrow and see if I can't remedy things a little. I'll go down to that high school tomorrow. I won't be a very good scholar fer Professor Herbert nohow. He won't keep me in atter school. I'll take a different kind of lesson down there and make 'im acquainted with it."

"Now, Luster," says Mom, "you jist stay away from there. Don't cause a lot o' trouble. You can be jailed fer a trick like that. You'll get th' Law atter you. You'll jist go down there and show off and plague your own boy Dave to death in front o' all th' scholars!"

"Plague or no plague," says Pa, "he don't take into consideration what all I haf to do here, does he? I'll show 'im it ain't right to keep one boy in and let the rest go scot-free. My boy is good as th' rest, ain't he? A bullet will make a hole in a school-teacher same as it will anybody else. He can't do me that way and get by with it. I'll plug 'im first. I aim to go down there bright and early in the mornin' and get all this straight! I aim to see about bug larnin' and this runnin' all over God's creation hunt-in' snakes, lizards, and frogs. Ran-sackin' th' country and goin' through cherry orchards and breakin' th' trees down atter lizards! Old Eif Crabtree ought to a-poured th' hot lead into 'em instead o' chargin' six dollars fer th' tree! He ought to a-got old Herbert the first one!"

I ate my supper. I slipped upstairs and lit the lamp. I tried to forget the whole thing. I studied plane geome-try. Then I studied my biology lesson. I could hardly study for thinking about Pa. "He'll go to school with me in the morning. He'll take a gun

for Professor Herbert! What will Pro-fessor Herbert think of me! I'll tell him when Pa leaves that I couldn't help it. But Pa might shoot him. I hate to go with Pa. Maybe he'll cool off about it tonight and not go in the morning."

Pa got up at four o'clock. He built a fire in the stove. Then he built a fire in the fireplace. He got Mom up to get breakfast. Then he got me up to help feed and milk. By the time we had our work done at the barn, Mom had breakfast ready for us. We ate our breakfast. Daylight came and we could see the bare oak trees cov-ered white with frost. The hills were white with frost.

"Now, Dave," says Pa, "let's get ready fer school. I aim to go with you this mornin' and look into bug larnin', frog larnin', lizard and snake larnin', and breakin' down cherry trees! I don't like no sicha foolish way o' larnin' myself!"

Pa hadn't forgot. I'd have to take him to school with me. He would take me to school with him. I was glad we were going early. If Pa pulled a gun on Professor Herbert there wouldn't be so many of my class-mates there to see him.

I knew that Pa wouldn't be at home in the high school. He wore overalls, big boots, a blue shirt and a sheepskin coat, and a slouched black hat gone to seed at the top. He put his gun in its holster. We started trudging toward the high school across the hill.

It was early when we got to the County High School. Professor Her-bert had just got there. I just thought as we walked up the steps into the schoolhouse: "Maybe Pa will find out Professor Herbert is a good man. He just doesn't know him. Just like I felt toward the Lambert boys across the hill. I didn't like them until I'd seen them and talked to them; then I liked them and we were friends. It's a lot in knowing the other fellow."

"You're th' Professor here, ain't you?" says Pa.

"Yes," says Professor Herbert, "and you are Dave's father."

"Yes," says Pa, pulling out his gun and laying it on the seat in Professor Herbert's office. Professor Herbert's eyes got big behind his black-rimmed glasses when he saw Pa's gun. Color came into his pale cheeks.

"Jist a few things about this school I want to know," says Pa. "I'm tryin' to make a scholar out'n Dave. He's the only one out'n eleven youngins I've sent to high school. Here he comes in late and leaves me all th' work to do! He said you's all out bug huntin' yesterday and broke a cherry tree down. He had to stay two hours atter school yesterday and work out money to pay on that cherry tree! Is that right?"

"Wwwwy," says Professor Herbert, "I guess it is."

He looked at Pa's gun.

"Well," says Pa, "this ain't no high school. It's a bug school, a lizard school, a snake school! It ain't no school nohow!"

"Why did you bring that gun?" says Professor Herbert to Pa.

"You see that little hole," says Pa as he picked up the long blue forty-four and put his finger on the end of the barrel. "A bullet can come out'n that hole that will kill a schoolteacher same as it will any other man. It will kill a rich man same as a poor man. It will kill a man. But atter I come in and saw you, I know'd I wouldn't need it. This maul o' mine could do you up in a few minutes."

Pa stood there, big, hard, brown-skinned, and mighty beside of Professor Herbert. I didn't know Pa was so much bigger and harder. I'd never seen Pa in a schoolhouse before. I'd seen Professor Herbert. He always looked big before to me. He didn't look big standing beside of Pa.

"I was only doing my duty," says Professor Herbert, "Mr. Sexton, and following the course of study the state provided us with."

"Course o' study!" says Pa. "What study? Bug study? Varmint study? Takin' youngins to th' woods. Boys and girls all out there together a-gala-vantin' in the brush and kickin' up their heels and their poor old Ma's and Pa's at home a-slavin' to keep 'em in school and give 'em a education!"

Students are coming into the schoolhouse now. Professor Herbert says: "Close the door, Dave, so others won't hear."

I walked over and closed the door. I was shaking like a leaf in the wind. I thought Pa was going to hit Professor Herbert every minute. He was doing all the talking. His face was getting red. The red color was coming through the brown, weather-beaten skin on Pa's face.

"It jist don't look good to me," says Pa, "a-takin' all this swarm of youngins out to pillage th' whole deestrict. Breakin' down cherry trees. Keepin' boys in atter school."

"What else could I have done with Dave, Mr. Sexton?" says Professor Herbert. "The boys didn't have any business all climbing that cherry tree after one lizard. One boy could have gone up in the tree and got it. The farmer charged us six dollars. It was a little steep, I think, but we had it to pay. Must I make five boys pay and let your boy off? He said he didn't have the dollar and couldn't get it. So I put it in for him. I'm letting him work it out. He's not working for me. He's working for the school!"

"I jist don't know what you could a-done with 'im," says Pa, "only a-larruped 'im with a withe! That's what he needed!"

"He's too big to whip," says Professor Herbert, pointing at me. "He's a man in size."

"He's not too big fer me to whip," says Pa. "They ain't too big until they're over twenty-one! It jist didn't look fair to me! Work one and let th' rest out because they got th' money. I don't see what bugs has got to do with a high school! It don't look good to me nohow!"

Pa picked up his gun and put it back in its holster. The red color left Professor Herbert's face. He talked more to Pa. Pa softened a little. It looked funny to see Pa in the high-school building. It was the first time he'd ever been there.

"We're not only hunting snakes, toads, flowers, butterflies, lizards," says Professor Herbert, "but, Mr. Sexton, I was hunting dry timothy

grass to put in an incubator and raise some protozoa."

"I don't know what that is," says Pa. "Th' incubator is th' new-fangled way o' cheatin' th' hens and raisin' chickens. I ain't so sure about th' breed o' chickens you mentioned."

"You've heard of germs, Mr. Sexton, haven't you?" says Professor Herbert.

"Jist call me Luster if you don't mind," says Pa, very casual like.

"All right, Luster, you've heard of germs, haven't you?"

"Yes," says Pa, "but I don't believe in germs. I'm sixty-five years old and I ain't seen one yet!"

"You can't see them with your naked eye," says Professor Herbert. "Just keep that gun in the holster and stay with me in the high school today. I have a few things I want to show you. That scum on your teeth has germs in it."

"What," says Pa, "you mean to tell me I've got germs on my teeth!"

"Yes," says Professor Herbert. "The same kind as we might be able to find in a living black snake if we dissect it!"

"I don't mean to dispute your word," says Pa, "but darned if I believe it. I don't believe I have germs on my teeth!"

"Stay with me today and I'll show you. I want to take you through the school anyway. School has changed a lot in the hills since you went to school. I don't guess we had high schools in this county when you went to school."

"No," says Pa, "jist readin', writin', and cipherin'. We didn't have all this bug larnin', frog larnin', and findin' germs on your teeth and in the middle o' black snakes! Th' world's changin'."

"It is," says Professor Herbert, "and we hope all for the better. Boys like your own there are going to help change it. He's your boy. He knows all of what I've told you. You stay with me today."

"I'll shore stay with you," says Pa. "I want to see th' germs off'n my teeth. I jist want to see a germ. I've never seen one in my life. 'Seein' is believin',' Pap allus told me."

Pa walks out of the office with Professor Herbert. I just hoped Professor Herbert didn't have Pa arrested for pulling his gun. Pa's gun has always been a friend to him when he goes to settle disputes.

The bell rang. School took up. I saw the students when they marched in the schoolhouse look at Pa. They would grin and punch each other. Pa just stood and watched them pass in at the schoolhouse door. Two long lines marched in the house. The boys and girls were clean and well dressed. Pa stood over in the schoolyard under a leafless elm, in his sheepskin coat, his big boots laced in front with buckskin and his heavy socks stuck above his boot tops. Pa's overalls legs were baggy and wrinkled between his coat and boot tops. His blue work shirt showed at the collar. His big black hat showed his gray-streaked black hair. His face was hard and weather-tanned to the color of a ripe fodder blade. His hands were big and gnarled like the roots of the elm tree he stood beside.

When I went to my first class I saw Pa and Professor Herbert going around over the schoolhouse. I was in my geometry class when Pa and Professor Herbert came in the room. We were explaining our propositions on the blackboard. Professor Herbert and Pa just quietly came in and sat down for a while. I heard Fred Wurts whisper to Glenn Armstrong: "Who is that old man? Lord, he's a rough-looking scamp." Glenn whispered back: "I think he's Dave's Pap." The students in geometry looked at Pa. They must have wondered what he was doing in school. Before the class was over, Pa and Professor Herbert got up and went out. I saw them together down on the playground. Professor Herbert was explaining to Pa. I could see the prints of Pa's gun under his coat when he'd walk around.

At noon in the high-school cafeteria Pa and Professor Herbert sat together at the little table where Professor Herbert always ate by himself. They ate together. The students watched the way Pa ate. He ate with his knife instead of his fork. A lot of students felt sorry for me after they found out he was my father. They didn't have to feel sorry for me. I wasn't ashamed of Pa after I found out he wasn't going to shoot Professor Herbert. I was glad they had made friends. I wasn't ashamed of Pa. I wouldn't be as long as he behaved.

In the afternoon when we went to biology Pa was in the class. He was sitting on one of the high stools beside the microscope. We went ahead with our work just as if Pa wasn't in the class. I saw Pa take his knife and scrape tartar from one of his teeth. Professor Herbert put it under the lens and adjusted the microscope for Pa. He adjusted it and worked awhile. Then he says: "Now, Luster, look! Put your eye right down to the light. Squint the other eye!"

Pa put his head down and did as Professor Herbert said: "I see 'im," says Pa. "Who'd a ever thought that? Right on a body's teeth! Right in a body's mouth! You're right certain they ain't no fake to this, Professor Herbert?"

"No, Luster," says Professor Herbert. "It's there. That's the germ. Germs live in a world we cannot see with the naked eye. We must use the microscope. There are millions of them in our bodies. Some are harmful. Others are helpful."

Pa holds his face down and looks through the microscope. We stop and watch Pa. He sits upon the tall stool. His knees are against the table. His legs are long. His coat slips up behind when he bends over. The handle of his gun shows. Professor Herbert pulls his coat down quickly.

"Oh, yes," says Pa. He gets up and pulls his coat down. Pa's face gets a little red. He knows about his gun and he knows he doesn't have any use for it in high school.

"We have a big black snake over here we caught yesterday," says Professor Herbert. "We'll chloroform him and dissect him and show you he has germs in his body, too."

"Don't do it," says Pa. "I believe you. I jist don't want to see you kill the black snake. I never kill one. They are good mousers and a lot o' help to us on the farm. I like black snakes. I jist hate to see people kill 'em. I don't allow 'em killed on my place."

The students look at Pa. They seem to like him better after he said that. Pa with a gun in his pocket but a tender heart beneath his ribs for snakes, but not for man! Pa won't whip a mule at home. He won't whip his cattle.

Professor Herbert took Pa through the laboratory. He showed him the different kinds of work we were doing. He showed him our equipment. They stood and talked while we worked. Then they walked out together. They talked louder when they got out in the hall.

When our biology class was over I walked out of the room. It was our last class for the day. I would have to take my broom and sweep two hours to finish paying for the split cherry tree. I just wondered if Pa would want me to stay. He was standing in the hallway watching the students march out. He looked lost among us. He looked like a leaf turned brown on the tree among the treetop filled with growing leaves.

I got my broom and started to sweep. Professor Herbert walked up and says: "I'm going to let you do that some other time. You can go home with your father. He is waiting out there."

I laid my broom down, got my books, and went down the steps.

Pa says: "Ain't you got two hours o' sweepin' yet to do?"

I says: "Professor Herbert said I could do it some other time. He said for me to go home with you."

"No," says Pa. "You are goin' to do as he says. He's a good man. School has changed from my day and time. I'm a dead leaf, Dave. I'm behind. I don't belong here. If he'll let me I'll get a broom and we'll both sweep one hour. That pays your debt. I'll hep you pay it. I'll ast 'im and see if he won't let me hep you."

"I'm going to cancel the debt," says Professor Herbert. "I just wanted you to understand, Luster."

"I understand," says Pa, "and since I understand he must pay his debt fer th' tree and I'm goin' to hep him."

"Don't do that," says Professor Herbert. "It's all on me."

"We don't do things like that," says Pa; "we're just and honest people. We don't want somethin' fer nothin'. Professor Herbert, you're wrong now and I'm right. You'll haf to listen to me. I've larned a lot from you. My boy must go on. Th' world has left me. It changed while I've raised my family and plowed th' hills. I'm a just and honest man. I don't skip debts. I ain't larned 'em to do that. I ain't got much larnin' myself, but I do know right from wrong atter I see through a thing."

Professor Herbert went home. Pa and I stayed and swept one hour. It looked funny to see Pa use a broom. He never used one at home. Mom used the broom. Pa used the plow. Pa did hard work. Pa says: "I can't sweep. Durned if I can. Look at th' streaks o' dirt I leave on th' floor!

Seems like no work a-tall fer me. Brooms is too light 'r somethin'. I'll jist do th' best I can, Dave. I've been wrong about th' school."

I says: "Did you know Professor Herbert can get a warrant out for you for bringing your pistol to school and showing it in his office! They can railroad you for that!"

"That's all made right," says Pa. "I've made that right. Professor Herbert ain't goin' to take it to court. He likes me. I like 'im. We jist had to get together. He had the remedies. He showed me. You must go on to school. I am as strong a man as ever come out'n th' hills fer my years and th' hard work I've done. But I'm behind, Dave. I'm a little man. Your hands will be softer than mine. Your clothes will be better. You'll allus look cleaner than your old Pap. Jist remember, Dave, to pay your debts and be honest. Jist be kind to animals and don't bother th' snakes. That's all I got agin th' school. Puttin' black snakes to sleep and cuttin' 'em open."

It was late when we got home. Stars were in the sky. The moon was up. The ground was frozen. Pa took his time going home. I couldn't run like I did the night before. It was ten o'clock before we got the work finished, our suppers eaten. Pa sat before the fire and told Mom he was going to take her and show her a germ some time. Mom hadn't seen one either. Pa told her about the high school and the fine man Professor Herbert was. He told Mom about the strange school across the hill and how different it was from the school in their day and time.

Getting the Main Idea

There is surely no point in reading a story unless, when you are through, you know the main idea of it. Can you give the main idea of "Split Cherry Tree" in no more than one sentence?

In a single sentence, can you write the main idea of the paragraph indicated by each of the following beginnings?

1. I thought once I'd run through the woods . . . (page 6)
2. The bell rang. (page 10)
3. At noon in the high-school cafeteria . . . (page 10)
4. "We don't do things like that . . ." (page 12)
5. It was late when we got home. (page 12)

Getting Ideas Through Words

We can easily miss an important idea in a story when we do not know the meaning of a word. The words in italics below appeared in the story. Choose the word or group of words in each line that most nearly gives the meaning of the word in italics.

1. *holster:* (a) holdup   (b) leather case for pistol   (c) firearm
2. *casual:* (a) offhand   (b) bitter   (c) causal
3. *dissect:* (a) to determine   (b) to cut for examination   (c) to display
4. *disputes:* (a) dissatisfactions   (b) distances   (c) arguments
5. *warrant:* (a) document authorizing arrest   (b) guarantee   (c) warning

Understanding Three Persons

1. What do you learn about Pa on pages 7, 9, and 12?
2. What do you find out about Dave on pages 5 and 10?
3. What kind of man was Professor Herbert? See pages 9, 11, and 12.

⋇ LAURA INGALLS WILDER

Caught in a Blizzard

An old Indian had warned that the winter of 1880–81 would be severe in the Dakota Territory. Blizzards would cut off all supplies from the outside. For safety's sake, the Ingalls family moved into town for the winter.

One afternoon while Laura and her sisters were at school, a blizzard struck. How could they get home? It would be easy to lose direction in the swirling whiteness. A few missteps and the children would be hopelessly lost on the prairie that surrounded the little town.

LAURA and Carrie were enjoying school so much that they were sorry when Saturday and Sunday interrupted it. They looked forward to Monday. But when Monday came, Laura was cross because her red flannel underwear was so hot and scratchy.

It made her back itch, and her neck, and her wrists; and where it was folded around her ankles, under her stockings and shoe-tops, that red flannel almost drove her crazy.

At noon she begged Ma to let her change to cooler underthings. "It's too hot for my red flannels, Ma!" she protested.

"I know the weather's turned warm," Ma answered gently. "But this is the time of year to wear flannels, and you would catch cold if you took them off."

Laura went crossly back to school

and sat squirming because she must not scratch. She held the flat geography open before her, but she wasn't studying. She was trying to bear the itching flannels and wanting to get home where she could scratch. The sunshine from the western windows had never crawled so slowly.

Suddenly there was no sunshine. It went out, as if someone had blown out the sun like a lamp. The outdoors was gray, the windowpanes were gray, and at the same moment a wind crashed against the schoolhouse, rattling windows and doors and shaking the walls.

Miss Garland started up from her chair. One of the little Beardsley girls screamed, and Carrie turned white.

Teacher and all the others were staring at the windows, where nothing but grayness could be seen. They all looked frightened. Then Miss Garland said, "It is only a storm, children. Go on with your lessons."

The blizzard was scouring against the walls, and the winds squealed and moaned in the stovepipe.

All the heads bent over the books as Teacher had told them to do. But Laura was trying to think how to get home. The schoolhouse was a long way from Main Street, and there was nothing to guide them.

All the others had come from the East that summer. They had never seen a prairie blizzard. But Laura and Carrie knew what it was. Carrie's head was bowed limply above her book, and the back of it, with the white parting between the braids of fine, soft hair, looked small and helpless and frightened.

There was only a little fuel at the schoolhouse. The school board was buying coal, but only one load had been delivered. Laura thought they might outlive the storm in the schoolhouse, but they could not do it without burning all the costly patent desks.

Without lifting her head Laura looked up at Teacher. Miss Garland was thinking and biting her lip. She could not decide to dismiss school because of a storm, but this storm frightened her.

"I ought to tell her what to do," Laura thought. But she could not think what to do. It was not safe to leave the schoolhouse, and it was not safe to stay there. Even the twelve patent desks might not last long enough to keep them warm until the blizzard ended. She thought of her wraps and Carrie's, in the entry. Whatever happened she must somehow keep Carrie warm. Already the cold was coming in.

There was a loud thumping in the entry. Every pupil started and looked at the door.

It opened and a man stumbled in. He was bundled in overcoat, cap, and muffler, all solid white with snow driven into the woolen cloth. They could not see who he was until he pulled down the stiffened muffler.

"I came out to get you," he told Teacher.

He was Mr. Foster, the man who owned the ox team and had come in from his claim to stay in town for the winter at Sherwood's, across the street from Teacher's house.

Miss Garland thanked him. She rapped her ruler on the desk and said, "Attention! School is dismissed. You may bring your wraps from the entry and put them on by the stove."

Laura said to Carrie, "You stay here. I'll bring your wraps."

The entry was freezing cold; snow was blowing in between the rough boards of the walls. Laura was chilled before she could snatch her coat and hood from their nail. She found Carrie's and carried the armful into the schoolhouse.

Crowded around the stove, they all put on their wraps and fastened them snugly.

Laura wrapped the muffler snugly over Carrie's white face and took firm hold of her mittened hand. She told Carrie, "Don't worry, we'll be all right."

"Now, just follow me," said Mr. Foster, taking Teacher's arm. "And keep close together."

He opened the door, led the way with Miss Garland. Mary Power and

Minnie each took one of the little Beardsley girls. Ben and Arthur followed them closely; then Laura went out with Carrie into blinding snow.

They could hardly walk in the beating, whirling wind. The schoolhouse had disappeared. They could see nothing but swirling whiteness and snow and then a glimpse of each other, disappearing like shadows.

Laura felt that she was smothering. The icy particles of snow whirled scratching into her eyes and smothered her breathing. Her skirts whipped around her, now wrapped so tightly that she could not step, then whirled and lifted to her knees. Suddenly tightening, they made her stumble. She held tightly to Carrie, and Carrie, struggling and staggering, was pulled away by the wind and then flung back against her.

"We can't go on this way," Laura thought. But they had to.

She was alone in the confusion of whirling winds and snow except for Carrie's hand that she must never let go. The winds struck her this way and that. She could not see nor breathe, she stumbled and was falling, then suddenly she seemed to be lifted and Carrie bumped against her. She tried to think. The others must be somewhere ahead. She must walk faster and keep up with them or she and Carrie would be lost. If they were lost on the prairie they would freeze to death.

But perhaps they were all lost. Main Street was only two blocks long. If they were going only a little way to north or south they would miss

the block of stores, and beyond was empty prairie for miles.

Laura thought they must have gone far enough to reach Main Street, but she could see nothing.

The storm thinned a little. She saw shadowy figures ahead. They were darker gray in the whirling gray-whiteness. She went on as fast as she could, with Carrie, until she touched Miss Garland's coat.

They had all stopped. Huddled in their wraps, they stood like bundles close together in the swirling mist. Teacher and Mr. Foster were trying to talk, but the winds confused their shouts so that no one could hear what they said. Then Laura began to know how cold she was.

Her mittened hand was so numb that it hardly felt Carrie's hand. She was shaking all over, and deep inside her there was a shaking that she could not stop. Only in her very middle there was a solid knot that ached, and her shaking pulled this knot tighter so that the ache grew worse.

She was frightened about Carrie. The cold hurt too much, Carrie could not stand it. Carrie was so little and thin, she had always been delicate, she could not stand such cold much longer. They must reach shelter soon.

Mr. Foster and Teacher were moving again, going a little to the left. All the others stirred and hurried to follow them. Laura took hold of Carrie with her other hand, that had been in her coat pocket and was not quite so numb.

She kept tight hold of Carrie and hurried to follow Mr. Foster and Teacher as fast as she could. Her chest sobbed for air, and her eyes strained open in the icy snow-particles that hurt them like sand. Carrie struggled bravely, stumbling and flopping, doing her best to stay on her feet and keep on going. Only for instants when the snow-whirl was thinner could they glimpse the shadows moving ahead of them.

Laura felt that they were going in the wrong direction. She did not know why she felt so. No one could see anything. There was nothing to go by—no sun, no sky, no direction in the winds blowing fiercely from all directions. There was nothing but the dizzy whirling and the cold.

It seemed that the cold and the winds, the noise of the winds and the blinding, smothering, scratching snow, and the effort and the aching, were forever. Pa had lived through three days of a blizzard under the bank of Plum Creek. But there were no creek banks here. Here there was nothing but bare prairie. Pa had told about sheep caught in a blizzard, huddled together under the snow. Some of them had lived. Perhaps people could do that, too. Carrie was too tired to go much farther, but she was too heavy for Laura to carry. They must go on as long as they could, and then. . .

Then, out of the whirling whiteness, something hit her. The hard blow crashed against her shoulder and all through her. She rocked on her feet and stumbled against something solid. It was high, it was hard, it was the corner of two walls. Her hands felt it, her eyes saw it. She had walked against some building.

With all her might she yelled, "Here! Come here! Here's a house!"

All around the house the winds were howling so that at first no one heard her. She pulled the icy stiff muffler from her mouth and screamed into the blinding storm. At last she saw a shadow in it, two tall shadows thinner than the shadowy wall she clung to—Mr. Foster and Teacher. Then other shadows pressed close around her.

No one tried to say anything. They crowded together and they were all there—Mary Power and Minnie, each with a little Beardsley girl, and Arthur Johnson and Ben Woodworth with the small Wilmarth boys.

They followed along the side of that building till they came to the front of it, and it was Mead's Hotel, at the very north end of Main Street.

Beyond it was nothing but the railroad track covered with snow, the lonely depot and the wide, open prairie. If Laura had been only a few steps nearer the others, they would all have been lost on the endless prairie north of town.

For a moment they stood by the hotel's lamplit windows. Warmth and rest were inside the hotel, but the blizzard was growing worse and they must all reach home.

Main Street would guide all of them except Ben Woodworth. No other buildings stood between the hotel and the depot where he lived. So Ben went into the hotel to stay till the blizzard was over. He could afford to do that because his father had a regular job.

Minnie and Arthur Johnson, taking

the little Wilmarth boys, had only to cross Main Street to Wilmarth's grocery store and their home was beside it. The others went on down Main Street, keeping close to the buildings. They passed the saloon, they passed Royal Wilder's feed store, and then they passed Barker's grocery. The Beardsley Hotel was next, and there the little Beardsley girls went in.

The journey was almost ended now. They passed Couse's Hardware store and they crossed Second Street to Fuller's Hardware. Mary Power had only to pass the drugstore now. Her father's tailor shop stood next to it.

Laura and Carrie and Teacher and Mr. Foster had to cross Main Street now. It was a wide street. But if they missed Pa's house, the haystacks and the stable were still between them and the open prairie.

They did not miss the house. One of its lighted windows made a glow that Mr. Foster saw before he ran into it. He went on around the house corner with Teacher to go by the clothesline, the haystacks, and the stable to the Garland house.

Laura and Carrie were safe at their own front door. Laura's hands fumbled at the doorknob, too stiff to turn it. Pa opened the door and helped them in.

He was wearing overcoat and cap and muffler. He had set down the lighted lantern and dropped a coil of rope. "I was just starting out after you," he said.

In the still house Laura and Carrie stood taking deep breaths. It was so quiet there where the winds did not push and pull at them. They were still blinded, but the whirling icy snow had stopped hurting their eyes.

Laura felt Ma's hands breaking away the icy muffler, and she said, "Is Carrie all right?"

"Yes, Carrie's all right," said Pa.

Ma took off Laura's hood and unbuttoned her coat and helped her pull out of its sleeves. "These wraps are driven full of ice," Ma said. They crackled when she shook them and little drifts of whiteness sifted to the floor.

"Well," Ma said, " 'All's well that ends well.' You're not frostbitten. You can go to the fire and get warm."

Laura could hardly move, but she stooped and with her fingers dug out the caked snow that the wind had driven in between her woolen stockings and the tops of her shoes. Then she staggered toward the stove.

It was so wonderful to be there, safe at home, sheltered from the winds and the cold. Laura thought that this must be a little bit like Heaven, where the weary are at rest. She could not imagine that Heaven was better than being where she was, slowly growing warm and comfortable.

Cold Understanding

These questions will help you check your understanding of the story:
1. Why was the blizzard so very dangerous?
2. What picture of the schoolhouse do you get?
3. How did the girls arrive home safely?
4. Why was Laura concerned about Carrie?
5. What kind of girl was Laura?

The Main Idea

Look at the fifth paragraph in the story. Here are three possible titles for it. Which do you think gives the main idea of the paragraph?
1. A Geography Lesson
2. Itching Red Flannels
3. Laura's Interest in School

Write a title for each of the paragraphs indicated by these beginnings:
1. Suddenly there was no sunshine. (page 14)
2. Laura felt that she was smothering. (page 16)
3. But perhaps they were all lost. (page 16)
4. Then, out of the whirling whiteness, . . . (page 17)
5. It was so wonderful to be there, . . . (page 18)

Guessing and Checking Word Meanings

Look at the words in italics. If you do not know what they mean, can you guess their meaning by the way they are used? Check your guesses with your dictionary.
1. "It's too hot for my red flannels, Ma!" she *protested*.
2. "Attention! School is *dismissed*."
3. She was alone in the *confusion* of whirling winds . . .
4. Only for instants . . . could they *glimpse* the shadows moving ahead of them.
5. It was so wonderful to be there, safe at home, *sheltered* from the winds and the cold.

Colorful Ways of Saying Things

The author of the story has used words to make you see pictures. Here are two examples:
1. The sunshine from the western windows had never crawled so slowly.
2. Suddenly there was no sunshine. It went out as if someone had blown out the sun like a lamp.

Can you find sentences in the story that make you see and hear and feel the following?
1. the noise of the storm
2. the blinding whiteness
3. the strength of the winds
4. the bitter coldness

◀ᴵᶜ ERIC KNIGHT

The Rifles of the Regiment

It was after the fall of Dunkirk that the colonel and his men were trying to make their way to the French coast. If they did reach the coast, what could they do then? The old colonel seemed to have ridiculous ideas about a retreating regiment—ideas that he clung to even after the night he fought with Fear.

COLONEL HEATHERGALL has become a bit of a regimental legend already. In the mess of the Loyal Rifles they say, "Ah, but Old Glass-eye! He was a one for one. A pukka sahib[1]! I'll never forget once . . ."

Then off they go on some story or other about "Old Glass-eye."

But the regiment doesn't know the finest and truest story of all: when he fought all night with Fear—and won.

Colonel Heathergall met Fear in a little shack atop a cliff near the French village of Ste. Marguerite-en-Vaux. He had never met Fear before —not on the Somme nor in India nor in Palestine—because he was the type brought up not to know fear. Fear is a cad—you just don't recognize the bounder.

The system has its points. Not being even on nodding acquaintance with Fear had allowed the colonel to keep the Loyal Rifle Regiment going in France long after all other British troops had gone—they were still fighting, working their way westward to-

[1]*pukka sahib*. Out-and-out master.

ward the Channel, nearly two weeks after Dunkirk was all over.

The men—those that were left— were drunk with fatigue. When they marched between fights, they slept. When they rested, they went into a sort of coma, and the sergeants had to slap them to waken them.

"They're nearly done," the adjutant said. "Shouldn't we jettison equipment?"

"All right," the colonel said, finally. "Equipment can be destroyed and left behind. But not rifles! Regiment's never failed to carry its rifles in—and carry 'em out. We'll take our rifles with us—every last single rifle."

The adjutant saluted.

"Er—and tell 'em we'll cut through soon," the colonel added. "Tell 'em I say we'll find a soft spot and cut through soon."

But the Loyal Rifles never did cut through. For there was then no British army left in France to cut through to. But the regiment didn't know that. It marched west and north and attacked, and went west and north again. Each time it brought out its rifles and left its dead. First the sergeants were carrying two rifles, and then the men, and then the officers.

The Loyal Rifles went on until—they could go no farther. For they had reached the sea. It was on a headland looking out over the Channel beside the fishing port of Ste. Marguerite-en-Vaux.

In the late afternoon the colonel used the regiment's last strength in an attempt to take Ste. Marguerite, for there might be boats there, fishing smacks, something that could carry them all back to England. He didn't find boats. He found the enemy with tanks and artillery, and the regiment withdrew. They left their dead, but they left no rifles.

The colonel sent out scouts. They brought him the report. They were cut off by the Germans—ringed about with their backs to the sea; on a cliff top with a two-hundred-foot drop to the beach below.

The regiment posted pickets, and dug foxholes, and fought until darkness came. Then they waited through the night for the last attack that was sure to come.

And it was that night, in his headquarters at the cliff-top shack that Colonel Heathergall, for the first time in his well-bred, British, military life, met Fear.

Fear had a leprous face. Its white robes were damp, and it smelled of stale sweat.

Colonel Heathergall, who had not heard the door close, saw the figure standing there in the undarkness.

"Who—who is it?"

Fear bowed and said, "You know me, really, Colonel. All your arrogant, aristocratic British life you've snubbed me and pretended you didn't know me, but really you do, don't you? Let us be friends."

The colonel adjusted his monocle. "What do you want?" he asked.

"I've come to tell you," Fear said, "that it's time for you to surrender the regiment. You're finished."

"You're a slimy brute," the colonel said. "I won't surrender. There must be some way out! That R.A.F. plane this morning! I'm sure it saw us—the way the chap waggled his wings. He'd go get help. The navy—they'll come!"

Fear laughed. "And if they come, then what? How would you get down that cliff? . . . You *can't* get down—and you know it!"

"We could cut south and find a better spot—the men still have fight left," the colonel said desperately.

"The men," Fear said, "they'll leave their broken bodies wherever you choose. They've got the stuff. And, oh, yes, you too, have courage, in your way. The huntin'-shootin'-fishin' sort of courage. The well-bred, polo-field kind of courage. But that's got nothing to do with *this* kind of war. You haven't the right to ask your men to die to preserve that sort of record. Have you?"

The colonel sat still, not answering.

Fear spoke again: "The enemy will be here soon. Your men are exhausted. They can't do any more. Really, you'd be saving their lives if you surrender. No one would blame you. . . ."

The colonel shook his head. "No," he said. "We can't do that. You see

—we never have done that. And we can't now. Perhaps we are outmoded. I and my kind may be out of date—incompetent—belonging to a bygone day. But . . ." He looked around him as if for help. Then he went on desperately: "But—we've brought out all the rifles."

"Is that all?" mocked Fear.

"All?" the colonel echoed. "Is that all?"

Then at last he squared his shoulders. "All? Why, you bloody civilian, it's everything! I may die—and my men may die—but the regiment! It doesn't. The regiment goes on living. It's bigger than me—it's bigger than the men. Why, you slimy, dugout king of a base-wallah[2]—it's bigger than you!"

And exactly as he said that, Fear fled. And there came a rap on the door, and the adjutant's voice sounded.

"Come in," the colonel said quietly.

"Are you alone, sir?" the adjutant asked.

"Yes," the colonel said. "Quite alone. What is it?"

"Report from the signal officer, sir. He has carried an ordinary torch with him, and he feels the colonel will be interested to know that he's in visual communication with the navy—destroyers or something. They say they're ready to put off boats to take us off."

"Tell him my thanks to CO of whatever naval force there is there. Message to company commanders:

Withdraw pickets quietly. Rendezvous cliff top north of this HQ at three-fifty-five ack emma.[3] Er—pretty good chaps in the navy—I've heard."

"Indeed, sir," the adjutant said.

So they assembled the men of the Loyal Rifle Regiment on the cliff top, where they could see out and below them the brief dots and dashes of light that winked. And there, too, in the night wind, they could feel the space and know the vast drop to the beach. Some of the men lay flat and listened for the sound of the sailors two hundred feet below them.

The officers waited, looking toward the colonel. It was the major who spoke: "But—but how on earth are we going to get down there, Colonel?"

Colonel Heathergall smiled privately within himself. "The rifles," he said softly. "The rifles, of course. I think we'll just about have enough."

And that's how the regiment escaped. They made a great chain of linked rifle slings, and went down it one at a time. The colonel came last, of course, as custom dictated.

Below, they picked up the rifles, whole and shattered, that they had thrown from the cliff top, and, wading out into the sea, carried them to the boats.

By this time the Germans were awake; and they let loose with everything they had. The sailors used fine naval language, and said that Dunkirk was a panic compared to this so-and-so bloody mess.

But they got the men into the boats. The navy got in and got them out.

---

[2] *base-wallah.* A soldier stationed at one base permanently.

[3] *ack emma.* Code for A.M.

That's the way the Loyal Rifle Regiment came home nearly two weeks after the last troops from Dunkirk had landed in Blighty.[4] . . . .

In the mess they still talk of the colonel. "Old Glass-eye," they say. "Ah, there was a colonel for you.

[4]*Blighty.* England.

Saved the outfit, he did. Knew the only way it'd ever get out would be down a cliff—so he made 'em carry all the rifles halfway across France. Knew he'd need the slings for that cliff. Foresight, eh? . . . Great chap, Old Glass-eye. Never knew the meaning of Fear."

Never Knew the Meaning of——

Think through the story you have just read and answer these questions:

1. Why was the colonel's fight with Fear important to the outcome of the story?
2. What kind of man was the colonel? Why was his adherence to military rules important to the outcome?
3. What picture does the story give you of the situation after Dunkirk?

Making New Words Your Own

On your paper, list five words you find in the story which are not a part of your vocabulary. Find out what they mean and use them until they are really yours.

◀︎ Mona Gardner

The Dinner Party

A dinner party may not sound like a very good setting for a nerve-shattering adventure. This story will surprise you.

I first heard this story in India, where it is told as if true—though any naturalist would know it couldn't be. Later I learned that a magazine version of it appeared shortly before the First World War. This account, and its author, I have never been able to track down.

——Originally published in *The Saturday Review of Literature.* Copyright, 1942, by Saturday Review Associates, Inc.

THE COUNTRY is India. A colonial official and his wife are giving a large dinner party. They are seated with their guests—army officers and government attachés and their wives, and a visiting American naturalist—in their spacious dining room, which has a bare marble floor, open rafters, and wide glass doors opening onto a veranda.

A spirited discussion springs up between a young girl who insists that women have outgrown the jumping-on-a-chair-at-the-sight-of-a-mouse era and a colonel who says that they haven't.

"A woman's unfailing reaction in any crisis," the colonel says, "is to scream. And while a man may feel like it, he has that ounce more of nerve control than a woman has. And that last ounce is what counts."

The American does not join in the argument but watches the other guests. As he looks, he sees a strange expression come over the face of the hostess. She is staring straight ahead, her muscles contracting slightly. With a slight gesture she summons the native boy standing behind her chair and whispers to him. The boy's eyes widen: he quickly leaves the room.

Of the guests, none except the American notices this or sees the boy place a bowl of milk on the veranda just outside the open doors.

The American comes to with a start. In India, milk in a bowl means only one thing—bait for a snake. He realizes there must be a cobra in the room. He looks up at the rafters—the likeliest place—but they are bare. Three corners of the room are empty, and in the fourth the servants are waiting to serve the next course. There is only one place left—under the table.

His first impulse is to jump back and warn the others, but he knows the commotion would frighten the cobra into striking. He speaks quickly, the tone of his voice so arresting that it sobers everyone.

"I want to know just what control everyone at this table has. I will count three hundred—that's five minutes—and not one of you is to move a muscle. Those who move will forfeit 50 rupees.[1] Ready!"

The 20 people sit like stone images while he counts. He is saying ". . . two hundred and eighty . . ." when, out of the corner of his eye, he sees the cobra emerge and make for the bowl of milk. Screams ring out as he jumps to slam the veranda doors safely shut.

"You were right, Colonel!" the host exclaims. "A man has just shown us an example of perfect control."

"Just a minute," the American says, turning to his hostess. "Mrs. Wynnes, how did you know that cobra was in the room?"

A faint smile lights up the woman's face as she replies: "Because it was crawling across my foot."

[1]*rupees.* A rupee is a silver coin used as the monetary unit of British India.

◦◦◦

How Did You Know That——?

1. How does the setting of the story make this kind of adventure possible?
2. What clues led the American to believe that a cobra was in the room?

3. How does the conversation at the table tell you that a woman will experience the awful adventure with the cobra?

4. Did the ending of the story surprise you? Should you have been surprised if you were reading with the eyes of a "detective"?

WORDS AND PICTURES

In a few words the author of this story has helped readers to see with "the mind's eye." What mental picture do you have of each of the following?

1. The dining room in which the story takes place
2. The hostess as the cobra crawled across her foot
3. The native boy as the hostess told him about the cobra

What is the meaning of these words and groups of words?

1. naturalist
2. magazine version
3. government attachés
4. spacious dining room
5. muscles contracting
6. impulse
7. commotion
8. stone images
9. sees the cobra emerge
10. perfect control

⟞ HOWARD PEASE

Passengers for Panama

Often adventure has a tinge of mystery. Here is one of the famous Tod Moran stories. After reading this story, you will agree that for once Tod must have had his fill of adventure, mystery, and South American revolutions.

THE THIRD MATE of the *Araby* was puzzled. From the foredeck of his old tramp steamer he looked uneasily across a deserted wharf at the little Caribbean port of La Guaira, lying quiet and undisturbed at the foot of the Andes. Too quiet, thought Tod Moran as his gaze swept the empty street. At ten in the morning, with a

ship just arrived in port, a whole town doesn't take a siesta—even in Venezuela. Something was certainly up. Something serious.

"The skipper wants ter see yer in the saloon cabin, sir."

Tod swung about and met the gaze of a small cockney seaman. "Is the dock superintendent still with him, Toppy?"

" 'E's just goin' ashore. I 'eard 'im tell the skipper we can't discharge our cargo 'ere."

——From: *Night Boat and Other Tod Moran Stories* by Howard Pease. Copyright 1942 by Howard Pease, reprinted by permission of Doubleday & Company, Inc.

In surprise Tod's gaze crossed to a man hurrying down the gangway. The port official paused uncertainly when he reached the dock, while his glance darted to right and left; then he started on a run for the corrugated-iron shed.

"What's got into everybody this morning?" Tod demanded.

Toppy grinned. "Don't yer worry. Cap'n Jarvis said we'd unload anyway. No matter wot's wrong."

"Then I'll bet we do," said Tod, turning toward the port alleyway. All at once he pulled up short. Raising his head with a startled movement, he listened.

From somewhere behind the shed sounded the crack of a rifle.

Tod nodded grimly. This was South America, all right.

In the saloon cabin he found Captain Jarvis pacing up and down. "Take a seat, Third. I've a job laid out for you."

Tod dropped into a swivel chair before the green baize table. "What's up now, sir?"

Tom Jarvis faced him. "We couldn't have chosen a worse time to arrive in Venezuela. General Gomez, the president, has died. Revolution has broken out in Caracas—that's the capital, thirty miles inland from here. The dock superintendent says the people there are burning the city, looting the homes and buildings, killing everybody who belonged to the old regime." Jarvis paused and fixed his eyes upon Tod. "And one of us must go to Caracas. Right now."

Tod sat up straight. "Thirty miles isn't far. What do you want me to do?"

"Get in touch with the Venezuelan Import Company. Get a receipt for their goods while I have the men unload. The company will have to put a guard over it because the dock superintendent here won't take the responsibility."

Tod nodded thoughtfully. "Can't we telephone to Caracas?"

"The wires are down. No trains running, either. The city is cut off from the rest of the world."

"Could I make it in a car?"

"If we can find one to rent. Apparently the drivers are afraid their automobiles will be confiscated by the rebels. And furthermore, the officials here have announced they'll issue no permits to visit the capital until things quiet down." Jarvis grasped the back of a swivel chair. "Tod, we have a cargo waiting for us on the dock in San Francisco. We can't afford to waste time here. If I manage to get you a permit and perhaps a car, do you think you can make it to Caracas?"

"I'll sure try." Tod stood up. "When do I start?"

"As soon as we see the chief of police. Get your passport. Your vaccination certificate, too."

"How about a gun?"

"No hardware on this trip, young man. If you were searched, you'd land in jail—and where could I find a new third mate?" Jarvis crossed to the door. "Let's get going. If you hurry, you should be back here by six tonight."

Captain Jarvis was altogether too optimistic. At six o'clock that evening Tod Moran had just arrived in Caracas. Seated in a private office of the Venezuelan Import Company, he was facing the manager across a polished table.

"You were mad to come to Caracas today." Luis Sanchez shook his gray head in disapproval as he eyed the *Araby's* third mate. "The people are in complete control. No one is supposed to enter or leave the city."

"So I've been told," Tod said. "But you see I'm here just the same. Things aren't as bad as I thought they'd be."

Tod, in fact, had expected to hear rifle volleys and see snipers on the roofs of buildings. Instead, the city had almost the aspect of a celebration in progress. Crowds, laughing and shouting, milled gaily through the narrow streets to the Plaza Bolivar. True, he had seen automobiles burning upside down; he had seen mobs break into buildings, looting the homes and offices of members of the former regime. He had glimpsed a man being marched away between armed guards—to a firing squad against a stone wall, he suspected. But on the surface, at least, a holiday spirit seemed to have taken possession of the city.

"How, Señor Moran, did you get here?"

Tod looked up. "It was slow going, I admit. Captain Jarvis spent two hours in getting me a permit. Another hour was wasted in finding a car. Then the driver insisted upon driving himself for fear he might lose his car. We were stopped at the edge of town and searched, but my American passport worked like a talisman."

"Ah, you North Americans!" sighed the manager. "You are all a leetle bit mad—is it not so?"

Tod grinned. "That's just what we sometimes think about you South Americans."

"Just now perhaps you are right." Señor Sanchez frowned steadily at the polished table. "But to understand, you would have to know how much we have suffered in the last twenty years. Listen, señor. Hardly a family in Caracas has not had a brother or son sent to prison to rot. Not even our own thoughts did we dare express aloud—for even whispers were heard. And now since this tyrant Gomez is dead, is it surprising that the people are happy? Is it surprising that they kill the members of the hated government? That they burn property bought with stolen public money? No, señor. It is justice."

The man rose suddenly. "But I must not detain you. Here is the receipt. And here also is a letter to the warehouse manager who will take over our goods. Come. I will let you out. I stay here tonight to see that no one breaks in."

Tod followed him through the outer office to the big closed door. First Luis Sanchez unbolted a little grilled window in the door and looked out. "But your car. It is not there."

"The driver went to the Union Garage to fill up with gas."

"It takes him nearly one hour to do that?" Señor Sanchez was dubious. "Let us hope he has not run into trouble."

Tod looked over the man's shoulder. The street was quiet in the fading light. Only a few passers-by were visible as they walked quickly past the closed shops opposite. From the direction of the Plaza Bolivar, however, came shouts and roars of triumph.

At that moment a small black coupé drew up before the door of the import company. "There he is now," Tod said with relief.

"What? You come in a car like that?"

"It was the only one we could find. We were lucky to get anything."

Señor Sanchez eyed Tod's car with an intent look. The driver, clad in chauffeur's livery, got down from the seat and came toward the door. A knock sounded on the thick wood.

"Coming right out," Tod called through the little grille.

Luis Sanchez drew Tod to one side of the dimly lighted office. "Señor," he said in a voice low and excited, "is that the chauffeur who brought you here?"

"Why, yes."

"Where did you find him? In La Guaira?"

"No. Just outside the city."

"Ah, I thought so!" Luis Sanchez clutched Tod's arm. "Tell me. What happened?"

"Nothing much. Captain Jarvis and I rented this little car and got permission from the chief of police. But when we got outside the town and began climbing the mountain road, the driver stopped. He said he was afraid to go any farther. He was afraid to enter Caracas."

"Señor Moran, that was a lie."

Tod's eyes widened. "What do you mean?"

"I see it all now." Luis Sanchez lowered his voice. "Listen. Tell me if I am correct. Your chauffeur tells you he is afraid. He says he will get a friend who will drive you the rest of the way. And he did, yes?"

Tod nodded, puzzled. "But how did you know that the fellow outside isn't the chauffeur I started out with?"

The black eyes of Luis Sanchez gleamed. "And this friend, señor, this driver who brought you here, he is no chauffeur. Even in his driver's suit and cap, even in those dark glasses he wears, I recognize him. He is Paul Velasco, nephew of General Gomez. He is a rich man with a price on his head. If anyone in the streets recognizes him, he will be killed. Your car will be burned. And you——" Luis Sanchez looked at Tod intently. "You would at least be sent to prison."

"But I don't understand." Tod leaned against a counter, surprise crossing his face. "Why should this Paul Velasco return to Caracas if he is in danger here?"

"Ah, that you might ask him. Perhaps there is money he would take with him before he flees the country. Who knows?"

Tod strode across to the little grille and looked out. Up to this time he had paid little attention to his driver. Now he looked with new eyes at this man who sat so alert and immovable behind the wheel. Of course. The fellow was anything but a chauffeur. Well groomed, well fed, his round face had the quick, intent look of a successful business executive. And his uneasiness on the trip over the mountain was not merely fear of losing a car that did not belong to him. It was fear of losing his own life.

Tod turned back to the manager. "This is certainly a nice fix for me to get into! I've got to get back to the *Araby* tonight. And I need that car."

"Then take it. Drive it yourself." Señor Sanchez coughed nervously. "I do not like that man before my door. Were he recognized—— Please hurry."

"But what will happen to him if I leave him here?"

"Is that any affair of yours? Were you not tricked into bringing him here?" Luis Sanchez shook his gray head. "No one is more hated here than this Paul Velasco. He had charge of a prison for political prisoners. His cruelty is a byword."

"If he's that sort, then I'll waste no pity." Tod held out his hand. "Goodby, Señor Sanchez. Thank you for everything."

His companion unbolted the heavy door. "Be sure you do not go so much as one short block with that driver, Señor Moran. It was a miracle he was not recognized before this. Were you not stopped at the barrier as you entered the city?"

"Yes, but the guards let us through with only a few questions. I won't chance it again, though, when I leave. I'll get rid of him right away."

"*Adios, señor.*" Luis Sanchez stood in the doorway as Tod crossed the sidewalk to the car.

Night was closing down upon the city. Along the narrow street the stores were dark, the windows shuttered. Only here and there in the three-storied buildings opposite was a light visible. Prudent people were remaining indoors tonight.

There was an ominous gleam in the glance Tod flung his driver. "Señor Velasco," he said, "get down. I shall drive back to the coast. Alone."

The man at the wheel gave a start of dismay. His round face paled. His lips twitched as he looked at Tod. "The American señor is mistaken. I do not understand."

"You don't?" Tod's hand, closing on the little door, suddenly flung it open. "Get out! I don't intend to get into trouble over your affairs. I've a ship leaving La Guaira before morning."

Behind them Luis Sanchez cried from the doorway, "Hurry, señor! Look. A mob is coming from the Plaza Bolivar."

Tod glanced down the street. Swinging toward him was a shadowy mass of people, marching without haste, singing loudly. From an iron balcony above them a man was waving and shouting encouragement. He could hear the shrill cries: "*¡Abajo la tirania!*"

Tod smiled grimly. Down with tyranny. With the swelling roar of the mob in his ears, he suddenly realized his predicament.

"Get out," he repeated. "I'm driving from now on."

The man at the wheel spoke swiftly. "Señor, let me stay with you till we get out of this section of town. Then I leave."

Tod hesitated. The mob was coming closer. "All right. Get going." He flung himself into the seat.

A shout of protest came from the door of the import company, but Tod had no time to answer. The black coupé shot ahead in high gear.

Tod glared at the man beside him. "Why in thunder didn't you tell me who you were?"

"Because then the señor would not have let me drive him."

"And how much did you pay the owner to turn over his car and license to you?"

"One thousand bolivares."

A low whistle escaped Tod's lips. Nearly two hundred and sixty dollars! He looked at the man closely. "It must have been important business that brought you back to Caracas."

"It was, señor. Very."

At the corner the car slowed up. A woman was trudging down the middle of the street, a huge carved chair on her back. A group of men standing on the corner waved their hands and laughed.

"*¡Abajo la tirania!*" the woman called.

"*¡Viva Venezuela!*" the men shouted in chorus.

Tod couldn't help but smile. At least one woman would have a new chair to grace her house tonight. Loot, probably, from the home of an enemy.

Once safely round the corner, Tod put a hand on the driver's arm. "Stop here. It's time you got out."

"Never, señor, could you find your way to the barrier."

"Couldn't I ask the way?"

The man laughed shortly. "How many people in Caracas do you think speak English? No one would understand you. You would lose the car, too."

Tod loosed his hold. Why in thunder had he been such a fool? He should have suspected that a Venezuelan who spoke English so fluently was no ordinary chauffeur.

"Very well." Tod gave in. "You can drive me to the edge of town. Then out you go."

Ahead of them a street junction flamed with light. He could see several armed police charging past the corner.

"The rebels burn another house," said the driver bitterly. "That is the way I found my own home. Merely the walls standing."

Tod flung the man a quick glance. The plump face was twisted in bitter lines. "You are really Paul Velasco?" Tod asked.

"Why deny the truth?"

"And you had charge of one of the prisons where General Gomez kept his political enemies?"

"True. But they are all free today."

"Those that are still alive, you mean."

"What would you, señor?" The man shrugged as the car swung swiftly across the intersection and gained the darker street ahead. "Someone must rule. His Excellency, General Gomez, was a tyrant, but a benevolent tyrant. Venezuela is a wealthy country, thanks to him and to the oil wells of Maracaibo. He made much money for his country."

"And much money for himself and his friends as well?"

"Assuredly. Why not?"

Tod sat up straight. "Why, Señor Velasco, did you come back to Caracas? Why face this danger again? For money?"

"I have plenty in the bank in Panama, señor."

"I see. Looking into the future, eh?" Tod's voice was filled with scorn. "Tell me, have you hidden any in this car? In the rumble seat?"

The man shook his head. "No, señor."

"You'd better not. We're sure to be searched again. And I want to get to La Guaira. Tonight."

Tod's eyes suddenly narrowed. Their car was speeding down a dark and silent street, and he now saw that the way ahead was blocked by another roving mob bent on mischief. Torches blazed in the night air. The sound of singing came to him above the steady hum of the car's motor. "Maybe, señor," Tod said, "we'd better turn around."

The brakes screamed as the driver stopped. For the first time he switched on the headlights. A row of grilled windows and locked doors sprang into view.

Tod leaned out the door and glanced back. His throat contracted. Another crowd was coming toward them from the rear, torches waving. They were caught between the mobs. "Wait." Tod raised his hand. "You'd better get out and hide."

"But where? These doors are all locked and bolted. The riffraff rule the streets tonight."

"Then we've got to go ahead. Can we make it?"

"Listen, señor. When we reach the crowd you show your American passport. It is our car they will cast greedy eyes at—not us."

"All right." Tod was doubtful. "I don't like it. How far are we from the edge of town?"

"About one kilometer."

Slowly they got under way and headed toward the approaching mob. The street grew lighter; the waving torches flared high against the balconied buildings; the singing reverberated through the narrow street.

"Better slow up," Tod cautioned.

The driver pulled his cap lower over his eyeglasses. He seemed almost to shrink within himself, his olive skin pale, his lips moving soundlessly. Tod reached into his pocket for his passport. Then the mob was upon them. In an instant they were surrounded.

In surprise Tod saw the man at his side thrust his foot on the brake and wave a hand wildly outside. "¡Abajo la tirania!" Paul Velasco shouted as though he really meant it.

Fifty voices took up the cry in triumph. The mob at once became friendly. They were men and women, Tod saw, who were shabbily dressed, their faces wreathed in smiles as though the day of glory had arrived. And perhaps for them it had.

"Señor Moran, shout with them."

The words in his ear moved Tod to action. He leaned far out and waved his passport. "¡Viva Venezuela!" he cried at the top of his lungs.

The crowd about the car waved them on. "Americano," they called gaily. "¡Americano!"

They moved slowly forward. The crowd gave way. Tod began to breathe more freely as they passed the few stragglers in the rear.

Abruptly a man sprang toward their car, a torch aloft in one hand. Jumping to the running board, he snatched off the driver's glasses. "Pablo Velasco!" He raised his voice in hate and derision. "Velasco—Velasco!"

The driver struck with a fist. Under the impact of the blow the man toppled from the running board. The car hurtled forward. Behind them a cry of rage went up from the crowd. Men came running in swift pursuit.

"Hurry!" Tod leaned forward. They must get away at any cost. For good or bad, he was in this affair up to his neck. He could never hope to explain to these irate people that he was innocent of complicity. He could only trust to luck and the speed of their black coupé.

The car gained a side street, turned, and plunged ahead down a narrow winding lane between low, dark buildings. The cries fell away behind them.

"A close call," Tod said with a relieved sigh.

The driver was staring straight ahead.

A sudden thought flashed into Tod's mind. He turned to the man at his side. "Are the telephones still working in Caracas?"

"Si, señor."

"Then they'll phone to the barrier! And there's only one road to La Guaira." A wave of despair swept over him. "The guards will stop us. What'll we do?"

"I know a leetle country lane, señor. It winds through a coffee plantation and reaches the highway halfway up the mountain."

"But won't it be guarded, too?"

"Perhaps. But I do not believe there will be a telephone there."

"All right." Tod peered ahead into the gloom. "When we get to that road, out you get. Understand?"

"But, señor"—the man's deep rich tones were pleading—"if I do not escape from the city with you, I am lost. No one will hide me. I have no home now."

"Why didn't you think of that before you came back?"

"I did, señor. But I had to come just the same. Perhaps I could hide in the rumble seat."

Tod shook his head. "We're sure to be searched again. They'd never overlook the rumble compartment."

"I know. But you could lock it. You have a permit from the prefect of police. A passport, too. Some lowly official might let you pass."

"On a little byroad?" Tod laughed grimly. "He'll be suspicious because I don't travel by the highway."

"That, señor, is a chance we must take."

"You mean you're willing to. But I'm not."

"Señor, it will mean my death."

Tod's voice showed no hint of sympathy. "And just how many deaths were you responsible for here in Caracas? No, Señor Velasco. It is justice."

"Señor Moran, I beg of you. Give me this one chance."

"Nothing doing." Tod looked ahead down the darkened street. Suddenly he sat up. Suppose this man at his side, desperate, fighting for his life, should attempt to steal the car? Attempt to put his fare quietly out of the way? Tod's lithe young body grew taut. Holding himself in readiness, he waited for any move.

But the hands on the wheel did not stir. Only the voice went on. "Señor, it is not for myself I ask this. It is for the sake of my wife and son."

"So you've a family?" Tod frowned as he regarded the man. "I suppose not one of the men you let rot in prison left a family behind?"

"*Si, señor*. Many of them. But I was carrying out orders."

Tod's lips came tightly together. "Listen, Señor Velasco," he said after a moment. "You can't make me give in because of your family. They're nothing to me. And anyway, how do I know you're telling the truth?"

The man drew up suddenly at the curb. Across the sidewalk a shuttered window was opened a trifle, a sliver of light flashed out to the pavement, then the shutter was slammed shut again. The street was once more dark and silent.

"You are getting out here, señor?" Tod was surprised. "Are we near the edge of town?"

"Half a kilometer more." The man stepped to the sidewalk and moved to the rear of the car. Taking a key from his pocket, he unlocked the rumble seat.

"I suppose you've got something hidden there," said Tod, springing out. "Get your stuff and beat it. I'm through with you."

The man threw open the little compartment. Two heads appeared.

Tod stared in astonishment. They had been carrying two passengers locked in the confined space of the rumble seat, two passengers who had made no murmur of protest against their cramped quarters. One was a woman whose eyes in the dim light showed terror. The other was a slender boy who stood up quickly with a glad cry.

The man spoke briefly, almost curtly in Spanish to the two, while Tod looked at them with a sinking sensation. This wasn't fair, he told himself. Not fair at all. He must get back to the *Araby* if she was to sail by morning. His loyalty to the ship came first.

"Señor!" The pleading tone of the man brought Tod up short. "My wife, Señora Velasco. My son, Alberto. They were in the city, hiding at the home of a servant. They could not escape alone. No one dared help them. That is why I returned."

Tod put out a hand and leaned against the fender of the rear wheel. He did not dare meet the glance of the woman who eyed him so beseechingly or look at the boy who contemplated him in silence, only half understanding.

"Señor, our one chance is to leave the city in your car. I beg of you, do this thing for my wife's sake! For my son's sake! Once at La Guaira I can pay enough to get us out of the country. But no money will give us leave to pass the barrier tonight."

Tod's jaw tightened. His eyes narrowed as he cast a quick glance up and down the street. "You win. We'll try. Lock them in again."

"Ah, señor——"

"Don't waste time." Tod's tone was brusque. "Hurry."

A moment later the car was racing ahead once more. Now and then they shot past people who looked at them with suspicion. They came to the northern suburb. Open country lay almost within their grasp.

Before a lighted grocery store an armed guard stood waiting. Tod leaned forward, breathless. His driver pulled his cap lower over his eyes. Their car slowed down.

The guard stepped forward to the driver's side. "*Cédula de Identidad, señor.*"[1]

Tod thrust his papers across the wheel. "To La Guaira."

The guard, short and dark, looked over the papers slowly. There was a pistol prominently displayed on his hip. Abruptly one hand went to his side. He handed the papers back to Tod, while his black eyes searched the face of the driver.

"Get out!" There was no mistaking his words. "Get out, Señor Pablo Velasco." His hand brought up the pistol until it pointed directly at the driver.

Tod did not move from his seat. In dismay he saw the man at his side slide out from behind the wheel and face the guard. Paul Velasco's face seemed drained of all its blood; but his dark eyes were keen, intent.

The guard pointed to the rumble seat. "Open, señor."

Paul Velasco did not comply. Instead he reached toward an inner pocket of his coat, and the guard's

pistol moved forward on the instant. But it was only a purse the man brought forth. He spoke swiftly in a low tone. Gold coins glittered in the light streaming out from the open door of the store.

The guard looked over his shoulder and, nodding, took the purse. He motioned his prisoner toward the store.

"Señor Moran." Paul Velasco's voice was husky with emotion. "Move over and drive. Drive like mad. A telephone message reached the store. The guard dare not let me go. It would mean his death. But you as an American he will overlook. You may pass if you hurry."

That was all that Señor Velasco said. No mention of the two passengers in the rear compartment. No mention of what Tod was to do with them. But Tod Moran understood. He moved across to the wheel. His hand touched the gear shift. "Señor," he said, and his voice was low, "you may count on me."

"Then I shall thank you to my last dying moment."

Tod looked straight ahead. He pulled the clutch into low gear. The car jerked forward. Into second it moved, into high. It gathered speed as it struck the lane running into open country. The steady murmur of its motor was like the drumming beat of its driver's heart.

At ten that night Tod Moran reached La Guaira. When he drove out upon the wooden wharf his eyes sought his ship, moored there with her portholes agleam in the night. Her cargo for Venezuela had already

[1] *Cédula de Identidad, senor:* Identification paper, sir.

been discharged; it lay piled on the dock.

As he sprang out a small seaman came running down the gangway.

"Where's the skipper, Toppy?"

"In 'is cabin, sir. 'E's worried about yer."

Toppy's eyes opened wide when Tod unlocked the rumble seat and ushered out his two passengers. The woman's eyes were dry. Grief too deep for tears showed on her face. The boy clung to her, afraid.

"We can take you both to Panama, señora. You have friends there?"

She nodded. He hurried them up the gangway.

When they entered the saloon cabin, Captain Jarvis sprang to his feet in amazement. "Sufferin' catfish, Third! What's the meaning of this?"

"Two passengers for Panama, sir. They're to have my cabin."

"Impossible. Are you crazy?"

Tod handed over the letters from the manager of the import company in Caracas. "Please, Captain Tom. I'll explain later. Get Toppy to take this letter to the warehouse. Everything ready for shoving off?"

"Yes. But what in thunder——"

"You've got to trust me, sir. Only get us out of this harbor. Before we're stopped. A man gave his life to let these two people get away. Trust me, sir. I'll explain as soon as these two are hidden."

Captain Jarvis looked from the third mate's face to the pleading eyes of the woman and boy. "Very well," he said harshly. "Two passengers for Panama. Get them out of sight. We'll put to sea right now."

❖❖❖

No Escape Yet

1. How was Tod able to escape?
2. Why was Paul Velasco unable to escape? What sacrifice did he make?
3. Why did Paul Velasco go back into the city?
4. Where in the story does Señor Velasco try to justify his bad deeds?
5. At the beginning of the adventure Tod was not entirely a good detective. What events should he have suspected?

Intelligent Guessing

You probably do not run to the dictionary every time you meet a strange word in your reading. Instead, you do some intelligent guessing. You try to determine the meaning through the general sense of the passage. Then later, if you are still in doubt, you check with your dictionary.

Look at the words in italics. From the way they are used, can you tell what they mean? After you have done your intelligent guessing, check with the dictionary.

1. Tod swung about and met the gaze of a small *cockney* seaman.
2. . . . he had seen mobs break into buildings, *looting* the homes and offices of members of the former *regime*.

3. "We were stopped at the edge of town and searched, but my American passport worked like a *talisman*."

4. "Were you not stopped at the *barrier* as you entered the city?"

5. There was an *ominous* gleam in the glance Tod flung his driver.

6. . . . the singing *reverberated* through the narrow street.

7. He could never hope to explain to these *irate* people that he was innocent of *complicity*.

8. Tod's *lithe* young body grew *taut*.

9. Tod's tone was *brusque*.

10. When he drove out upon the wooden wharf, his eyes sought his ship, *moored* there with her *portholes agleam* in the night.

◄ ARMSTRONG SPERRY

"White-water!"

Have you ever harpooned a whale? If you haven't, you can learn how to do it from this story. And hold tight when you hear the call "White-water!"

I COUNTED myself lucky indeed in being a member of Mr. Gardner's crew, where Rimatara was boat steerer and Juan Silva pulled bow oar. Skip Howard was appointed midship oarsman, while the Ferret was responsible for the lines in the tubs. I pulled stroke oar, and was expected to bail in emergencies, as well as help with the sail.

"A whale," Mr. Gardner dinned into us, time after time, "ain't so different from a sailor: each one's got his own peculiarities. You've got to keep a weather eye peeled if you don't want a stove boat. Whales I'm talkin' about now. Why, I've seen a pesky little fifty-bar'l[1] cow put up a fight that lasted twenty-four hours, stove three boats, and killed seven men. And on t'other hand, I've known a hundred-bar'l bull that hardly raised a fluke[2] from first iron to fin-out. Generally speakin', though, a whale will follow one of three courses. He'll turn and come at you head on and try to smash your boat. Or he may take a notion to light out for the horizon, towin' you along for a Nantucket sleigh ride. Or mebbe he'll just turn flukes and sound. That's why you've got to keep the line clear in the tubs, Ferret! Let it foul just once, and we'll all be dragged to Granny Howlan's washtub."

Mr. Gardner taught us the proper way to muffle our oarlocks, something of the fine art of paddling, how to manage sheet and sail, and above all

[1] *fifty-bar'l.* Fifty barrels of whale oil.

——From *Danger to Windward* by Armstrong Sperry, published by The John C. Winston Company.

[2] *fluke.* A part of a whale's tail.

never to forget the special duties of our individual positions. For a good boat crew is a team playing a fine game, each man supplementing the efforts of his mates and trying to anticipate every move of the opponent.

In such manner our training went on, rigorously, day after long day. But it was not until we were somewhere in latitude 37° South and longitude 12° West that we heard the long-awaited cry:

"Blows! Blows! White-water! Blo-o-ows!"[3]

The off watch came tumbling up from below. The cook popped out of his galley, while the mates went racing aloft to see what they could make of it. Davy Macy took the quarter-deck at a bound, sprang into the ratlines, spyglass in hand. The whole ship was thrown into an unbelievable pandemonium of excitement by that magic cry. Those of us on deck, however, could see no sign of spout or whale.

"Ah blows!" again came the lookout's call, ringing across the morning stillness of the air. "Blo-o-ows!"

"Where away?" the captain shouted back.

"Three pints[4] off lee bow, sir. Blo-ows!"

"One," counted the captain.

"Blows! She white-waters!" Again the lookout.

"Two!" from the captain.

"Blo-o-ows!"

"Three!"

"Blo-o-ows!"

<hr>

[3] *blows.* Ejections of moisture-laden air from the lungs of the whale.
[4] *pints.* Points of a compass.

"Four!"

"Blows—"

"Sperm whales, by Jupiter!" cried Mr. Titus, while Davy Macy raked the horizon with his glass.

By this time the spouts were visible to us all—low and "bushy" spouts with the telltale forward rake which bespoke the sperm whale. Here was a whole "pod" of them, some three miles off our lee bows. The monsters lay disporting themselves in the waves, some lazily rolling fin-up, others lobtailing, or making the white-water fly as they flung their vast bodies clear of the sea. It was an amazing spectacle, one which seemed somehow to belong to the childhood of creation; and I caught my breath in wonder and delight.

"They're milling, sir," the lookout warned. "Pintin' to wind'ard now."

"Trim the yards, Mr. Titus," ordered the captain. "Brace her up as sharp as she'll go. All hands stand by the boats." And to the helmsman he rapped: "Keep her up a couple of points . . . There, steady's you go . . . Watch her close!"

"Aye, aye, sir."

Orders were executed almost as rapidly as issued. Sails, spars, braces, and helm—all flexed and functioned like sinews in answer to superior command.

The whales had come up again to breathe, and the lookout was ready for them. "Blows! Blo-o-ows!"

"Blast my toplights!" Mr. Gardner exclaimed. "Hundred-bar'lers, every one. And a dozen of 'em, or I'm a greenie."

David Macy snapped shut his spyglass. "Stand by to lower away!" he bellowed.

Four whaleboats hit the water almost simultaneously, each with boat header and harpooner already in position. Then we of the crew went swarming down the tackles to take the positions for which we'd been trained. By this time the shipkeepers (as the men were called who stayed behind) had trimmed the *Good Intent's* yards to the wind, so that simply putting the helm down deadened her way, allowing the boats to run clear without fouling one another. There was no frantic waste motion, no fumbling; but in every face the most intense anxiety was manifest. Men muted their voices to a whisper, as if fearful that a loud word might drown the distant spouting of the whales.

The breeze was enough to make the sails of greater use than oars, and there was sufficient sea to admit of an easy approach to our quarry; so we stepped the mast and made fast the stays, hoisted and peaked the canvas, paid out the sheet. Like a deer with the hounds at her heels the little whaleboat leaped forward. In no time our boat had gained some fifty yards' advantage over the other three, which soon were widely scattered. The *Good Intent* dropped astern, while signals in her rigging apprised us constantly of the movements of the whales.

Presently, by the disappearance of the colors at the ship's main-truck, we understood that the whales had sounded. Since they had not appeared to be in flight when first sighted, however, it was assumed that they would rise again not far from the place where they had turned flukes. Accordingly when we were within a quarter mile of this spot, we hove to our craft, Mr. Gardner deciding to remain that distance to windward, since it would be easy enough to sail down but more difficult to pull up should we fall to leeward. An occasional wave, lifting us high, disclosed the other boats likewise hove to, but separated by considerable distance.

Now we lay in silence, awaiting the reappearance of our prey; and so taut were we with nervous expectancy that we scarce dared to draw breath. Every eye was strained to catch the slightest motion, every ear peaked to hear the faintest sound. For no one could tell how soon the whales would again surface. Our throats constricted with waiting; our eyes were half-blinded with staring across the sunlit brilliance of the sea.

In his eagerness, Skip had pulled himself up on the bow chock, and was anxiously peering over the waves as the boat rose to a swell. "I think I heard a spout," he whispered.

At that moment a square blue flag appeared at the ship's main-truck, and almost simultaneously came Mr. Gardner's joyous cry: "Blows!" And he pointed excitedly to a bushy spout to starboard, just melting out of sight.

"Blo-o-ws—" Rimatara breathed, gently. "There, and *there*. Blows!"

"By Godfrey!" the mate exulted. "Seven or eight big bulls. I can see 'em clear as rain. Steady now, boys, we'll sail directly down to 'em."

The ship's ensign, dipping at the

peak, informed us that of the four boats ours was nearest to the prey, and most favorably disposed.

"Down with that mast!" the mate ordered.

The peak of the sail was dropped, and the boat swung up into the wind's eye, hove to and almost stationary. The mast was quickly unstepped and made fast.

"Pull a little, boys—"

We shot her ahead for a few strokes, then peaked oars. Now we could hear the spouting of the whales clear enough: a long-drawn whistling exhaust, once heard, never to be forgotten. A cloud of humid vapor, escaping from the pent-up lungs, fanned our necks with rank moisture; and I'm certain it's as well that we greenies rowed with our backs to the quarry and our eyes astern; for I must confess to feeling scared and breathless. I fastened my gaze upon the bronzed, impassive face of Mr. Gardner, towering above me in the stern sheets. That face, so rock-strong with purpose, seemed the one reassurance at that unnerving moment.

"We'll have to stand across a little to come up behind 'em," muttered the mate, singling out one huge bull as our prey. "Don't get on his eye—"

Again came the long-sighing whistle and the cloud of vapor. Involuntarily I flung a glance over my shoulder, forgetting that it was against the rules. There I beheld a monstrous black form, glistening in the waves. My heart gave a great leap and hung fire.

"Eyes astern!" warned the mate. "I'll knock seven bells out of anyone who looks around. Rimatara—stand by your iron!"

A needless command. Already the Polynesian was in position, iron held poised, knee resting on the lubber chock, taut for action.

"A little starboard—" whispered the mate.

The boat was now laid round. As she rose to a wave, the whale seemed almost under us. And now—

"Give it to him!" bellowed the mate.

Rimatara hurled his iron. It buried to its hitches. A beautiful shot.

"The other iron!"

But already it had left the harpooner's hand. The instantaneous *whiz* of the line through the chock told that we were "fast."

"Peak your oars!" came the command. "Wet line, wet line, Ferret. Can't you see it's smoking, you leatherhead?"

Flake after flake of line went skimming overboard with a velocity almost beyond conception. One tub was soon empty and half of the second gone before a slackening in the speed of its exit suggested that the whale had run his length and was now probably returning to the surface. With a dash across the thwarts Mr. Gardner and Rimatara exchanged places. The lances were out of their becket and on the rest. Mr. Gardner seized one and stood ready.

The whale reappeared on the surface, not a ship's length ahead of us. Suddenly he breached, leaping nearly his entire length out of the sea. He fell back with a mighty thunderclap of sound. The water displaced by that monstrous body created a wash which, for a moment, threatened to swamp our boat.

"Haul in slack line, you lubbers!" shouted the mate. "Let's get up to him. Take the line to the bow cleat and pull up."

But by the time we had managed to get in the heavy wet line, the whale was forging slowly ahead with the horizon as his destination.

"Haul up!" again came the command, and we strained our utmost to obey. Slowly, inch by inch, we pulled the boat up to our quarry, while Mr. Gardner stood ready with the lance. But just as we got within dart, the whale again sounded. To my horror, the bow of our boat was sucked half under; and those not prepared for this contingency were thrown sprawling.

By the time the whale had reappeared, and I had bailed us clear, the entire school had surfaced. All were going off at a rate of several knots, of course taking our whale with them. Our boat leaped unexpectedly forward, harnessed as it was to this leviathan. Here was the "Nantucket sleigh ride" with a vengeance! White wings of foam swept back from our bows. We were as drenched as if we had fallen into the sea. Our boat was dragged like a toy on a string, while a wake stretched behind us to the horizon. We could only hold on, and pray, as we saw the *Good Intent* disappearing astern and felt ourselves being hauled willy-nilly through the boiling waters. Not one of us spoke. Only Mr. Gardner and Rimatara seemed unmoved by this extraordi-

nary occurrence. The Polynesian stood by the stern sheets, throwing an occasional turn of the line over the loggerhead: cool and unruffled, as if danger were the very salt of life. The mate, braced against the wild motion of the boat, still held his lance at ready.

For what seemed an interminable time our speed went unslackened. The stern tub was almost empty of line, and the waist tub was being drawn on heavily. It must have been a good half hour (though it seemed vastly longer) before the line went out slower as the whale checked his frantic pace. Our boat fell forward so unexpectedly that its abrupt lack of movement was more disconcerting than the "sleigh ride."

"Haul line there, boys!" shouted the mate. "Look lively now."

Feet braced against the thwarts, we gripped the line and hauled with all our might. Inch by bitter inch we won it back, while Rimatara held what we made with his turn on the loggerhead. Foot by foot the Manila line yielded, to be coiled in a wide heap in the stern sheets, for in its wet state a neat coil would have been impossible. Now I could see the whale lying quite still upon the water, and my teeth began to chatter with excitement as Mr. Gardner braced his knee in the clumsy cleat. His cap had been lost overboard; his shirttails floated on the breeze; sweat and spray streaked his face. But his hands were steady as they gripped the lance.

"Pull me up to the beast," he breathed. "Take a turn around the bow thwart and hold me to him!"

Suddenly the boat scraped against the whale's barnacled side. We held her there. Then, bending almost double, the mate hove his lance. In it went, like a knife into butter, burying itself to the pole hitches: a full six feet of cold iron. Then for a split second the man churned his weapon, withdrew it, sent home his thrust again and again.

A tremendous quiver ran through the vast body. Clotted vapor leaped from the whale's spiracle.

"Blood!" shouted the mate—that cry which the whaleman at all times utters with joy. "He's rolling it out, boys, thick as tar. Stern all now. Quick!"

None too soon. The whale had rolled in his death flurry. Now he began to beat the waters with sweeping flukes. He darted hither and yon in frenzied bursts of speed. Even from a safe distance it was indeed fearsome to behold the devastating power of those thrashing flukes, and in the convolutions of this dying leviathan there was a sort of tragic splendor. We learned afterward that the other boats, more than two miles away from the scene, could hear the reverberations of that titanic struggle.

"Watch out now, lads—"

The mate's words were hardly spoken when the whale, goaded to final effort, lunged upright full length from the water. With a tremendous splash he fell back. Then, as a stream of clotted crimson gushed from the spout hole, the vast glistening carcass rolled fin-out, lay awash upon the sea.

"He's head on to the sun," the mate exulted, beside himself with triumph. "Never knew it to fail!"

And I remembered then that all old whalemen believed that a whale died face to the sun. Whether this be true, or only one more superstition of the fo'c'sle, I cannot say. But one curious fact I noted with this whale, as well as those we subsequently took: it drifted at a good rate right into the wind's eye. Possibly this may be accounted for by the disproportionate weight of the head. Also the wash of the flukes, acting somewhat like the "sculling" of an oar at the stern of a boat, tends to propel the carcass in the direction it is pointing. Sharks, those wary footpads of the deep, were gathering for the feast. The water was teeming and alive with them: blue sharks and gray, the hammerhead and the dreaded tiger. Some of them, darting past, seemed as long as our boat; and the white gleam of their bellies, the gaping jaws so cruelly studded with teeth, were a sight to make the blood run cold.

In the hours that followed, as the long day drew to its close, we were to discover that towing a dead whale involved backbreaking labor. With a spade, Rimatara cut a hole in the flukes of our victim, reeving a warp through solid gristle. Trailing this line, we began the long hard journey back to the *Good Intent*. Sweat ran into our eyes, blinding us; blisters rose on calloused hands—blister upon blister. Our throats were parched; our muscles tortured each with a separate ache. But on we rowed.

"Bend to it, lads," the mate encouraged. "There's a pound of Irish

Twist[5] waiting for every man-Jack of you. Handsomely now—bend to it!"

The swift dark of these latitudes followed close upon the heels of sunset, and still we rowed. A first star hung above the rim of the sea, seemingly so close at hand that one thought to feel its pallid warmth. With a sensation of vast relief we discovered that our ship, dim in the distance, had taken advantage of a rising breeze and was bearing down to us. We lay on our oars then and watched her approach, with lights in her rigging, looking for all the world like some strange sea monster come to avenge the death of one of her kind.

We quickly discovered that the other whaleboats had already returned on board without having made fast to a single whale. We of the waist boat found ourselves the heroes of the hour, rating extra portions of duff[6] at supper, which we wolfed down like men famished.

The sea was rising, the night quite dark, and it seemed as if the most difficult part of our day's work remained still to be done. To secure the whale alongside, in a position for cutting in, it was necessary to pass a chain around that part of its body known as the "small"; the tapering extremity to which the flukes are joined (although it is not actually "small" by any means, except in comparison to the rest of the vast hulk). This operation, simple though it may sound, was carried out only with extreme difficulty. You see, a dead whale lies upon its side with one fin out, floating just awash, the flukes and the small both completely submerged. Consequently, it is no slight undertaking to pass the necessary line, particularly at night in a heavy sea; but performing the impossible is a commonplace aboard a whale ship. A light line was weighted at the middle with ten-pound shot; each boat then took one end of the line and, being stationed on either side of the whale, pulled slowly toward the head, with the intention of passing the "bight" beneath the carcass.

Several times the attempt was made; but each time our line was caught in the fork of the flukes, now perpendicular in the water and reaching to considerable depth. At the fifth trial, our efforts were successful. A hawser was then bent to the line while the chain was slowly paid out overboard. One end of the chain passed through a ring at the opposite extremity, forming a slip noose, or "running bight," as it was called. This noose was quickly tightened about the small, and then the carcass was hauled up to the ship's side and made fast for the night.

It was past eight bells before we of the waist boat climbed wearily aboard, after some sixteen hours of hard and dangerous labor. Orders were then given to get up the cutting gear in readiness for the morrow. When the watch had been set, we staggered below to our bunks and tumbled in, wet clothing and all, to snatch a few hours of blessed oblivion before our day should commence again.

[5] *Irish Twist.* A kind of tobacco.
[6] *duff.* A kind of pudding.

Whaling Takes Understanding

1. What three ways may a whale act after it has been harpooned?
2. What were some of the things Mr. Gardner taught the crew on his whaleboat?
3. When does a whale blow?
4. What are the steps in capturing a whale?
5. Why is the job of making a dead whale fast to the ship a difficult one?

Whaling Vocabulary

What does each of the following mean?

bail	sperm whales
fluke	whales had sounded
blows	harpooner
white-water	spiracle
spout	eight bells

Interesting Ways of Saying Things

Here are some expressions used in the story. Can you tell what each means?

weather eye peeled	Peak your oars!
Nantucket sleigh ride	head on to the sun
Granny Howlan's washtub	rim of the sea
whole "pod" of them	wolfed down
I'm a greenie	blessed oblivion

Seeing and Hearing and Smelling

Here are three interesting examples of ways by which the author appeals to our senses. Can you find other good examples?

1. . . . our eyes were half-blinded with staring across the sunlit brilliance of the sea.
2. A cloud of humid vapor, escaping from the pent-up lungs, fanned our necks with rank moisture. . . .
3. Again came the long-sighing whistle and the cloud of vapor.

Recognizing Main Ideas of Paragraphs

Turn to each of the paragraphs indicated below. Can you in a single sentence give the main idea that Armstrong Sperry is trying to express? Make very sure you are giving the *main idea* and not a detail.

1. "A whale," Mr. Gardner dinned into us, time after . . . (page 36)
2. By this time the spouts were visible . . . (page 37)
3. Now we lay in silence, . . . (page 38)
4. Feet braced against the thwarts, we gripped . . . (page 40)
5. And I remembered then that all old whalemen believed . . . (page 41)

◄◄ W. H. HUDSON

The Serpent with the Cross

W. H. Hudson spent years on the pampas—those treeless plains of the Argentine. His stories of that country ring with truth. This story is no exception. One afternoon he and a friend were planning a trip for the next day. Suddenly an accident occurred. The result of that accident led to an uncomfortable experience with a poisonous snake.

AT LENGTH, one hot afternoon, we were sitting on our rugs on the clay floor of the hut, talking of our journey on the morrow. We spoke of the better fare and other delights we would find at the end of the day at the house of an English settler we were going to visit. While talking, I took up his revolver to examine it for the first time. My friend had just begun to tell me that it was a revolver with a peculiar character of its own, and with idiosyncrasies, one of which was that the slightest touch, or even vibration of the air, would cause it to go off when on the cock.

He was just telling me this, when off the revolver went with a terrible bang and sent a conical bullet into my left knee, an inch or so beneath the kneecap. The pain was not much, the sensation resembling that caused by a smart blow on the knee; but on attempting to get up I fell back. I could not stand. Then the blood began to flow in a thin but continuous

——Reprinted (slightly adapted for readability) from *Tales of the Gauchos* by W. H. Hudson, by permission of Alfred A. Knopf, Inc. Copyright 1946 by Alfred A. Knopf, Inc.

stream from the round symmetrical bore which seemed to go straight into the bone of the joint. Nothing that we could do would serve to stop it.

Here we were in a pretty fix! Thirty-six miles from the settlement, and with no conveyance that my friend could think of except a cart at a house several miles up the river, but on the wrong side! He, however, in his anxiety to do something, imagined, or hoped, that by some means the cart might be got over the river. So, after thoughtfully putting a can of water by my side, he left me lying on my saddle rugs; and, after fastening the door on the outside to prevent the intrusion of unwelcome prowlers, he mounted his horse and rode away. He had promised that, with or without some wheeled thing, he would be back not long after dark. But he did not return all night; he had found a boat and boatman to transport him to the other side only to learn that his plan was impracticable. Then returning with the disappointing tidings, he found no boat to recross, and so in the end was obliged to tie his horse to a bush and lie down to wait for morning.

For me night came only too soon. I had no candle; and the closed, windowless cabin was intensely dark. My wounded leg had become inflamed and pained a great deal, but the bleeding continued until the handkerchiefs we had bound round it were saturated. I was fully dressed; and as the night grew chilly, I pulled my big cloth poncho,[1] that had a soft fluffy lining, over me for warmth. I soon gave up expecting my friend, and knew that there would be no relief until morning. But I could neither doze nor think, and could only listen. From my experience during those black anxious hours I can imagine how much the sense of hearing must be to the blind and to animals that exist in dark caves.

At length, about midnight, I was startled by a slight curious sound in the intense silence and darkness. It was in the cabin and close to me. I thought at first it was like the sound made by a rope drawn slowly over the clay floor. I lighted a wax match; but the sound had ceased, and I saw nothing. After a while I heard it again; but it now seemed to be out of doors and going round the hut, and I paid little attention to it. It soon ceased, and I heard it no more. So silent and dark was it thereafter that the hut I reposed in might have been a roomy coffin in which I had been buried a hundred feet beneath the surface of the earth. Yet I was no longer alone, if I had only known it. I now had a

messmate and bedfellow who had subtly crept in to share the warmth of the cloak and of my person—one with a broad arrow-shaped head, set with round lidless eyes like polished yellow pebbles, and a long smooth limbless body, strangely segmented and vaguely written all over with mystic characters in some dusky tint on an indeterminate grayish tawny ground.

At length, about half-past three to four o'clock, a most welcome sound was heard—the familiar twittering of a pair of scissor-tail tyrant birds from a neighboring willow tree. After an interval, there came the dreamy, softly rising and falling, throaty warblings of the white-rumped swallow. A loved and beautiful bird is this, that utters his early song circling round and round in the dusky air, when the stars begin to pale. His song, perhaps, seems sweeter than all others, because it corresponds in time to that rise in the temperature and swifter flow of the blood—the inward resurrection experienced on each morning of our individual life. Next in order the red-billed finches begin to sing—a curious, gobbling, impetuous performance, more like a cry than a song. These are pretty reed birds, olive green, buff-breasted, with long tails and bright red beaks. The intervals between their spasmodic bursts of sound were filled up with the fine frail melody of the small brown and gray crested song sparrows. Last of all was heard the long, leisurely uttered chanting cry of the brown carrion hawk, as he flew past; and I knew that the morning was beautiful in the east. Little by lit-

---

[1] *poncho.* A cloak which looks like a blanket with a slit in the middle for the head.

tle the light began to appear through the crevices, faint at first, like faintly traced pallid lines on a black ground, then brighter and broader until I, too, had a dim twilight in the cabin.

Not until the sun was an hour up did my friend return to me to find me hopeful still, and with all my faculties about me, but unable to move without assistance. Putting his arms around me, he helped me up. Just as I had got erect on my sound leg, leaning heavily on him, out from beneath the poncho lying at my feet glided a large serpent of a venomous kind, the *Craspedocephalus alternatus*, called in the vernacular "the serpent with a cross." Had my friend's arms not been occupied with sustaining me he, no doubt, would have attacked it with the first weapon that offered, and in all probability killed it, with the result that I should have suffered from a kind of vicarious remorse ever after. Fortunately it was not long in drawing its coils out of sight and danger into a hole in the wall. My hospitality had been unconscious, nor, until that moment, had I known that something had touched me. I rejoice to think that the secret deadly creature, after lying all night with me, warming its chilly blood with my warmth, went back unbruised to its den.

❖❆❖

To Consider

1. Why is the story called "The Serpent with the Cross"?
2. How is time an important element in the story?
3. What details does Hudson include to show the unusual setting of the story? Read sentences which give a picture of the setting.
4. Why was Hudson glad that his friend did not kill the snake?
5. How can you tell that this is a true story?

Words, Words, Words

The interesting words given in Column A appear in the story. Can you match them correctly with the words and phrases in Column B?

A	B
1. idiosyncrasies	a. poisonous
2. vibration	b. hasty
3. conical	c. encroachment
4. symmetrical	d. experiencing for another
5. conveyance	e. peculiarities
6. intrusion	f. cone-shaped
7. poncho	g. fitful
8. segmented	h. a quivering
9. impetuous	i. vehicle
10. spasmodic	j. balanced
11. venomous	k. divided into sections
12. vicarious	l. a cloak made like a blanket

Following the Author's Time Line

Hudson's story about the serpent is easy to follow because the passage of time is so clearly indicated. In the very first sentence Hudson tells what time of day it was. From there to the end of the story he keeps the reader informed as to the time. Hudson is a master of this chronological method of telling a story.

Can you point out the sentences in the story in which the passage of time is indicated?

❧ Mildred Plew Meigs

Pirate Don Durk of Dowdee

Here is the story of a pirate. He was terribly wicked,
but he was also so perfectly gorgeous to see that even
the mermaids "deep down in the ocean" went splash
at the mere thought of him.

Ho, for the Pirate Don Durk of Dowdee!
He was as wicked as wicked could be;
But oh, he was perfectly gorgeous to see!
    The Pirate Don Durk of Dowdee.

His conscience, of course, was as black as a bat;
But he had a floppety plume on his hat;
And when he went walking, it jiggled—like that!
    The plume of the Pirate Dowdee.

His coat it was crimson and cut with a slash,
And often as ever he twirled his mustache.
Deep down in the ocean the mermaids went splash,
    Because of Don Durk of Dowdee.

Moreover, Dowdee had a purple tattoo;
And stuck in his belt where he buckled it through
Were a dagger, a dirk, and a squizzamaroo,
    For fierce was the Pirate Dowdee.

So fearful he was he would shoot at a puff;
And always at sea when the weather grew rough,
He drank from a bottle and wrote on his cuff,
    Did Pirate Don Durk of Dowdee.

——Used by permission of Clifford H. Meigs.

Oh, he had a cutlass that swung at his thigh,
And he had a parrot called Pepperkin Pye
And a zigzaggy scar at the end of his eye,
    Had Pirate Don Durk of Dowdee.

He kept in a cavern, this buccaneer bold,
A curious chest that was covered with mold;
And all of his pockets were jingly with gold!
    Oh jing! went the gold of Dowdee.

His conscience, of course, it was crook'd like a squash;
But both of his boots made a slickery slosh;
And he went through the world with a wonderful swash,
    Did Pirate Don Durk of Dowdee.

It's true he was wicked as wicked could be;
His sins they outnumbered a hundred and three;
But oh, he was perfectly gorgeous to see,
    The Pirate Don Durk of Dowdee.

❖❰❖

Wicked and Gorgeous

1. How do you know that Pirate Don Durk was perfectly gorgeous to see? What details of his beauty does the poet give?

2. Is there any truth in this poem? Don't say a quick no.

Rhymes for the Pirate

Look at the rhyme scheme of the poem. Which lines in each stanza rhyme? Now look at the rhyming words that are used. Are all of them real words?

Sound Advice

Leave adventure
To the masses;
Take your time
And shine your glasses.

LOOKING BACKWARD THROUGH THE CHAPTER

1. In what ways are Dave and Laura alike in character? Prove your opinion by specific passages in the stories.
2. What do you think of the two characters Pirate Don Durk of Dowdee and Paul Velasco?
3. How do Sperry and Hudson give the ring of reality to their stories?
4. In what different places do the stories and poems in this chapter take place?

SHARPENING YOUR WITS

Who Wrote What?

Match the titles in the first column with the authors in the second. Try to do this without looking back at the stories.

1. "White-water!"   a. Mildred Plew Meigs
2. Passengers for Panama   b. W. H. Hudson
3. Split Cherry Tree   c. Laura Ingalls Wilder
4. The Serpent with the Cross   d. Armstrong Sperry
5. Pirate Don Durk of Dowdee   e. Howard Pease
6. Caught in a Blizzard   f. Jesse Stuart

Who Did What?

Can you name these characters?
1. A boy who accidentally helped to break a tree
2. A girl who took care of her sister in a blizzard
3. A man who had an experience with a snake
4. A seaman who was mixed up in a revolution
5. A fierce but handsome pirate
6. A Polynesian who was boat steerer of a whaling crew

What Do These Mean?

Can you "guess" what these words mean from the way they are used in the sentences?
1. ". . . all this swarm of youngins out to *pillage* th' whole deestrict."
2. She was alone in the *confusion* of whirling winds . . . .
3. ". . . but my American passport worked like a *talisman*."
4. But already it had left the *harpooner's* hand.
5. . . . it was a revolver with a peculiar character of its own, and with *idiosyncrasies*.

ADVENTURING FURTHER

1. Perhaps you would like to read other stories of adventure. If you would, the list on pages 50 and 51 may be the "open sesame" to some exciting times.
2. Examine the news articles in your newspaper for several days. Do you find any which might be the basis for good adventure stories? Report your findings to the class.

3. Write briefly on one of these topics or on one of similar nature:
   a. An Unforgettable Character
   b. The Importance of Setting
   c. Characters Talk as They Are
   d. My Father (*or* My Mother)
   e. Moments of Crisis Prove the Person

4. Take an inventory of your reading habits. Obviously the chief purpose of reading is to get the main idea that the author is trying to present. When you read, do you *know* what you read? Practice reading a number of stories; and, as you read, keep asking yourself: *What is the main idea?*

STORIES OF ADVENTURE

Brier, Howard M., *Sky Freighter*, 1942 (Random House).
   The flying of freight to radium mines in arctic Canada.

Brink, Carol R., *Magical Melons*, 1944 (Macmillan).
   A true picture of pioneer Wisconsin and of Caddie Woodlawn, her family, and friends.

Calahan, Harold A., *Back to Treasure Island*, 1935 (Vanguard Press).
   More about Long John Silver, Black Dog, and Jim Hawkins.

Church, Richard, *Five Boys in a Cave*, 1951 (Day).
   Jim and his four friends in a perilous descent.

Du Bois, William Pène, *Twenty-one Balloons*, 1947 (Viking).
   Professor Sherman's fantastic trip in a balloon.

Du Soe, Robert C., *Three without Fear*, 1947 (Longmans).
   Exciting experiences of a shipwrecked American boy and two orphaned Indian children.

Edmonds, Walter D., *Tom Whipple*, 1942 (Dodd).
   A young boy's trip to Russia and his visit with the emperor.

Enright, Elizabeth, *Spiderweb for Two*, 1951 (Rinehart).
   Surprise coded messages for the Melendys.

Field, Rachel L., *Hitty; Her First Hundred Years*, 1929 (Macmillan).
   A doll's-eye view of her hundred years' eventful life.

Gray, Elizabeth Janet, *Adam of the Road*, 1942 (Viking).
   A very real boy's search for his father and dog in England during the thirteenth century.

Herron, Edward A., *The Big Country*, 1953 (Aladdin).
   The Alaskan background as a setting for a rugged battle with nature.

Kent, Louise Andrews, *He Went with Marco Polo*, 1935 (Houghton).
   A young gondolier's adventures and travels with Marco Polo.

Leeming, Joseph (editor), *Riddles, Riddles, Riddles*, 1953 (F. Watts).
   Another "triple title" fun book.

McSwigan, Marie, *Snow Treasure*, 1942 (Dutton).
An exciting tale of children smuggling gold out of Norway during the Nazi occupation.

Marshall, Rosamond V., *None but the Brave*, 1942 (Houghton).
Adventure and sword play in Holland in the sixteenth century.

Molloy, Anne, *The Monkey's Fist*, 1953 (Houghton).
Tugboating and smuggling equal adventure.

Pease, Howard, *Captain of the Araby*, 1953 (Doubleday).
Rousing South Sea mystery.

Ransome, Arthur, *Swallows and Amazons*, 1931 (Lippincott).
English children, a parrot, and a pirate on a small island.

Saint Exupéry, Antoine de, *The Little Prince*, 1943 (Reynal).
An encounter with the Little Prince, after a forced landing in the Sahara—a modern fairy tale.

Sanger, Frances, *The Silver Teapot*, 1948 (Westminster).
Mystery and suspense mingled with history in an exciting tale of the Battle of Bennington.

Sperry, Armstrong, *Thunder Country*, 1952 (Macmillan).
Harrowing adventures in the Venezuelan jungles.

Sterne, Emma Gelders, *The Long Black Schooner*, 1954 (Aladdin).
The story of a remarkable voyage to freedom.

Stevenson, Robert Louis, *Treasure Island*, 1924 (Scribner).
The classic of adventure tales—pirates, mutiny, and buried treasure.

Torjesen, Elizabeth, *Captain Ramsay's Daughter*, 1953 (Lothrop).
Life and adventures of a whaling family in the Nantucket of the 1830's.

Villiers, Alan, *And Not to Yield*, 1953 (Scribner).
Seaworthy adventures on a training ketch, after World War II.

Wheelwright, Jere, *Gentlemen, Hush!* 1948 (Scribner).
Reconstruction days after the War between the States.

Wilder, Laura Ingalls, *These Happy Golden Years*, 1953 (Harper).
More about Laura, her family, and Almanzo, plus romance and teaching.

Tooth
and Claw

Lobo, the King of Currumpaw

"Lobo" is one of the finest stories about a wolf ever written. The fact that it is a true story makes it even more exciting.

(Note the time when you begin reading in order to tell how long it takes you to read this story.)

I

CURRUMPAW is a vast cattle range in northern New Mexico. It is a land of rich pastures and teeming flocks and herds, a land of rolling mesas[1] and precious running waters that at length unite in the Currumpaw River, from which the whole region is named. And the king whose despotic power was felt over its entire extent was an old gray wolf.

Old Lobo, or the king, as the Mexicans called him, was the gigantic leader of a remarkable pack of gray wolves that had ravaged the Currumpaw Valley for a number of years. All the shepherds and ranchmen knew him well; and, wherever he appeared with his trusty band, terror reigned supreme among the cattle and wrath and despair among their owners. Old Lobo was a giant among wolves and was cunning and strong in proportion to his size. His voice at night was well known and easily distinguished from that of any of his fellows. An ordinary

wolf might howl half the night about the herdsman's bivouac without attracting more than a passing notice; but when the deep roar of the old king came booming down the canyon, the watcher bestirred himself and prepared to learn in the morning that fresh and serious inroads had been made among the herds.

Old Lobo's band was but a small one. This I never quite understood, for usually, when a wolf rises to the position and power that he had, he attracts a numerous following. It may be that he had as many as he desired, or perhaps his ferocious temper prevented the increase of his pack. Certain is it that Lobo had only five followers during the latter part of his reign. Each of these, however, was a wolf of renown. Most of them were above the ordinary size: one in particular, the second in command, was a veritable giant; but even he was far below the leader in size and prowess. Several of the band, besides the two leaders, were especially noted. One of those was a beautiful white wolf that the Mexicans called Blanca; this was supposed to be a female, possibly

---

[1] *mesas*. Flat-topped land with sloping sides.
——Reprinted from *Wild Animals I Have Known* by Ernest Thompson Seton; copyright 1896, 1926 by Ernest Thompson Seton; used by permission of the publishers, Charles Scribner's Sons.

Lobo's mate. Another was a yellow wolf of remarkable swiftness, which, according to current stories had, on several occasions, captured an antelope for the pack.

It will be seen, then, that these wolves were thoroughly well known to the cowboys and shepherds. They were frequently seen and oftener heard; and their lives were intimately associated with those of the cattlemen, who would so gladly have destroyed them. There was not a stockman on the Currumpaw who would not readily have given the value of many steers for the scalp of any one of Lobo's band, but they seemed to possess charmed lives and defied all manner of devices to kill them. They scorned all hunters, derided all poisons, and continued, for at least five years, to exact their tribute from the Currumpaw ranchers to the extent, many said, of a cow each day. According to this estimate, therefore, the band had killed more than two thousand of the finest stock, for, as was only too well-known, they selected the best in every instance.

II

In the fall of 1893, I made the acquaintance of the wily marauder, and at length came to know him more thoroughly than anyone else. Some years before I had been a wolf hunter; but my occupations since then had been of another sort, chaining me to stool and desk. I was much in need of a change, and when a friend, who was also a ranch owner on the Currumpaw, asked me to come to New Mexico and try if I could do anything with this predatory pack, I accepted the invitation and, eager to make the acquaintance of its king, was as soon as possible among the mesas of that region. I spent some time riding about to learn the country; and at intervals, my guide would point to the skeleton of a cow to which the hide still adhered, and remark, "That's some of his work."

It became quite clear to me that, in this rough country, it was useless to think of pursuing Lobo with hounds and horses, so that poison or traps were the only available expedients. At present we had no traps large enough, so I set to work with poison.

I need not enter into the details of a hundred devices that I employed to circumvent this *loup-garou*[2]; there was no combination of strychnine, arsenic, cyanide, or prussic acid, that I did not essay; there was no manner of flesh that I did not try as bait; but morning after morning, as I rode forth to learn the result, I found that all my efforts had been useless. The old king was too cunning for me.

A single instance will show his wonderful sagacity. Acting on the hint of an old trapper, I melted some cheese together with the kidney fat of a freshly killed heifer, stewing it in a china dish and cutting it with a bone knife to avoid the taint of metal. When the mixture was cool, I cut it into lumps, and making a hole in one side of each lump, I inserted a large dose of strychnine and cyanide, contained in a capsule that was impermeable by any odor; finally I sealed the holes up with

[2] *loup-garou.* Werewolf.

pieces of the cheese itself. During the whole process, I wore a pair of gloves steeped in the hot blood of the heifer and even avoided breathing on the baits. When all was ready, I put them in a rawhide bag rubbed all over with blood and rode forth dragging the liver and kidneys of the beef at the end of a rope. With this I made a ten-mile circuit, dropping a bait at each quarter of a mile and taking the utmost care, always, not to touch any with my hands.

Lobo, generally, came into this part of the range in the early part of each week and passed the latter part, it was supposed, around the base of Sierra Grande. This was Monday; and that same evening, as we were about to retire, I heard the deep bass howl of his majesty. On hearing it one of the boys briefly remarked, "There he is; we'll see."

The next morning I went forth, eager to know the result. I soon came on the fresh trail of the robbers, with Lobo in the lead—his track was always easily distinguished. An ordinary wolf's forefoot is 4½ inches long, that of a large wolf 4¾ inches; but Lobo's, as measured a number of times, was 5½ inches from claw to heel. I afterward found that his other proportions were commensurate, for he stood three feet high at the shoulder, and weighed 150 pounds. His trail, therefore, though obscured by those of his followers, was never difficult to trace. The pack had soon found the track of my drag and, as usual, followed it. I could see that Lobo had come to the first bait, sniffed about it, and finally had picked it up.

Then I could not conceal my delight. "I've got him at last," I exclaimed; "I shall find him stark within a mile," and I galloped on with eager eyes fixed on the great broad track in the dust. It led me to the second bait and that also was gone. How I exulted—I surely have him now and perhaps several of his band. But there was the broad paw mark still on the drag; and though I stood in the stirrup and scanned the plain I saw nothing that looked like a dead wolf. Again I followed—to find now that the third bait was gone—and the king wolf's track led on to the fourth, there to learn that he had not really taken a bait at all but had merely carried them in his mouth. Then having piled the three on the fourth, he scattered filth over them to express his utter contempt for my devices. After this he left my drag and went about his business with the pack he guarded so effectively.

This is only one of many similar experiences which convinced me that poison would never avail to destroy this robber; and though I continued to use it while awaiting the arrival of the traps, it was only because it was meanwhile a sure means of killing many prairie wolves and other destructive vermin.

About this time there came under my observation an incident that will illustrate Lobo's diabolic cunning. These wolves had at least one pursuit which was merely an amusement: it was stampeding and killing sheep, though they rarely ate them. The sheep are usually kept in flocks of from one thousand to three thousand under one or more shepherds. At night they are gathered in the most sheltered place available, and a herdsman sleeps on each side of the flock to give additional protection. Sheep are such senseless creatures that they are liable to be stampeded by the veriest trifle; but they have deeply ingrained in their nature one, and perhaps only one, strong weakness; namely, to follow their leader. And this the shepherds turn to good account by putting half a dozen goats in the flock of sheep. The latter recognize the superior intelligence of their bearded cousins; and when a night alarm occurs, they crowd around them and usually are thus saved from a stampede and are easily protected. But it was not always so.

One night late in last November, two Perico shepherds were aroused by an onset of wolves. Their flocks huddled around the goats, which being neither fools nor cowards, stood their ground and were bravely defiant; but alas for them, no common wolf was heading this attack. Old Lobo, the werewolf, knew as well as the shepherds that the goats were the moral force of the flock; so, hastily running over the backs of the densely packed sheep, he fell on these leaders, slew them all in a few minutes, and soon had the luckless sheep stampeding in a thousand different directions. For weeks afterward I was almost daily accosted by some anxious shepherd who asked, "Have you seen any stray OTO sheep lately?" and usually I was obliged to say I had; one day it was, "Yes, I came on some five or six carcasses by Diamond Springs"; or

another, it was to the effect that I had seen a small "bunch" running on the Malpai Mesa; or again, "No, but Juan Meira saw about twenty, freshly killed, on the Cedra Monte two days ago."

At length the wolf traps arrived, and with two men I worked a whole week to get them properly set out. We spared no labor or pains; I adopted every device I could think of that might help to insure success. The second day after the traps arrived, I rode around to inspect and soon came upon Lobo's trail running from trap to trap. In the dust I could read the whole story of his doings that night. He had trotted along in the darkness; and although the traps were so carefully concealed, he had instantly detected the first one. Stopping the onward march of the pack, he had cautiously scratched around it until he had disclosed the trap, the chain, and the log, then left them wholly exposed to view with the trap still unsprung; and passing on, he treated over a dozen traps in the same fashion.

Very soon I noticed that he stopped and turned aside as soon as he detected suspicious signs on the trail, and a new plan to outwit him at once suggested itself. I set the traps in the form of an H; that is, with a row of traps on each side of the trail, and one on the trail for the crossbar of the H. Before long, I had an opportunity to count another failure. Lobo came trotting along the trail and was fairly between the parallel lines before he detected the single trap in the trail. But he stopped in time, and why or how he knew enough I cannot tell—

the Angel of the wild things must have been with him—but without turning an inch to the right or left, he slowly and cautiously backed on his own tracks, putting each paw exactly in its old track until he was off the dangerous ground. Then returning at one side he scratched clods and stones with his hind feet till he had sprung every trap. This he did on many other occasions; and although I varied my methods and redoubled my precautions, he was never deceived, his sagacity seemed never at fault, and he might have been pursuing his career of rapine today but for an unfortunate alliance that proved his ruin and added his name to the long list of heroes who, unassailable when alone, have fallen through the indiscretion of a trusted ally.

III

Once or twice I had found indications that everything was not quite right in the Currumpaw pack. There were signs of irregularity, I thought; for instance, there was clearly the trail of a smaller wolf running ahead of the leader, at times, and this I could not understand until a cowboy made a remark which explained the matter. "I saw them today," he said, "and the wild one that breaks away is Blanca." Then the truth dawned upon me, and I added, "Now, I know that Blanca is a she-wolf, because were a he-wolf to act thus, Lobo would kill him at once."

This suggested a new plan. I killed a heifer and set one or two rather obvious traps about the carcass. Then cutting off the head, which is considered useless offal and quite beneath the notice of a wolf, I set it a little apart and around it placed two powerful steel traps properly deodorized and concealed with the utmost care. During my operations I kept my hands, boots, and implements smeared with fresh blood, and afterward sprinkled the ground with the same, as though it had flowed from the head; and when the traps were buried in the dust, I brushed the place over with the skin of a coyote, and with a foot of the same animal made a number of tracks over the traps. The head was so placed that there was a narrow passage between it and some tussocks; and in this passage I buried two of my best traps, fastening them to the head itself.

Wolves have a habit of approaching every carcass they get the wind of, in order to examine it, even when they have no intention of eating of it; and I hoped that this habit would bring the Currumpaw pack within reach of my latest stratagem. I did not doubt that Lobo would detect my handiwork about the meat and prevent the pack approaching it; but I did build some hopes on the head, for it looked as though it had been thrown aside as useless.

Next morning, I sallied forth to inspect the traps, and there, oh, joy! were the tracks of the pack and the place where the beef head and its traps had been was empty. A hasty study of the trail showed that Lobo had kept the pack from approaching the meat; but one, a small wolf, had evidently gone on to examine the head as it lay apart and had walked right into one of the traps.

We set out on the trail and within a mile discovered that the hapless wolf was Blanca. Away she went, however, at a gallop; and although encumbered by the beef head, which weighed over fifty pounds, she speedily distanced my companion, who was on foot. But we overtook her when she reached the rocks, for the horns of the cow's head became caught and held her fast. She was the handsomest wolf I had ever seen. Her coat was in perfect condition and nearly white.

She turned to fight and, raising her voice in the rallying cry of her race, sent a long howl rolling over the canyon. From far away upon the mesa came a deep response, the cry of Old Lobo. That was her last call, for now we had closed in on her and all her energy and breath were devoted to combat.

Then followed the inevitable tragedy, the idea of which I shrank from afterward more than at the time. We each threw a lasso over the neck of the doomed wolf and strained our horses in opposite directions until the blood burst from her mouth, her eyes glazed, her limbs stiffened and then fell limp. Homeward then we rode, carrying the dead wolf and exulting over this, the first deathblow we had been able to inflict on the Currumpaw pack.

At intervals during the tragedy, and afterward as we rode homeward, we heard the roar of Lobo as he wandered about on the distant mesas, where he seemed to be searching for Blanca. He had never really deserted her; but

knowing that he could not save her, his deep-rooted dread of firearms had been too much for him when he saw us approaching. All that day we heard him wailing as he roamed in his quest; and I remarked at length to one of the boys, "Now, indeed, I truly know that Blanca was his mate."

As evening fell, he seemed to be coming toward the home canyon, for his voice sounded continually nearer. There was an unmistakable note of sorrow in it now. It was no longer the loud, defiant howl, but a long, plaintive wail; "Blanca! Blanca!" he seemed to call. And as night came down, I noticed that he was not far from the place where we had overtaken her. At length he seemed to find the trail; and when he came to the spot where we had killed her, his heartbroken wailing was piteous to hear. It was sadder than I could possibly have believed. Even the stolid cowboys noticed it and said they had "never heard a wolf carry on like that before." He seemed to know exactly what had taken place, for her blood had stained the place of her death.

Then he took up the trail of the horses and followed it to the ranch house. Whether in hopes of finding her there or in quest of revenge, I know not; but the latter was what he found, for he surprised our unfortunate watchdog outside and tore him to little bits within fifty yards of the door. He evidently came alone this time, for I found but one trail next morning; and he had galloped about in a reckless manner that was very unusual with him. I had half expected this and had set a number of additional traps about the pasture. Afterward I found that he had indeed fallen into one of these; but such was his strength, he had torn himself loose and cast it aside.

I believed that he would continue in the neighborhood until he found her body at least, so I concentrated all my energies on this one enterprise of catching him before he left the region and while yet in this reckless mood. Then I realized what a mistake I had made in killing Blanca, for by using her as a decoy I might have secured him the next night.

I gathered in all the traps I could command, one hundred and thirty strong steel wolf traps, and set them in fours in every trail that led into the canyon; each trap was separately fastened to a log, and each log was separately buried. In burying them, I carefully removed the sod; and every particle of earth that was lifted we put in blankets so that after the sod was replaced and all was finished, the eye could detect no trace of human handiwork. When the traps were concealed, I trailed the body of poor Blanca over each place and made of it a drag that circled all about the ranch; and finally I took off one of her paws and made with it a line of tracks over each trap. Every precaution and device known to me I used, and retired at a late hour to await the result.

Once during the night I thought I heard Old Lobo but was not sure of it. Next day I rode around; but darkness came on before I completed the circuit of the north canyon, and I had nothing to report. At supper one of the cowboys said, "There was a great row among the cattle in the north canyon this morning; maybe there is something in the traps there." It was afternoon of the next day before I got to the place referred to; and as I drew near, a great grizzly form arose from the ground, vainly endeavoring to escape, and there revealed before me stood Lobo, King of the Currumpaw, firmly held in the traps.

Poor old hero, he had never ceased to search for his darling; and when he found the trail her body had made, he followed it recklessly and so fell into the snare prepared for him. There he lay in the iron grasp of all four traps, perfectly helpless; and all around him were numerous tracks showing how the cattle had gathered about him to insult the fallen despot, without daring to approach within his reach. For two days and two nights he had lain there and now was worn out with struggling. Yet, when I went near him, he rose up with bristling mane and raised his voice and for the last time made the canyon reverberate with his deep bass roar, a call for help, the muster call of his band.

But there was none to answer him; and, left alone in his extremity, he whirled about with all his strength and made a desperate effort to get at me. All in vain: each trap was a dead drag of over three hundred pounds; and in their relentless fourfold grasp, with great steel jaws on every foot, and the heavy logs and chains all entangled together, he was absolutely powerless. How his huge ivory tusks did grind on those cruel chains! And when I ventured to touch him with my rifle barrel, he left grooves on it which are there to this day. His eyes glared green with hate and fury, and his jaws snapped with a hollow "chop" as he vainly endeavored to reach me and my trembling horse. But he was worn out with hunger and struggling and loss of blood, and he soon sank exhausted to the ground.

Something like compunction came over me, as I prepared to deal out to him that which so many had suffered at his hands.

"Grand old outlaw, hero of a thousand lawless raids, in a few minutes you will be but a great load of carrion. It cannot be otherwise." Then I swung my lasso and sent it whistling over his head. But not so fast; he was yet far from being subdued, and, before the supple coils had fallen on his neck, he seized the noose and, with one fierce chop, cut through its hard thick strands and dropped it in two pieces at his feet.

Of course I had my rifle as a last resource; but I did not wish to spoil his royal hide, so I galloped back to the camp and returned with a cowboy and a fresh lasso. We threw to our victim a stick of wood which he seized in his teeth; and before he could relinquish it, our lassoes whistled through the air and tightened on his neck.

Yet before the light had died from his fierce eyes, I cried, "Stay, we will not kill him; let us take him alive to the camp." He was so completely powerless now that it was easy to put a stout stick through his mouth, behind his tusks, and then lash his jaws with a heavy cord which was also fastened to the stick. The stick kept the cord in, and the cord kept the stick in, so he was harmless. As soon as he felt his jaws were tied, he made no further resistance and uttered no sound, but looked calmly at us and seemed to say, "Well, you have got me at last; do as you please with me." And from that time he took no more notice of us.

We tied his feet securely; but he never groaned, nor growled, nor turned his head. Then with our united strength we were just able to put him on my horse. His breath came evenly as though sleeping; and his eyes were bright and clear again, but did not rest on us. Afar on the great rolling mesas they were fixed, his passing kingdom, where his famous band was now scattered. And he gazed till the pony descended the pathway into the canyon and the rocks cut off the view.

By traveling slowly, we reached the ranch in safety; and after securing him with a collar and a strong chain, we staked him out in the pasture and removed the cords. Then for the first time I could examine him closely and proved how unreliable is vulgar report when a living hero or tyrant is concerned. He had *not* a collar of gold about his neck, nor was there on his shoulders an inverted cross to denote that he had leagued himself with Satan. But I did find on one haunch a great broad scar that tradition says was the fang mark of Juno, the leader of Tannerey's wolf hounds—a mark which she gave him the moment before he stretched her lifeless on the sand of the canyon.

I set meat and water beside him, but he paid no heed. He lay calmly on his breast, and gazed with those steadfast yellow eyes away past me down through the gateway of the canyon, over the open plains—his plains—nor moved a muscle when I touched him. When the sun went down, he was still gazing fixedly across the prairie. I expected he would call up his band when night came, and prepared for them; but he had called once in his extremity, and none had come; he would never call again.

A lion shorn of his strength, an eagle robbed of his freedom, or a dove bereft of his mate, all die, it is said, of a broken heart; and who will aver that this grim bandit could bear the threefold brunt, heart-whole? This only I know, that when the morning dawned, he was lying there still in his position of calm repose, but his spirit was gone—the old king wolf was dead.

I took the chain from his neck, a cowboy helped me to carry him to the shed where lay the remains of Blanca, and as we laid him beside her, the cattleman exclaimed: "There, you *would* come to her; now you are together again."

(Note the time; and check your speed of reading below, using the Reading Score Board.)

❖❮❖

WORTH THINKING ABOUT

1. In what ways did Lobo seem to have human traits and intelligence?
2. Why was the killing of the wolves necessary?
3. Why is the ending of the story especially good?
4. Do you know any stories—truth or fiction—which deal with the grief of animals?

SOMETHING NEW HAS BEEN ADDED

What interesting information did you find on each of these pages?

page 54   page 55   page 57   page 62

WORDS—PICTURES AND MEANINGS

Can you explain the meaning of each of the following?

teeming flocks	herdsman's bivouac	diabolic cunning	plaintive wail
despotic power	veritable giant	rallying cry	load of carrion

READING SCORE BOARD

Number of Words in Story: 4360

Number of Minutes	43 1/2	22	17 1/2	14 1/2	11	8 1/2
Reading Rate	100 w.p.m.	200 w.p.m.	250 w.p.m.	300 w.p.m.	400 w.p.m.	500 w.p.m.

Are you satisfied with the speed with which you read? Let us suppose that it took you 22 minutes to read the story. Someone else, reading 400 words a minute, was able to finish the story in 11 minutes. It does not take much mathematical ability to figure out the amount of time that the fast reader saved. Counting all the reading assignments that have to be done during a day, you can easily see that it pays to be a fast reader. Moreover, every test shows that speedy readers have a better understanding of what they read than do slow readers.

Now is the time to increase your rate of reading. First, how do you read? Do you read word by word like this?

Currumpaw   is   a   vast   cattle   range   in   northern

Or do you make your eyes take in several words at a time like this?

Currumpaw   is a   vast cattle range   in northern New Mexico.

It is a land   of rich pastures   and teeming flocks   and herds.

Reread some of the paragraphs of "Lobo," and try to determine how you read. If you are a word-by-word reader, *force* your eyes to take in several words at a time. The process will not be very comfortable at first; but if you really want to increase your reading speed, you will not mind a little discomfort.

ᐊ RUTHERFORD G. MONTGOMERY

Wapiti, the Elk

Wapiti is an Indian word meaning "king of the high country." The elk you will read about in this story proves by combat his right to the name *Wapiti*. Rutherford G. Montgomery has written many fine stories about animals but none more thrilling than this one.
(Note the time when you begin reading.)

THERE WERE eleven cows and three calves in the band. Wapiti kept them going until they came to a tall grass meadow with a stream flowing through it. Here the cows halted and started grazing. Wapiti marched about, whining coaxingly and grunting. He was bursting with savage pride, eager to defend his band, ready to challenge the whole world to come and fight. When one of the cows strayed farther than he thought proper, he went after her and drove her roughly back into the meadow.

Without ever having had his own band during the time of the mad moon, he knew what to do. The knowledge came to him the same as his desire to fight or to seek the high country when his antlers started forming. He was part of a grand plan and

——From *Wapiti, the Elk* by Rutherford G. Montgomery, by permission of Little, Brown & Co. Copyright 1952 by Rutherford G. Montgomery.

he acted his role without having to learn it.

If he had been cunning like the lobo or the cougar, he would have herded the cows into a secluded meadow where he could have kept them unmolested. But he wasn't cunning. He was angry and filled with a raging sense of power. He feared no other bull nor any creature of the wild. He invited battle by sending his challenge ringing through the woods, daring a rival to try to take any of his cows from him.

Late that first evening he was answered by a pair of squealers who were prowling about, driven by the same fury that filled Wapiti, but not being armed for combat. Wapiti marched toward the timber to give battle to the pair, but when they saw him they ran away and kept silent until they were deep in the woods. They finally set up a shrill chorus, but Wapiti did not go after them. From now on he would stay close to his band and meet there any challenger who cared to seek him.

Twice that night he moved the cows on because he was restless. And now the restlessness was taking hold of the cows so that they forgot to feed and moved eagerly when he prodded them on their way.

The band was not going any place; they were just running, working off a great energy which filled them. Their wandering was sure to bring them into contact with other bands. One morning, just as the sun was breaking through the morning mists, Wapiti stood on a knoll, sending his call ringing through the frosty air. His challenge was answered from a nearby ridge. For a matter of a half hour the two bulls roared defiance at each other as they slowly closed the gap which separated them. Finally Wapiti halted, waiting for the challenger to come out of the woods.

He remained poised against the sky, with the cows grazing below him. Lifting his muzzle, he bugled, ending the blast with savage grunts. From the timber close above him came an answer as loud and angry as his own.

When the intruder appeared, Wapiti broke his pose, and his wrath mounted with every step the challenger took. He stamped his foot furiously and screamed his rage. The approaching bull was the big blue, the same stag who had smashed Wapiti's horn the year before. Wapiti did not recognize him as a former enemy. He saw him only as another bull who wanted to fight.

At less than twenty feet apart, the two stags halted and stood glaring at each other, mouths open, breath whistling out in short blasts. Then they both dropped their heads and charged without wasting time in circling. Their antlers came together with such force that their forefeet were lifted high off the ground. For a matter of minutes they remained locked together, twisting their powerful necks, each trying to force the other off balance. Suddenly they parted and backed slowly away from each other, antlers sweeping low as shields against a sudden thrust. They circled slowly, looking for an opening. The cows and calves stopped grazing to watch, as though they knew this was no ordinary skirmish but a battle to be fought to the death.

With bellows of rage, the two lords of the high country lunged forward again. A thousand pounds of solid flesh were behind each set of antlers, and the sound of their meeting rang through the woods. With squeaks and grunts of rage the two twisted and strained, with little advantage going to either.

It was only after the fourth charge that Wapiti's youthful vigor began to make itself felt. For a brief moment he forced the big blue to his knees, but the blue was up quickly and drove Wapiti back a few steps. He seemed to realize he must hurl the young bull off balance and slash him to death at once or he would lose the fight. Wapiti dug his hoofs deep into the black earth to meet the thrust, but one hoof sank into a gopher hole and he was thrown off balance. With a savage grunt the blue drove his antlers past Wapiti's guard. They slashed deep, and blood flowed quickly. The smell of the blood added to the fury of the big blue and he lunged again, but this time Wapiti was ready and met the thrust with his antlers, hurling aside the stabbing lances of bone.

And now Wapiti's anger mounted to its highest pitch as he felt searing pain and smelled his own blood. When the big blue, his breath coming hard, staggered back for the moment's rest they had been taking between rounds, Wapiti lunged. In his fury he wanted nothing but to strike down the bull that had wounded him. His charge sent the big blue back and half turned him around. He was so spent he could not recover quickly, and Wapiti's antlers drove past his guard and thrust deep, sending the big bull down on his side. A groan burst from the big blue as he lashed with his hoofs and swept his antlers helplessly along the ground.

This was Wapiti's chance to finish his rival, but he was so weak and so much in need of breath that all he could do was to stand gasping and grunting while the big blue struggled to his feet and moved slowly toward the woods. It was several minutes before Wapiti recovered enough to roar triumphantly, and there was no answer from the big blue who was staggering on deeper into the forest.

Now Wapiti was truly champion, lord of the barrens, a monarch who had won his right to leadership in battle. Turning slowly, he marched toward the cows, and they instinctively moved closer together, their big eyes giving him the respect he had earned.

Sore and exhausted as he was, Wapiti started the band moving and kept them going through the day. When he did let them rest, he passed among them, giving each a sharp prod or a favor as the whim struck him.

This was Wapiti's hour of glory, the hour he had prepared for through long months of patient wandering, through the months of fearful waiting while his antlers formed and hardened. He marched along armed for battle, afraid of no living thing, eager to meet every challenge.

(Note the time. Check your speed by using the Reading Score Board, page 66.)

ANOTHER KIND OF BATTLE

1. How did Wapiti prove his right to be a leader?
2. Why was it necessary to prove his strength?
3. How did Wapiti conquer the big blue?
4. How do you know he acted often by instinct?
5. Can you give a correct title to each paragraph in the story?

CONQUERING WORDS

Find the word or group of words in each line that most nearly gives the meaning of the word in italics.

1. *coaxingly:* (a) constantly (b) urging gently (c) cautiously
2. *role:* (a) part (b) robot (c) rival
3. *unmolested:* (a) insincere (b) unhappy (c) not meddled with
4. *combat:* (a) argument (b) comfort (c) struggle
5. *knoll:* (a) small hill (b) valley (c) wasteland
6. *intruder:* (a) one behind (b) one pushing forward (c) one fighting
7. *skirmish:* (a) defeat (b) little fight (c) long battle
8. *vigor:* (a) vain attempt (b) vigilance (c) power
9. *searing:* (a) burning (b) sounding (c) clearing
10. *instinctively:* (a) carefully (b) naturally (c) slowly

READING SCORE BOARD

Number of Words in Story: 1210

Number of Minutes	12	6	5	4	3	2 1/2
Reading Rate	100 w.p.m.	200 w.p.m.	250 w.p.m.	300 w.p.m.	400 w.p.m.	500 w.p.m.

PRACTICE IN PHRASING

Try reading down these columns, forcing your eyes to take in an entire line at one glance:

Now Wapiti	and they instinctively	through the day.
was truly champion,	moved closer together,	When he did
lord of the barrens,	their big eyes	let them rest,
a monarch	giving him	he passed
who had won	the respect	among them,
his right	he had earned.	giving each
to leadership	Sore and exhausted	a sharp prod
in battle.	as he was,	or a favor
Turning slowly,	Wapiti started	as the whim
he marched	the band moving	struck him.
toward the cows,	and kept them going	

◄◄ CAROLYN WELLS

How to Tell the Wild Animals

Here are three very foolish poems about wild animals.
If you take them seriously, you'll surely be caught
napping.

> If ever you should go by chance
>   To jungles in the East;
> And if there should to you advance
>   A large and tawny beast,
> If he roars at you as you're dyin'
> You'll know it is the Asian Lion.
>
> Or if sometime when roaming round,
>   A noble wild beast greets you,
> With black stripes on a yellow ground,
>   Just notice if he eats you.
> This simple rule may help you learn
> The Bengal Tiger to discern.
>
> If strolling forth, a beast you view,
>   Whose hide with spots is peppered,
> As soon as he has lept on you,
>   You'll know it is the Leopard.
> 'Twill do no good to roar with pain,
> He'll only lep and lep again.
>
> If when you're walking round your yard,
>   You meet a creature there,
> Who hugs you very, very hard,
>   Be sure it is the Bear.
> If you have any doubt, I guess
> He'll give you just one more caress.
>
> Though to distinguish beasts of prey
>   A novice might nonplus,
> The Crocodiles you always may
>   Tell from Hyenas thus:
> Hyenas come with merry smiles;
> But if they weep, they're Crocodiles.

——Reprinted by permission of Dodd, Mead & Co. from *Baubles* by Carolyn Wells.

The true Chameleon is small,
    A lizard sort of thing;
He hasn't any ears at all,
    And not a single wing.
If there is nothing on the tree,
'Tis the Chameleon you see.

◄ A. E. HOUSMAN

The Elephant, or the Force of Habit

A tail behind, a trunk in front,
Complete the usual elephant.
The tail in front, the trunk behind,
Is what you very seldom find.

If you for specimens should hunt
With trunks behind and tails in front,
That hunt would occupy you long;
The force of habit is so strong.

◄ ARTHUR GUITERMAN

Habits of the Hippopotamus

The hippopotamus is strong
    And huge of head and broad of bustle;
The limbs on which he rolls along
    Are big with hippopotomuscle.

He does not greatly care for sweets
    Like ice cream, apple pie, or custard,
But takes to flavor what he eats
    A little hippopotomustard.

The hippopotamus is true
    To all his principles, and just;
He always tries his best to do
    The things one hippopotomust.

——"The Elephant, or the Force of Habit" reprinted by permission of The Society of Authors as the Literary Representative of the Trustees of the estate of the late A. E. Housman, and Messrs. Jonathan Cape, Ltd., publishers of A. E. Housman's *Collected Poems*.
——"Habits of the Hippopotamus" from the book *Gaily the Troubadour* by Arthur Guiterman. Copyright, 1936, by E. P. Dutton & Co., Inc.

He never rides in trucks or trams,
In taxicabs or omnibuses,
And so keeps out of traffic jams
And other hippopotomusses.

❧

QUESTIONS YOU AND A HIPPOPOTOMUST

1. Which of the poems did you enjoy most? Why?
2. What makes each of the poems funny?
3. Do you know any other silly poems about wild animals? If you do, take time to read them aloud to one another.

VARYING READING RATES

Remember, a good reader has several reading rates. He adapts his rate according to the type of material he reads and according to his purpose for reading.

What kind of rate would you probably use in reading each of the following?

1. A humorous poem
2. An article in an encyclopedia
3. A light novel
4. A history assignment
5. A science assignment
6. Most newspaper articles

❧ CARL AKELEY
AND MARY L. JOBE AKELEY

Elephant

Carl Akeley for a number of years was with the American Museum of Natural History. It was he who introduced the idea of showing animals in their native settings in museum exhibits. In order to get specimens of all kinds of animals and to know exactly what their native settings were, he found it necessary also to become an explorer. This story tells of a terrible experience he once had with an elephant in Africa.
(Note the time when you begin reading.)

THE elephant always may be trusted to provide the hunter with plenty of excitement. His great size, colossal strength, and magnificent courage are qualities that make him stand out as one of the most interesting as well as one of the most dangerous of beasts. Often he appears when least expected and frequently does the totally unex-

——From *Adventures in the African Jungle* by Carl and Mary L. Jobe Akeley. Copyright, 1930, by Mary L. Jobe Akeley. Used by permission of Dodd, Mead & Co., Inc.

pected. Walking unprepared into his presence is like stepping out of a quiet home in No Man's Land—it may be perfectly safe, but the odds are considerably against it.

One day in Uganda we followed the trail of two old bull elephants for five hours. We were in a big feeding ground; and the elephant tracks crossed, intermingled, and circled in a bewildering maze. I had told Bill, my faithful Kikuyu gun bearer, to follow the trail, more to test his ability than in the hope that he would succeed in bringing me to the herd. But I underrated Bill. Suddenly the boy stopped short and held up his cane as a signal for caution. Not more than twenty feet from us stood the two old bulls. They had not heard our approach nor had they caught our scent; but as I studied them from the shelter of a dense bush, I realized that we were in a very dangerous position.

I had no desire to kill an elephant, except one for my museum group—and that meant only an unusually fine specimen; but I had even less desire to be killed by an elephant. So, with two of them as close to me as if we had been in the same room, and with nothing between us but a flimsy screen of bushes, I could take no chances. I hesitated, trying to convince myself that the tusks were fine enough to justify a shot. Then, without warning, my decision was made for me. A great gray trunk was thrust inquiringly forward—forward until it nearly touched my gun barrel. The movement may have been an attempt to catch my scent. I do not know. I had one glimpse of angry eyes set in a solid wall-like head—and I fired. The animal, wounded in the neck, swung around and bolted. I could not watch him nor gauge the effect of my shot, as his companion was right in front of me. He paused for a moment; then, apparently familiar with the deadly language of the rifle, he made a quick retreat.

Bill and I followed for about a hundred yards. The wounded bull scented us, turned, and charged. I took aim; but there was no need to press the trigger, for the giant had made his last stand. His column-like legs swayed, crumpled beneath his weight, and the tremendous body lay outstretched on the ground. My bullet had pierced the jugular vein—a quick death. It had been a chance shot; but, fired from such a short distance, it was much more effective than such shots usually are.

I had luck that day. Not, however, until some years later, when I talked with other hunters in Nairobi, did I realize how good my luck really was. I talked with men there who had experiences similar to my own but who had not had my good fortune in escaping without injury. Great hunters who had been tossed and trampled—and lived to tell the tale.

Outram, by keeping cool in a great emergency, saved himself from a most unpleasant death. He had shot an elephant, and the beast had fallen. Believing it finished, Outram approached. "Suddenly," he said, "to my surprise and horror the *dead* elephant rose and rushed at me. He caught me with his trunk, and I went spinning through the air. I don't know whether in that brief flight I thought at all; but by the time I landed rather hard in the grass, amazement had given way to fear, and I was sure that something had to be done and done quickly.

"I could see the elephant coming after me to trample me into the ground. Fortunately he paused for a second to crush my helmet, which had fallen off during the attack. That second saved me. I got under the beast's tail, and there I clung while he wheeled and circled in a vicious attempt to get me in reach of trunk or tusks or feet. After a few moments of this sport, my injuries began to tell on me. The unequal contest could not have lasted much longer. Fortunately at the crucial moment my companion arrived and killed the elephant."

Hutchinson's story was similar to Outram's. An elephant caught him in the same way, wiped up the ground with him, and then threw him into the trampled vegetation; but he had presence of mind enough to mix himself up in the animal's legs until his gun boy could fire.

The angry beast that caught Alan Black more nearly carried his charge to a finish. The method of attack was the same; but when the elephant discarded him, Black landed in a bush that broke his fall. The elephant followed and stepped on him, returning two or three times to step on him again; but the bush into which Black had fallen served as a cushion and saved his life.

The elephant's trunk is the most remarkable organ any animal possesses. The arm of a man is notable because it may be swung about at any angle from the shoulder, but the elephant's trunk may be twisted and turned in any direction and at any point in its entire length. It is just as powerful in one position as in another. It is without bone—a great flexible cable of muscles and sinew, so tough that the sharpest knife will scarcely cut it. It is so delicate that the elephant may pluck the tenderest blade of grass, yet so strong that he may lift a tree weighing a ton and toss it about easily. With his great height and short, thick neck, the elephant would find it difficult indeed to feed if it were not for his trunk. However, it enables him to secure the choicest morsels on the ground or in the treetops and to strip a whole forest of bark and branches, if he feels like it. With his trunk he has a most extraordinary ability to detect the faintest scent and to punish or kill an enemy.

Since the elephant has something like a fair chance, elephant hunting, unlike a good deal of the shooting that is done in the name of sport, always seems to me a legitimate game. This splendid animal wields a pair of heavy weapons—his mighty tusks— each one of which may weigh as much as the average man; and they are backed by several tons of brute strength. With an agility and a sagacity not to be rivaled by any other beast of his size today, he is a worthy opponent for any sportsman. Elephant hunting is always a game full of interest and excitement because the elephant is such a wise old fellow that the hunter never learns all of his tricks.

Swiftly and surely the white man and the white man's rifles are getting the better of old Tembo.[1] Everywhere is he compelled to retreat before the advance of civilization. But occasionally the African elephant has his innings; and when he does, he winds up the episode with a dramatic flourish of trunk and tusks that the most spectacular handling of a gun cannot rival.

Every elephant hunter has known moments of nerve-torturing suspense—moments when his wits, his courage, and his skill with a gun have stood between him and an open grave. His opponent is adroit, fearless, resourceful, and possessed of tremendous strength. Of course, no one can put himself in the elephant's place and imagine the animal's feelings when it faces a rifle, but I am convinced that this great beast's attitude is one of supreme confidence. A man is handicapped, when he confronts a charging elephant, by his own state of mind. He knows he has "picked the fight." He knows he is the intruder. And he has a guilty feeling that creates in him a demoralizing fear that could never affect one who enters a contest with an absolute conviction of right.

"Here's something about half as big as one of my legs," says Tembo to himself. "A dwarfed thing equally objectionable to my eyes and nose. He's trying to frighten me with that little stick he's carrying, but I'll trample the runt and gore him and perhaps sit on him afterwards."

Then, when the "stick" emits a roar and a flash, if death is not instantaneous, the elephant is thoroughly

[1] *Tembo.* A nickname for elephants.

angered and becomes more dangerous than before. To the hunter it is a different story. He is not overconfident, through ignorance of his antagonist's power. Instead, he is handicapped by the knowledge that if his gun or his wits or his nerves fail him, he will be quickly finished by the charging beast.

If the man keeps his head, he has slightly more than half a chance in any combat with elephants; but if the elephant gets his man, it is fairly certain that there will be no need for the services of a doctor. There are exceptions to this rule—once in a while the victim survives—as I can testify.

I had been on a collecting expedition for the museum, and had obtained all the necessary specimens, when an old bull who tried the quiet waiting game "got" me. Descending from the ice fields of Mount Kenya, that snow-capped peak on the equator, we had made a temporary camp, intending to rest until our base camp could be portered to us. The interlude gave me an opportunity to make some pictures of the typical elephant country all about us. With a party of fifteen, including gun boys and a few porters, I went back up the mountain to an elevation of nine thousand feet at the edge of the dense bamboo forest.

Probably all would have gone well, and I might have obtained some valuable photographs, had we not run across the spoor of three large bulls. It was an old trail, and I knew it would take time to follow it, but the tracks were so unusual in size that I could not resist the temptation. There was always the chance that the trail might be crossed by a fresher one made as the bulls circled about feeding, but instead it led us on from noon until sundown without bringing us to any new sign.

The night on the mountain was so bitterly cold that we were glad to be up and on the move again at daybreak. There was frost in the air, and the morning was still misty when we entered a great elephant feeding ground. It was an open space where the rank growth attained eight or ten feet in height and where the animals milled about eating the vegetation and trampling it down until there was very little left. The place itself was a labyrinth of trails, and from it, as the spokes of a wheel radiate from a hub, were the clear and definite tracks of the departing elephants. Soon after we left this feeding ground, I came upon the fresh tracks of my three old bulls, so fresh that they must have been in that very spot an hour before.

But the network of paths led nowhere. For some time we wandered about in an attempt to follow the elephants; then, growing impatient, I left the clearing, intending to circle about it in the hope of finding on its outskirts the trail which the tuskers had taken. I had gone but a short distance when I found more fresh tracks. I stopped to examine them; and, as I did so, the crackling of bamboo not two hundred yards ahead caught my attention. The bulls were almost within rifle shot and were giving me the signal for the final stalk.

I waited while one of my trackers ran silently along the trail to a point about fifty yards away where it made an abrupt turn. He indicated the direction the animals had taken. Then I turned my attention to the porters, watching them select a place to lay down their loads in a clump of trees where they would be somewhat protected in case of a stampede. The second gun boy presented his rifle for inspection. I examined it, found everything in order, and sent the boy to a safe distance with the porters. The first gun boy presented his gun; I took it, handing him the rifle I had already examined. The second gun was now ready. I leaned it against my body and stood, my back to the wall of the forest, blowing upon my hands numbed by the cold and chafing them in order to have at a moment's notice a supple trigger finger. At the same time the first gun boy was taking the cartridges from his bandoleer[2] and holding them up so that I could be sure that each was a full steel-jacketed bullet—the only kind that will penetrate an elephant's head. There was no reason to suppose that the animals suspected our presence, and I prepared for the stalk with my customary caution and with more than my usual deliberation.

I was standing with my gun leaning against my hip, still warming my hands and still looking at the cartridges one after another. In a flash, one of the calmest moments of my hunting experience changed to the most profoundly intense moment of my entire life. I suddenly *knew* that an elephant was right behind me. Something must have warned me, but

---

[2] *bandoleer*. An ammunition box carried on a belt slung over the shoulder.

I have no idea what it was. I grabbed my gun; and as I wheeled around, I tried to shove the safety catch forward. It would not budge. I wanted desperately to look at it, but there was no time. I remember thinking that I must pull the trigger hard enough to fire. Then something struck me a staggering blow. I saw the point of a tusk right at my chest. Instinctively I seized it in my left hand, reached out for the other tusk with my right, and went down to the ground between them as the great body bore down upon me. One merciless little eye gleamed savagely above me as the elephant drove his tusks into the ground on either side of me, his rolled-up trunk against my chest. I heard a wheezy grunt as the great bull plunged forward, and I realized vaguely that I was being crushed beneath him. Then the light went out.

It was evening before I recovered consciousness, in a dazed sort of way. I was dimly aware of seeing a fire. I was lying where the old bull had left me, in a cold mountain rain, while my superstitious black boys, believing that I was dead, refused to touch me. I tried to shout, and I must have succeeded after a fashion, for a little later I felt myself being carried away by my legs and shoulders.

Later I had another lucid interval, in which I realized that I was in one of the porters' tents. Then I tried to piece together the events that had led to my accident. I supposed that my back was broken because I could not move. I felt no pain. I was miserably cold and numb, and that reminded me of a bottle of brandy, carried for emergencies. I ordered the boys to bring it to me and pour it down my throat. I also had them prepare for me some hot bovril, and gradually the numbness left me. Then I discovered that I could move my arm a little. I tried the same experiment with my leg and was successful. Though the effort brought pain, it told me that I had at least a chance for recovery.

When morning came, my mind was clear enough to inquire for my white companions at the camp below; and the boys told me that soon after the elephant knelt on me, they had dispatched a messenger asking for help. At that rate, assistance should have been close at hand. Fearing that the rescue party was lost on the mountain, I ordered my heavy gun to be fired every fifteen minutes; and within an hour my boys heard an answering shot from a smaller rifle.

When relief arrived, I was a sorry-looking spectacle. The blow from the elephant's trunk which had stunned me had also skinned my forehead, blackened and closed an eye, broken my nose, and torn open one cheek so that my teeth were exposed. Several of my ribs were broken, and my lungs were punctured. I was covered with mud and splashed with blood. But apparently it was my face that was the awful sight.

Just why I was not crushed completely, I shall never know. Beneath the old bull's weight, or even under the pressure of his enormous trunk, my body would have offered about as much resistance as a soda cracker. My only explanation—and I think it is the correct one—is that a root or rock under the surface of the ground must have stopped his tusks, and that seeing me unconscious he must have thought he had killed me. He had then left me and had charged about the clearing after the black boys.

My experience is just one more illustration of my idea that a combat between a man and an elephant is still a fairly equal contest. Even the express rifles of the twentieth century have not given the hunter an overwhelming advantage over this mighty beast.

(Note the time; and check your speed of reading with the Reading Score Board, page 76.)

❖❖❖

ARMCHAIR HUNTING

1. What are some of the things you have learned about the proper ways to hunt elephants?
2. How may an elephant fight back?
3. Why was Akeley hunting elephants?
4. What stories had he heard about the dangers of elephant hunting?
5. How was his life saved?

THE PROOF IS IN THE—PARAGRAPH

In reading the story you probably discovered Akeley's method of writing. He makes a statement of fact, and then he offers proof of the statement. List the items of proof given for each of these statements:

1. The elephant always may be trusted to provide the hunter with plenty of excitement.
2. The elephant's trunk is the most remarkable organ any animal possesses.
3. Since the elephant has something like a fair chance, elephant hunting, unlike a good deal of the shooting that is done in the name of sport, always seems to me a legitimate game.
4. When relief arrived, I was a sorry-looking spectacle.

THE RIGHT WORDS

What synonyms can you think of for the adjectives in italics?

1. *colossal* strength
2. *crucial* moment
3. great *flexible* cable
4. *nerve-torturing* suspense
5. *supple* trigger finger
6. *profoundly intense* moment
7. *merciless* little eye
8. *lucid* interval
9. *express* rifles
10. *overwhelming* advantage

What synonyms can you give for the adverbs in italics?

1. *bitterly* cold
2. wanted *desperately*
3. *Instinctively* I seized it
4. gleamed *savagely*
5. realized *vaguely*
6. was *dimly* aware

READING SCORE BOARD

Number of Words in Story: 2960.

Number of Minutes	30	15	12	10	7	6
Reading Rate	100 w.p.m.	200 w.p.m.	250 w.p.m.	300 w.p.m.	400 w.p.m.	500 w.p.m.

USING AN EYE-SPAN METER

An interesting device to use to force yourself to read faster is the eye-span meter. Cut out of cardboard a rectangle approximately 5" × 3" in size. Then in the rectangle cut a little slit approximately 3" × ¼". Fit the slit over the first line of print. Read that phrase at a single glance, and then drop the eye-span meter to the next line and the next.

The elephant	and magnificent courage	most dangerous
always may be trusted	are qualities	of beasts.
to provide	that make him	Often
the hunter	stand out	he appears
with plenty	as one of	when least expected
of excitement.	the most interesting	and frequently
His great size,	as well as	does the
colossal strength,	one of the	totally unexpected.

◄‖ OSA JOHNSON

Lions

Osa Johnson called her autobiography *I Married Adventure*. You will agree that it is a good name when you read this adventure which she and her husband, Martin, had while photographing lions in Africa. (Note the time when you begin to read.)

LIONS! For a year we lived with them in what Carl Akeley had called the "lions' den," that area some five hundred miles square in Tanganyika Territory to which Carl had taken us shortly before the illness which was to end his life. We worked with lions; we ate and slept with their roars all round us. At times, and with good

——From *I Married Adventure*, copyright, 1940, by Osa Johnson, published by J. B. Lippincott Company.

reason, we feared the great tawny cats; but in the end we grew, as Carl said we would, to respect and love them.

Our equipment consisted roughly of five tents, two water stills, ten motion-picture cameras, eleven still cameras, one hundred thousand feet of film, medical stores, foodstuffs, a typewriter and even a phonograph, and guns, of course. In all, there was something like four tons of stuff; and our big touring car, together with four trucks, carried the lot.

I drove the touring car with four natives hanging on wherever they could. Martin took the wheel of one of the trucks, which carried two tons of supplies and six black boys, while the next truck, equally overloaded, was driven by Urg, our newly acquired Swahili mechanic.

As we rolled into this vast and almost immeasurable domain that is the lion's "Happy Hunting Ground," I thought of Carl Akeley's resentment against the caging of these beautiful beasts. Here, the lion has an abundance for his every need, from food and air to freedom; and restraint is probably the one thing he cannot comprehend. Yet, for thousands of years, he has been hunted and captured and caged to satisfy the vanity of man. I am deeply in sympathy with those enlightened zoos, such as that at San Diego, dedicated to education rather than to entertainment, which are willing to appropriate sufficient ground to give their lion prizes some of the liberty and color of their native home.

Although the lion has counted more than any other factor in man's dread of Africa, curiously enough, man is the only enemy the lion really fears. Hunters from the days of the ancient Ptolemies and before have ranged the plains of Africa with all manner of weapons which were too much even for his magnificent strength and speed and cunning, and it has always surprised me that lions did not somehow remember and that they would trust us at all.

Government has now reduced the menace of the hunter as much as possible by high license fees and other protections, but there is still considerable wanton killing. Martin and I have always done all we could to encourage the setting aside of game preserves; and it was one of his special hopes to see the Serengetti Plains made into a protected area where lions could be hunted only with the camera, which now has finally become a fact under the direction of Game Warden Monty Moore and his splendid and heroic wife.

For the most part, the lion is a thoroughly agreeable personage. He lives a most leisurely existence, loafs and sleeps a great deal, has just as playful moods as a house cat and just as decided a personality. He minds his own business, is very fond of his family, and takes his duties as family protector and provider very seriously. As a youngster he usually attaches himself to a pride or "gang" of young males; and they roam about together, sometimes for years, having an hilarious time, sharing their food and their fun, until he finally settles down to domestic bliss and the raising of a family. When he becomes a grandfather and too old to keep up with his family and friends, he is ejected from the pride and left to roam about alone; and it is then that he often becomes a "rogue," probably a neurasthenic[1] condition not unfamiliar to humans.

Naturally, being of the cat family, he is carnivorous. He kills to eat. Except in self-defense, he seldom disturbs a living thing although I have known him to attack without provocation and have always been careful not to startle or annoy him. When attacked or wounded, he never retreats, but fights as long as there is a spark of life in his magnificent body.

Weighing anywhere between four hundred and five hundred pounds, this massive cat has great strength combined with feline suppleness. On short spurts he can overtake almost any other animal on the plains; and a single blow of his huge clawed foot, or crunch of his jaw, is almost certain death. Many of my friends, expert shots and fine sportsmen and fully aware of the ways of the lion, have been killed or disabled or severely mauled in a moment of recklessness.

Sir Alfred Pease, the well-known game hunter, made it a rule when hunting lions to keep at least two hundred yards between himself and the beast. His friend, George Grey—brother of Sir Edward Grey—hunting with him one day, failed to observe this rule and galloped to within ninety yards of a lion that had been slightly wounded. The animal charged. Sir Alfred tried heading it off and

[1] *neurasthenic.* Unhealthy; characterized by worry and emotional conflicts.

pumped several shots into it at close range; but the maddened creature, though terribly wounded, leaped upon Mr. Grey, lacerating him so cruelly that he died shortly afterwards.

Theodore Roosevelt wrote: "The hunter should never go near a lion until it is dead; and even when it is on the point of death, he should not stand near nor approach his head from the front."

In order to obtain a really complete pictorial history of the lion, it became apparent that we must photograph his nocturnal as well as his daylight habits.

Fortunately, Martin had experimented at length and successfully with night camera work and knew all the mechanical requirements. Contrary to his usual procedure, however, of rigging up the flashlights and cameras and letting the mechanical devices do the work, he decided that he would probably have better results with lion if we stationed ourselves in our car and he operated the camera himself.

The method followed was to set four flash lamps on firmly planted poles about six feet above the ground, then to fasten the cameras securely to solid platforms three feet in front of and below each lamp. These were connected with dry batteries and controlled by a long "firing" wire. The cameras, especially made for this purpose, took pictures automatically at a speed of one three hundredths of a second when the light from the flash was at its maximum.

After setting up this apparatus, a much less pleasant task confronted us; the shooting of a zebra for bait. The guilty feeling we always had about this would have seemed ridiculous to anyone less concerned than ourselves; but the sight of the happy, rowdy little fellows always reminded Martin of his pony, Socks, and put me in a mood where I wanted to pet and certainly not to shoot them.

First, in this connection, of course, there was the ignominious business of sneaking away from camp. Assuredly, since we wouldn't admit to each other that we were sentimental about zebra, we weren't going to attempt to explain our actions to the black boys.

Our routine usually followed the same pattern. Having located a herd and moved within shooting distance of it, we would glance furtively at each other; and then, either Martin or I would yawn. I usually managed to get in ahead of my husband on this.

"Ho, hum," I would say. "You haven't done much shooting lately. It's about time you practiced up."

"Oh, as to that," he would reply carelessly, "as long as I'm only the cameraman around here and you're the one who holds the gun, I think you should keep in practice."

"Well," I would then say, "I don't feel like shooting today. I think my head aches."

"Oh, all right," my husband would growl, "but if I just wound one of the poor fellows, don't blame me."

With this he'd jerk his gun to his shoulder and pretend to take aim.

This was my cue to sigh. "Never mind," I'd say. "Let's pick out an old one or a lame one and get it over with."

Martin's look of relief at this always endeared him to me. Then we would stand for quite a long time, weighing the relative age or lameness of this zebra or that zebra. Finally one would be selected, I would shoot him, and in silence we would go back to camp. Our boys were then sent, of course, to fetch the victim of my gun and place him at a spot exactly fifteen feet from the cameras. Ouranga always directed this part of the flashlight operation; and it was he, too, who, waiting until it was quite dark, cut the entrails from the carcass and dragged them about the site. He always added a mumbled incantation to this disagreeable business and took credit for the results—if good. Seated in our car at a discreet distance by this time, with gun and "firing" wire ready, we sent all the blacks, including the theatrical Ouranga, back to camp.

The wretched hyenas were invariably the first to find our zebra. Sometimes a well-aimed rock would disperse them; but when they came in packs and seemed on the point of eating all the bait, we were usually forced to shoot one or two to show them we were in earnest.

"If only the lions would eat the darned old hyenas," Martin grumbled, "everything would be fine."

"Shhh," I whispered. "I think I hear something."

"Oh, there won't be anything doing tonight," my husband said drowsily. "I wish I were in bed." This said, he promptly went to sleep.

The sky was overcast; there was no moon and the darkness was black and thick and cold. I remembered how quietly lions moved on their padded paws. I also derived what comfort I could from the fact that we had sat in open cars many times before, with lions all around us, and that so far we had not been eaten.

Then I heard a tearing sound, and a chewing and gulping and crunching and, along with this, a sort of purring growl.

I nudged Martin, but he was too fast asleep for gentle methods to have effect. I pinched him. He said, "Ouch"; the crunching accompanied only by a deep growl went steadily on.

"Golly!" my husband said. He turned on his electric torch; and there, sitting right in front of us and wearing one of the finest manes I have ever seen, was surely the king himself; the king of all the Tanganyika lions. Lifting his great head slowly, the big animal looked disdainfully straight into our light. A piece of zebra flesh, torn and dripping, dangled from his mouth; but not even this could detract from his majesty.

My husband now put our flashlights and cameras into operation. The lion dropped his piece of meat, bared his teeth and roared; and then, with an abruptness that left me trembling and my gun still pointed at his head, he went back to his feast.

Others of his family joined him. Several of them were his wives, apparently; and the smaller ones might have been his half-grown sons. They were a fine-looking lot and formed a perfect picture.

"Oh, that's great! That's great!" I heard Martin whispering to himself.

He pressed the button. Nothing happened. Again he pressed it with all his might, and there was no sign of a flash. Frantically he pulled the wires from the button and touched them together, but still without result.

"Well," he said, "I guess there's nothing else to do."

He was looking straight out to where the lions were feeding.

I knew what he meant, but I wouldn't believe him. "What do you mean?" I demanded.

"I've got to get out there and fix it, that's all."

He was out of the car before I could stop him. I caught him by the collar.

"You're crazy," I said, half crying.

"Give me the sawed-off gun," was all he said.

So I drove the lions off the kill by throwing the powerful searchlight of our car in their faces, tooting the auto horn and yelling, covering Martin the while with my gun. The lions retreated about twenty yards; and in a few brief minutes, which seemed like an eternity, my husband found the loose connection and returned to the car.

"Don't you ever do that again!" I said, practically in collapse.

Martin went straight to work, though I saw that he was shaking a little.

The lion king, having eaten his fill, apparently decided now to investigate the flashlights and cameras. He even gave one of the cameras an experimental bite.

"You let that camera alone!" my husband yelled, completely beside himself.

The majestic cat glanced our way

indifferently, then began chewing at the base on which the camera was fastened. The whole thing went over.

Martin got out of the car again and began throwing rocks and anything else that came to hand. To add to the complication, one of the younger lions now decided to follow the cue of the older lion, and seizing one of the wires, tugged at it until he had torn it and several other wires from their fastenings.

We sat there throwing rocks, shooting our guns into the air, yelling until we were hoarse; but not until those two lions had pulled down every wire, battery, camera, and pole of our equipment were they satisfied. Then they strolled off, their tails waving proudly; and our night of flashlight photography was definitely at an end.

A few days later we came upon a large pride of young males resting under a cluster of trees, and we stopped to watch. They were extremely curious and began edging up to look us over. They were so playful and frisky that Martin obtained some new and very valuable film. We decided to lunch there and climbed out through the aperture at the top of the truck and sat down to enjoy our sandwiches and to watch.

At the sight of our food, the lions came up close to the car and sat down like a bunch of hungry beggars. I threw them some partridge legs, which they tasted and then licked their chops as much as to say, "Pretty high-toned food for a jungle lion."

For an hour they played about us, within a few feet of the car, bit at the tires and nipped at one another and had a rowdy time. We even called them by name (not for exact resemblance of course): Roy Chapman Andrews, the most dapper of them; Lowell Thomas, the one who roared most; George Dryden, the one who bit the tires and seemed most interested in the rubber business; Merian Cooper, the wise and well-mannered one who kept his distance through most of the fracas. And the lions seemed satisfied with the comparisons.

Perhaps it was experiences of this sort that made us a little reckless; that had us thinking of the huge felines in terms of fireside tabbies. At any rate, we were on foot one very hot day—our camera and gunbearers were with us, of course—when we turned a sort of corner past a jagged rock and there, not twenty yards from us, was a sleeping lion.

The big creature was on his feet almost instantly and facing us. He drew his ears back, switched his tail, and snarled—three signs I didn't at all like. My husband proceeded busily, however, to set up his camera.

"I don't like his looks, Martin," I said cautiously. At the same time I signaled for my gun.

"Oh, he's all right," my husband said. "A little cranky, maybe, but just bluffing." He started to crank the camera.

Then, with a low growl, the lion started slowly toward us, his tail lashing from side to side. How at such a moment I could notice, and sharply at that, the ripple of his hard shoulder muscles under his shining yellow coat, I don't know.

"He's going to charge, Martin—I tell you he is!"

"I don't think so," my husband said, biting hard on his cigar.

The lion, crouching tensely now, stared at us in what seemed to be an all-consuming hatred. Then he charged.

Martin's hand continued mechanically to crank the camera.

The animal looked as large as a bull as he leaped toward us—his mane flying, fangs bared. I seemed to be watching in a prolonged, timeless sort of daze; and then, without really being aware of what I was doing, I shot. Afterwards I couldn't even recall taking aim.

The lion seemed to hesitate in midair and then fell just thirteen feet from the camera's tripod.

(Note the time; and check your speed of reading, using the Reading Score Board.)

❖❆❖

READING SCORE BOARD

Number of Words in Story: 2800.

Number of Minutes	28	14	11	9 1/3	7	5 1/2
Reading Rate	100 w.p.m.	200 w.p.m.	250 w.p.m.	300 w.p.m.	400 w.p.m.	500 w.p.m.

COMPREHENSION CHECK

Complete each of these statements:

1. It was =?= who first took the Johnsons to the "lions' den."
2. The purpose of the Johnsons' trip to Africa was to =?=, not to kill them.
3. As a youngster, a lion attaches himself to a pride, or =?=.
4. A full-grown lion weighs between =?= and =?= pounds.
5. Big-game hunters advise =?= even when the beast is fatally wounded.
6. In order to take =?= picture of lions feeding, the Johnsons rigged up cameras and flashlights.
7. A =?= was used as bait.
8. Usually the =?= arrived before the lions.
9. Because the lions were so playful, the Johnsons named some of them =?=.
10. But one lion that was definitely not playful was killed by Osa only =?=.

FOLLOWING OSA'S EXPLANATION

In the first part of the article, Osa explains some facts about lions. You can tell almost by a glance that these paragraphs are explanations, just as you can tell that the last part is a story. Which part do you think you will read more slowly? Why?

If you will look at the first sentence of each of Osa's paragraphs of explanation, you will have a good reading guide. Almost always she tells you in that first sentence (her topic sentence) what the paragraph is going to be about. Check her paragraphs of explanation now, and see whether you can find the guideposts.

Osa's Jungle Words

What do these words and phrases mean?

immeasurable domain	incantation
cunning	majestic cat
pride	feline
carnivorous	all-consuming hatred
nocturnal	fangs

Reading Phrases, Not Words

Use your eye-span meter to read down these columns. Force your eyes to take in each line at a single glance, and work for speed.

Although	the lion	which were too much
the lion	really fears.	even for his
has counted	Hunters	magnificent strength
more than any	from the days	and speed
other factor	of the ancient Ptolemies	and cunning.
in man's dread	and before	For the most part,
of Africa,	have ranged the plains	the lion
curiously enough,	of Africa	is a thoroughly
man is	with all manner	agreeable personage.
the only enemy	of weapons	

◀◀ Theodore J. Waldeck

Lions on the Hunt

Here is the story of Sur-Dah, a hungry young lion. Whenever you are hungry, you go after food. Sur-Dah did the same thing, but his method of obtaining food was not a calm walk to the icebox.
(Note the time when you begin reading the story.)

BOOM—BA-BA—BOOM! Boom—ba-ba—boom!

The sound seemed to come from far off, yet from all around. Never stopping, never hesitating, its rhythmic throb hung in the stagnant air as if it were a part of the heat that scourged the earth. Now it rose in

——From *Lions on the Hunt* by Theodore J. Waldeck. Copyright 1942 by Theodore J. Waldeck. Reprinted by permission of The Viking Press, Inc., New York.

volume, now it fell to faint vibrance, only to grow loud again.

Sur-Dah liked neither the heat nor the throbbing.

Lithe, lean, tawny, the young lion swung through the gloom in the wake of his mother and brother, all three in search of meat to still their aching hunger. The day had given way to the night with a quickness as if a curtain had been dropped over the sun, and with nightfall had come the time to hunt.

As always, his mother took the lead. As always, his brother followed, while Sur-Dah brought up the rear. It made Sur-Dah more than a little contemptuous, this silly weakness of his brother for staying so near his mother that the tufted tip of her tail fairly brushed his nose.

He, Sur-Dah, was not afraid to lag behind! He was no longer a cub, with the apprehensive, sniveling ways of cubhood! He was full grown, with a sleek mane that swept proudly down from his head and shoulders. True, his mane was not yet grown to its greatest length. But it was only the shortness of his mane and the clear smoothness of his hide, unmarred by the scars of battle, that stamped him as a young lion just coming into his full powers, not quite matured in wisdom and cunning.

The time would soon come when he would no longer sleep at his mother's side, follow her in the hunt, guide himself by her command. Already he felt a strange feeling of dissatisfaction at his dependency. Soon he would leave her, strike out for himself—make his own way!

The three great cats were as silent as three disembodied shadows as they trotted along in single file. Into a clump of gnarled mimosa trees the mother led the way, then down a narrow *donga*[1] and across the dry bed of what had once been a rushing stream.

Sur-Dah uttered a low growl of dissatisfaction. They had often hunted at this very stream, and the zebras and other sweet-flavored game had come here by the score to drink. Now its water had vanished, and its mud bottom was scorched and cracked with dryness. Even though the sun had long since dipped beneath the horizon, the searing heat remained.

And worse yet, Sur-Dah's belly was maddeningly hollow.

What was wrong, that meat was so scarce? What was ailing his mother, who used to lead them so unerringly to the places where game might be found? Why was it that she found so little game now?

Many moons back, Sur-Dah had feasted at will on zebra, okapi, or gazelle. Many moons back, he had gorged himself nightly on rich red meat so plentiful that he could not eat it all but had left well-nigh half of each kill for the skulking scavenger hyenas to finish off. So it had been during the rainy season, when life was easy and hunger was unknown; and Sur-Dah, with his mother and brother, had grown comfortable and fat and even a little lazy.

Not so now. Now the rain was a stranger to the veldt.[2] Now the sun god held full sway over Zululand. Every morning he rose in the form of a gigantic, blood-red ball, growing smaller but more malignant as he soared. Every night he sank, again a sullen red ball, giving no hope for the morrow.

And with the heat, a blight had come to the earth. First the breadfruit trees had lost their fruit, then their foliage. The leaves of the acacias

[1] *donga.* A watering place.

[2] *veldt.* A grassland in South Africa.

had withered and died, fluttering to the ground and leaving the branches gaunt and bare. The waving green grass of the veldt no longer waved, nor was it green. So sere and brittle had it become that even the soft-footed Sur-Dah was hard put to pass through without making it crackle.

Then the water holes had dried, one by one, so that only a few remained. The small streams had vanished, the large ones dwindling to a mere trickle. Here and there lay the whitening bones of animals that had dropped from hunger and thirst. Always, during the daytime, the vultures wheeled and circled so high in the sky that they seemed mere specks. And still the blood-red, malignant sun god ruled. . . .

Boom—ba-ba—boom! Boom—ba-ba—boom!

If meat would not come to them, they could wait no longer. They must go and find it!

Dust, dust—always dust—but no food!

Of one thing Sur-Dah became aware with quickening interest. Borne through the moonlight-silvered air were the frequent roars of other lions —many of them. First the call came from one direction, then another; from far off, and near by. And finally the old lioness stopped in midstride, one heavy forepaw raised, and emitted her roar.

Sur-Dah had heard his mother's roar many times before. He had heard it so often, knew it so well, that he would recognize it among a thousand. But tonight he detected a new note in

it—a strange, almost desperate note that fired his blood and made excitement course through his veins.

Sur-Dah did not understand the meaning of it. But of one thing he felt sure. Tonight something was different, something was changed.

Tonight something was going to happen. . . .

His mother stood for a moment, listening. Then through the gloom came an answering roar. His mother struck off without a moment's delay in the direction of the sound. The two younger lions, both mystified, followed.

Soon, as they slunk through the tall dead grass, they heard the confused, rumbling murmur of many lions. An instant later they came out of a cluster of gnarled mimosa trees and into the open, where the veldt stretched out for mile after mile in the moonlight, with only a tree here and there, and an occasional mighty boulder, to interrupt its vast flatness.

There, directly before them, were the tawny figures of perhaps a dozen lions. Some of them lay quietly waiting—for what, Sur-Dah did not know. Others paced back and forth with nervous, jerky strides, their heads hanging low, tufted tails switching, deep voices muttering in menace. Both males and females were there, and even young cubs not quite full grown—waiting, all waiting.

Boom—ba-ba—boom! Boom—ba-ba—boom!

Never stopping, never hesitating, the faraway throbbing pulsed through the night. Now it rose in volume, now it fell. Sur-Dah listened, and there was that in the sound which made the hair on his spine rise, his tail switch nervously.

Boom—ba-ba—boom! Boom—ba-ba—boom!

His heart thumped painfully. Something was changed, this night! Something was different.

Something was going to happen.

Sur-Dah's heart was still thumping against his ribs as he followed his mother and the other lions in the direction of the ceaseless throbbing. But in the midst of his ignorance and vague apprehension as to what was afoot, he experienced a keen thrill of pleasure. He was traveling with the pack—an accepted member of it. Whatever happened, he would acquit himself in a manner that would do honor to his mother and himself!

The throbbing grew steadily louder in his ears. With it now was mixed a strange jumble of other noises—an incessant rattle, a low and guttural grunting, now and then the thump of one object against another.

It was all new, all foreign to Sur-Dah, but he had a presentiment that he would soon learn what it was. He noted that this migration of the lions was not at all like the hunt, for on the hunt a lion made no sound. Now, on the other hand, the black-maned leader gave vent to a full-throated roar from time to time, and others joined with him.

At that moment Sur-Dah, close behind his mother and brother, emerged from a shallow *donga* and loped through a cluster of baobab trees. Coming out on a level plain several miles in breadth and covered only with short dry grass and an occasional boulder, he involuntarily stopped short at what he saw.

Redness was in the sky—licking, leaping, fiery redness that issued from the ground and seemed to reach to the very heavens. Like a column of sunlight, it split a hole in the darkness, making the moonbeams seem wan in comparison.

It was from behind a high barrier, the like of which Sur-Dah had never seen before, that the flames seemed to originate. It was from here, too, that the confused jumble of sounds came.

Had he been alone, he would have been unwilling to go closer to these orange-red flames which he instinctively hated and feared. Yet he saw that the heavy-maned leader, far in the van, did not hesitate.

And then Sur-Dah heard another sound which made him recall suddenly that he was in an agony of hunger. It was a chorus of low, uneasy bawls which, though he had never heard them before, he felt sure were the calls of animals that were his rightful prey. With the calls came the rich, pungent scent of meat.

Meat! Sur-Dah licked his chops, and his tail switched in nervous anxiety. Meat . . . prey . . . it was near him, and yet he could not see it. It must be behind the barrier, whose jagged black silhouette loomed so high in the light of the flames beyond. And if it was behind that mighty barrier, how could it be taken?

The lions, more than a score of them, were now near the thorny *gange*[3] of Kaweyo's village. And the leader, after a moment of careful deliberation, began running straight toward the high barricade.

Sur-Dah watched with bated breath. Surely he was not foolish enough to attempt to hurdle that sheer wall! Surely he did not intend——

But he did! With a tremendous spring, the leader launched his body into the air. Over the top of the thorn fence he sailed, a tawny streak of power in the firelight—and dropped from sight into the enclosure whence came the smell, the sounds, and the redness.

Sur-Dah had never before witnessed such a magnificent leap. Every fiber of him thrilled at the power and courage of it. But now the leader had vanished into the blackness. What had become of him? Would he return?

Even as the young lion wondered, his question was answered. Back over the barricade came the leader, and clutched firmly in his jaws was a medium-sized animal with horns and hooves, somewhat resembling an antelope.

Sur-Dah writhed with combined envy and admiration at this exhibition of prowess. This leader could not only leap the wall—he could hurdle it while weighted down with a burden!

With his prey in his mouth, the leader stopped momentarily in front of the watching pack, as if to demonstrate that there was meat to be had for those courageous enough to take

it. Then he stalked off by himself to enjoy his kill and fill his empty belly. The others knew better than to follow. He had won his prey, and it was his alone. Let the rest get their own!

From inside the enclosure there suddenly issued a series of excited yells. The throbbing, the grunting, and the rattling stopped; and in their place came the sound of running feet. Though Sur-Dah did not know it, it was the abrupt termination of the ceremonial dance by the order of Kaweyo. A goat had been snatched from the flock; and the animals, goats and cattle alike, were wild with terror, threatening to stampede because of the dreaded smell of lion in their nostrils.

To Sur-Dah, the leap he had witnessed was a stirring challenge. If the leader could accomplish it, so could he! And though his legs were quaking strangely beneath him, he ran out to the forefront of the pack. Other lions, who had been hesitating in indecision, joined him. With Sur-Dah in the lead, they were about to essay a leap over the *gange*, when all at once the sky seemed to rain down on them with fearsome, fiery weapons.

At the top of the *gange*, many warriors appeared, bearing with them flaming brands which they had carried from the fire. Yelling savagely, they flung the brands directly at the encircling lions. Arcs of flame cut the air, with a great sizzling and throwing of sparks—flame that struck the ground and shattered into many flames.

One of them fell near Sur-Dah, and

---

[3] *gange*. A wall made of poles covered with thorny bushes.

in a twinkling his courage vanished. He leaped away from the hissing embers—leaped away and rejoined his mother. What were these crackling, sputtering weapons, edged with barbs of dancing sunlight and carrying the pungent smell of smoke? Sur-Dah did not know; and though he was not lacking in fortitude, he had no desire to find out.

Despite his retreat, he noted in his mother's eyes a glow of pride in his willingness to take the lead. He noticed with surprise that his brother was nowhere to be seen; but he did not know that his mother's appreciation of his valor was heightened by the fact that at the first sight of flame, his brother had turned tail and taken to his heels into the veldt.

The warriors, still shouting at the top of their voices, had left the *gange* and raced back to the fire for more embers. Seeing them leave, Sur-Dah again edged closer, the tempting smell of cattle and goats driving him almost frantic with eagerness. Behind him came the others, who had retreated when he did.

But the warriors were back in an instant, bearing more firebrands. Again the flaming weapons were hurled from the barrier. Again the hungry cats gave ground before the onslaught, snarling and spitting in impotent rage.

But this time a tiny spurt of flame appeared at the bottom of the barrier. One of the warriors, in his haste to fling a hot ember, had broken part of it off; and it had fallen to the ground immediately outside of the *gange*.

In a moment the *gange*, brittle-dry after the long drought, was an angry sheet of fire. From the warriors came sharp cries of terror. Only too well they knew that if their fence burned down, they would be at the mercy of the lions. Lacking water with which to fight the fire, they desperately beat their shields against the burning wall. They had not even had time to remove their headdresses; and the feathers on one brave's head, caught by a spark, leaped into quick flame.

Howling with pain, he dropped his shield and rolled on the ground, trying to put the fire out. Others came to his aid; and in a moment he was saved, though much of his hair was burned from his head.

Meanwhile, danger threatened the warriors from a new quarter. The bawling of the cattle was growing louder and more frantic. They had got out of control of the boys who were tending them and were milling about in the enclosure, blind with fear, terrified at the noise, the flames, the shouting, and above all at the smell of lion which came to them through it all. In a tight circle they moved, their nostrils distended, their eyes wide, looking for a means of escape. The women of the village strove to quiet them, but it was of no use.

The warriors, their eyebrows singed and their paint-daubed faces streaked with sweat, managed at last to extinguish the fire. There remained a gaping hole in the *gange*, as wide as a man is tall—and the frightened cattle spied it.

With one accord they bolted for the opening. Before the warriors could stop them, twelve, sixteen—twenty of the cows had slipped through, little knowing that in their unreasoning fear they were heading straight for disaster.

To the Zulu warriors, their cows were their most valuable possessions—their meat, their drink, their life. Without a moment's hesitation, a dozen-odd men led by Kaweyo himself, spears upraised and shields held before them, rushed out to drive back the lions and rescue the cattle.

Sur-Dah, close beside his mother and almost groaning with excitement, saw her go tense as a half-grown heifer plunged blindly toward her. With a smooth running jump she was on the animal's back, breaking its neck with one mighty stroke of her heavy forepaw. Its despairing bawl only half uttered, the young cow went down, dead as it struck the ground.

The lioness seized her prey by the nape of the neck and sought to drag it away. But the heifer, though not full grown, was heavy; and it was all she could do to pull it inch by inch.

Sur-Dah, trembling in every limb, eager and yet afraid to begin devouring the cow where it lay, did not know what to do. But when his mother turned on him with an impatient snarl, he understood. He ran up beside her, got his teeth in the heifer's neck, and helped his mother drag the animal away.

So engrossed was he that he forgot about the clamor that raged all about. He did not notice the warrior who ran up, his upraised arm bearing a gleaming assegai.[4]

4 *assegai.* A wooden spear.

The arm came down with a snap. The assegai flashed through the air.

Sur-Dah's mother uttered a short, sharp yelp of pain. She loosed her hold on the cow. Surprised, Sur-Dah glanced at the retreating warrior, then at his mother. She was sitting on her haunches, craning her neck and biting at a long, slender shaft which protruded from her side.

The shaft . . . it puzzled Sur-Dah. Yet he realized that there was no time to be lost. They must drag the cow away from the noise and the shouting —drag it away to a quiet place where it would be safe for him and his mother to eat their fill. As for his brother, he was gone, and good riddance—where, Sur-Dah neither knew nor cared.

But his mother made no move to come and help. She kept biting at the object in her side, uttering a whimper as she did so.

Sur-Dah was vaguely annoyed. Well, then—he would do it alone! Tonight, for the first time, he had come to full realization of his powers; and he reveled in it.

It was heavy work, but Sur-Dah made good headway. Glowing inwardly with pride at his strength, which he could see was even greater than his mother's, he pulled the inert heifer across the dry grass toward the grove of baobabs.

He gained the fringe of trees with his burden and kept on in the direction of a grassy hollow that was shielded by heavy brush on one side and by a mighty clifflike boulder on the other. Beyond him his mother crawled painfully, the shaft still in her side, her breath coming in short, labored gasps.

Sur-Dah at last reached the hollow, fairly frenzied by the smell of flesh in his nostrils. The sounds from the *kraal*[5] were faint in the distance now; and his hunger was such that he felt almost unsteady on his legs.

But his mother, to his amazement, made no move to devour her kill. Slowly she followed Sur-Dah into the hollow, lay down on her belly with her head resting on her outstretched forepaws, and gazed at him, now and then uttering a low growl of distress.

Sur-Dah was nonplused. His mother had made the kill—she should be first to enjoy it.

He walked over to her and touched his nose against hers. Affectionately she licked him with a tongue that seemed strangely dry and rough. But still she made no move.

Sur-Dah could wait no longer. The pangs in his middle would not be denied now that meat lay before his very eyes. Greedily he began to devour the tender, still-warm flesh of the young cow. As he ate he could feel new strength coursing into his veins.

Never was meat so succulent, so fragrant, so satisfying!

Only one thing marred his complete contentment. His mother. . . . From time to time he glanced at her, puzzled, wondering, inquiring. What was troubling her? Why did she not eat? It gave him a vague feeling of shame that he should be gorg-

ing himself while she still went hungry.

When he had eaten his fill, he dragged the cow's carcass over to where she lay and placed it directly before her nose.

Even then she did not stir. And Sur-Dah, crouched low, looking steadily at her, realized that something was seriously wrong. His mother, who had been almost starving, would not eat.

The sorrowful truth dawned on him with sudden clarity. His mother was dying. Even as the cow had died under her blow, now she herself was dying for some reason he could not comprehend.

He lay down beside her—felt her sides heaving spasmodically, heard her low growling grow fainter. Not knowing what else to do, he licked her ears, her face. By the pale yellow moonlight he could see that her eyes were becoming filmy and glazed.

She had been with him since the daylight had first shone into his opening eyes. She had saved him, long ago, from the charge of a bull rhinoceros by grasping him in her jaws and hurling him to one side. By night and by day she had been with him, teaching him the lore of the veldt, teaching him to stalk, to hunt, to be wary of danger.

Soon she would be with him no more. . . .

With grief and fear in his heart, Sur-Dah lay beside her. At last a brief tremor passed through her body. Then she went limp and rolled over on her side, the slender shaft of the assegai projecting upward from her ribs.

[5] *kraal*. Village.

For a long time Sur-Dah sat looking at her. She did not move again.

The world was big, vast, frighten-ing. . . . And Sur-Dah was alone—utterly alone!

He turned and trotted slowly off into the veldt.

(Note the time; and check your speed of reading with the Reading Score Board, page 92.)

◆◖◆

LOOKING BELOW THE SURFACE

1. What is meant by the "law of survival"? How does it apply to this story?
2. How does Sur-Dah feel toward the leader of the pack?
3. What lines in the story indicate Sur-Dah's ambition?
4. What do you discover about the relationship between a mother lion and her young?
5. What picture do you get of the life of the Zulus?
6. From what point of view is the story told—man's or beast's? Can you name another story told from the same point of view?

PICTURE-MAKING WORDS

Can you find a synonym for each of these colorful adjectives which are used in the story?

1. *lithe:* (a) pliant (b) listless (c) little
2. *tawny:* (a) tawdry (b) strong (c) tan
3. *contemptuous:* (a) contented (b) scornful (c) contemptible
4. *sniveling:* (a) snuffling (b) snippy (c) sniping
5. *gnarled:* (a) twisted (b) goaded (c) crippled
6. *sullen:* (a) envious (b) glum (c) despicable
7. *incessant:* (a) indefinite (b) incautious (c) uninterrupted
8. *pungent:* (a) sharp (b) sweet (c) punctual
9. *encircling:* (a) surrounding (b) encouraging (c) encroaching
10. *frantic:* (a) fragrant (b) wild (c) mild

Here are ten picture-making verbs used in the story. Choose a synonym for each.

1. *gorged:* (a) glutted (b) gory (c) gorgeous
2. *emitted:* (a) emigrated (b) remitted (c) uttered
3. *slunk:* (a) sunk (b) galloped (c) moved stealthily
4. *pulsed:* (a) pursued (b) throbbed (c) puffed
5. *emerged:* (a) embraced (b) disappeared (c) appeared
6. *loomed:* (a) appeared (b) looked (c) discovered
7. *launched:* (a) lunched (b) plunged (c) drowned
8. *writhed:* (a) twisted (b) wrought (c) teased
9. *stalked:* (a) followed (b) stamped (c) approached
10. *bolted:* (a) darted (b) lagged (c) stumbled

READING SCORE BOARD

Number of Words in Story: 3710.

Number of Minutes	37	18 1/2	15	12 1/3	9 1/4	7 1/2
Reading Rate	100 w.p.m.	200 w.p.m.	250 w.p.m.	300 w.p.m.	400 w.p.m.	500 w.p.m.

KEY WORDS HOLD THE KEY

As you have already discovered, every line of print contains certain words which are more important than others. Good readers automatically look for those words; the little unimportant words they pick up with the tail of the eye.

In the following paragraph, direct your eyes chiefly to the words printed in heavy type. You will find that those words give you the clues to meaning. You will find also that by concentrating on these words instead of on the unimportant words, your rate of reading will increase.

Sur-Dah uttered a low **growl** of **dissatisfaction.** They had often **hunted** at this very **stream,** and the **zebras** and other sweet-flavored **game** had come here by the score **to drink.** Now its **water** had **vanished,** and its **mud bottom** was scorched and cracked with **dryness.**

Together determine what the key words are in a number of the paragraphs in the story "Lions on the Hunt." Then practice reading other material, making your eyes search out the key words in each line.

◀️ SIR ARTHUR QUILLER-COUCH

Sage Counsel

Wild-animal hunting is undoubtedly dangerous. Perhaps it would be just as wise, therefore, to follow the advice given in the last two lines.

The lion is the beast to fight:
    He leaps along the plain,
And if you run with all your might,
    He runs with all his mane.
        I'm glad I'm not a Hottentot,
        But if I were, with outward cal-lum
        I'd either faint upon the spot
        Or hie me up a leafy pal-lum.

The chamois is the beast to hunt:
    He's fleeter than the wind,
And when the chamois is in front
    The hunter is behind.
        The Tyrolese make famous cheese
        And hunt the chamois o'er the chaz-zums:
        I'd choose the former, if you please,
        For precipices give me spaz-zums.

The polar bear will make a rug
    Almost as white as snow;
But if he gets you in his hug,
    He rarely lets you go.
        And polar ice looks very nice,
        With all the colors of a prissum:
        But, if you'll follow my advice,
        Stay home and learn your catechissum.

❖❖❖

More Sage Counsel and Inquiries

1. A pun, or play on words, may be the lowest form of wit; but it's amusing, nevertheless. Can you find a pun in the first four lines?
2. What other foolery does Sir Arthur Quiller-Couch do with words?
3. In the second stanza, how should *wind* be pronounced?

Sage Counsel—about Reading

Have you ever watched a person read poetry to himself, carefully whispering each word? His lips, and probably his tongue and throat muscles, were all working overtime. Sometimes this bad habit is carried over into the reading of prose. Whenever the habit is present, there is no doubt that the rate of reading is slowed down tremendously. So, take "sage counsel"; and avoid that habit like the plague.

◄**J. H. WILLIAMS**

A Tiger Attacks

Here is a story of a tiger's cunning. A newborn elephant would make a delicious meal, but how could the tiger get it? Two adult elephants, Mee Tway and Ma Shwe, were guarding the baby with their lives. Moreover, the elephant riders, called oozies, were not far away. Step by step, the tiger laid his plans.
(Note the time when you begin reading.)

BEFORE it was dark the tiger left his lair and crossed the creek a long way below the elephants' pitch. He worked stealthily upstream until his sensitive nostrils picked up the scent of the newborn calf being wafted down on the evening breeze. For some distance he boldly followed the open game-track along the bank of the creek. Then he re-entered the jungle, and for a time squatted motionless on his haunches, working himself up for the attack. There was more in this than hunger and a succulent meal; there was prowess. To attack two elephants and kill the calf would be an achievement worthy of the king of the Burmese jungle.

He could not decide in advance whether he would attack the mother or the auntie first. That would depend on how they were standing when he moved in to attack. But he knew that he could not seize the calf until he had stampeded both the adults. He must spring on the back of one and so lacerate her that she

fled for safety; then he must unseat himself and stampede the other long enough to give him time to seize the precious calf and carry it off like a cat with a rat in its mouth.

But before he could attack, he knew that he must circle the clearing, because the best line of attack was from upstream. His patience was superb. Twice he moved up to within fifty yards of the clearing, but each time the breeze was coming downstream too fast for him to risk his scent being carried to them when he moved above.

The moon rose higher and higher, but it was not till well after midnight that the breeze dropped. Utter silence fell on the jungle, a silence so deathly that few human beings can endure it without making some sound or movement to reassure themselves. But the elephants made no sound. The two adults stood side by side, as unmoving as statues in the moonlight; and between the forelegs of his mother, with his little head just filling the gap, stood the baby calf, as motionless as they.

Occasionally the ears of the adult animals moved forward as if straining

——From: *Bandoola* by J. H. Williams. Copyright 1953 by J. H. Williams, reprinted by permission of Doubleday & Company, Inc. and Rupert Hart-Davis Limited.

to hear a sound. Then Mee Tway broke the silence—for no reason—she just thumped the end of her trunk on the ground, and it rang hollowly with a metallic sound.

It eased the tension, but it started the tiger on his first circuit round the clearing. He was fifty yards out and he had decided to make his attack from the creek side. Four times he circled without crackling a leaf or a twig — the perfect hunter. He no longer walked with slow, stealthy step. He was now so near that at any moment he might see his quarry in the clearing. His poise was low on the ground. He moved forward with his powerful hind legs tensed under his body, ready instantly to spring. The tip of his tail quivered.

At last he saw the picture he had dreamed of: an elephant's flank clearly silhouetted, and only ten bounds and a leap away. His enormous power was released as he bounded forward and with a seven-foot spring landed on Mee Tway's back. His forepaws dug deep into the barrel of the elephant's back. The vicious grip of the foreclaws held his weight, while with his hinder claws he lacerated the sides of the wretched elephant. With a murderous snarl he sank his teeth into the elephant's shoulder.

For a second Mee Tway was taken by surprise. Then bellowing with panic fear she was off, making for the nearest jungle, where she could shake this savage terror from her back.

As she reached the edge of the untrodden elephant grass she hesitated for a moment; and in that moment the tiger retracted his claws and slid off, as a child might slide from a bareback pony. Immediately he turned and bounded back to attack Ma Shwe, standing under the Nyaung tree with the buttresses of the tree protecting her flanks. She had the advantage of position. The tiger could only attack head on. He had no opportunity to maneuver. She was terrified, but she stood her ground, with the calf huddled between her forelegs.

She took one chance. As the tiger checked before her, she took a pace forward and lashed at him with her trunk. With a lightning swing his right paw struck, the very movement of a cat at a terrier's face. The sharp claws struck home and Ma Shwe shrieked and bellowed with pain; for the trunk is the most sensitive and vital organ of the elephant. But she did not stampede. She replaced her off forward foot to protect the calf, who hadn't moved an inch.

But in that moment the tiger had gained his flank position and sprang up on her withers. His foreclaws dug their hold and his hind-claws tore at her flesh. She rolled and shook herself to fling him off, but still she didn't stampede and still he clung and tore.

Her trunk hung limp. She had no means of touching her calf. The injury had made it quite numb and useless. She felt herself weakening. Was there no relief from this murderous weight?

Then suddenly it seemed as if the Nyaung tree had fallen on her. Something struck her with the force of an avalanche. She sank to her knees with the impact, without damaging the calf. And when she rose again, the murderous weight was gone. Mee Tway had returned, goaded to fury by her wounds, and charged at the tiger clinging to the mother's flank.

The king of the Burmese jungle fell to the ground. He was badly hurt in pride and body. But he managed to slide away back to his jungle lair.

Now the two defiant elephants stood side by side once more, the blood streaming from their wounds, but the calf stood perfect and untouched. They raised their heads and roared and trumpeted a challenge to all the tigers of the Ningyan Forest.

The only answer was the shouting of the oozies coming to the rescue.

(Check your speed of reading with the Reading Score Board.)

◆‹‹◆

YOUR TURN TO ATTACK

1. Explain, step by step, the tiger's plan to get the baby elephant.
2. Next, explain the cause for his failure.

READING SCORE BOARD

Number of Words in Story: 1030

Number of Minutes	10 1/3	5 1/6	3 1/2	2 1/2	2
Reading Rate	100 w.p.m.	200 w.p.m.	300 w.p.m.	400 w.p.m.	500 w.p.m.

GOING ALWAYS FORWARD

When you are reading, are you ever tempted to look back to pick up a word or an idea that you think you missed? This looking-back habit (*regression* is the name for it) reduces both speed and comprehension. Suppose you do not understand a word or two (or a half dozen or more); nine chances out of ten, you are going to get the main idea anyway. Make your eyes move forward, always forward, and never, never backward.

Get someone to test you for possible regressions. Have him watch your eyes as you read. To do this, he can use a mirror or a newspaper with a peek hole in it. With the newspaper method, you will read an article in the paper while your tester watches, through the peek hole, the movements of your eyes. If he finds that you do have the habit of looking back to pick up words, then you will simply have to discipline yourself. You will have to make yourself read forward even though you feel you will not understand a thing if you do not look back.

"I didn't have the heart to shoot him—and, besides, he seems quite happy as a rug."

AL BOIME

Mack.   The American Magazine

"I see where they've caught all those monkeys that escaped from the zoo, except one!"

GORILLA

AL JOHNS

SHIRVANIAN

"Watch him jump when I let it go."

◄⊂ RAYMOND L. DITMARS

Buying "Dynamite"

For several years Raymond L. Ditmars had charge of the Reptile Collection at the Bronx Zoo in New York. Snakes were his business. Therefore his nerve-tingling adventure with two king cobras, told in the following story, was all in the line of business.
(Note the time when you begin reading.)

ONE MORNING I received a telephone call from one of the older animal dealers whose disordered gloomy places are fast disappearing. The man was excited and urged me to hurry down, that he had two big king cobras loose. We wanted to buy a pair of these creatures, but I didn't relish the job of capturing them. Nevertheless, the head keeper and I started down. We carried a large fiber satchel in which were two deep burlap bags and a staff with a noose at the end.

The king cobra holds the palm as the largest and most active of all poisonous serpents. It grows to be fifteen feet long and is built like a great whip. From its size and extremely deadly venom it is by far the most formidable of any serpent. But added to all this is its curiously alert mentality or intelligence and its common habit of deliberately pursuing and attacking humans. It is Indo-Malayan and fortunately not generally common.

We found the dealer in a bad state of excitement. He had had a ship-

ment of birds from India, and among the cages was a large case of the usual Oriental teakwood with a few holes at the top. It was heavy, and he had carried it up to a room where he broke up boxes and cages, intending to knock off the top and carry the "python" it appeared to contain to the downstairs snake cages. As he expected to find a twelve- to fifteen-footer, stupid on being exposed to the light after its long journey, he anticipated no trouble in two men carrying the beast—one at the head and another at the tail—leaving the box behind to be broken up.

He knocked off part of the cover and at the first glance was surprised to see so much space in the case. He expected to find the highly piled coils of the Indian python. The weight of the case had deceived him, as teak is very heavy. Another look told the story. There were many loops of pale olive, no thicker than a man's wrist. As the dealer brandished the hammer in fright, an orange-colored head with glowing eyes rose straight up. He backed for the door; and the apparition continued to rise directly upward until the cobra had reared to the level of the man's breast, giving him a fearless preparatory stare. By this time the man had retreated through the door, stepping on the feet of the assistant who had come to help him. They both fell backward against the balustrade in the dark hall-way. Just as the dealer closed the door he caught the flash of a second cobra rearing beside the first, the two like great candlesticks. And they stared venomously at him!

I know only too well that curious stare of the king cobra. Its eyes are strangely brilliant—not luminous—but *alert*. The stare is piercing, as if to analyze and anticipate one's moves. The color of the reptile's eyes usually matches the hue of its throat and head, which are of ruddy yellow like an orange skin, giving the anterior portion of the snake distinct character in contrast to the pale olive body.

The dealer was terrified that the snakes would escape. There were two windows in the room; but they were safe because the place had been used for transferring large birds, and the sashes were covered with fine but strong mesh, cut in panels stapled over the entire casing from top to bottom. The room, however, was about eight-een feet square; and it was filled with trash, broken boxes and their covers, which were piled waist and shoulder high. There were rats in the old build-ings; and the floor of the room had not been examined for years, owing to the litter. The dealer feared that rats might have gnawed through the floor to make a meeting place of the room and to enlarge their traveling channels. If so, the cobras could es-

cape into the building. He wrung his hands at the thought of king cobras at liberty in downtown New York and implored me to get busy. I'll confess that right there I was somewhat ap-prehensive about going up to that room.

The first thing the dealer did was to take a key from his pocket and un-lock the door. Then he backed off while we peeked in. There was noth-ing in sight. Fortunately, there was some cleared space on our side. The door swung inward and jammed on the floor when halfway opened. I mo-mentarily closed it to make more room. There was a stout piece of wooden strip loose on the floor, which the head keeper appropriated as a staff. We had the two burlap bags and the stick with the noose.

Next we cautiously peered around, gently shoving a broken box here and there before we saw the first snake. A greenish fold protruded from be-neath a case. The cobra was asleep. But I knew what he would do if we touched him: boil out from the shel-ter and rear in combat attitude, pos-sibly come right at us. However, I figured we could handle him with the two sticks if the second cobra didn't join the party.

"Go around behind me and open the door so we have a getaway; I'm going to stir him up!" I cautioned the head keeper. He quietly moved be-hind me and grasped the handle. *The door was locked!*

My anger at the cowardly dealer for locking us in was hard to repress. But I had to grind my teeth and knock softly at the door. We didn't dare start any vibration by kicking it. There was no response. It was probable that the man was cowering downstairs.

We were in a fine mess! The door was too stout to be kicked through, and the windows were covered with mesh. I told my companion not to hesitate, but swing hard and disable the cobra if he came at us. As there was nothing to do but start, I poked the greenish coil.

Instantly there was a hiss like a muffled sneeze, deeper in tone than the characteristic sneezing hiss of the common Indian cobra—and out and up the serpent came, turning to us with his intent stare. His neck slowly expanded into the long narrow hood of his species, showing black and white spots between the scales.

That slow expanding of the hood was a favorable sign. The snake was hesitating between anger and surprise. I knew that here was the critical moment to get him. If the noose didn't work, he would get one of us— or there would be a dead cobra.

My assistant slowly waggled his stick as I reached forward and upward with the noose. I saw the cobra's intent eyes give a flicking glance at the noose. There was also a slight movement of his head. But instantly the eyes gathered intensity in their gaze at me. Quickly the thin noose slipped over his head. But still he didn't move. A side swing of the pole tightened the noose, and we pulled him down, the constricting cord narrowing his hood about three inches from the head.

The way that long body poured out from under the boxes was terrifying. There were fully twelve feet of him.

He furiously chewed the stick, embedding his fangs again and again in it. When my assistant got his stick across the snake's head, I grasped the brute by the neck. This is not so dangerous as it sounds if one knows how to do it. The idea was to back him into our bag. Meanwhile he was raising an awful rumpus in the room, throwing his body around and crashing over boxes right and left. I yanked my end toward a corner, the other man pulling the serpent hand over hand to the bag, then starting to shove the tail portion in.

We were successfully backing our first cobra in when we saw the other one. Impressions are sometimes instantaneous. I remember now that the throat markings were different, and I realized the two were a pair. She gave us more of a shock than the first, being high on the boxes and rearing fully four feet besides. She looked balefully over the scene like an avenger about to descend.

"Swing for that one!" I shouted, gathering the bag around the first snake. He was helping, if anything, in backing into the bag in his effort to pull his head away. Catching the edge of the bag I waited for him to yank back hard—and when he did I let go. It was a fifty-fifty chance. He might have shot out like a rocket; but he didn't, and he was not given an instant's handicap. There is a way of letting go such a bag with one hand and spinning it with the other that instantly seals the serpent inside. I learned this years before and had taught it to all the keepers of the Reptile Department. The trick caught His

Majesty by surprise and gave us two or three minutes' leeway before he could push his head past the twists. All this was happening in less time than it takes to tell it.

At this moment there was an awful clatter beside me. It was my assistant trying to hold down the head and neck of the second snake. Now it was my turn to waggle the noose staff and stand ready. The lady pulled loose once and made a magnificent sweep at us but missed by a couple of feet. We nearly climbed the wall in our scrambling jumps to duck that strike. A cobra doesn't strike like a viper, the latter being so quick there is a mere flash in the action. The king cobra sweeps forward in its strike, and by a jump you can evade the movement if it isn't followed.

Now it was the cobra or ourselves, and I was prepared to end it with a kill when the head keeper made a swing between a blow and a push and pinned the creature's neck against the top of a tilting case. The case lay fairly firm. I followed this by jamming the noosing staff nearer the head and holding with all my strength as she lashed and whipped her body all around the room.

"I have a good grip—pin the head!" I yelled. My man's stick advanced over the head. All at once we had her, grasped firmly by the neck like the first. Here was victory! By using his knee to lever the stick in down pressure, he pinioned her with one hand and grasped her with the other.

With my assistant now holding the snake's neck in a two-fisted grip and half squatting on the reptiles' anterior

quarter, I tied the first bag. During the action with the lady cobra it had been rising and pitching from side to side like a drunken thing. We backed number two into a bag, which was a lively but not difficult act as there was nothing else to bother us. The next thing for us to do was to get the heaviest piece of wood in the room and batter down that infernal door. Here was a chance to vent our feelings. The racket we made in the job was satisfying to both of us. One panel was split in several places. A moment later we should have had splinters flying into the hall when the door opened and the owner peeked in. One look at his face was enough to still the thoughts of the verbal abuse which was ready on my lips. The dealer, who was an oldish man, was as pale as clay, perspiring and shaking. He gasped for a statement of results, and I told him we had both cobras.

I have never seen a man recover his poise so quickly. He was keen for a dicker. Within five minutes he was rubbing his hands and telling us what a fine pair of cobras we had. The head keeper gave me a slow wink. We were also recovering our own poise and breath. King cobras were sold for about a hundred dollars apiece in those days before the war, a price that meant a good profit for the dealer. Such a price may seem ridiculous for a creature of the kind; but the truth of the matter was that daring native snake-catchers would occasionally trap or snare king cobras, bring them into the Chinese animal dealers' shops in Singapore, and receive their price.

Then the buyer, having a tremendous respect for the specimen, would get rid of it as quickly as he could. Such creatures were shipped along with other animals, and there was an extremely small market for them. I had for some time been objecting to this indiscriminate shipping of deadly snakes and insisting that they should be transported only under the most responsible care. There was too much danger of their boxes being broken during careless handling or accident.

But to return to the action: "I'll give you a hundred dollars for the *two* snakes," I told the dealer.

He wouldn't listen to such a price but was crafty enough to quote slightly lower than the average. I turned to the head keeper:

"Take them both upstairs and turn them loose where we found them."

That was enough. It closed the dicker. It was our revenge for the locked door.

(Note the time; and check your speed of reading with the Reading Score Board, page 103.)

❖‹‹❖

KNOWING HOW

Can you tell, step by step, how to catch a cobra?

A KIND OF TELEVISION

What pictures flashed upon the screen of your mind when you read these phrases and sentences in the story?
1. disordered gloomy places
2. loops of pale olive
3. orange-colored head with glowing eyes
4. the two like great candlesticks
5. A greenish fold protruded from beneath a case.
6. The way that long body poured from under the boxes was terrifying.
7. rising and pitching from side to side like a drunken thing
8. The dealer, who was an oldish man, was as pale as clay, perspiring and shaking.

KEY WORDS

How is each of these words important to the story?
1. king cobras
2. satchel
3. venom
4. Oriental teakwood
5. python
6. hood
7. noose
8. a dicker
9. specimen
10. revenge

SUPPORTING DETAILS

In his story, Ditmars stops occasionally to explain important facts. Fortunately, he knows exactly how to make his explanation clear. He states the main idea in a topic sentence, and then he gives a number of details which prove his statement. Here are three topic sentences which he uses for paragraphs of explanation. List the details which he uses to prove each of the topic sentences.

1. The king cobra holds the palm as the largest and most active of all poisonous serpents. (page 98)

2. The dealer was terrified that the snakes would escape. (page 99)

3. The way that long body poured out from under the boxes was terrifying. (page 100)

READING SCORE BOARD

Number of Words in Story: 2270.

Number of Minutes	23	11 1/2	9	7 1/2	5 1/2	4 1/2
Reading Rate	100 w.p.m.	200 w.p.m.	250 w.p.m.	300 w.p.m.	400 w.p.m.	500 w.p.m.

⟐ GREY OWL

Rabbit Hunting Made Easy

Grey Owl was born of a Scotch father and an Apache mother. He was adopted by the Ojibway and given the name of Grey Owl because of his love for night traveling. For years he lived in a cabin in northern Canada—one hundred miles from the nearest settlement. In the following, Grey Owl is telling a story which he heard another man tell. Between the lines you will recognize his own knowledge of the woods and his sense of humor.

(Note the time when you begin reading.)

RED LANDREVILLE had a sense of humor above the ordinary. I think he must have made his stories up as he went along, on the spur of the moment. He was an artist. His sense of humor was unquenchable, though he seldom smiled; and he could be crushed by no misfortune whatsoever. Anything but an expert packer, he

——From *Tales of an Empty Cabin* by Grey Owl. Used by permission of Grey Owl Estate and The Macmillan Company of Canada, Ltd.

once fell on a portage, face down, with his load on top of him. I was behind him, and dropping my own load I helped him out from under. I asked him how he felt. His face was cut and his teeth were full of sand and pine needles; but he spat them out and replied that he had never felt better in his life and that if he did, he would be inclined to think the world was framing on him.

I first noticed Red sitting among a

group of Rangers outside the head-quarters cabin at Bisco, the starting point for those who would penetrate the vast wilderness areas that lay spread out for hundreds of miles in all directions. The traveling was by canoe and portage only, and sufficiently arduous for even well-experienced bushmen; and I saw, with certain mis-givings, that several of those present, including Landreville, were going to be more ornamental than useful. Though certainly Landreville was no ornament. Tall and thin, with a homely, freckled face surmounted by a shock of violently red hair, he was talking with a kind of sarcastic twist to his lips that caused me to think that he was fomenting trouble among the men. So I stopped and listened. He waved me courteously to a seat on the bare ground, and said, "Look, Chief, these guys won't believe me; isn't that true about the rabbits? You know."

Not wanting to spoil a story I re-plied, on general principles, "Sure, it's true; what is it?"

"Well," he answered, "the way the Indians catch them, with pepper. You know." I didn't know, but it was all right with me.

He asked me to explain the method to the group, knowing very well that I had not the faintest idea of what he was getting at; but I had not the time, I claimed, being busy, and sug-gested he do so. "You tell it," I said.

So he did. And then I completely forgot all about my pretense of busi-ness and sat there and listened to Red Landreville.

I gathered that one of the group,

an athletically built university man (who had been foisted upon us), had been asking innumerable questions concerning the coming voyage. How-ever brilliant as a student, he was utterly out of place in these surround-ings, and green as grass—as I, too, would have been in college halls. In this he was forgivable except that he had made the rather bad mistake of boasting that he didn't really need the job and that he had got himself enrolled so he could have a holiday in the woods and at the same time be paid for it. He turned out to be a dead loss; and considering that he would be only a drawback and was filling the place of some working man who needed the money to live, this re-mark had grated rather on the sensi-bilities of those present who earned their living by the sweat of their brow. This gentleman in his thirst for knowledge asked numerous and rather dumb questions instead of try-ing to profit by what he saw and had enquired among many other things how it was possible to get fresh meat in the woods. On being told that white people were not allowed to kill anything but fish and rabbits in the Summer, he had asked how one caught the rabbits. Red had at once volunteered the information. The method, he said, was a secret known only to the Indians and himself, and he begged those present not to divulge it lest the Indians take revenge on him for betraying the secret.

"You see how easy it is," he com-menced. "Rabbits have a way of sit-ting around at night in circles, like we are," he indicated his listeners, "and they sit there thumping their hind feet on the ground—don't they?" He referred to me, and I had to admit that this was true. Having very adroitly made me an accessory, he continued: "Well, they always go to the same place to hold their *fiestas*[1]; and where they sit gets kinda worn, in a circle. Well, you go around through the bush until you find a place like that; and then you put stones inside the ring, one in front of where you think each rabbit is going to sit. Some stones will be right, and some won't; but that's all right because you don't want to kill 'em all. All you got to do is to sprinkle some red pepper on the

rocks and go away. You see, when the rabbits bang their hind feet on the ground, they kinda bob their heads down; did I get that right?" he looked at me. Being now hopelessly involved, I agreed with him again. He gave me a friendly nod, as from one craftsman to another. He resumed: "Well, when they bang their feet, they bob their heads, see; and when they bob their heads, they get the pepper that's on the stone in their noses, and then they commence to sneeze and sneeze *and* sneeze, banging their heads until they knock their fool brains out on the stones. All you do is go round in the morning and collect. Nothin' to it!"

[1] *fiestas.* Holiday festivities.

(Note the time, and check your speed of reading with the Reading Score Board.)

❖❖❖

READING CHARACTER BETWEEN THE LINES

Point out the lines which tell you something of the character of each:
1. Red Landreville   2. the university man   3. Grey Owl

GETTING THE POINT

Exactly how, according to Red, does one catch rabbits the easy way?

"CATCHING" WORDS—NOT RABBITS

What do the following words mean?

portage	arduous	misgivings	adroitly
penetrate	bushmen	divulge	accessory

READING SCORE BOARD

Number of Words in Story: 940.

Number of Minutes	10	5	4	3	2 1/2	2
Reading Rate	100 w.p.m.	200 w.p.m.	250 w.p.m.	300 w.p.m.	400 w.p.m.	500 w.p.m.

◂⊰ LAURA E. RICHARDS

The Buffalo

The Buffalo, the Buffalo,
He had a horrid snuffle, oh!
And not a single Indian chief
Would lend the beast a handkerchief,
Which shows how very, very far
From courtesy those people are.

◂⊰ CHARLES EDWARD CARRYL

The Plaint of the Camel

The camel, like the buffalo, has cause for complaint.
You would complain, too, if you had the troubles of
those animals.

Canary birds feed on sugar and seed,
    Parrots have crackers to crunch;
And as for poodles, they tell me the noodles
    Have chickens and cream for their lunch.
        But there's never a question
        About MY digestion—
          ANYTHING does for me!

Cats, you're aware, can repose in a chair,
    Chickens can roost upon rails;
Puppies are able to sleep in a stable,
    And oysters can slumber in pails.
        But no one supposes
        A poor Camel dozes—
          ANY PLACE does for me!

Lambs are enclosed where it's never exposed,
    Coops are constructed for hens;
Kittens are treated to houses well heated,
    And pigs are protected by pens.
        But a Camel comes handy
        Wherever it's sandy—
          ANYWHERE does for me!

People would laugh if you rode a giraffe,
    Or mounted the back of an ox;
It's nobody's habit to ride on a rabbit,
    Or try to bestraddle a fox.
        But as for a Camel, he's
        Ridden by families—
          ANY LOAD does for me!

A snake is as round as a hole in the ground,
    And weasels are wavy and sleek;
And no alligator could ever be straighter
    Than lizards that live in a creek,
        But a Camel's all lumpy
        And bumpy and humpy—
          ANY SHAPE does for me!

OBJECTS OF DISTRESS

1. Both the buffalo in Richards's poem and the camel in Carryl's were obviously in sad plights. Can you tell exactly why each was suffering?

2. What lines in each poem do you think are particularly amusing? Do you suppose our own complaints ever sound as amusing to others as do the camel's?

LOOKING BACKWARD THROUGH THE CHAPTER

1. Which stories, sketches, and poems in this chapter are told from the animal's point of view? Which are told from the point of view of a human being?

2. Which of the selections emphasize setting as well as plot? What different kinds of locale are used?

3. Which of the authors express an attitude toward the killing of animals? Explain.

4. Can you cite incidents in the selections which produce fright in the reader? sadness? amusement?

5. What interesting facts have you learned about the methods of hunting animals and about animal life in general?

PUTTING ON YOUR THINKING CAP

Who Wrote Them?

Without looking back at the selections to refresh your memory, can you list the authors of the following?

1. Lobo
2. Lions
3. Sage Counsel
4. The Buffalo
5. Wapiti, the Elk
6. The Plaint of the Camel
7. Lions on the Hunt
8. Elephant
9. Buying "Dynamite"
10. Rabbit Hunting Made Easy

What Are They About?

On your paper, complete each of these statements:

1. =?= is about a young animal that is wild with hunger.
2. =?= is the story of an old animal that died grieving for his mate.
3. =?= tells about the capture of two king cobras.
4. =?= tells about an animal with a "horrid snuffle."
5. =?= pictures a tiger's attack on elephants.
6. =?= relates the experience of a man in Africa in search of specimens for a museum.
7. =?= gives the thrills that may come to one who photographs wild animals.
8. =?= is a humorous story about catching certain little animals.
9. =?= follows the theme that "anything does" for one particular animal.
10. =?= suggests that you "Stay home and learn your catechissum."

What Do These Mean?

Can you do some "intelligent guessing" with these words in italics? What do you think they mean? Later, check with the dictionary.

1. And the king whose *despotic* power was felt over its entire extent was an old gray wolf.
2. . . . this was no ordinary *skirmish* but a battle to be fought to the death.
3. . . . I realized *vaguely* that I was being crushed beneath him.
4. Naturally, being of the cat family, he is *carnivorous*.
5. He was no longer a cub, with the apprehensive, *sniveling* ways of cubhood!
6. It closed the *dicker*. It was our *revenge* for the locked door.
7. . . . he felt *searing* pain and smelled his own blood.
8. The traveling was by canoe and *portage* only, and sufficiently *arduous* for even well-experienced *bushmen*.
9. . . . Wapiti's youthful *vigor* began to make itself felt.
10. *Instinctively* I seized it in my left hand.

OTHER THINGS TO DO

1. There are many other interesting stories about wild animals. The list on page 109 has a number of good suggestions.
2. Spend some time telling stories about wild animals that you know. They may be true stories or ones you have read in books.

3. Everyone at one time or another has the itch to write. Perhaps this is your moment. Here are some ideas that may interest you:

    a. A true hunting story

    b. A wild animal you have tamed

    c. A story told from a pet's point of view

    d. How the cat got his whiskers (or the camel his hump, or the zebra his stripes, and so on)

    e. Some foolish verses about animals

4. Take stock of your skill in reading. How would you answer these questions?

    a. Are you checking yourself, as you read, on whether you understand the meaning of the material?

    b. Is your rate of reading improving?

    c. Are you adding to your vocabulary?

STORIES ABOUT ANIMALS

Buzzati, Dino, *The Bears' Famous Invasion of Sicily*, 1947 (Pantheon).
    The influence of human beings on the bears who conquer Sicily.

De la Mare, Walter J., *Mr. Bumps and His Monkey*, 1942 (Winston).
    A sailor and his African monkey.

Clark, Denis, *Black Lightning*, 1954 (Viking).
    A coal-black leopard in the jungle.

George, John L. and Jean C., *Masked Prowler*, 1950 (Dutton).
    Life cycle of a raccoon.

Grey Owl, *Sajo and the Beaver People*, 1936 (Scribner).
    Two beaver kittens rescued by an Indian hunter.

Henderson, Luis M., *Amik, the Life Story of a Beaver*, 1948 (Morrow).
    Natural life of a wild animal.

Henry, Marguerite, *Misty of Chincoteague*, 1947 (Rand McNally).
    Freedom-loving wild ponies on islands off the shore of Virginia.

Holling, Holling C., *Minn of the Mississippi*, 1951 (Houghton).
    A three-legged snapping turtle's journey down the Mississippi.

Kipling, Rudyard, *The Jungle Book*, 1932 (Doubleday).
    Jungle life of a boy brought up by a family of wolves.

Kjelgaard, Jim, *Haunt Fox*, 1954 (Holiday).
    A fox of the wilds.

McCracken, Harold, *Flaming Bear*, 1951 (Lippincott).
    Quest for a huge bear which seemed to glow in the night.

Montgomery, Rutherford G., *Carcajou*, 1936 (Caxton Printers).
    The life and death struggles of a wolverine.

Mukerji, Dhan Gopal, *Hari, the Jungle Lad*, 1924 (Dutton).
    How a jungle lad learns the ways of the wild.

Heroes

The Golden Fleece

A famous story of Greek mythology tells of a young man who dared fire-breathing bulls and dragons and the like for a special kind of fleece. Perhaps the fact that it was *golden* fleece spurred Jason on.
(Notice the time when you begin reading in order to tell how long it takes you to read this story.)

IN VERY ancient times there lived in Thessaly a king and queen named Athamas and Nephele. They had two children, a boy and a girl. After a time Athamas grew indifferent to his wife, left her, and took another. Nephele suspected danger to her children from the influence of the stepmother, and took measures to send them out of her reach. Mercury[1] assisted her, and gave her a ram with a golden fleece, on which she set the two children, trusting that the ram would convey them to a place of safety.

The ram vaulted into the air with the children on his back, taking his course to the East, till when crossing the strait that divides Europe and Asia, the girl, whose name was Helle, fell from his back into the sea, which from her was called the Hellespont,— now the Dardanelles. The ram continued his career till he reached the kingdom of Colchis, on the eastern shore of the Black Sea, where he safely landed the boy Phryxus, who was hospitably received by Æetes, king of the country. Phryxus sacrificed the ram to Jupiter,[2] and gave the Golden Fleece to Æetes, who placed it in a consecrated grove, under the care of a sleepless dragon.

There was another kingdom in Thessaly near to that of Athamas, and ruled over by a relative of his. The king Æson, being tired of the cares of government, surrendered his crown to his brother Pelias on condition that he should hold it only during the minority of Jason, the son of Æson. When Jason was grown up and came to demand the crown from his uncle, Pelias pretended to be willing to yield it, but at the same time suggested to the young man the glorious adventure of going in quest of the Golden Fleece, which it was well known was in the kingdom of Colchis, and was, as Pelias pretended, the rightful property of their family.

Jason was pleased with the thought and forthwith made preparations for the expedition. At that time the only species of navigation known to the Greeks consisted of small boats or canoes hollowed out from trunks of trees, so that when Jason employed Argus to build him a vessel capable of

[1] *Mercury.* God of speed; the messenger of the gods.
——From Helen Sewell: *A Book of Myths.* Copyright 1942 by The Macmillan Company and used with their permission.

[2] *Jupiter.* King of the gods.

containing fifty men, it was considered a gigantic undertaking. It was accomplished, however, and the vessel named *Argo*, from the name of the builder.

Jason sent his invitation to all the adventurous young men of Greece, and soon found himself at the head of a band of bold youths, many of whom afterwards were renowned among the heroes and demigods of Greece. Hercules, Theseus, Orpheus, and Nestor were among them. They are called the Argonauts, from the name of their vessel.

The *Argo* with her crew of heroes left the shores of Thessaly and having touched at the Island of Lemnos, thence crossed to Mysia and thence to Thrace. Here they found the sage Phineus, and from him received instruction as to their future course. It seems the entrance of the Euxine Sea was impeded by two small rocky islands, which floated on the surface, and in their tossings and heavings occasionally came together, crushing and grinding to atoms any object that might be caught between them. They were called the Clashing Islands. Phineus instructed the Argonauts how to pass this dangerous strait.

When they reached the islands they let go a dove, which took her way between the rocks, and passed in safety, only losing some feathers of her tail. Jason and his men seized the favourable moment of the rebound, plied their oars with vigour, and passed safe through, though the islands closed behind them, and actually grazed their stern. They now rowed along the shore till they arrived at the eastern end of the sea, and landed at the kingdom of Colchis.

Jason made known his message to the Colchian king, Æetes, who consented to give up the Golden Fleece if Jason would yoke to the plough two fire-breathing bulls with brazen feet, and sow the teeth of the dragon which Cadmus had slain, and from which it was well known that a crop of armed men would spring up, who would turn their weapons against their producer. Jason accepted the conditions, and a time was set for making the experiment. Previously, however, he found means to plead his cause to Medea, daughter of the king. He promised her marriage, and as they stood before the altar of Hecate, called the goddess to witness his oath. Medea yielded, and by her aid, for she was a sorceress, he was furnished with a charm, by which he could encounter safely the breath of the fire-breathing bulls and the weapons of the armed men.

At the time appointed, the people assembled at the grove of Mars, and the king assumed his royal seat, while the multitude covered the hill-sides. The brazen-footed bulls rushed in, breathing fire from their nostrils that burned up the herbage as they passed. The sound was like the roar of a furnace, and the smoke like that of water upon quick-lime. Jason advanced boldly to meet them. His friends, the chosen heroes of Greece, trembled to behold him. Regardless of the burning breath, he soothed their rage with his voice, patted their necks with fearless hand, and adroitly slipped over them the yoke, and compelled them to drag the plough.

The Colchians were amazed; the Greeks shouted for joy.

Jason next proceeded to sow the dragon's teeth and plough them in. And soon the crop of armed men sprang up, and, wonderful to relate! no sooner had they reached the surface than they began to brandish their weapons and rush upon Jason. The Greeks trembled for their hero, and even she who had provided him a way of safety and taught him how to use it, Medea herself, grew pale with fear. Jason for a time kept his assailants at bay with his sword and shield, till, finding their numbers overwhelming, he resorted to the charm which Medea had taught him, seized a stone and threw it in the midst of his foes. They immediately turned their arms against one another, and soon there was not one of the dragon's brood left alive. The Greeks embraced their hero, and Medea, if she dared, would have embraced him too.

It remained to lull to sleep the dragon that guarded the fleece, and this was done by scattering over him a few drops of a preparation which Medea had supplied. At the smell he relaxed his rage, stood for a moment motionless, then shut those great round eyes, that had never been known to shut before, and turned over on his side, fast asleep. Jason seized the fleece, and with his friends and Medea accompanying, hastened to their vessel before Æetes the king could arrest their departure, and made the best of their way back to Thessaly, where they arrived safe, and Jason delivered the fleece to Pelias, and dedicated the *Argo* to Neptune.[3]

What became of the fleece afterwards we do not know, but perhaps it was found after all, like many other golden prizes, not worth the trouble it had cost to procure it.

[3] *Neptune.* God of the sea.

(Note the time; and check your speed of reading with the Reading Score Board, page 115.)

❖❰❖

THINKING IT OVER

1. Extraordinary things happen in myths and legends. What incidents in "The Golden Fleece" are unbelievable?

2. Why did Jason want the Golden Fleece?

3. How was he able to get it?

4. *Three* is supposed to be a magic number. How does the number *three* enter into this story?

5. Why is the last paragraph especially good? Can you give other examples of the truth that is expressed?

THE GREEKS HAD A WORD FOR IT

These Greek words have become a part of our language. What do they mean?

1. *Hellespont*
2. *herculean* strength
3. *Orpheus* societies
4. wisdom of *Nestor*
5. *martian* array
6. *Pegasus*

What do you think is the origin of each of these words? Your *Webster's Students Dictionary* will help you if you are not sure.

pedagogue	hyacinth	psalm
alphabet	echo	tantalize
enthusiasm	halcyon	stigma
gymnasium	panic	synonym

A BAD ENDING

The love affair of Jason and Medea ended very badly. If you can, find a story that tells what happened to them.

Then write a single paragraph, telling what you think of Jason or Medea. Use this as your topic sentence: Jason (or Medea) is an unforgettable character.

READING SCORE BOARD

Number of Words in Story: 1170.

Number of Minutes	12	6	5	4	3	2 1/3
Reading Rate	100 w.p.m.	200 w.p.m.	250 w.p.m.	300 w.p.m.	400 w.p.m.	500 w.p.m.

◀ KATHARINE PYLE

Thor[1] Loses and Finds His Hammer

The following story comes from Norse mythology. Thor was the great god of thunder, and from him we get our word *Thursday* (Thor's Day). Thor could protect the gods and goddesses by his great thunder-making hammer. Hence, when he lost his hammer, something had to be done at once.
(**Note the time when you begin reading.**)

THOR's hammer was the protection of the gods. The giants, who were the Asas' bitter enemies, feared it as they feared nothing else; and always Thor kept it where he could catch it up at any moment. But on a certain morning he awoke to find his hammer gone. Someone had stolen it in the night. At once he suspected Loki[2]; for Loki was a mischief-maker. Nothing pleased him more than giving others trouble or distress.

In haste Thor sent for Loki, but he soon found the mischief-maker knew no more about the loss than he himself. Loki, indeed, was sore afraid

[1] *Thor.* God of thunder.
——From *Heroic Tales from the Norse*, by Katharine Pyle. Copyright, 1928, 1934, by J. B. Lippincott Company.

[2] *Loki.* God of mischief.

when he heard Thor's hammer had been stolen. "If the giants learn of this," he said, "it may prove a dangerous thing for the Asas. They might even take courage to come here to Asgard and attack us." He then told Thor to keep the loss as secret as he could.

"But how shall we win the hammer back?" asked Thor.

"Let me think for a moment's time," said Loki; then presently—"First of all we will go to Freya.³ From her I will borrow her falcon dress and put it on. Then as a falcon I will fly about the world until I find the hammer. After that it will be for thee to win it back. But we will tell none but Freya of all this."

The plan pleased Thor, and at once the two Asas went to Freya's palace. There Thor told her of his loss and asked if she would lend her falcon dress to Loki so that he might fly forth in search of Miölner.⁴

Freya cried, "If it were of silver, he should have it, Thor; and if it were of gold, still I would lend it to him," and at once she fetched the dress. Loki put it on and became a falcon. He said farewell to Freya and to Thor; and spreading wide his wings, away he sped—down to Midgard.

There a fearful storm was raging, rain and hail and wind; the lightning flashed and thunder rolled across the heavens. Loki needed no more than that to tell him who had Thor's hammer. The giant Thrym had the power to send out storms, but never before had he been able to make thunder

and lightning; only with Thor's hammer could he do that. Loki waited until the storm was over, then winged his way to Jötunheim and to Thrym's palace.

Thrym gave him greeting. "How goes it with the Asas upon Asgard's heights?" he asked.

"It goes but ill with them," Loki answered. "Thor is in a rage because thou hast stolen his hammer. Where hast thou hidden it, Thrym?"

Thrym answered, "Where thou wilt never find it, Loki. It is hidden eight miles down below the mountains of Jötunheim."

Loki asked, "Wilt thou sell it back to us?"

"Yes, for a price," Thrym answered. "Let the Asas give me Freya for a wife, and Thor shall have his hammer back."

Loki said, "That is a price that will never be paid. Of all the goddesses there is not one as fair as Freya. The gods would never let her go from Asgard. Moreover, she is Odur's wife; he would never give her up. Ask for some other thing, oh Thrym."

Thrym answered, "There is nothing else that I desire. My treasure house is full of treasures; servants obey my word; I have steeds for pleasure and cows with golden horns. Unless I can have Freya as the price, I will keep Thor's hammer."

Loki said, "I will carry that message back to Asgard, but I fear the gods will never agree to give thee Freya."

At once he put on his falcon dress again and returned to Asgard. There he told Thor he had learned where the hammer was—that Thrym had

³ *Freya.* Goddess of love and beauty.
⁴ *Miölner.* The name of Thor's hammer.

stolen it; told him, too, all the giant had said.

Thor cried, "Let us at once seek Freya. She must go to Thrym, for until I have my hammer back the Asas are not safe—no, not even here in Asgard."

Loki said, "Be not hasty, Thor. Let us first call a meeting of the gods, and we will all talk this matter over. Freya, too, shall come to our meeting."

To this Thor after some talk agreed, though most unwillingly. The gods were bidden to Gladsheim, the great council hall; and Freya, too, was told to come.

After they had all assembled there, Thor rose and told them how his hammer had been stolen; told them, too, who had taken it. Pale grew the Asas when they heard. Thor told, as well, how Loki had gone to bargain for the hammer, and of the price Thrym asked for the return of it. Then turning to where Freya sat he said, "Now make thyself ready as quickly as thou canst, Freya. I myself will ride with thee to Jötunheim and deliver thee to Thrym. Then I can bring my hammer back with me."

Then Freya was filled with such wrath, her necklace Brisingamen burst apart and fell down clashing on the floor. "Shall I, who am the wife of Odur, go like a lovesick maid to Jötunheim to be the wife of Thrym?" she cried. "That shall never be. Better death than that."

Odur, too, was filled with fury, and others of the gods as well, though some thought Thor spoke wisely. But the white Heimdall rose and called for silence. Wise was he beyond most others, and the gods fell silent to listen to him.

"There is no need for Freya to go to Jötunheim," he said. "There is another way of winning back the hammer. Thor shall dress as a bride in women's robes and ornaments; he shall wear Freya's necklace on his breast, and draw a veil across his face, and go to Thrym, and in some way win back his Miölner."

Then Thor's eyes flashed fire. Sparks flew from his beard. "Never will I consent to this," he cried. "The mighty Thor will never act the bride and make himself a laughingstock for gods and men."

But Loki cried sharply, "Silence, Thor! This thing must be, for Freya will not go, and only so canst thou win back thy hammer; only so can we be safe, and our homes and wives as well. I will myself dress as thy serving maid, and ride with thee to Thrym-heim."

Then Thor at last gave way, though sullenly. They dressed him as a bride with shining robes, and bracelets on his arms, and fastened Brisingamen about his neck. They braided his hair right cunningly so that it appeared as a woman's, and last of all they drew a veil across his face.

Loki, too, made ready, and presently the two set out riding high in Thor's chariot. Thor's wrath and shame were still so great that as they journeyed on, the mountain smoked, and flames rose from the earth.

Thrym was watching for his guests. As they drew near, he hastened out to meet them. He would have drawn aside Thor's veil and kissed the pretended bride, but Thor leaped back with such a furious bound that all who saw it wondered. Loki cried in haste, "Thy bride is shy, and she is strange in Jötunheim. Let her alone, and she will soon grow used to it."

Then Thrym took Thor's hand and led him into the palace hall. Thor hung his head and would not speak, and once again Loki said, "She is too shy; she will talk presently." So Thrym was satisfied.

A great wedding feast had been prepared, and presently they all sat round the board with Thor at Thrym's right hand. Thor arranged his veil so his mouth was free to eat and drink. Brisingamen, Freya's necklace, glittered on his breast so that Thrym's eyes were dazzled by it. Scarce could he see aught else.

Greatly the giants ate, but Thor ate even more. Whole oxen he devoured, and sheep and salmon, fruit and cakes; all that had been prepared for the women he ate himself, and he drank greatly, too.

Thrym was amazed. He said, "Methinks my bride hath a mighty hunger, and a mighty thirst."

Loki said, "For eight days she hath eaten nothing, and no drop hath passed her lips, so greatly hath she longed for thee and Jötunheim."

Then for the third time Thrym was satisfied.

When the feast was ended, Thrym's old sister came to ask for a marriage present from the bride. She begged for jewels from Thor's breast, or for the rings from his fingers; but he gave

her nothing then, though later he gave her that for which she neither asked nor wished.

Thrym cried, "Now shall our wedding joy be sealed by a bride-gift"; and he brought Thor's hammer to him in his hands. At sight of it Thor's eyes flashed fire so that they seemed to burn even through his veil, and Thrym said, "How sharp are the bride's eyes!"

Loki said, "They burn with love for thee!"

And now Thrym laid the hammer across the knees of the pretended bride.

At once Thor seized it in his hand and rose; he tore aside his veil, he tore aside his woman's robes, and swung the hammer high; and Thrym and all giants cried aloud with fear, seeing who it was and knowing they had been tricked. Then they would have fled away, but Thor threw his hammer first of all at Thrym, and he fell, and afterward at the others, and always when it was thrown a giant fell, and always the hammer at once returned to Thor's hand again. Many were the Jotuns who were slain that day; and to Thrym's sister Thor gave smacks instead of jewels, and blows instead of rings. After that Thor and Loki burned Thrym's castle down and left it a heap of ruins. So they returned triumphantly to Asgard, and there were great rejoicings there; for now Thor had his hammer once again and the gods could dwell in peace and safety in their glittering houses on Asgard's heights.

(Note the time; and check your speed of reading with the Reading Score Board, page 119.)

PROOF FOR TRUTH

Can you cite passages to prove each of these statements?
1. Loki was more than a mischief-maker.
2. Thor was fearless.
3. Thor was selfish.
4. Three is a number used often in such stories as this.
5. For a number of reasons the giants should have known the "bride" was a god.

WORDS MAKE PICTURES

What does each of these expressions mean to you?

sore afraid   lovesick maid
falcon dress   shining robes
fearful storm   pretended bride
council hall   heap of ruins
necklace Brisingamen   glittering houses

WORDS GIVE MEANING

On your paper write *Syn.* (synonym) or *Ant.* (antonym) for each of the following pairs of words. Synonyms, you remember, are words that mean almost the same; antonyms are words with opposite meanings.

1. distress—joy
2. forth—onward
3. steeds—horses
4. bidden—asked
5. assembled—disbanded
6. wrath—anger
7. sullenly—smilingly
8. cunningly—crudely
9. devoured—ate
10. triumphantly—victoriously

GODS TALK STRANGELY

How would you say each of the following thoughts? Find other sentences in the story which have a godlike ring, and say them as you would normally say them.
1. Let me think for a moment's time.
2. It goes but ill with them.
3. Where hast thou hidden it, Thrym?
4. Let us at once seek Freya.
5. Then Freya was filled with such wrath, her necklace Brisingamen burst apart and fell clashing on the floor.

READING SCORE BOARD

Number of Words in Story: 1700.

Number of Minutes	17	8 1/2	7	5 2/3	4 1/4	3 1/2
Reading Rate	100 w.p.m.	200 w.p.m.	250 w.p.m.	300 w.p.m.	400 w.p.m.	500 w.p.m.

❧ DOROTHY HOSFORD

Beowulf's Encounter with Grendel

An Anglo-Saxon poet back in the tenth century wrote about the adventures of a Danish hero named Beowulf. Single-handed, Beowulf was able to destroy Grendel, a terrible man-eating monster. Here is the story of that famous encounter.
(Note the time when you begin reading.)

LONG AGO there lived a king of the Danes, Hrothgar by name, who was a noble lord of his people. He had won such honor and glory in war that all his kin obeyed him gladly and his band of followers was great.

One day it came to the mind of Hrothgar that he would bid his henchmen[1] build a great hall, mightier than had ever been seen by the sons of earth. There would he rule his people and divide among them the spoils of battle. When the word was spoken, his kinsmen came from far and wide to help with the building of the hall. Soon it stood ready, high and wide-gabled, towering strong in the land. The hall was named Heorot. Within its walls Hrothgar was faithful to his promises and dealt fairly with his people and gave unto them many a treasure.

So Hrothgar and his clansmen dwelt in cheerfulness and plenty; harps and the sound of clear singing rang out in the hall. Bards[2] sang of the early time of man when God first made the world: how the sun and the moon were set in the heavens to make a light for man; how the earth was made lovely with trees and green growing things, and how God gave life to all creatures that breathe and move. All was peace in the land of Hrothgar.

But in the wild fens[3] and moorlands there dwelt a monster whose name was Grendel. He heard these sounds of joy with fierce anger. When the night was dark, he crept forth to the hall of the Danes. The band of warriors lay sleeping after their feast, unmindful of danger or sorrow. Grendel, with grim and greedy claws, tore thirty of the thanes[4] from their resting places and sped to his dark home, exultant over his spoil.

When daybreak came, men saw the evil that Grendel had done. Sorrow overcame their joy, and a great cry was raised in the dawn. Word was brought to Hrothgar, the king; and he sat on his high-seat, joyless, heavy with sorrow, grieving the loss of his

---

[1] *henchmen.* Followers.
[2] *bards.* Singers of heroic songs.
——From *By His Own Might: The Battles of Beowulf* by Dorothy Hosford. Copyright, 1947, by Henry Holt and Company, Inc.

[3] *fens.* Low swamplands.
[4] *thanes.* Men holding land through military service.

thanes. Yet when darkness came, Grendel returned to the hall once more and again wrought violence and destruction upon the sleeping warriors. None could resist his strength. From that time forth he would often, when the black night covered the land, steal from his moorlands and attack the hall. Great numbers of the Danes perished in his grasp.

Thus Grendel gained mastery over them all. After a time the great hall of Heorot stood deserted and empty each night, and long it remained so. Now that the hate of the demon was clearly shown, none dared sleep within the hall. Fear of Grendel made them seek a safer place.

For twelve long years Hrothgar, lord of the Danes, endured this sorrow. In time it became known far and wide, as the tale was told from one man to another, how Grendel had striven against Hrothgar and how he had brought sorrow and destruction upon him. Grendel would make no pact of peace with the Danes, nor would he give ransom for those he had slain. Night after night he prowled the misty moors, and lay in ambush for old and young. And none but Grendel sought out the gold-bright hall of Heorot in the dark night.

The earls of the Danes often assembled in council to devise ways to combat this unseen terror, but none could be found. All who offered to face Grendel lost their lives to him; no man had strength against him. So the great sorrow and heart-rending misery endured. The woe of Hrothgar was unceasing. Nothing could heal his sorrow; too great was the strife and misery that had come upon his people.

Far off in his home a thane of Hygelac, named Beowulf, famed among the Geats, heard of the deeds of Grendel. He was a man of mighty valor, noble and powerful. At once he made ready. He would sail far over the sea and seek out the king of the Danes, who had need of men. Nor did Beowulf's kinsmen discourage him from the dangerous journey, though they loved him dearly.

Then this bold Geat chose the comrades he would take with him, the keenest warriors he could find, fourteen in number. Time passed, and the ship was ready; the boat was drawn up under the bluff, where the waves were churning the sea with the sand. The warriors bore to the vessel their shining war gear, their mail,[5] and weapons. The men pushed off and the boat, built of strong timbers, was on its way. Like a bird sped by the wind, the ship moved over the waters. They sailed over their course with such swiftness that on the second day they sighted the land of the Danes. They saw the sea-cliffs shining, the steep hills, and the broad headlands. Their journey was ended.

The Geats anchored their ship and went ashore, with their gear of battle and their clashing armor. They thanked the Almighty Father for bringing them safely over the paths of the sea.

The road, laid with stones, showed the men the way. Their mail glistened, and the steel rings of their

[5] *mail.* Armor made of interlinked metal rings.

armor sang as they strode toward the hall. Outside the hall, they set their broad shields and bucklers against the wall and stacked together their weapons and gray-tipped spears. Weary from their sea journey, they rested themselves on the benches.

Then came to them a warrior of the Danes, who was Hrothgar's herald and messenger. He asked them of their home and kindred: "From whence come you, bearing your burnished shields and armor of war?"

The lord of the Geats answered him: "We are Hygelac's table-comrades. Beowulf is my name. I will tell my errand to your lord, the mighty prince, the son of Healfdene, if he grant that we may greet him."

The name of the warrior was Wulfgar. He was a prince known for his bold deeds and his wise counsel. He made answer to Beowulf: "I will ask the king of the Danes, the giver of rings, concerning your errand and quickly bring such answer as he gives."

Then he went in haste to where Hrothgar sat, old and white-haired, with his earls about him. Wulfgar spoke to his lord and master:

"Men have come hither from far over the ocean ways, from the land of the Geats. The chief man among them is called Beowulf. They ask this boon,[6] my master, that they may have speech with you. Do not refuse, gracious Hrothgar, to give them hearing. They seem warriors worthy of respect; their leader, surely, is a man of prowess."

Hrothgar, lord of the Danes, answered: "I knew him as a child. The wise Ecgtheow was his father. Now his son has come boldly hither and sought out his friend. I have heard, too, from seamen who have carried my gifts to the court of the Geats, that this man has the strength of thirty in his hand. The Almighty Father, I trust, has sent him to us as aid against the terror of Grendel. Haste, and bid them come hither and give them this word—that they are welcome guests to the folk of the Danes."

Wulfgar returned to the door of the hall and spoke Hrothgar's words of welcome to the Geats.

Beowulf, the mighty one, rose with his thanes about him. They went where the herald led them, through the hall of Heorot to the high-seat of the king.

Then Beowulf stood forth in his bright coat of linked mail, and spoke:

"Hail, Hrothgar! Hygelac's kinsman and follower am I. Fame already have I gained as a youth. I have heard in my homeland of the deeds of Grendel. Seafarers tell how this hall of yours, the best of buildings, stands empty and idle when nightfall comes. So my thanes advised me, O sovereign Hrothgar, to seek you here, for they knew full well my strength and courage. They themselves had seen me come from battle flecked with the blood of my foes, when I had worsted them and bound five together. Amid the waves I have slain monsters of the sea when they sought the destruction of the Geats. Now Grendel, that monster cruel, shall be mine to quell in single combat.

"So, prince of the Danes, I ask one boon of you. Refuse it not, friend of

6 boon. Favor.

the people, lord of the warriors, since I have come so far. Let me, alone with my brave men, now cleanse this hall. Furthermore, I have heard that this monster, in his wantonness, recks[7] not of weapons. So I will scorn to carry sword or shield to the battle; but with grip of hand alone will I face that fiend and fight for life, foe against foe.

"In the hands of the Almighty Father will be the victory. If Grendel wins, he will devour my men in this hall of gold as he has devoured others. Nor will you need to perform burial rites for me. Grendel will bear my body as prey to his den in the fastness, with my lifeblood will he redden his lair. If I go down in the battle, send to Hygelac the war gear that has ever guarded my breast. It is the work of Wayland, the smith, finely wrought. There is none to equal it. And let Fate fare as she must."

Then spoke Hrothgar: "You have sought us out to bring aid and comfort in our need, my friend Beowulf. It is a soreness in my heart to say to anyone what desolation Grendel has wrought for me with his hatred and his evil. My band of warriors grows less, for Fate has swept them into Grendel's grasp. But the Almighty Father is able to turn this deadly foe from his deeds. My armed men have often sworn, as they sat at banquet, that they would remain here in the mead-hall[8] and meet Grendel's attack with flash of swords. Then, when the morning came, the hall was dyed with blood, the benches stained and broken. And more of my heroes had met their death. But come, sit down at banquet, and tell my men of your plans and purpose."

The brave Geats took their places at the long bench set aside for them. A henchman, bearing the carved cup in his hand, served them and poured the clear mead. Bards sang their ancient songs and the warriors, both Geats and Danes, made merry.

The sounds of merriment and feasting filled the hall, till after a time Hrothgar rose to seek his rest for the night. He knew a battle awaited Grendel, when the sun was gone and the dark night was come and the monster should seek out the great hall. The warriors stood and Hrothgar greeted Beowulf, one warrior to another, and wished him safe outcome, mastery over the hall:

"Never to any man before, since I could lift hand or shield, have I given in trust this noble hall of the Danes, save now to you. Take now and hold this fairest of houses. Remember you are great; make known your might; watch for the foe. No wish of yours shall go unfulfilled, if you come forth with your life from this battle."

Then the king and queen went forth from the hall, attended by the whole company of Danes.

Beowulf, in the hall, took off his corselet[9] of iron and the helmet from his head. He gave them and his richly carved sword to his henchman and bade him guard them. Before he sought his bed, Beowulf, valiant hero of the Geats, spoke these proud words:

"I count myself as great in battle, in deeds of war, as Grendel. Not with

---

[7] recks. Is concerned.
[8] mead-hall. A place for eating and drinking.

[9] corselet. Armor used to cover the body.

the sword shall I give him over to the sleep of death, though I have that power. He has no skill with weapons. Therefore we both shall spurn the sword this night. If he seek me here, I shall meet him unarmed. Let the Almighty Father award the mastery as He sees fit."

Beowulf laid him down on his bed; and his warriors, weary, stretched themselves to rest. Not one of them thought that he would ever go forth alive from that place or return again to his home and the folk from whom he came. They remembered how many warriors Grendel had seized in that hall of the Danes. But they sank to slumber, worn with their journeying; all save one. Beowulf, wakeful, ready, waited fiercely through the night the oncoming battle.

Then from the moorland, from the misty crags, Grendel came. Mighty in his wrath, he made ready to seize upon the warriors gathered in the mead-hall. Under the clouds he strode until the great hall, brave with gold, came into sight. Many times he had sought out the home of Hrothgar, but never before had such hardy warriors awaited him. Straight to the hall came the evil one. The door, though fastened with bands forged in the fire, gave way when his fists struck it; and he burst into the hall fierce in his rage. He strode across the shining floor. Flashes, like flame, came from his eyes. He spied the hero band sleeping together. And he laughed in his heart and thought that before morning he would rend the life from each of them and have his fill of feasting. But it was fated that never, after

that night, should he feed again on the race of men.

Beowulf, strong in his might, watched his foe eagerly to see how he would set about the onslaught. Nor did the monster pause. Straightway he seized a sleeping warrior and destroyed him, devouring his blood and body. Then he stepped forward again and grasped the hero Beowulf where he lay on his bed. The fiend reached for him with his claw, but Beowulf clutched Grendel's arm and threw his weight against it. At once that monster knew that never in this world, on any of the ways of the earth, had he met with so mighty a handgrip. He was afraid and trembled in his heart, but he could not escape. He would fain have fled to his fastness, to that den of devils. This was not as it had been in other raids upon the hall.

Then the hardy Beowulf remembered his battle-boast. Up he sprang and laid fast hold upon his foe. Grendel's fingers cracked in that iron grip, but the fiend strove fiercely to wrench himself free. He longed to escape to the fens, yet he knew his power was caught in the strength of this grim one. Din filled the hall. Panic fell upon the Danes, upon all who heard the uproar. Maddened were the strugglers; the house resounded with their clashing. It was a wonder that the hall held firm, that it did not fall to earth with the rage of their battle. Strong iron bands, without and within, held it fast, though many a gold-decked mead bench crashed to the floor. The wise Danes had built their house to withstand all onslaughts, save the creeping embrace of fire.

The turmoil grew. Suddenly a strange outcry rose through the night. The Danes quaked with terror as they heard the monster's wail of pain and defeat. Caught in Beowulf's fierce grip, Grendel cried aloud in anguish. Beowulf would not suffer that murderous one to live.

Now many of Beowulf's warriors drew their weapons to aid their lord. They did not know, as they came close to Grendel, striking at him from every side with their swords, that no blade fashioned on earth could do him harm. He had laid his spell on every weapon, and none could hurt him. But the evil one, who had wrought murder many a time in days past, found that his strength now failed him. The bold kinsman of Hygelac held him fast. As they struggled, the monster took a fearful hurt; a great wound showed on his shoulder, his sinews cracked, and the bones broke. Now was the victory given to Beowulf; and Grendel, sick unto death, fled to his den in the dark moor. He knew that his wound was mortal—that the end of his days had come, the last of his life on earth.

By this bloody battle the Danes had at last won peace. Beowulf, strong in arm and brave of heart, had brought safety to Hrothgar's hall. The Geat had made good his battle-boast to the Danes, and the sorrow they had long endured was ended now. It was proof of this, when Beowulf laid down in the hall the limb, the whole arm and shoulder of Grendel, which he had torn from him in the struggle.

(Note the time; and check your speed of reading with the Reading Score Board, page 126.)

◆《◆

A Fight to the Death

1. How was Beowulf able to kill Grendel when all others had failed?
2. What picture do you get of the monster?
3. What picture do you get of the way people lived in those long-ago times? What entertainment did they have? How did the warriors dress? What kind of houses did they have? Cite passages in the story that tell the answers to these questions.

Another Kind of Language

Did you notice how different the language of the story sounds from that which you use every day? Notice the frequent use of adjectives as in (1) *gold-decked mead bench*, (2) *richly carved sword*, (3) *bright coat of linked mail*. Notice, too, the way characters are described; for example: (1) *the king of the Danes, the giver of rings*, (2) *Beowulf, valiant hero of the Geats*.

What other interesting differences do you find? How do you account for these differences? What does this show about language: is it changing or unchanging?

UNDERSTANDING THE WORDS

What do the words in italics in the following phrases mean?

1. all his *kin*
2. *spoils* of battle
3. *bards* sang
4. wild *fens* and *moorlands*
5. *wrought* violence
6. *prowled* the misty moors
7. shining war *gear*
8. the *herald* led them
9. ask one *boon*
10. *spurn* the sword
11. set about the *onslaught*
12. the *turmoil* grew
13. had laid his *spell*
14. wound was *mortal*

WRITING THE WORDS

In writing about the story of Beowulf (in any kind of writing, for that matter), we must be careful to spell correctly. Many foolish little mistakes are made in substituting one homonym for another. Homonyms, as you have learned long before this, are words that are alike in pronunciation but different in meaning and frequently in spelling. So if we write about Beowulf's great hall, we want to be sure to spell the adjective *great* and not *grate*.

Write these phrases from dictation:

1. the *sons* of earth
2. *all* was peace
3. he *heard* these sounds
4. a great cry was *raised*
5. the *tale* was *told*
6. could *heal* his sorrow
7. *sail* far over the sea
8. time *passed*
9. their *mail* glistened
10. *bade* him guard them

READING SCORE BOARD

Number of Words in Story: 2810.

Number of Minutes	28	14	11 1/4	9 1/3	7	5 1/2
Reading Rate	100 w.p.m.	200 w.p.m.	250 w.p.m.	300 w.p.m.	400 w.p.m.	500 w.p.m.

✠ MARY MACLEOD

How Arthur Was Crowned King

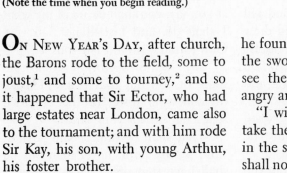
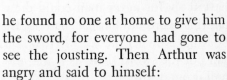

Most authorities believe that Arthur lived in the sixth century A.D. During the fourteen centuries between then and now there has been plenty of time for stories about him to grow and grow. Historians generally agree that he fought against the armies that invaded England. Legend has it that he did many miraculous things.

Arthur was the son of Uther Pendragon, King of Britain. Because of the jealous lords, Arthur would have been killed as a child had he not been hidden away by Merlin, the magician. For years the young Arthur lived in the family of Sir Ector, believing that he was Sir Ector's own son. Even Sir Ector did not realize the boy's identity.

This story tells how Arthur came to discover who he really was.

(Note the time when you begin reading.)

ON NEW YEAR'S DAY, after church, the Barons rode to the field, some to joust,[1] and some to tourney,[2] and so it happened that Sir Ector, who had large estates near London, came also to the tournament; and with him rode Sir Kay, his son, with young Arthur, his foster brother.

As they rode, Sir Kay found he had lost his sword, for he had left it at his father's lodging; so he begged young Arthur to go and fetch it for him.

"That will I, gladly," said Arthur, and he rode fast away.

But when he came to the house,

he found no one at home to give him the sword, for everyone had gone to see the jousting. Then Arthur was angry and said to himself:

"I will ride to the churchyard and take the sword with me that sticketh in the stone, for my brother, Sir Kay, shall not be without a sword this day."

When he came to the churchyard, he alighted, and tied his horse to the stile, and went to the tent. But he found there no knights, who should have been guarding the sword, for they were all away at the joust. Seizing the sword by the handle he lightly and fiercely pulled it out of the stone, then took his horse and rode his way, till he came to Sir Kay, his brother, to whom he delivered the sword.

As soon as Sir Kay saw it, he knew well it was the sword of the Stone;

[1] *joust*. To battle another knight from horseback.

[2] *tourney*. To engage in a tournament, or tilting contest, with many knights.

——From *King Arthur and His Noble Knights* by Mary MacLeod. Copyright, 1949. Reprinted by permission of J. B. Lippincott Company.

so he rode to his father Sir Ector, and said:

"Sir, lo, here is the sword of the Stone, wherefore I must be King of this land."

When Sir Ector saw the sword, he turned back and came to the church, and there they all three alighted and went into the church, and he made his son swear truly how he got the sword.

"By my brother Arthur," said Sir Kay, "for he brought it to me."

"How did you get this sword?" said Sir Ector to Arthur.

And the boy told him.

"Now," said Sir Ector, "I understand you must be King of this land."

"Wherefore I?" said Arthur; "and for what cause?"

"Sir," said Ector, "because God will have it so; for never man could draw out this sword but he that shall rightly be King. Now let me see whether you can put the sword there as it was and pull it out again."

"There is no difficulty," said Arthur, and he put it back into the stone.

Then Sir Ector tried to pull out the sword and failed; and Sir Kay also pulled with all his might, but it would not move.

"Now you shall try," said Sir Ector to Arthur.

"I will, well," said Arthur, and pulled the sword out easily.

At this, Sir Ector and Sir Kay knelt down on the ground before him.

"Alas," said Arthur, "mine own dear father and brother, why do you kneel to me?"

"Nay, nay, my lord Arthur, it is not so; I was never your father, nor of your blood; but I know well you are of higher blood than I thought you were."

Then Sir Ector told him all, how he had taken him to bring up, and by whose command; and how he had received him from Merlin. And when he understood that Ector was not his father, Arthur was deeply grieved.

"Will you be my good, gracious lord, when you are King?" asked the knight.

"If not, I should be to blame," said Arthur, "for you are the man in the world to whom I am the most beholden, and my good lady and mother your wife, who has fostered and kept me as well as her own children. And if ever it be God's will that I be King, as you say, you shall desire of me what I shall do, and I shall not fail you; God forbid I should fail you."

"Sir," said Sir Ector, "I will ask no more of you but that you will make my son, your foster brother Sir Kay, seneschal[3] of all your lands."

"That shall be done," said Arthur, "and by my faith, never man but he shall have that office while he and I live."

Then they went to the Archbishop and told him how the sword was achieved, and by whom.

On Twelfth Day all the Barons came to the Stone in the churchyard, so that any who wished might try to win the sword. But not one of them all could take it out, except Arthur. Many of them therefore were very angry and said it was a great

---

[3] *seneschal.* A steward taking care of the management of an estate.

shame to them and to the country to be governed by a boy not of high blood, for as yet none of them knew that he was the son of King Uther Pendragon. So they agreed to delay the decision till Candlemas, which is the second day of February.

But when Candlemas came, and Arthur once more was the only one who could pull out the sword, they put it off till Easter; and when Easter came, and Arthur again prevailed in presence of them all, they put it off till the Feast of Pentecost.

Then by Merlin's advice the Archbishop summoned some of the best knights that were to be got—such knights as in his own day King Uther Pendragon had best loved, and trusted most—and these were appointed to attend young Arthur and never to leave him night or day till the Feast of Pentecost.

When the great day came, all manner of men once more made the attempt; and once more not one of them all could prevail but Arthur. Before all the Lords and Commons there assembled, he pulled out the sword, whereupon all the Commons cried out at once:

"We will have Arthur for our King! We will put him no more in delay, for we all see that it is God's will that he shall be our King, and he who holdeth against it, we will slay him."

And therewith they knelt down all at once, both rich and poor, and besought pardon of Arthur, because they had delayed him so long.

And Arthur forgave them, and took the sword in both his hands, and offered it on the altar where the Archbishop was; and so he was made knight by the best man there.

After that, he was crowned at once, and there he swore to his Lords and Commons to be a true King and to govern with true justice from thenceforth all the days of his life.

(Note the time; and check your speed of reading with the Reading Score Board, page 130.)

❖❚❖

Character in a Few Lines

1. Quote two remarks made by Sir Kay that show something of his character.
2. Point out two or three passages in the story which reveal Sir Ector's character.
3. Indicate places in the story that show Arthur's kindness, patience, and honesty.

Words of Long Ago—and Now

In each line can you find a word or group of words that means almost the same as the word in italics?

Nouns...
1. *joust:* (a) tilting match between two men   (b) roast beef   (c) frolic
2. *tourney:* (a) itinerary   (b) bandage   (c) warlike game
3. *tournament:* (a) match   (b) combat of skill with many contestants (c) exhibition

4. *stile:* (a) step or set of steps   (b) pointed instrument   (c) fence
5. *seneschal:* (a) morning song   (b) aging   (c) steward
6. *Candlemas:* (a) the day after Christmas   (b) February 2nd—a feast day (c) Christmas Eve communion
7. *Feast of Pentecost:* (a) Church festival held on Whitsunday   (b) marriage feast   (c) celebration of founding of church sect
8. *Lords:* (a) titled noblemen, owners of feudal land   (b) manors   (c) despots
9. *Commons:* (a) Commonwealth   (b) mass of the people   (c) habitations

Verbs

10. *alighted:* (a) dismounted   (b) sprang up   (c) became active
11. *am beholden:* (a) am adorned   (b) am indebted   (c) am seen
12. *was achieved:* (a) was honored   (b) was obtained   (c) was affected
13. *prevailed:* (a) protested   (b) persisted   (c) succeeded
14. *summoned:* (a) raised   (b) called   (c) admonished
15. *besought:* (a) looked for   (b) scolded   (c) implored

MORE ABOUT ARTHUR

1. Read other stories about Arthur and spend some time telling them in class.
2. See whether you can find out about the following:

Excalibur   Lancelot
Lady of the Lake   Galahad
Round Table   Merlin
Guinevere   Death of Arthur

3. Perhaps you would like to put into play form the story "How Arthur Was Crowned King" and present it before your class.

READING SCORE BOARD

Number of Words in Story: 1110.

Number of Minutes	11	5 1/2	4 1/2	3 2/3	2 3/4	2 1/5
Reading Rate	100 w.p.m.	200 w.p.m.	250 w.p.m.	300 w.p.m.	400 w.p.m.	500 w.p.m.

◄◄ J. WALKER McSPADDEN

How Robin Hood Met Little John

According to the knowing ones, Robin Hood's real name was Robert Fitzooth; and he was born about 1160. One story has it that he was a gay young nobleman who ran through his fortune and was finally outlawed by the king for his many debts. So he went to Sherwood Forest and became an outlaw. Many other brave young men joined him there. Thus there came to be the famous band of Robin Hood and his Merry Men.

With his followers, Robin Hood lived boldly and dangerously. He robbed the rich to care for the poor; he shot the king's deer for meat and matched his wits with the Sheriff of Nottingham. One of the best-known members of the band was Little John. This story tells how he and Robin Hood first met. (Note the time when you begin reading.)

"O here is my hand," the stranger reply'd,
   "I'll serve you with all my whole heart:
My name is John Little, a man of good mettle;
   Ne'er doubt me for I'll play my part."

"His name shall be altered," quoth William Stutely.
   "And I will his godfather be:
Prepare then a feast, and none of the least,
   For we will be merry," quoth he.

Aʟʟ summer Robin Hood and his merry men roamed in Sherwood Forest, and the fame of their deeds ran abroad in the land. The Sheriff of Nottingham waxed wroth[1] at the report, but all his traps and excursions failed to catch the outlaws. The poor people began by fearing them, but when they found that the men in Lincoln green who answered Robin Hood's horn meant them no harm, but despoiled the oppressor to relieve the oppressed, they 'gan to have great liking for them. And the band increased by other stout hearts till by the end of the summer fourscore good men and true had sworn fealty.[2]

But the days of quiet which came on grew irksome to Robin's adventurous spirit. Up rose he one gay morn, and slung his quiver over his shoulders.

"This fresh breeze stirs the blood, my lads," quoth he, "and I would be seeing what the gay world looks like in the direction of Nottingham town. But tarry ye behind in the borders of the forest, within earshot of my bugle call."

[1] *waxed wroth.* Grew angry.
——From *Robin Hood* by J. W. McSpadden, published by The World Publishing Company.

[2] *fealty.* Allegiance.

Thus saying he strode merrily forward to the edge of the wood and paused there a moment, his agile form erect, his brown locks flowing and his brown eyes watching the road; and a goodly sight he made, as the wind blew the ruddy color into his cheeks.

The highway led clear in the direction of the town, and thither he boldly directed his steps. But at a bend in the road he knew of a bypath leading across a brook which made the way nearer and less open, into which he turned. As he approached the stream, he saw that it had become swollen by recent rains into quite a pretty torrent. The log foot-bridge was still there; but at this end of it a puddle intervened which could be crossed only with a leap, if you would not get your feet wet. But Robin cared little for such a handicap. Taking a running start, his nimble legs carried him easily over and balanced neatly upon the end of the broad log. But he was no sooner started across than he saw a tall stranger coming from the other side. Thereupon Robin quickened his pace, and the stranger did likewise, each thinking to cross first. Midway they met, and neither would yield an inch.

"Give way, fellow!" roared Robin, whose leadership of a band, I am afraid, had not tended to mend his manners.

The stranger smiled. He was almost a head taller than the other.

"Nay," he retorted, "fair and softly! I give way only to a better man than myself."

"Give way, I say," repeated Robin, "or I shall have to show you a better man."

His opponent budged not an inch but laughed loudly. "Now by my halidom!" he said good-naturedly, "I would not move after hearing that speech, even if minded to it before; for this better man have I sought my life long. Therefore show him to me an it please you."

"That will I right soon," quoth Robin, planting his feet sturdily apart. "I'll show you right Nottingham play."

And with that, Robin Hood drew a broad goose-wing arrow from his quiver and set it to the string of his bow, then aimed the shaft full at the big fellow's breast. But the other merely laughed in scorn.

"I'll tan your hide for you, if you offer to loose that string," he said quietly.

"You prate like a fool," said Robin. "For were I but to bend my bow, I could send a shaft through your heart before you could strike a single blow."

"You talk like a coward," retorted the stranger. "You are well armed with a long bow, while I have nought but a staff in my hand."

"I scorn the name of coward," said Robin, beginning to feel ashamed of himself. "I'll lay by my long bow and fight you on even terms. Bide you here a little while till I cut me a cudgel like unto that you have been twiddling in your fingers." So saying he sought his own bank again with a leap, laid aside his long bow and arrows, and cut him a stout staff of oak, straight, knotless, and a good six feet in length. But still it was a full foot shorter than his opponent's. Then back came he boldly.

"I mind not telling you, fellow," said he, "that a bout with archery would have been an easier way with me. But there are other tunes in England besides that the arrow sings." Here he whirred the staff about his head by way of practice. "So make you ready for the tune I am about to play upon your ribs. Have at you! One, two——"

"Three!" roared the giant, smiting at him instantly.

Well was it for Robin that he was quick and nimble of foot; for the blow that grazed a hair's breadth from his shoulder would have felled an ox. Nevertheless while swerving to avoid this stroke, Robin was poising for his own, and back came he forthwith—whack!

Whack! parried the other.

Whack! whack! whack! whack!

The fight waxed fast and furious. It was strength pitted against subtlety, and the match was a merry one. The mighty blows of the stranger went whistling around Robin's ducking head, while his own swift undercuts were fain to give the other an attack of indigestion. Yet each stood firmly in his place, not moving backward or forward a foot for a good half hour, nor thinking of crying "Enough!" though some chance blow seemed likely to knock one or the other off the narrow foot-bridge. The giant's face was getting red, and his breath came snorting forth like a bull's. He stepped forward with a furious onslaught to finish this audacious fellow. Robin dodged his blow lightly,

then sprang in swiftly and unexpectedly and dealt the stranger such a blow upon the short ribs that you would have sworn the tanner was trimming down his hides for market.

The stranger reeled and came within an ace of falling, but regained his footing right quickly.

"By my life, you can hit hard!" he gasped forth, giving back a blow almost while he was yet staggering.

This blow was a lucky one. It caught Robin off his guard. His stick had rested a moment while he looked to see the giant topple into the water, when down came the other upon his head, whack! Robin saw more stars in that one moment than all the astronomers have since discovered, and forthwith he dropped neatly into the stream.

The cool rushing current quickly brought him to his senses, howbeit he was still so dazed that he groped blindly for the swaying reeds to pull himself up on the bank. His assailant could not forbear laughing heartily at his plight, but was also quick to lend his aid. He thrust down his long staff to Robin crying, "Lay hold of that, an your fists whirl not so much as your head!"

Robin laid hold and was hauled to dry land for all the world like a fish, except that the fish would never have come forth so wet and dripping. He lay upon the warm bank for a space to regain his senses. Then he sat up and gravely rubbed his pate.

"By all the saints!" said he. "You hit full stoutly. My head hums like a hive of bees on a summer morning."

Then he seized his horn, which lay

near, and blew thereon three shrill notes that echoed against the trees. A moment of silence ensued, and then was heard the rustling of leaves and crackling of twigs like the coming of many men; and forth from the glade burst a score or two of stalwart yeomen,[3] all clad in Lincoln green, like Robin, with good Will Stutely and the widow's three sons at their head. "Good master," cried Will Stutely, "how is this? In sooth there is not a dry thread on your body."

"Why, marry," replied Robin, "this fellow would not let me pass the footbridge; and when I tickled him in the ribs, he must needs answer by a pat on the head which landed me overboard."

"Then shall he taste some of his own porridge," quoth Will. "Seize him, lads! He shall have a proper ducking!"

"Nay, let him go free," said Robin. "He's a stout fellow. Forbear, the fight was a fair one; and I abide by it. I surmise you also are quits?" he continued, turning to the stranger with a twinkling eye.

"I am content," said the other, "for verily you now have the best end of the cudgel. Wherefore, I like you well and would fain know your name."

"Why," said Robin, "my men and even the Sheriff of Nottingham know me as Robin Hood, the outlaw."

"Then am I right sorry that I beat you," exclaimed the man, "for I was on my way to seek you and to try to join your merry company. But after my unmannerly use of the cudgel, I fear we are still strangers."

3 *yeomen.* Attendants.

"Nay, never say it!" cried Robin. "I am glad I fell in with you; though, sooth to say, I did all the falling!"

And amid a general laugh the two men clasped hands, and in that clasp the strong friendship of a lifetime was begun.

"But you have not yet told us your name," said Robin, bethinking himself.

"Whence I came, men call me John Little. An you will let me join your band, ne'er doubt me, I'll play my part."

"Enter our company then, John Little; enter and welcome. The rites are few; the fee is large. We ask your whole mind and body and heart even unto death."

"I give the bond, upon my life," said he.

Thereupon Will Stutely, who loved a good jest, spoke up and said: "The infant in our household must be christened, and I'll stand godfather. This fair little stranger is so small of bone and sinew, that his old name is not to the purpose." Here he paused long enough to fill a horn in the stream. "Hark ye, my son"—standing on tiptoe to splash the water on the giant—"take your new name on entering the forest. I christen you Little John."

At this jest the men roared long and loud.

"Give him a bow, and find a full sheath of arrows for Little John," said Robin joyfully. "Can you shoot as well as fence with the staff, my friend?"

"I have hit an ash twig at forty yards," said Little John.

Thus chatting pleasantly, the band turned back into the woodland and sought their secluded dell, where the trees were the thickest, the moss was the softest, and a secret path led to a cave, at once a retreat and a stronghold. Here under a mighty oak they found the rest of the band, some of whom had come in with a brace of fat does. And here they built a ruddy fire and sat down to the meat and drink, Robin Hood in the center with Will Stutely on the one hand and Little John on the other. And Robin was right well pleased with the day's adventure, even though he had got a drubbing; for sore ribs and heads will heal, and 'tis not every day that one can find a recruit as stout of bone and true of soul as Little John.

(Note the time; and check your speed of reading with the Reading Score Board, page 136.)

◆◄◆

Hark Ye!

1. What sort of person was Robin Hood?
2. Why will he always be a popular character?
3. In what ways does Little John show himself worthy to be a member of Robin Hood's band?
4. How did Little John get his name?
5. Find passages in the story that tell about the following items:
   a. clothing of the merry men
   b. methods of fighting
   c. food
   d. membership requirements of the band
6. Did Robin Hood and Little John fight fairly?
7. What do you know about Will Stutely?
8. What other stories about Robin Hood do you know?
9. Why, do you think, does the story begin with a poem?

Old Ways of Speaking

Since the Robin Hood ballads, on which the stories are based, were first sung hundreds of years ago, some of the language of that long ago remains. You found these phrases in the story. In twentieth-century language, what do they mean?

waxed wroth	long staff
despoiled the oppressor	stalwart yeoman
fourscore good men	would fain know your name
grew irksome	secluded dell
tarry ye behind	ruddy fire
cut me a cudgel	a drubbing

Colorful Ways of Speaking

Study the story for the many words and phrases which help the reader to see the outlaws and the forest.

UNLOCKING WORDS

If you are reading a story and run across a word that doesn't look familiar, what do you do? Do you throw up your hands and quit? Or do you look at it to see whether there is a part of it you know? Often a prefix or a suffix is added to a word and makes it look different. A prefix, you remember, is a group of letters added at the beginning of a root word to change its meaning. A suffix is a group of letters added at the end of a root word for the same purpose.

What root words do you recognize in the following?

adventurous	outlaw	extraordinary	judgment
quickened	unwillingly	customary	constitution
knotless	sorrowful	misdeed	dangerous
unexpectedly	disrespect	distrust	withstand
heartily	misunderstanding	kinship	co-operation

What new words can you make of each of the following by adding a prefix or a suffix or perhaps both?

reject	miser	hold	place
hard	pity	direct	beard

READING SCORE BOARD

Number of Words in Story: 1930.

Number of Minutes	19 1/2	10	7 3/4	6 1/2	5	4
Reading Rate	100 w.p.m.	200 w.p.m.	250 w.p.m.	300 w.p.m.	400 w.p.m.	500 w.p.m.

◀◀ ALFRED NOYES

A Song of Sherwood

Sherwood in the twilight, is Robin Hood awake?
Gray and ghostly shadows are gliding through the brake,
Shadows of the dappled deer, dreaming through the morn,
Dreaming of a shadowy man that winds a shadowy horn.

Robin Hood is here again; all his merry thieves
Hear a ghostly bugle-note shivering through the leaves,
Calling as he used to call, faint and far away,
In Sherwood, in Sherwood, about the break of day.

Merry, merry England has kissed the lips of June;
All the wings of fairyland were here beneath the moon,
Like a flight of rose leaves fluttering in a mist
Of opal and ruby and pearl and amethyst.

Merry, merry England is waking as of old,
With eyes of blither hazel and hair of brighter gold;
For Robin Hood is here again beneath the bursting spray
In Sherwood, in Sherwood, about the break of day.

Love is in the greenwood building him a house
Of wild rose and hawthorn and honeysuckle boughs;
Love is in the greenwood, dawn is in the skies,
And Marian is waiting with a glory in her eyes.

Hark! The dazzled laverock[1] climbs the golden steep!
Marian is waiting; is Robin Hood asleep?
Round the fairy grass-rings frolic elf and fay,
In Sherwood, in Sherwood, about the break of day.

Oberon,[2] Oberon, rake away the gold,
Rake away the red leaves, roll away the mold,
Rake away the gold leaves, roll away the red,
And wake Will Scarlett from his leafy forest bed.

Friar Tuck and Little John are riding down together
With quarterstaff and drinking-can and gray goose feather.
The dead are coming back again, the years are rolled away
In Sherwood, in Sherwood, about the break of day.

Softly over Sherwood the south wind blows.
All the heart of England hid in every rose
Hears across the greenwood the sunny whisper leap,
Sherwood in the red dawn, is Robin Hood asleep?

Hark, the voice of England wakes him as of old
And, shattering the silence with a cry of brighter gold,
Bugles in the greenwood echo from the steep,
Sherwood in the red dawn, is Robin Hood asleep?

Where the deer are gliding down the shadowy glen
All across the glades of fern he calls his merry men —
Doublets of the Lincoln green glancing through the May
In Sherwood, in Sherwood, about the break of day —

[1] *laverock.* A lark.
[2] *Oberon.* King of the fairies.

Calls them and they answer; from aisles of oak and ash
Rings the *Follow! Follow!* and the boughs begin to crash,
The ferns begin to flutter and the flowers begin to fly,
And through the crimson dawning the robber band goes by.

Robin! Robin! Robin! All his merry thieves
Answer as the bugle-note shivers through the leaves,
Calling as he used to call, faint and far away,
In Sherwood, in Sherwood, about the break of day.

❖❁❖

"TURN BACKWARD"

1. Why do people always wish for the return of the "good old days"?
2. Why might many wish for the return of Robin Hood?
3. Which of the Robin Hood characters are spoken of in the poem?
4. Which lines of the poem give you vivid pictures of the greenwood?

GHOSTLY WORDS

Noyes has used a number of different words to make the reader feel the ghostliness of the scene. The whole poem is a shadowy, ghostly picture. What words do you find in addition to these: *twilight, gray?*

Some poems become more meaningful to us after we have read them several times. It is well to let the scenes pictured by the words "grow in our minds." Now reread the poem, and select the lines that give you the clearest and the most interesting pictures. Are there lines that you would like to memorize?

❁❁ TOIVO ROSVALL

Tyl Ulenspiegel Shows His Wisdom

Tyl Ulenspiegel is said to have lived in Germany in the fourteenth century. His stories about himself are clumsy, bragging, mischievous accounts. For centuries he has been remembered as a clever clown.
(Note the time when you begin reading.)

WHEN Tyl Ulenspiegel left Magdeburg, he traveled all the way to Prague in Bohemia, a city full of good and pious and very learned people. And Ulenspiegel boasted and told everyone that he could answer any questions that anybody might ask him—in truth, he could certainly do it better

——From *Story Parade.* Used by permission of the author.

than most of the good professors at the University. He was willing to prove it, too, and nailed notices on the doors of the University and challenged anybody to give him a question that he could not answer truthfully.

The Rector of the University shook his head in anger: that anyone should dare! The professors were annoyed, and even the students were dismayed and talked about it in excited groups and wondered who this learned Tyl Ulenspiegel really was. The University was in an uproar, and they all decided that they must punish the daring fellow. *They* certainly would put questions to him that he would never be able to answer, no matter how wise or how clever he was. He would not be able to give a correct solution; and then they would quietly pounce upon him, shame him before everyone, and declare him the fool he really was.

A meeting was called right away. The conference lasted for hours, as conferences have a way of doing; and finally questions that seemed more than difficult enough were found. It was decided that the Rector himself, he who was most offended at the boldness of the fellow, should ask the questions.

Tyl Ulenspiegel was hastily summoned to the University to prove his wisdom before everyone there assembled and to be judged if he were wise and learned enough to be made one of the members of the famous University of Prague. He appeared in the hall in a long black robe, looking really learned and wise and exactly like a scholar. He nodded right and left, smiled, and stood on the little platform beside the Rector. "I am ready," he said.

"Ah!" sighed the Rector. "You have challenged us to a contest of wisdom——" here Tyl bowed and smiled once more—"and if you answer our questions truthfully, you will be made a member of our famous University."

"I feel honored," Tyl Ulenspiegel bowed.

"First: tell me how many particles, exactly how many particles are there in all the waters of the seas? If you cannot solve the problem, you will be severely punished."

"I can solve and answer your question, sir," replied Tyl. "It is quite simple. If you will only stop all the water on the earth from running, then I will quickly measure the particles for you, give you the results, and prove that I am right. It is easy enough, you see."

"It is impossible for me to stop the waters from flowing," the Rector admitted reluctantly, "so I shall not demand that you count the particles. But tell me, if you are so wise, how many days have passed from Adam's time to this very day?"

"Only seven days," Tyl answered calmly.

"Only seven days?" everyone wondered, and there was a loud whispering in the hall. "Only seven days?"

"Yes. Sunday, Monday, Tuesday, Wednesday, Thursday, Friday, and Saturday. When the first seven days had gone by, there followed seven more. So it has been, and so it will be until the end of the world."

The Rector murmured and hurried on to his third question. "Come, exactly where is the middle of the earth?

"Here, in Prague. Right here where I am standing is the middle of the world. And if you don't believe me, then measure it with a piece of string. If it falls short by only the thickness of a straw, you can call me a fool."

"Rather than measure it, I will take your word for it," the Rector retorted dryly. "But if you are so clever, surely you can tell me how far it is from heaven to earth?"

"Oh, heaven is not so far from here," Tyl Ulenspiegel explained. "When someone is speaking in heaven, you can hear it distinctly here below. Only climb into heaven, sir, and I will speak quite softly here; and you will be able to hear every word. And if you don't hear me, then you can surely say that I am a liar."

"Well, I am satisfied. I suppose I would hear you even if you only whispered," admitted the Rector. "But, sir, how big is heaven?"

"How big is heaven? It is a thousand ells wide and a thousand fathoms deep, to the fraction of an inch. If you doubt my word, take the sun and the moon, the stars and all the planets out of the sky, and then measure it. You will find it exactly so, to the fraction of an inch. Believe me!"

What could they say? It was impossible to make a fool of Tyl Ulenspiegel. They could do nothing but admit that he was a wise fellow. Indeed, he was wise enough to wear the long black robe and be a member of their University. But Tyl Ulenspiegel got tired of looking learned, tired of wearing the long black robe. A few days later he took it off and went away, eager to play another trick, to make people laugh and see how foolish they really were.

(Note the time; and check your speed of reading with the Reading Score Board, page 141.)

❖❖❖

SHOWING YOUR WISDOM

1. What two or three qualities of character does Tyl show?
2. Why was he able to answer each of the questions?
3. Can you make up questions similar to those the Rector asked?
4. Why do you think Tyl could not stay at the University?
5. Why is this kind of folk story always popular? To what traits of human nature does it appeal?

MORE AND MORE WORDS

There is no doubt that the more words we know, the better we can understand the stories we read. And the better we understand a story, the more likely we are to enjoy it. Stretching our vocabularies, then, is really a paying proposition.

One way to stretch a vocabulary is to learn to know whole families of words.

For example, here are a number of nouns. What is the corresponding adjective for each of them?

honor	contempt	ruin
truth	awe	sin
offense	luck	wind
fame	mythology	grief
reluctance	mystery	thought

READING SCORE BOARD

Number of Words in Story: 890.

Number of Minutes	9	7	6	4 1/2	3 3/5	3
Reading Rate	100 w.p.m.	125 w.p.m.	150 w.p.m.	200 w.p.m.	250 w.p.m.	300 w.p.m.

LOOKING BACKWARD THROUGH THE CHAPTER

1. What different countries are represented in the selections?
2. How do the selections represent the different countries? Point out details which show customs and beliefs and something of the history of the country.
3. What qualities do the legendary heroes seem to have in common?
4. Why is a legendary hero always greater than an ordinary person?
5. How do you think these stories had their beginnings?

MEMORY TEASING

Who Is the Hero?

Can you name the hero who did each of the following?
1. Pulled a sword from a stone
2. Tamed fire-breathing bulls
3. Killed a monster by pulling its arm out of the socket
4. Gathered a band of outlaws together and lived in Sherwood Forest
5. Boasted that he could answer any questions that anyone would ask him

Which Hero Is Described?

To which hero does each of the following apply?
1. They dressed him as a bride with shining robes, and bracelets on his arms, and fastened Brisingamen about his neck.
2. It was impossible to make a fool of ——. They could do nothing but admit that he was a wise fellow.
3. —— is here again; all his merry thieves
   Hear a ghostly bugle-note shivering through the leaves.
4. After that, he was crowned at once, and there he swore to his Lords and Commons to be a true King and to govern with true justice from thenceforth all the days of his life.
5. —— next proceeded to sow the dragon's teeth and plough them in.

What Do These Mean?

Choose the word or phrase in each line that most nearly gives the meaning of the word in italics:

1. *herculean:* (a) colossal (b) mighty (c) magnificent
2. *turmoil:* (a) tumult (b) whirlpool (c) quarrel
3. *onslaught:* (a) deluge (b) attack (c) battle
4. *joust:* (a) tilt (b) judgment (c) feast day
5. *besought:* (a) attained (b) implored (c) acquired

MORE ABOUT HEROES

1. Perhaps you would like to read other stories about heroes. See the list below.
2. Make up a hero representing your community. What stories could be told about him?
3. Try your hand at writing different kinds of hero stories. Here are some suggestions.

   a. Write a modern version of the story of Tyl Ulenspiegel with you yourself acting as Tyl.

   b. Write about an athletic contest in the same kind of language used in the story about Arthur.

STORIES OF HEROES

Baldwin, James, *The Story of Roland,* 1883 (Scribner).
  The story of Charlemagne's noble knight and Roland's tragic death.

Baldwin, James, *The Story of Siegfried,* 1882 (Scribner).
  The Siegfried legends based on German folklore.

Buff, Mary M. and Conrad, *The Apple and the Arrow,* 1951 (Houghton).
  William Tell and his son.

Church, Alfred J., *The Aeneid for Boys and Girls,* 1908 (Macmillan).
  A simplified prose version of Virgil's tales of Aeneas.

Church, Alfred J., *The Iliad for Boys and Girls,* 1907 (Macmillan).
  Homer's epic of the Trojan War, with all its battles and the intrigues among the gods and goddesses and heroes.

Colum, Padraic, *The Golden Fleece,* 1921 (Macmillan).
  Greek myths and hero tales.

Hawthorne, Nathaniel, *The Wonder Book and Tanglewood Tales,* 1946 (Houghton).
  Free retelling of Greek tales and myths.

Homer, *The Odyssey,* translated by G. H. Palmer, 1929 (Houghton).
  Translation into rhythmic prose of the thrilling adventures of Ulysses after the downfall of Troy.

Malory, Sir Thomas, *The Boy's King Arthur*, edited for boys by Sidney Lanier, 1917 (Scribner).
Arthur, Lancelot, Tristram, Galahad, and other Knights of the Holy Grail.

Munchausen, *Adventures of Baron Munchausen*, illus. by Gustave Doré, 1944 (Pantheon).
Fantastic adventures of the German Baron.

Norton, André, *Huon of the Horn*, 1951 (Harcourt).
The Charlemagne saga after the death of Roland.

Pyle, Howard, *The Merry Adventures of Robin Hood*, 1932 (Scribner).
Robin Hood of the ballads presented in story form.

Pyle, Katharine, *Heroic Tales from the Norse*, 1930 (Lippincott).
Stories of the Norwegian gods.

Robinson, Mabel, *King Arthur and His Knights*, 1953 (Random House).
Legendary characters of the Round Table.

Seredy, Kate, *The White Stag*, 1937 (Viking).
Attila and the march on the Huns.

Sherwood, Merriam, *Tales of the Warrior Lord*, 1930 (Longmans).
Translation into prose of the poem telling the deeds of the Spanish hero, the Cid.

Fables
and
Strange Tales

The Hare and the Tortoise

Aesop was such a good storyteller that his stories, or fables, have been read and enjoyed for twenty-five hundred years. The truths that he emphasized in his little stories about animals are as fundamental to human nature today as they were in Greece six hundred years before the birth of Christ. That is the reason Aesop's fables never decline in popularity.

A HARE insulted a Tortoise upon account of his slowness and vainly boasted of her own great speed in running. "Let us make a match," replied the Tortoise; "I will run with you five miles for five pounds, and the fox yonder shall be the umpire of the race." The Hare agreed; and away they both started together. But the Hare, by reason of her exceeding swiftness, outran the Tortoise to such a degree that she made a jest of the matter; and, finding herself a little tired, squatted in a tuft of fern that grew by the way and took a nap; thinking that, if the Tortoise went by, she could at any time fetch him up with all the ease imaginable. In the meantime while the Tortoise came jogging on with slow but continued motion and the Hare, out of a too-great security and confidence of victory, oversleeping herself, the Tortoise arrived at the end of the race first.

✦《✦

SPECIFIC DETAILS

You found it easy, didn't you, to get the *main idea* of the fable? Let us see now how many specific details you picked up with "the tail of your eye."

1. How many miles was the race to cover?
2. How much money was involved in the bet?
3. On what did the Hare take a little nap?

Could you answer the three questions easily? In this chapter let us continue to concentrate on getting the main idea, on increasing our rate of reading, and on stretching our vocabularies. Then let us add another objective. Let us try to make our eyes pick up little specific details which may add interest and meaning.

BASIC MEANINGS IN WORDS

What is the meaning of these words and phrases?

1. insulted
2. vainly boasted
3. a jest
4. fetch him up
5. came jogging on
6. a too-great security
7. confidence of victory

◄**《 Jean de La Fontaine**

The Raven and the Fox

About two thousand years after Aesop wrote his fables, a Frenchman by the name of Jean de La Fontaine put many of those fables in verse form. Here is one of them. It is typical of all La Fontaine's fables, in the simple but charming style and in the good story it has to tell.

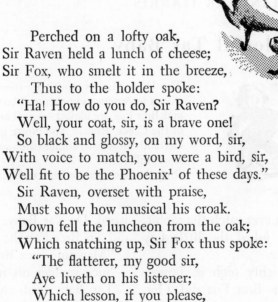

> Perched on a lofty oak,
> Sir Raven held a lunch of cheese;
> Sir Fox, who smelt it in the breeze,
> Thus to the holder spoke:
> "Ha! How do you do, Sir Raven?
> Well, your coat, sir, is a brave one!
> So black and glossy, on my word, sir,
> With voice to match, you were a bird, sir,
> Well fit to be the Phoenix[1] of these days."
> Sir Raven, overset with praise,
> Must show how musical his croak.
> Down fell the luncheon from the oak;
> Which snatching up, Sir Fox thus spoke:
> "The flatterer, my good sir,
> Aye liveth on his listener;
> Which lesson, if you please,
> Is doubtless worth the cheese."
> A bit too late, Sir Raven swore
> The rogue should never cheat him more.

◄**《◆**

Another Truth

1. What is the lesson to be learned from "The Raven and the Fox"?
2. How true *today* is the lesson that the Raven learned?

Some Details

1. What was the Raven eating?
2. How did the Fox find out about the Raven's lunch?
3. What did the Raven decide after he had been fooled?

[1] *Phoenix.* A wonderful bird supposed to be the embodiment of the sun-god.

MEANINGS

What is the meaning of the words in italics?
1. *Perched* on a *lofty* oak
2. So black and *glossy*
3. Sir Raven, *overset* with praise
4. *Aye* liveth on his listener
5. The *rogue* should never cheat him more.

+€ JOEL CHANDLER HARRIS

The Wonderful Tar Baby

The Uncle Remus stories are some of the best-loved stories in American literature. The names Brer Rabbit and Brer Fox are almost as well known as the names of the Greek, Roman, and Norse gods and goddesses. Certainly those two animals are more amusing, as this story will show.
(Note the time when you begin reading.)

DIDN'T the fox ever catch the rabbit, Uncle Remus? asked the little boy the next evening.

He come mighty nigh it, honey, sho's you bawn—Brer Fox did. One day Brer Fox went ter wuk en got 'im some tar, en mix it wid some turkentime, en fix up a contraption w'at he call a Tar Baby, en he tuck dish yer Tar Baby en he sot 'er in de big road, en den he lay off in de bushes fer to see w'at de news wuz gwineter be. En he didn't hatter wait long, needer, kaze bimeby yer come Brer Rabbit pacin' down de road—*lippity-clippity, clippity-lippity*—des ez sassy ez a jaybird. Brer Fox, he lay low. Brer Rabbit come prancin' 'long twel he spy de Tar Baby, en den he fotch up on his behime legs like he wuz 'ston-ished. De Tar Baby, she sot dar, she did, en Brer Fox, he lay low.

"Mawnin'!" sez Brer Rabbit, sezee —"nice wedder dis mawnin'," sezee.

Tar Baby aint sayin' nothin', en Brer Fox, he lay low.

"How does yo' sym'toms seem ter segashuate?" sez Brer Rabbit, sezee.

Brer Fox, he wink his eye slow, en lay low, en de Tar Baby, she aint sayin' nothin'.

"How you come on, den? Is you deaf?" sez Brer Rabbit, sezee. "Kaze if you is, I kin holler louder," sezee.

Tar Baby stay still, en Brer Fox, he lay low.

"Youer stuck up, dat's w'at you is," sez Brer Rabbit, sezee, "en I'm gwineter kyore you, dat's w'at I'm a-gwineter do," sezee.

Brer Fox, he sorter chuckle in his

——Used by permission of Lucien Harris.

stomach, he did, but Tar Baby aint sayin' nothin'.

"I'm gwineter larn you how ter talk ter 'spectable folks ef hit's de las' ack," sez Brer Rabbit, sezee. "Ef you don't take off dat hat en tell me howdy, I'm gwineter bus' you wide open," sezee.

Tar Baby stay still, en Brer Fox, he lay low.

Brer Rabbit keep on axin' 'im, en de Tar Baby, she keep on sayin' nothin', twel present'y Brer Rabbit draw back wid his fis', he did, en *blip* he tuck 'er side er de head. Right dar's whar he broke his merlasses jug. His fis' stuck, en he can't pull loose. De tar hilt 'im. But Tar Baby, she stay still, en Brer Fox, he lay low.

"Ef you don't lemme loose, I'll knock you agin," sez Brer Rabbit, sezee, en wid dat he fotch 'er a wipe wid de udder han', en dat stuck. Tar Baby, she aint sayin' nothin', en Brer Fox, he lay low.

"Tu'n me loose, fo' I kick de natal stuffin' outen you," sez Brer Rabbit, sezee, but de Tar Baby, she aint sayin' nothin'. She des hilt on, en den Brer Rabbit lose de use er his foots in de same way. Brer Fox, he lay low. Den Brer Rabbit squall out dat ef de Tar Baby don't tu'n 'im loose he butt 'er crank-sided. En den he butted, en his head got stuck. Den Brer Fox, he sa'ntered fort', lookin' des ez inner-cent ez one er yo' mammy's mockin'-birds.

"Howdy, Brer Rabbit," sez Brer Fox, sezee. "You look sorter stuck up dis mawnin'," sezee, en den he rolled on de groun', en laffed en laffed twel he couldn't laff no mo'.

Uncle Remus, asked the little boy the next evening, did the fox kill and eat the rabbit when he caught him with the Tar Baby?

Law, honey, w'at I tell you w'en I fus' begin? I tole you Brer Rabbit wuz a monstus soon creetur—leas'ways dat's w'at I laid out fer ter tell you. Well den, honey, don't you go en make no calkalations, kaze in dem days Brer Rabbit en his fambly wuz at de head er de gang w'en any racket wuz on han', en dar dey stayed. 'Fo' you begins fer ter wipe yo' eyes 'bout Brer Rabbit, you wait en see whar-'bouts Brer Rabbit gwineter fetch up at.

W'en Brer Fox fine Brer Rabbit mixed up wid de Tar Baby, he feel mighty good, en he roll on de groun' en laff. Bimeby he up'n say, sezee:

"Well, I speck I got you dis time, Brer Rabbit," sezee; "maybe I aint, but I spect I is. You bin runnin' roun' here sassin' atter me a mighty long time, but I spect you done come ter de een' er de row. You bin cuttin' up yo' capers en bouncin' roun' in dis neighborhood twel you come ter b'lieve yo'se'f de boss er de whole gang. En den youer allers some'rs whar you got no business," sez Brer Fox, sezee. "Who ax you fer ter come en strike up a 'quaintance wid dish yer Tar Baby? En who stuck you up dar whar you is? Nobody in de roun' worril. You des tuck en jam yo'se'f on dat Tar Baby widout waitin' fer any invite," sez Brer Fox, sezee, "en dar you is, en dar you'll stay twel I fixes up a bresh-pile en fires her up, kaze I'm gwineter bobbycue you dis day, sho," sez Brer Fox, sezee.

Den Brer Rabbit talk mighty 'umble.

"I don't keer w'at you do wid me, Brer Fox," sezee, "so you don't fling me in dat briar patch. Roas' me, Brer Fox," sezee, "but don't fling me in dat briar patch," sezee.

"Hit's so much trouble fer ter kin'le a fire," sez Brer Fox, sezee, "dat I spect I'll hatter hang you," sezee.

"Hang me des ez high ez you please, Brer Fox," sez Brer Rabbit, sezee, "but do fer de Lord's sake don't fling me in dat briar patch," sezee.

"I aint got no string," sez Brer Fox, sezee, "en now I speck I'll hatter drown you," sezee.

"Drown me des ez deep ez you please, Brer Fox," sez Brer Rabbit, sezee, "but do don't fling me in dat briar patch," sezee.

"Dey aint no water nigh," sez Brer Fox, sezee, "en now I spect I'll hatter skin you," sezee.

"Skin me, Brer Fox," sez Brer Rab-bit, sezee, "snatch out my eyeballs, t'ar out my years by de roots, en cut off my legs," sezee, "but do please, Brer Fox, don't fling me in dat briar patch," sezee.

Co'se Brer Fox wanter hu't Brer Rabbit bad ez he kin, so he kotch 'im by de behime legs en slung 'im right in de middle er de briar patch. Dar wuz a consider'ble flutter whar Brer Rabbit struck de bushes, en Brer Fox sorter hang roun' fer ter see w'at wuz gwineter happen. Bimeby he year somebody call 'im, en way up de hill he see Brer Rabbit settin' cross-legged on a chinkapin log combin' de pitch outen his ha'r wid a chip. Den Brer Fox know dat he bin swop off mighty bad. Brer Rabbit wuz bleedz fer ter fling back some er his sass, en he holler out:

"Bred en bawn in a briar patch, Brer Fox—bred en bawn in a briar patch!" en wid dat he skip out des ez lively ez a cricket in de embers.

(Note the time; and check your speed of reading with the Reading Score Board, page 151.)

❧

"SORTER STUCK UP"

1. Why does Joel Chandler Harris have the rabbit outwit the fox?
2. Do you see any application of this story to real life?
3. How does dialect help the story?

LITTLE INTERESTING FACTS

1. How many parts of Brer Rabbit got stuck to the Tar Baby?
2. Where did Brer Rabbit say he did not want to be thrown?

READING PHRASES—NOT WORDS

As you read the stories in this chapter, try to force your eyes to pick up groups of words rather than single words. You will find that your speed of reading will increase tremendously as soon as you break yourself of the word-by-word habit.

◄**J. FRANK DOBIE**

Coyote between Two Sheep

A native of Texas, J. Frank Dobie is an authority on the folklore of the Southwest. The following story by him comes straight out of the sheep country, where coyotes are a constant threat. It is natural that there should be stories dealing with sheep and coyotes and that in some, at least, the sheep should outwit their natural enemy.

(This story has 490 words in it. Try to read it with your best speed; and, of course, be sure to get the meaning.)

As SEÑOR COYOTE was going down the road, he met two sheep.

"Aha," he said, "I see I am not going to be hungry long."

"But, Brother Coyote, what do you mean?" one of the sheep asked.

"I mean," said the coyote, "to invite one of you kinsmen to be my dinner."

"Which one?" the other sheep asked.

"The one that has the best meat," the coyote answered, and he felt for the fat on each of their tails.

"Do not try to cat me," said the first sheep, "I am too lean."

"Do not try to eat me," said the second sheep, "I am too tough."

"Will it take the kidney fat from both of you to make a respectable dinner?" the coyote asked.

"No, no," the sheep said in one voice.

"Then I'll tell you what we'll do," the coyote said. He looked very wise. "I will draw a line here across the road. There, see." And he scratched a plain line in the dirt across the road. "Now, Nephew Lean Sheep, you go down the road about fifty paces to that mesquite[1] bush with the pink just showing on its beans. Now, Uncle Tough Sheep, you go up the road

——From *The Voice of the Coyote* by J. Frank Dobie. Used by permission of Little, Brown & Company.

[1] *mesquite.* A spiny kind of shrub that grows in Southwestern United States and in Mexico.

about fifty paces to that all-thorn bush in which the butcherbird has her nest. You understand?"

"Yes, yes," Lean Sheep and Tough Sheep bleated together.

"Very well," *Señor* Coyote went on. "You will be at your station, each looking this way and ready to run. I will count 'one, two, three.' When I say 'three,' each of you starts running toward the line here. I will be standing to one side of the road looking right down the line. The sheep that crosses the line first I will slap on the back and at the same time cry out 'First.' To the second sheep I will tell a secret."

The coyote was immensely pleased with his plan. He knew that the separated sheep would not dare run off.

"Nephew Lean Sheep," he cried, "get to your mesquite. Uncle Tough Sheep, get to your all-thorn bush."

The two obeyed.

"Are you ready?" he called.

"Yes, yes, Brother Coyote," the sheep answered.

"One, two, three," the coyote counted. He stood at the edge of the road facing down the line. He looked to the right and Nephew Lean Sheep was coming. He looked to the left and Uncle Tough Sheep was coming. After that he did not take his eyes from the mark. He put one paw up ready to tag the lead racer. Then he put it down. "No," he said to himself low, "they are going to butt into each other exactly at my nose."

His laughter at the joke ended when the sheep rammed into his sides at the same time. Before he got his breath back, Nephew Lean Sheep and Uncle Tough Sheep were two specks side by side close to their master's house.

(Note the time, and check your speed of reading with the Reading Score Board.)

❖⟨⟨❖

An Outwitted Coyote

1. Which details in this story show what part of the country it comes from?
2. Why did Harris tell about a rabbit and a fox; Dobie, sheep and a coyote?
3. What similarity do you see in the stories by Harris and Dobie?
4. Exactly what was the coyote's plan?

Reading Score Board

Number of Words in Story: 490.

Number of Minutes	5	2 1/2	2	1 2/3	1 1/4	1
Reading Rate	100 w.p.m.	200 w.p.m.	250 w.p.m.	300 w.p.m.	400 w.p.m.	500 w.p.m.

How did your eyes *phrase* the lines in the story?

❦ CHARLES EDWARD CARRYL

Robinson Crusoe's Story

Robinson Crusoe, according to Daniel Defoe's story, was shipwrecked and then stranded on an uninhabited island for years and years. What did he do during all those years? Well, in this poem Carryl gives some of his amusing ideas on the subject.

The night was thick and hazy
    When the *Piccadilly Daisy*
Carried down the crew and captain in the sea;
    And I think the water drowned 'em,
    For they never, never found 'em,
And I know they didn't come ashore with me.

Oh! 'twas very sad and lonely
    When I found myself the only
Population on this cultivated shore;
    But I've made a little tavern
    In a rocky little cavern
And I sit and watch for people at the door.

I spent no time in looking
    For a girl to do my cooking,
As I'm quite a clever hand at making stews;
    But I had that fellow Friday,
    Just to keep the tavern tidy
And to put a Sunday polish on my shoes.

I have a little garden
    That I'm cultivating lard in,
As the things I eat are rather tough and dry;
    For I live on toasted lizards,
    Prickly pears, and parrot gizzards,
And I'm really very fond of beetle pie.

The clothes I had were furry,
    And it made me fret and worry

——From *Davy and the Goblin* by Charles Edward Carryl. Reprinted by permission of and arrangement with Houghton Mifflin Company, the authorized publishers.

When I found the moths were eating off the hair;
    And I had to scrape and sand 'em,
    And I boiled 'em and I tanned 'em,
Till I got the fine morocco suit I wear.

    I sometimes seek diversion
    In a family excursion
With the few domestic animals you see;
    And we take along a carrot
    As refreshment for the parrot,
And a little can of jungleberry tea.

    Then we gather as we travel,
    Bits of moss and dirty gravel,
And we chip off little specimens of stone;
    And we carry home as prizes
    Funny bugs, of handy sizes,
Just to give the day a scientific tone.

    If the roads are wet and muddy,
    We remain at home and study—
For the Goat is very clever at a sum—
    And the Dog, instead of fighting,
    Studies ornamental writing,
While the Cat is taking lessons on the drum.

    We retire at eleven,
    And we rise again at seven;
And I wish to call attention, as I close,
    To the fact that all the scholars
    Are correct about their collars,
And particular in turning out their toes.

CAN'T BE TRUE

Part of the humor of the poem lies in its silly contradictions. For example, Robinson Crusoe says he built a tavern; and we know that taverns are found only in places where there are people. What other examples of contradiction and impossibility do you find in the poem?

❧ CARL SANDBURG

The Story of Jason Squiff and Why He Had a Popcorn Hat, Popcorn Mittens, and Popcorn Shoes

This story is strictly American. It is about an extremely strange character named Jason Squiff. Jason couldn't rely on his wits, like Tyl Ulenspiegel (because he probably wasn't oversupplied); so he put his faith in a whincher.
(Note the time when you begin reading.)

JASON SQUIFF was a cistern cleaner. He had greenish yellowish hair. If you looked down into a cistern when he was lifting buckets of slush and mud, you could tell where he was, you could pick him out down in the dark cistern, by the lights of his greenish yellowish hair.

Sometimes the buckets of slush and mud tipped over and ran down on the top of his head. This covered his greenish yellowish hair. And then it was hard to tell where he was, and it was not easy to pick him out down in the dark where he was cleaning the cistern.

One day Jason Squiff came to the Bimber house and knocked on the door.

"Did I understand," he said, speaking to Mrs. Bimber, Blixie Bimber's mother, "do I understand you sent for me to clean the cistern in your back yard?"

——From *Rootabaga Stories* by Carl Sandburg, copyright, 1922, by Harcourt, Brace and Company, Inc.

"You understand exactly such," said Mrs. Bimber, "and you are welcome as the flowers that bloom in the spring, tra-la-la."

"Then I will go to work and clean the cistern, tra-la-la," he answered, speaking to Mrs. Bimber. "I'm the guy, tra-la-la," he said further, running his excellent fingers through his greenish yellowish hair which was shining brightly.

He began cleaning the cistern. Blixie Bimber came out in the back yard. She looked down in the cistern. It was all dark. It looked like nothing but all dark down there. By and by she saw something greenish yellowish. She watched it. Soon she saw it was Jason Squiff's head and hair. And then she knew the cistern was being cleaned and Jason Squiff was on the job. So she sang tra-la-la and went back into the house and told her mother Jason Squiff was on the job.

The last bucketful of slush and mud came at last for Jason Squiff. He squinted at the bottom. Something was shining. He reached his fingers down through the slush and mud and took out what was shining.

It was the gold buckskin whincher Blixie Bimber lost from the gold chain around her neck the week before when she was looking down into the cistern to see what she could see. It was exactly the same gold buckskin whincher shining and glittering like a sign of happiness.

"It's luck," said Jason Squiff, wiping his fingers on his greenish yellowish hair. Then he put the gold buckskin whincher in his vest pocket and spoke to himself again, "It's luck."

A little after six o'clock that night Jason Squiff stepped into his house and home and said hello to his wife and daughters. They all began to laugh. Their laughter was a ticklish laughter.

"Something funny is happening," he said.

"And you are it," they all laughed at him again with ticklish laughter.

Then they showed him. His hat was popcorn, his mittens popcorn, and his shoes popcorn. He didn't know the gold buckskin whincher had a power and was working all the time. He didn't know the whincher in his vest pocket was saying, "You have a letter Q in your name and because you have the pleasure and happiness of having a Q in your name you must have a popcorn hat, popcorn mittens, and popcorn shoes."

The next morning he put on another hat, another pair of mittens, and another pair of shoes. And the minute he put them on they changed to popcorn.

So he tried on all his hats, mittens, and shoes. Always they changed to popcorn the minute he had them on.

He went downtown to the stores. He bought a new hat, mittens, and shoes. And the minute he had them on they changed to popcorn.

So he decided he would go to work and clean cisterns with his popcorn hat, popcorn mittens, and popcorn shoes on.

The people of the Village of Cream Puffs enjoyed watching him walk up the street, going to clean cisterns. People five and six blocks away could see him coming and going with his popcorn hat, popcorn mittens, and popcorn shoes.

When he was down in a cistern, the children enjoyed looking down into the cistern to see him work. When none of the slush and mud fell on his hat and mittens, he was easy to find. The light of the shining popcorn lit up the whole inside of the cistern.

Sometimes, of course, the white popcorn got full of black slush and black mud. And then when Jason Squiff came up and walked home, he was not quite so dazzling to look at.

It was a funny winter for Jason Squiff.

"It's a crime, a dirty crime," he said to himself. "Now I can never be alone with my thoughts. Everybody looks at me when I go up the street.

"If I meet a funeral, even the pall bearers begin to laugh at my popcorn hat. If I meet people going to a wedding, they throw all the rice at me as if I am a bride and a groom all together.

"The horses try to eat my hat wherever I go. Three hats I have fed to horses this winter.

"And if I accidentally drop one of my mittens, the chickens eat it."

Then Jason Squiff began to change. He became proud.

"I always wanted a white beautiful hat like this white popcorn hat," he said to himself. "And I always wanted white beautiful mittens and white beautiful shoes like these white popcorn mittens and shoes."

When the boys yelled, "Snow man! yah-de-dah-de-dah, Snow man!" he just waved his hand to them with an upward gesture of his arm to show he was proud of how he looked.

"They all watch for me," he said to himself, "I am distinguished—am I not?" he asked himself.

And he put his right hand into his left hand and shook hands with himself and said, "You certainly look fixed up."

One day he decided to throw away his vest. In the vest pocket was the gold buckskin whincher, with the power working, the power saying, "You have a letter Q in your name and because you have the pleasure and happiness of having a Q in your name you must have a popcorn hat, popcorn mittens, and popcorn shoes."

Yes, he threw away the vest. He forgot all about the gold buckskin whincher being in the vest.

He just handed the vest to a rag man. And the rag man put the vest with the gold buckskin whincher in a bag on his back and walked away.

After that Jason Squiff was like other people. His hats would never change to popcorn nor his mittens to popcorn nor his shoes to popcorn.

And when anybody looked at him down in a cistern cleaning the cistern or when anybody saw him walking along the street they knew him by his greenish yellowish hair which was always full of bright lights.

And so—if you have a Q in your name, be careful if you ever come across a gold buckskin whincher. Remember different whinchers have different powers.

(Note the time; and check your speed of reading with the Reading Score Board, page 158.)

(Note the time; and check your speed of reading with the Reading Score Board, page 158.)

❖❖❖

A Few Words about Jason—and Reading

1. Where do you first suspect that this is going to be an unusual story?
2. How did Jason Squiff happen to get popcorn hats, shoes, and mittens?
3. What amusing things happened to Jason Squiff with his popcorn outfit?
4. How did Jason make the best of his amusing predicament?
5. In reading the story, into what natural phrases did your eyes break it?

The Right Words for Jason

How are these words and phrases important to the story?

1. greenish yellowish hair
2. tra-la-la
3. gold buckskin whincher
4. a Q in your name
5. Village of Cream Puffs
6. shining popcorn

READING SCORE BOARD

Number of Minutes	12	6	4 2/3	4	3	2 1/3
Reading Rate	100 w.p.m.	200 w.p.m.	250 w.p.m.	300 w.p.m.	400 w.p.m.	500 w.p.m.

◄◄ ELLA YOUNG

Three Golden Apples

Ella Young is famous for her stories of Irish folklore. The following is one of her most delightful. Miss Young admits that she invented the character of Ballor's Son. The Pooka, however, she says, has "many hiding-holes in Irish folklore"; and Angus had "temples to his honor once, over a great part of Europe." In the story by Sandburg that you have just read, Jason Squiff had a magic "whincher." In the following story you will find several kinds of strange Irish magic. The three golden apples that you are going to read about are definitely not the apple-a-day-keeps-the-doctor-away variety.

(Note the time when you begin reading.)

BALLOR'S SON woke in the morning with a grievance in his mind.

"What's the good of having a king for your father," he said to himself, "if you never get anything that you want? I wish I wasn't Ballor's only son. I wish I lived in a country where there was sunshine in the sky and apples on the trees—Oh, I wish I were a beggar-boy with the world to wander in!"

He felt so sorry for himself that he began to cry, softly at first and then loudly—very loudly indeed.

———From *The Unicorn with Silver Shoes* by Ella Young, copyright 1932, and published by Longmans, Green and Co.

The First Lord-in-Waiting hurried in, with the Second Lord-in-Waiting at his heels.

"O Noble Prince," said the First Lord, "what distresses you?"

"I want an apple tree!" said Ballor's Son. "I want a white horse that can go over land and water; I want a silver branch with three golden apples on it!"

"Alas!" said the First Lord-in-Waiting, wiping a tear out of his eyes.

"Alas!" said the Second Lord, copying him.

"Alas!" said the two of them together. "You've been listening to Faery Tales, Most Noble Prince!"

"I have not!" said Ballor's Son, stoutly.

"Where did you get word, then," said the First Lord, "of a Horse that goes over land and sea, or of the Silver Branch with Golden Apples?"

"I got word of them from a boy I met in the Garden of Twisted Trees in the dusk of yestereve, the time I ran away from you all. He told me of those things—and other things, too. Oh, I wish I had him to talk to now!"

"Don't wish a bad wish like that," said the First Lord, severely, "or you may find yourself in Faery-Land, for it was a lad out of Faery-Land that told you of the Golden Apples and of the White Horse. That Horse belongs to Mananaun the King of Faery-Land; and the Golden Apples belong to his son, Angus."

"And to what person does the Pooka belong?" said Ballor's Son.

"The Pooka," said the First Lord, "is a tricky little spirit that belongs to Faery-Land; and the less you trouble your head about these things the better!"

"How does one go to Faery-Land?" asked Ballor's Son.

"No one in this country knows," said the First Lord, "and of a certainty you, Most Noble Prince, are not going there."

Ballor's Son shut his lips tightly; he had got as much information as he was likely to get, and he had made up his mind.

He was so very good all day that he was given his best royal crown to wear and his best royal mantle. He had both these on him when he stole away in the dusk to look for Faery-Land.

Beyond the Garden of Twisted Trees there was a high wall, and on the top of the wall a row of sharp iron spikes. The sky was beyond the wall, and nothing else that Ballor's Son could see. He went from end to end of the wall, looking for a doorway, or a loose place in the stones where he could climb, or a broken place where he could crawl out; but he found everywhere the same solid smooth iron-spiked wall.

He sat down on the ground, and nothing but the thought of the First and Second Lords-in-Waiting prevented him from lifting up his voice in a wail fitting to the occasion.

"I *won't* cry," he said to himself. "No, I won't cry—to please them!"

All at once he knew that he was not alone. Beside him stood the boy he had spoken with the evening before. He was a slender lad with pale gold hair and shining gray eyes.

"Put your hand in mine," he said to Ballor's Son, "and I will take you into Faery-Land."

Ballor's Son reached a hand. He heard a sound like a clap of thunder, and shut his eyes tight. When he opened them, he was all by himself in a wood. He had never seen trees like the trees of that wood, so tall-growing, so ancient, so splendid-looking. On all the boughs the leaves were young and green, and the sunlight flaming through them made patterns on the moss about his feet. A little path wound away and away into the heart of the wood. Ballor's Son went along the path. It seemed to him that he walked and walked and walked for hours before he came to an open space, and peering through the branches, saw an old man seated on a stone.

Ballor's Son thought that he must be very old, because his hair was gray to whiteness; but when he looked closer, that hair was all like silver flame and the old man had a radiance in his face. He was wrapped in a cloak of purple that had nine capes, each one more richly embroidered than the other. By his side stood a young man with a sunburnt face and poor and tattered clothes. They were talking together. Ballor's Son sharpened his ears to listen.

"Are you not tired," asked the old man, "are you not tired, Angus, of walking the roads of the world with the bitter wind in your face and the clogging dust on your feet? Are you still eager to leave riches and go a-begging?"

"I am still eager," said the young man, "for change, though it be from blue to gray, and for the road where all things may happen!"

Just then, a Pooka came out from between the trees. It looked like a little snow-white kid with golden horns and silver hoofs, but it could take any shape it had a fancy for. When it saw Angus, it smiled and made one jump on to his shoulder.

"Look at this!" said Angus, "I never can say anything important without being interrupted!"

"What do you want?" he said to the Pooka, pretending to be cross.

"Oh, nothing at all, only to listen to your wise talk; it does me good," said the Pooka, prancing on Angus's

shoulder. "I'll soon be the wisest Pooka in the world!"

At this Ballor's Son burst out of hiding.

"Pooka! Pooka! Pooka!" he yelled, "I want you, come here!"

The Pooka jumped behind Angus. Ballor's Son tried to seize it. Angus put out a hand.

"Who are you?" he said.

"I am a Royal Prince," said the boy, trying to look big.

"You have princely manners," said Angus.

"I am Ballor's own son. I have come out to look for treasure, and if you have anything, I command you to give it to me at once."

"What would you like?" said Angus.

"I would like the White Horse of Mananaun, or three Golden Apples, or a Hound out of Faery-Land."

"They say it's lucky to be good to poor folk," said Angus; "if you are good to us perhaps you may find a treasure."

"If you do not get up at once and hunt about for a treasure for me, I will tell my father, Ballor, and he will wither you off the face of the earth!"

"Oh, give me a little time," said Angus, "and I'll look for something."

The Pooka, who had been listening to everything, now skipped out from his hiding place with a turnip in his mouth—he was holding it by the green leaves.

"The very thing!" said Angus. "Here is a treasure!" He took the turnip in his hands and passed his fingers over it. The turnip became a great white egg, and the leaves turned into gold and crimson spots and spread themselves over the egg.

"Now look at this!" said Angus. "It is an enchanted egg. You have only to keep it till you do three Good Actions, and then it will hatch out into something splendid."

"Will it hatch into Mananaun's White Horse?" asked Ballor's Son.

"It depends on the Good Actions you do; everything depends on that."

"What is a Good Action?"

"Well, if you were to go quietly away, and never tell anyone you had seen us, it would be a Good Action."

"I'll go," said Ballor's Son. He took the egg in his hands, kicked up a toeful of earth at the Pooka, and went.

He hadn't gone far when he heard a bird singing. He looked and saw a little bird on a furze bush.

"Stop that noise!" he said.

The bird kept on singing. Ballor's Son flung the egg at it. The egg turned into a turnip, and struck a hare that was crouching in the ferns by the furze bush. The hare jumped out of the furze bush.

"My curse on you!" cried Ballor's Son, "for a brittle egg! What came over you to hatch into nothing better than a hare! My Grief and my Trouble! What came over you to hatch out at all when this is only my second Good Action?"

He turned to go back to his own country. At first he walked with big steps puffing his cheeks vaingloriously, but little by little a sense of loss overcame him; and as he thought how nearly he had earned the White Horse of Mananaun, or three Golden Apples, or some greater treasure, two

tears slowly rolled down his snub nose.

Angus and the old man and the Pooka were still in the little clearing when Ballor's Son passed back through it. The moment he came in sight, the Pooka changed himself into a squirrel and ran up the oak tree; Angus changed himself into an oak leaf and fell softly on a bank of moss; the old man sat quite still and looked at Ballor's Son.

"The egg hatched out," said Ballor's Son. "It was a bad egg. I wish that I had thrown it at the beggarman's head!"

The old man smiled and picked up the oak leaf. He pressed his hands over it, and it became a great golden egg with green and purple spots on it.

"Give it to me! Give it to me!" yelled Ballor's Son; "it's better than the first egg, and the first egg is broken. Give it to me."

"This egg is too precious for you," said the old man. "I must keep it in my own hands."

"Then I will blast you and all the forest and every living thing! I have only to roar three times, and three armies of my people will come to help me. Give me the egg, or I will roar."

"I will keep this egg in my own hands," said the old man.

Ballor's Son shut his eyes tight and opened his mouth very wide to let out a great roar, and it is likely he would have been heard at the other end of the world if the Pooka hadn't dropped a handful of acorns into his mouth. The roar never came out. Ballor's Son choked and spluttered. The old man patted him on the back and shook him. He shook him very hard, and after a while Ballor's Son got his breath. Then he said:

"I will not blast you this time; I will do a Good Action. I will let you carry the egg, and you can be my slave and treasure-finder!"

"I am Mananaun," said the old man.

"Oh," cried Ballor's Son, "O, I want a white—"

He heard the Pooka laughing behind him.

"What are you laughing at?" he cried, turning sharply round.

There was no Pooka! There was no laughter! He turned again. There was an old man, and no bank of moss!

He rubbed his eyes, he shut them and opened them three times, he dug his knuckles into them—there was no Pooka, no bank of moss, no old man!

"What ails you, Ballor's Son?" said a voice. It came from a tree above him, and looking up he saw a white bird with a ruby-colored breast and emerald eyes.

"I'm the most unfortunate prince that ever lived!" said Ballor's Son. "I've lost my Luck-Egg."

"I've lost three Seeds of Good-Luck, myself," said the bird.

"What are Seeds of Good-Luck?" asked Ballor's Son. "Are they as good as Luck-Eggs?"

"That depends," said the bird, "on the person who plants them—they might grow into anything!"

"Where did you lose them?" asked Ballor's Son.

"In the hollow of the tree I'm sitting on," said the bird.

"I'll get them," said Ballor's Son, and he began to break his way into the hollow of the tree. It was hard work, but he kept at it till he could put head and shoulder and a searching hand into the hollow. He found three hard, shining seeds. Straightening himself he cried:

"I've got them, White Bird."

The bird had gone.

"I'll keep them myself," said Ballor's Son.

"Will you?" asked a voice with laughter in it—a voice that he knew.

It was the Pooka come back!

This time he looked like a great stag with branching horns. His hide was silver spotted with gold.

"Give the seeds to me," he said, "and I will let you ride on my back."

"No," cried Ballor's Son, "I will give the seeds to the owner!"

"That will be a Good Action," said the Pooka.

"White Bird! White Bird! White Bird!" cried Ballor's Son.

From the far blueness of the sky the white bird descended, whirling and poising and falling as lightly as a petal of apple blossom or a flake of wind-lifted snow.

"Give the seeds to Angus, the Beggar-Man, with my blessing," cried the white bird, circling and poising.

"Angus! Angus! Angus!" called Ballor's Son, and before the last word left his mouth the beggar-man was standing between the trees.

Ballor's Son gave him the seeds.

Angus took the seeds. He put one on his forehead where it shone like a king's jewel. He threw one into the air and it became a golden bird, circling and poising with its ruby-breasted fellow. He planted one. It came up a little slender apple tree. It grew and blossomed, and three big yellow apples hung on it—the sweetest apples in the world! Angus gathered the apples. He kept one. He gave one to the Pooka.

"Good luck, and may your hand never be empty," said the Pooka.

He gave one to Ballor's Son.

"Here," said he, "is fruit untasted save in Faery-Land. Keep it till you go into your own country, or no one will believe you ever had it."

"Good luck, and may your hand never be empty," said Ballor's Son. He stepped blithely homeward, but he hadn't taken three steps before he fell to munching the apple—that is why no one believed him when he got home.

(Note the time; and check your speed of reading with the Reading Score Board, page 164.)

❖❖❖

Irish Magic

1. What different kinds of magic took place in the story?
2. What seems to be the magic number in the story? How many times is it used?
3. Did the trip that Ballor's Son took into Faery-Land help him? How?
4. What do you know about Angus, the Pooka, and the old man?

Small Details—But Magic-making

1. What three things did Ballor's Son say he wanted?
2. In what magical way did Ballor's Son go to Faery-Land?
3. What did Faery-Land look like?
4. What vegetable turned into an enchanted egg?
5. Where were the three Seeds of Good-Luck lost?

Faery Pictures

Did you notice the many words and phrases used to give exact pictures of things and persons? Here are a few. How many others do you find?
a. white horse
b. silver branch with three golden apples
c. Garden of Twisted Trees

Faery Words

Can you match the words and phrases in these columns?

I   II

Nouns
1. spirit   a. brightness
2. mantle   b. rabbit
3. radiance   c. loose sleeveless cloak
4. hare   d. elf

Verbs

1. prevented
2. peering
3. blast
4. munching

a. chewing noisily
b. forestalled
c. looking into space attentively
d. to rend in pieces by explosion

Adjectives

1. enchanted
2. brittle
3. precious
4. unfortunate

a. easy to break
b. highly prized
c. having ill luck
d. bewitched

Adverbs

1. severely
2. vaingloriously
3. lightly
4. blithely

a. with excessive vanity
b. harshly
c. joyously
d. airily

READING SCORE BOARD

Number of Words in Story: 2410.

Number of Minutes	24	16	13 3/4	12	10	8	6
Reading Rate	100 w.p.m.	150 w.p.m.	175 w.p.m.	200 w.p.m.	250 w.p.m.	300 w.p.m.	400 w.p.m.

◄◄ WASHINGTON IRVING

Rip Van Winkle

Here is the famous story of the man who fell asleep on a mountainside and did not wake up for twenty years. No wonder he was confused! You'd be confused, too, after a twenty-year nap.
(Note the time when you begin reading.)

WHOEVER has made a voyage up the Hudson must remember the Kaatskill Mountains. They are a dismembered branch of the great Appalachian family and are seen away to the west of the river, swelling up to a noble height and lording it over the surrounding country. Every change of season, every change of weather, indeed, every hour of the day, produces some change in the magical hues and shapes of these mountains; and they are regarded by all the good wives, far and near, as perfect barometers. When the weather is fair and settled, they are clothed in blue and purple, and print their bold outlines on the clear evening sky; but, sometimes, when the rest of the landscape is cloudless, they will gather a hood of gray vapors about their summits, which, in the last rays of the setting sun, will glow and light up like a crown of glory.

At the foot of these fairy mountains, the voyager may have descried the light smoke curling up from a village, whose shingle roofs gleam among the trees, just where the blue tints of the upland melt away into the fresh green of the nearer landscape. It is a little village, of great antiquity, having been founded by some of the Dutch colonists, in the early times of the province, just about the beginning of the government of the good Peter Stuyvesant (may he rest in peace!); and there were some of the houses of the original settlers standing within a few years, built of small yellow bricks brought from Holland, having latticed windows and gable fronts, surmounted with weathercocks.

In that same village, and in one of these very houses (which, to tell the precise truth, was sadly timeworn and weather-beaten), there lived many years since, while the country was yet a province of Great Britain, a simple good-natured fellow, of the name of Rip Van Winkle. He was a descendant of the Van Winkles who figured so gallantly in the chivalrous days of Peter Stuyvesant and accompanied him to the siege of Fort Christina. He inherited, however, but little of the martial character of his ancestors. I have observed that he was a simple good-natured man; he was, moreover, a kind neighbor and an obedient henpecked husband. Indeed, to the latter circumstance might be owing that meekness of spirit which gained him such universal popularity; for those men are most apt to be obsequious and conciliating abroad, who are under the discipline of shrews at home. Their tempers, doubtless, are rendered pliant and malleable in the fiery furnace of domestic tribulation; and a curtain lecture is worth all the sermons in the world for teaching the virtues of patience and long-suffering. A termagant[1] wife may, therefore, in some respects, be considered a tolerable blessing; and if so, Rip Van Winkle was thrice blessed.

Certain it is, that he was a great favorite among all the good wives of the village, who, as usual, with the amiable sex, took his part in all family squabbles and never failed, whenever they talked those matters over in their evening gossipings, to lay all the blame on Dame Van Winkle. The children of the village, too, would shout with joy whenever he approached. He assisted at their sports, made their playthings, taught them to fly kites and shoot marbles, and told them long stories of ghosts, witches, and Indians. Whenever he went dodging about the village, he was surrounded by a troop of them, hanging on his skirts, clambering on his back, and playing a thousand

[1] *termagant.* Scolding.

tricks on him with impunity; and not a dog would bark at him throughout the neighborhood.

The great error in Rip's composition was an insuperable aversion[2] to all kinds of profitable labor. It could not be from the want of assiduity[3] or perseverance; for he would sit on a wet rock, with a rod as long and heavy as a Tartar's lance, and fish all day without a murmur, even though he should not be encouraged by a single nibble. He would carry a fowling piece on his shoulder for hours together, trudging through woods and swamps, and up hill and down dale, to shoot a few squirrels or wild pigeons. He would never refuse to assist a neighbor even in the roughest toil, and was a foremost man at all country frolics for husking Indian corn or building stone fences; the women of the village, too, used to employ him to run their errands and to do such little odd jobs as their less obliging husbands would not do for them. In a word Rip was ready to attend to anybody's business but his own; but as to doing family duty, and keeping his farm in order, he found it impossible.

In fact, he declared it was of no use to work on his farm; it was the most pestilent little piece of ground in the whole country; everything about it went wrong, and would go wrong, in spite of him. His fences were continually falling to pieces; his cow would either go astray or get among the cabbages; weeds were sure to grow quicker in his fields than any-

where else; the rain always made a point of setting in just as he had some outdoor work to do; so that though his patrimonial estate had dwindled away under his management, acre by acre, until there was little more left than a mere patch of Indian corn and potatoes, yet it was the worst conditioned farm in the neighborhood.

His children, too, were as ragged and wild as if they belonged to nobody. His son Rip, an urchin begotten in his own likeness, promised to inherit the habits, with the old clothes of his father. He was generally seen trooping like a colt at his mother's heels, equipped in a pair of his father's cast-off galligaskins,[4] which he had much ado to hold up with one hand, as a fine lady does her train in bad weather.

Rip Van Winkle, however, was one of those happy mortals, of foolish, well-oiled dispositions, who take the world easy, eat white bread or brown, whichever can be got with least thought or trouble, and would rather starve on a penny than work for a pound. If left to himself, he would have whistled life away in perfect contentment; but his wife kept continually dinning in his ears about his idleness, his carelessness, and the ruin he was bringing on his family. Morning, noon, and night, her tongue was incessantly going; and everything he said or did was sure to produce a torrent of household eloquence. Rip had but one way of replying to all lectures of the kind, and that, by frequent use, had grown into a habit. He shrugged his shoulders, shook his head, cast up

2 *aversion.* Dislike.
3 *assiduity.* Diligence.

4 *galligaskins.* Breeches.

his eyes, but said nothing. This, however, always provoked a fresh volley from his wife; so that he was fain to draw off his forces and take to the outside of the house—the only side which, in truth, belongs to a henpecked husband.

Rip's sole domestic adherent was his dog Wolf, who was as much henpecked as his master; for Dame Van Winkle regarded them as companions in idleness and even looked upon Wolf with an evil eye, as the cause of his master's going so often astray. True it is, in all points of spirit befitting an honorable dog, he was as courageous an animal as ever scoured the woods— but what courage can withstand the ever-during and all-besetting terrors of a woman's tongue? The moment Wolf entered the house his crest fell, his tail drooped to the ground or curled between his legs, he sneaked about with a gallows air, casting many a sidelong glance at Dame Van Winkle, and at the least flourish of a broomstick or ladle, he would fly to the door with yelping precipitation.

Times grew worse and worse with Rip Van Winkle as years of matrimony rolled on; a tart temper never mellows with age, and a sharp tongue is the only edged tool that grows keener with constant use. For a long while he used to console himself, when driven from home, by frequenting a kind of perpetual club of the sages, philosophers, and other idle personages of the village, which held its sessions on a bench before a small inn, designated by a rubicund portrait of His Majesty George the Third. Here they used to sit in the shade

through a long lazy summer's day, talking listlessly over village gossip or telling endless sleepy stories about nothing. But it would have been worth any statesman's money to have heard the profound discussions that sometimes took place, when by chance an old newspaper fell into their hands from some passing traveler. How solemnly they would listen to the contents, as drawled out by Derrick Van Bummel, the schoolmaster, a dapper learned little man, who was not to be daunted by the most gigantic word in the dictionary; and how sagely they would deliberate upon public events some months after they had taken place.

The opinions of this junto[5] were completely controlled by Nicholas Vedder, a patriarch of the village and landlord of the inn, at the door of which he took his seat from morning till night, just moving sufficiently to avoid the sun and keep in the shade of a large tree, so that the neighbors could tell the hour by his movements as accurately as by a sundial. It is true he was rarely heard to speak, but smoked his pipe incessantly. His adherents, however (for every great man has his adherents), perfectly understood him and knew how to gather his opinions. When anything that was read or related displeased him, he was observed to smoke his pipe vehemently and to send forth short, frequent, and angry puffs; but when pleased, he would inhale the smoke slowly and tranquilly and emit it in light and placid clouds; and some-

[5] *junto.* Group of persons joined for a purpose.

times, taking the pipe from his mouth, and letting the fragrant vapor curl about his nose, would gravely nod his head in token of perfect approbation.

From even this stronghold the unlucky Rip was at length routed by his termagant wife, who would suddenly break in upon the tranquillity of the assemblage and call the members all to naught; nor was that august personage, Nicholas Vedder himself, sacred from the daring tongue of this terrible virago, who charged him outright with encouraging her husband in habits of idleness.

Poor Rip was at last reduced almost to despair; and his only alternative, to escape from the labor of the farm and clamor of his wife, was to take gun in hand and stroll away into the woods. Here he would sometimes seat himself at the foot of a tree and share the contents of his wallet with Wolf, with whom he sympathized as a fellow-sufferer in persecution. "Poor Wolf," he would say, "thy mistress leads thee a dog's life of it; but never mind, my lad, whilst I live thou shalt never want a friend to stand by thee!" Wolf would wag his tail, look wistfully in his master's face, and if dogs can feel pity I verily believe he reciprocated the sentiment with all his heart.

In a long ramble of the kind on a fine autumnal day, Rip had unconsciously scrambled to one of the highest parts of the Kaatskill Mountains. He was after his favorite sport of squirrel shooting, and the still solitudes had echoed and re-echoed with the reports of his gun. Panting and fatigued, he threw himself, late in the afternoon, on a green knoll covered with mountain herbage, that crowned the brow of a precipice. From an opening between the trees he could overlook all the lower country for many a mile of rich woodland. He saw at a distance the lordly Hudson, far, far below him, moving on its silent but majestic course, with the reflection of a purple cloud, or the sail of a lagging bark, here and there sleeping on its glassy bosom, and at last losing itself in the blue highlands.

On the other side he looked down into a deep mountain glen, wild, lonely, and shagged, the bottom filled with fragments from the impending cliffs and scarcely lighted by the reflected rays of the setting sun. For some time Rip lay musing on this scene; evening was gradually advancing; the mountains began to throw their long blue shadows over the valleys; he saw that it would be dark long before he could reach the village, and he heaved a heavy sigh when he thought of encountering the terrors of Dame Van Winkle.

As he was about to descend, he heard a voice from a distance, hallooing, "Rip Van Winkle! Rip Van Winkle!" He looked round but could see nothing but a crow winging its solitary flight across the mountain. He thought his fancy must have deceived him, and turned again to descend, when he heard the same cry ring through the still evening air: "Rip Van Winkle! Rip Van Winkle!"—at the same time Wolf bristled up his back, and giving a low growl, skulked to his master's side, looking fearfully down into the glen. Rip now felt a vague apprehension stealing over him; he looked anxiously in the same direction, and perceived a strange figure slowly toiling up the rocks and bending under the weight of something he carried on his back. He was surprised to see any human being in this lonely and unfrequented place, but supposing it to be some one of the neighborhood in need of his assistance, he hastened down to yield it.

On nearer approach he was still more surprised at the singularity of the stranger's appearance. He was a short square-built old fellow, with thick bushy hair and a grizzled beard. His dress was of the antique Dutch fashion—a cloth jerkin[6] strapped round the waist—several pair of breeches, the outer one of ample volume, decorated with rows of buttons down the sides, and bunches at the knees. He bore on his shoulder a stout keg that seemed full of liquor, and made signs for Rip to approach and assist him with the load. Though rather shy and distrustful of this new acquaintance, Rip complied with his usual alacrity; and mutually relieving one another, they clambered up a narrow gully, apparently the dry bed of a mountain torrent. As they ascended, Rip every now and then heard long rolling peals, like distant thunder, that seemed to issue out of a deep ravine, or rather cleft, between lofty rocks, toward which their rugged path conducted. He paused for an instant; but supposing it to be the muttering of one of those transient thunder showers which often take place in mountain heights, he proceeded. Pass-

6 *jerkin.* A jacket.

ing through the ravine, they came to a hollow, like a small amphitheater, surrounded by perpendicular precipices, over the brinks of which impending trees shot their branches, so that you only caught glimpses of the azure sky and the bright evening cloud. During the whole time Rip and his companion had labored on in silence; for though the former marveled greatly what could be the object of carrying a keg of liquor up this wild mountain, yet there was something strange and incomprehensible about the unknown, that inspired awe and checked familiarity.

On entering the amphitheater, new objects of wonder presented themselves. On a level spot in the center was a company of odd-looking personages playing at ninepins. They were dressed in a quaint outlandish fashion; some wore short doublets, others jerkins, with long knives in their belts, and most of them had enormous breeches, of similar style with that of the guide's. Their visages, too, were peculiar: one had a large beard, broad face, and small piggish eyes; the face of another seemed to consist entirely of nose, and was surmounted by a white sugar-loaf hat, set off with a little red cock's tail. They all had beards, of various shapes and colors. There was one who seemed to be the commander. He was a stout old gentleman, with a weather-beaten countenance; he wore a laced doublet, broad belt and hanger, high crowned hat and feather, red stockings, and high-heeled shoes with roses in them. The whole group reminded Rip of the figures in an old Flemish painting, in the parlor of Dominie Van Shaick, the village parson, and which had been brought over from Holland at the time of the settlement.

What seemed particularly odd to Rip was, that though these folks were evidently amusing themselves, yet they maintained the gravest faces, the most mysterious silence, and were, withal, the most melancholy party of pleasure he had ever witnessed. Nothing interrupted the stillness of the scene but the noise of the balls, which, whenever they were rolled, echoed along the mountains like rumbling peals of thunder.

As Rip and his companion approached them, they suddenly desisted from their play, and stared at him with such fixed statue-like gaze, and such strange, uncouth, lack-luster countenances, that his heart turned within him, and his knees smote together. His companion now emptied the contents of the keg into large flagons,[7] and made signs to him to wait upon the company. He obeyed with fear and trembling; they quaffed the liquor in profound silence and then returned to their game.

By degrees Rip's awe and apprehension subsided. He even ventured, when no eye was fixed upon him, to taste the beverage, which he found had much of the flavor of excellent Hollands. He was naturally a thirsty soul and was soon tempted to repeat the draught. One taste provoked another; and he reiterated his visits to the flagon so often that at length his senses were overpowered, his eyes

[7] *flagons.* Containers for liquors; usually with a handle, spout, and lid.

swam in his head, his head gradually declined, and he fell into a deep sleep.

On waking, he found himself on the green knoll whence he had first seen the old man of the glen. He rubbed his eyes—it was a bright sunny morning. The birds were hopping and twittering among the bushes, and the eagle was wheeling aloft and breasting the pure mountain breeze. "Surely," thought Rip, "I have not slept here all night." He recalled the occurrences before he fell asleep. The strange man with a keg of liquor—the mountain ravine—the wild retreat among the rocks—the woebegone party at ninepins—the flagon—"Oh! that flagon! That wicked flagon!" thought Rip—"What excuse shall I make to Dame Van Winkle!"

He looked round for his gun; but in place of the clean well-oiled fowling piece, he found an old firelock lying by him, the barrel incrusted with rust, the lock falling off, and the stock worm-eaten. He now suspected that the grave roisters of the mountain had put a trick upon him and, having dosed him with liquor, had robbed him of his gun. Wolf, too, had disappeared; but he might have strayed away after a squirrel or partridge. He whistled after him and shouted his name, but all in vain; the echoes repeated his whistle and shout, but no dog was to be seen.

He determined to revisit the scene of the last evening's gambol, and if he met with any of the party, to demand his dog and gun. As he rose to walk, he found himself stiff in the joints and wanting in his usual activity. "These mountain beds do not agree with me," thought Rip, "and if this frolic should lay me up with a fit of the rheumatism, I shall have a blessed time with Dame Van Winkle." With some difficulty he got down into the glen: he found the gully up which he and his companion had ascended the preceding evening; but to his astonishment a mountain stream was now foaming down it, leaping from rock to rock, and filling the glen with babbling murmurs. He, however, made shift to scramble up its sides, working his toilsome way through thickets of birch, sassafras, and witch hazel, and sometimes tripped up or entangled by the wild grapevines that twisted their coils or tendrils from tree to tree and spread a kind of network in his path.

At length he reached to where the ravine had opened through the cliffs to the amphitheater; but no traces of such opening remained. The rocks presented a high impenetrable wall over which the torrent came tumbling in a sheet of feathery foam and fell into a broad deep basin, black from the shadows of the surrounding forest. Here, then, poor Rip was brought to a stand. He again called and whistled after his dog; he was only answered by the cawing of a flock of idle crows, sporting high in air about a dry tree that overhung a sunny precipice; and who, secure in their elevation, seemed to look down and scoff at the poor man's perplexities. What was to be done? The morning was passing away, and Rip felt famished for want of his breakfast. He grieved to give up his dog and gun; he dreaded to meet his wife; but it would not do

to starve among the mountains. He shook his head, shouldered the rusty firelock, and, with a heart full of trouble and anxiety, turned his steps homeward.

As he approached the village he met a number of people, but none whom he knew, which somewhat surprised him, for he had thought himself acquainted with everyone in the country round. Their dress, too, was of a different fashion from that to which he was accustomed. They all stared at him with equal marks of surprise, and whenever they cast their eyes upon him, invariably stroked their chins. The constant recurrence of this gesture induced Rip, involuntarily, to do the same, when, to his astonishment, he found his beard had grown a foot long!

He had now entered the skirts of the village. A troop of strange children ran at his heels, hooting after him and pointing at his gray beard. The dogs, too, not one of which he recognized for an old acquaintance, barked at him as he passed. The very village was altered; it was larger and more populous. There were rows of houses which he had never seen before, and those which had been his familiar haunts had disappeared. Strange names were over the doors—strange faces at the windows—everything was strange. His mind now misgave him; he began to doubt whether both he and the world around him were not bewitched. Surely this was his native village, which he had left but the day before. There stood the Kaatskill Mountains—there ran the silver Hudson at a distance—there was every hill and dale precisely as it had always been—Rip was sorely perplexed—"That flagon last night," thought he, "has addled my poor head sadly!"

It was with some difficulty that he found the way to his own house, which he approached with silent awe, expecting every moment to hear the shrill voice of Dame Van Winkle. He found the house gone to decay—the roof fallen in, the windows shattered, and the doors off the hinges. A half-starved dog that looked like Wolf was skulking about it. Rip called him by name; but the cur snarled, showed his teeth, and passed on. This was an unkind cut indeed—"My very dog," sighed poor Rip, "has forgotten me!"

He entered the house, which, to tell the truth, Dame Van Winkle had always kept in neat order. It was empty, forlorn, and apparently abandoned. This desolateness overcame all his connubial[8] fears—he called loudly for his wife and children—the lonely chambers rang for a moment with his voice, and then all again was silence.

He now hurried forth, and hastened to his old resort, the village inn—but it too was gone. A large rickety wooden building stood in its place, with great gaping windows, some of them broken and mended with old hats and petticoats, and over the door was painted, "The Union Hotel, by Jonathan Doolittle." Instead of the great tree that used to shelter the quiet little Dutch inn of yore, there now was reared a tall naked pole, with something on the top that looked like a red nightcap; and from it was flut-

8 *connubial.* Pertaining to marriage.

tering a flag, on which was a singular assemblage of stars and stripes—all this was strange and incomprehensible. He recognized on the sign, however, the ruby face of King George, under which he had smoked so many a peaceful pipe; but even this was singularly metamorphosed. The red coat was changed for one of blue and buff, a sword was held in the hand instead of a scepter, the head was decorated with a cocked hat, and underneath was painted in large characters, GENERAL WASHINGTON.

There was, as usual, a crowd of folk about the door, but none that Rip recollected. The very character of the people seemed changed. There was a busy, bustling, disputatious tone about it, instead of the accustomed phlegm and drowsy tranquillity. He looked in vain for the sage Nicholas Vedder, with his broad face, double chin, and fair long pipe, uttering clouds of tobacco smoke instead of idle speeches; or Van Bummel, the schoolmaster, doling forth the contents of an ancient newspaper. In place of these, a lean, bilious-looking fellow, with his pockets full of handbills, was haranguing vehemently about rights of citizens—elections—members of congress—liberty—Bunker's Hill—heroes of seventy-six—and other words, which were a perfect Babylonish jargon to the bewildered Van Winkle.

The appearance of Rip, with his long grizzled beard, his rusty fowling piece, his uncouth dress, and an army of women and children at his heels, soon attracted the attention of the tavern politicians. They crowded round him, eyeing him from head to foot with great curiosity. The orator bustled up to him, and, drawing him partly aside, inquired "on which side he voted?" Rip stared in vacant stupidity. Another short but busy little fellow pulled him by the arm, and, rising on tiptoe, inquired in his ear, "Whether he was Federal or Democrat?" Rip was equally at a loss to comprehend the question, when a knowing, self-important old gentleman, in a sharp cocked hat, made his way through the crowd, putting them to the right and left with his elbows as he passed and planting himself before Van Winkle, with one arm akimbo, the other resting on his cane, his keen eyes and sharp hat penetrating, as it were, into his very soul, demanded in an austere tone, "what brought him to the election with a gun on his shoulder and a mob at his heels, and whether he meant to breed a riot in the village?"—"Alas! gentlemen," cried Rip, somewhat dismayed, "I am a poor quiet man, a native of the place, and a loyal subject of the king, God bless him!"

Here a general shout burst from the bystanders—"A tory! A tory! A spy! A refugee! Hustle him! Away with him!" It was with great difficulty that the self-important man in the cocked hat restored order; and, having assumed a tenfold austerity of brow, demanded again of the unknown culprit, what he came there for, and whom he was seeking? The poor man humbly assured him that he meant no harm, but merely came there in search of some of his neighbors, who used to keep about the tavern.

"Well — who are they? — name them."

Rip bethought himself a moment, and inquired, "Where's Nicholas Vedder?"

There was a silence for a little while, when an old man replied, in a thin piping voice, "Nicholas Vedder! Why, he is dead and gone these eighteen years! There was a wooden tombstone in the churchyard that used to tell all about him, but that's rotten and gone, too."

"Where's Brom Dutcher?"

"Oh, he went off to the army in the beginning of the war; some say he was killed at the storming of Stony Point—others say he was drowned in a squall at the foot of Antony's Nose. I don't know—he never came back again."

"Where's Van Bummel, the schoolmaster?"

"He went off to the wars, too, was a great militia general, and is now in congress."

Rip's heart died away at hearing of these sad changes in his home and friends and finding himself thus alone in the world. Every answer puzzled him, too, by treating of such enormous lapses of time and of matters which he could not understand: war—congress—Stony Point; he had no courage to ask after any more friends, but cried out in despair, "Does nobody here know Rip Van Winkle?"

"Oh, Rip Van Winkle!" exclaimed two or three, "Oh, to be sure! That's Rip Van Winkle yonder, leaning against the tree."

Rip looked, and beheld a precise counterpart of himself as he went up the mountain: apparently as lazy, and certainly as ragged. The poor fellow was now completely confounded. He doubted his own identity and whether he was himself or another man. In the midst of his bewilderment, the man in the cocked hat demanded who he was, and what was his name?

"God knows," exclaimed he, at his wit's end; "I'm not myself—I'm somebody else—that's me yonder—no—that's somebody else got into my shoes—I was myself last night, but I fell asleep on the mountain, and they've changed my gun, and every thing's changed, and I'm changed, and I can't tell what's my name, or who I am!"

The bystanders began now to look at each other, nod, wink significantly, and tap their fingers against their foreheads. There was a whisper, also, about securing the gun and keeping the old fellow from doing mischief, at the very suggestion of which the self-important man in the cocked hat retired with some precipitation. At this critical moment a fresh comely woman pressed through the throng to get a peep at the gray-bearded man. She had a chubby child in her arms, which, frightened at his looks, began to cry. "Hush, Rip," cried she, "hush, you little fool; the old man won't hurt you." The name of the child, the air of the mother, the tone of her voice, all awakened a train of recollections in his mind. "What is your name, my good woman?" asked he.

"Judith Gardenier."

"And your father's name?"

"Ah, poor man, Rip Van Winkle was his name, but it's twenty years since he went away from home with his gun and never has been heard of since—his dog came home without him; but whether he shot himself, or was carried away by the Indians, nobody can tell. I was then but a little girl."

Rip had but one question more to ask; but he put it with a faltering voice:

"Where's your mother?"

"Oh, she, too, had died but a short time since; she broke a blood vessel in a fit of passion at a New England peddler."

There was a drop of comfort, at least, in this intelligence. The honest man could contain himself no longer. He caught his daughter and her child in his arms. "I am your father!" cried he—"Young Rip Van Winkle once—old Rip Van Winkle now!—Does nobody know poor Rip Van Winkle?"

All stood amazed, until an old woman, tottering out from among the crowd, put her hand to her brow, and peering under it in his face for a moment, exclaimed, "Sure enough! It is Rip Van Winkle—it is himself! Welcome home again, old neighbor—Why, where have you been these twenty long years?"

Rip's story was soon told, for the whole twenty years had been to him but as one night. The neighbors stared when they heard it; some were seen to wink at each other and put their tongues in their cheeks: and the self-important man in the cocked hat, who, when the alarm was over, had returned to the field, screwed down the corners of his mouth and shook his head—upon which there was a general shaking of the head throughout the assemblage.

It was determined, however, to take the opinion of old Peter Vanderdonk, who was seen slowly advancing up the road. He was a descendant of the historian of that name, who wrote one of the earliest accounts of the province. Peter was the most ancient inhabitant of the village and well versed in all the wonderful events and traditions of the neighborhood. He recollected Rip at once and corroborated his story in the most satisfactory manner. He assured the company that it was a fact, handed down from his ancestor the historian, that the Kaatskill Mountains had always been haunted by strange beings. That it was affirmed that the great Hendrick Hudson, the first discoverer of the river and country, kept a kind of vigil there every twenty years, with his crew of the *Half Moon*; being permitted in this way to revisit the scenes of his enterprise and keep a guardian eye upon the river, and the great city called by his name. That his father had once seen them in their old Dutch dresses playing at ninepins in a hollow of the mountain; and that he himself had heard, one summer afternoon, the sound of their balls, like distant peals of thunder.

To make a long story short, the company broke up and returned to the more important concerns of the election. Rip's daughter took him home to live with her; she had a snug, well-furnished house and a stout cheery farmer for a husband, whom Rip recollected for one of the urchins that used to climb upon his back. As to Rip's son and heir, who was the ditto of himself, seen leaning against the tree, he was employed to work on the farm but evinced an hereditary disposition to attend to anything else but his business.

Rip now resumed his old walks and habits; he soon found many of his former cronies, though all rather the worse for the wear and tear of time, and preferred making friends among the rising generation, with whom he soon grew into great favor.

Having nothing to do at home, and being arrived at that happy age when a man can be idle with impunity, he took his place once more on the bench at the inn door and was reverenced as one of the patriarchs of the village and a chronicle of the old times "before the war." It was some time before he could get into the regular track of gossip or could be made to comprehend the strange events that had taken place during his torpor. How that there had been a revolutionary war—that the country had thrown off the yoke of old England—and that, instead of being a subject of His Majesty George the Third, he was now a free citizen of the United States. Rip, in fact, was no politician; the changes of states and empires made but little impression on him; but there was one species of despotism under which he had long groaned, and that was—petticoat government. Happily that was at an end; he had got his neck out of the yoke of matrimony and could go in and out whenever he pleased, without dreading the tyranny of Dame Van Winkle.

Whenever her name was mentioned, however, he shook his head, shrugged his shoulders, and cast up his eyes; which might pass either for an expression of resignation to his fate or joy at his deliverance.

He used to tell his story to every stranger that arrived at Mr. Doolittle's hotel. He was observed, at first, to vary on some points every time he told it, which was, doubtless, owing to his having so recently awaked. It at last settled down precisely to the tale I have related, and not a man, woman, or child in the neighborhood, but knew it by heart. Some always pretended to doubt the reality of it and insisted that Rip had been out of his head and that this was one point on which he always remained flighty. The old Dutch inhabitants, however, almost universally gave it full credit. Even to this day they never hear a thunderstorm of a summer afternoon about the Kaatskill, but they say Hendrick Hudson and his crew are at their game of ninepins; and it is a common wish of all henpecked husbands in the neighborhood, when life hangs heavy on their hands, that they might have a quieting draught out of Rip Van Winkle's flagon.

(Note the time; and check your speed of reading with the Reading Score Board, page 177.)

❖❖❖

FOR ALL TIMES

1. How is the story of Rip Van Winkle as true today as it ever was?
2. Does human nature change from generation to generation? Illustrate your conclusions by character traits found in Rip, his wife, and his son.
3. What details in the story show the Dutch background?

SOME SPECIFIC DETAILS

1. What kind of woman was Dame Van Winkle?
2. In what ways was Rip able to escape her?
3. What was Rip's "sole domestic adherent"?
4. Whom did Rip meet on the mountainside?
5. Why did the people call Rip a *tory* when he returned to the village after his long sleep?

ALMOST PERFECT PARAGRAPHS

Irving's stories are easy to read because he writes according to a pattern. In a paragraph of description or explanation (exposition), Irving is careful to give his reader a sentence which tells the topic he will discuss. His topic sentence then is followed by a number of sentences which enlarge upon the idea.

In the first paragraph of the story, you know from the first sentence that Irving is going to describe the Kaatskill Mountains. Can you find the topic sentences in the next eight paragraphs? Is each topic sentence a fair guide to what the paragraph contains?

How does recognizing topic sentences help you in your reading?

TELEVISION THROUGH WORDS

Irving is almost a master at creating pictures. His descriptions are so exact that you can almost *see* the places and the people. Look at the first paragraph of the story, for example. Notice how he uses the following phrases. What picture does each give you?

1. dismembered branch
2. swelling up to a noble height
3. lording it over the surrounding country
4. magical hues and shapes
5. clothed in blue and purple
6. a hood of gray vapors
7. like a crown of glory

What similar phrases do you find in other paragraphs?

INTELLIGENT GUESSING

From the general sense of the sentence, what do you think each of these means?

1. The great error in Rip's composition was an insuperable aversion to all kinds of profitable labor.

2. Morning, noon, and night, her tongue was incessantly going; and everything he said or did was sure to produce a torrent of household eloquence.

3. Panting and fatigued, he threw himself, late in the afternoon, on a green knoll covered with mountain herbage, that crowned the brow of a precipice.

4. By degrees Rip's awe and apprehension subsided.

5. He recollected Rip at once and corroborated his story in the most satisfactory manner.

READING SCORE BOARD

Number of Words in Story: 6100.

Number of Minutes	61	51	41	30 1/2	20 2/5	20 1/3	15 1/4	10 1/6
Reading Rate	100 w.p.m.	120 w.p.m.	150 w.p.m.	200 w.p.m.	250 w.p.m.	300 w.p.m.	400 w.p.m.	600 w.p.m.

LOOKING BACKWARD THROUGH THE CHAPTER

1. What similarities do you find in the fables and tales included in this chapter?
2. What "lessons" are pointed out in the fables that you read?
3. What different countries and parts of this country are represented in the stories?
4. What interesting little details from each of the stories in this chapter stick in your memory?
5. Which story did you like best? Why? Which poem?

SHARPENING YOUR WITS

Recognizing Characters

Identify the name of each of these:
1. A man slept for twenty years.
2. A rabbit gets badly "stuck up."
3. A man wears hat, mittens, and shoes made of very strange material.
4. An animal loses a race because of overconfidence.
5. A boy gets a magic apple but eats it.

Identifying Authors

Who wrote each of the following?
1. The Wonderful Tar Baby
2. Rip Van Winkle
3. Coyote between Two Sheep
4. The Story of Jason Squiff
5. The Hare and the Tortoise

Knowing Words

Each of the words in the first column was a key word in one of the selections in this chapter. Match it with the proper word or phrase in the second column.

I	II
1. jest	a. dread
2. rogue	b. joyously
3. mantle	c. a kind of rabbit
4. radiance	d. dislike
5. blithely	e. uselessly
6. aversion	f. confirmed
7. apprehension	g. cloak
8. vainly	h. trickster
9. hare	i. joke
10. corroborated	j. brightness

OTHER THINGS TO DO

1. If you would like to read other fables and strange tales, see the list on page 179.
2. Perhaps you would like to make up some fables of your own, basing them on the following subjects. Tell your fables in class.

a. a dog and a cat	d. a peacock and a sparrow
b. a cat and a mouse	e. a bird and a worm
c. a lark and a crow	f. a squirrel and a hunting dog

3. Perhaps you would like to write a myth explaining how some modern product was found. These may suggest ideas to you:

a. frozen foods	d. bubble gum
b. ice cream	e. lollipops
c. vitamins	f. snuff

A Reading Check

1. How many times do your eyes stop in reading a line of print in stories such as you have had in this chapter?
2. Are you forcing your eyes to pick up several words at a time?
3. Is your reading speed increasing?

Fables and Strange Tales

Aesop, *The Fables of Aesop*; selected, told anew, and their history traced by Joseph Jacobs, 1923 (Macmillan).
　　Greek fables with moral twists.

Babbitt, Ellen C., *Jataka Tales Retold*, 1912 (Appleton).
　　Fables about animals from a Buddhist sacred book.

Chrisman, Arthur Bowie, *Shen of the Sea*, 1925 (Dutton).
　　Short stories of China, with a folklore background.

Dolbier, Maurice, *The Half-pint Jinni, and Other Stories*, 1948 (Random House).
　　Witty enchantment tales of Baghdad.

Finger, Charles J., *Tales from Silver Lands*, 1924 (Doubleday).
　　Legendary stories the author learned from the Indians of South America.

Frost, Frances Mary (editor), *Legends of the United Nations*, 1943 (Whittlesey House).
　　Folk tales of England, Poland, China, Czechoslovakia, India, United States, Netherlands, Mexico, France, Yugoslavia, Brazil, Canada, Australia, and Belgium.

Gibson, Katharine, *The Golden Bird, and Other Stories*, 1927 (Macmillan).
　　Ten legends from Greece, Egypt, Persia, China, and France.

Harris, Joel Chandler, *Favorite Uncle Remus*; selected, arranged, and edited by George Van Santvoord and Archibald C. Coolidge, 1948 (Houghton).
　　Selections of sixty classic tales from Uncle Remus.

Lagerlöf, Selma, *The Wonderful Adventures of Nils*, 1907 (Doubleday).
　　Swedish folklore woven about a tale of a mischievous boy transformed by an elf.

Leach, Maria, *The Soup Stone*, 1954 (Funk & Wagnalls).
　　Collection of stories about superstitions and customs.

O'Faoláin, Eileen, *Miss Pennyfeather and the Pooka*, 1946 (Random House).
　　Strange tale of Miss Pennyfeather's fairy horse.

Thorne-Thomsen, Gudrun, *East o' the Sun and West o' the Moon*, 1946 (Row).
　　Norwegian folk tales simply told but full of the spirit of adventure.

Weaver, Jack, *Mr. O'Hara*, 1953 (Viking).
　　Entrancing Irish tall tales.

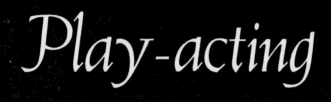

Play-acting

Homework

Obviously, plays can be read silently; but the most fun comes from dramatizing them. You will enjoy acting out the three plays in this chapter. The first play, "Homework," may remind you of some of the ridiculous things that go on at home in the pursuit of homework.

Characters

PAPA PEPPER
MRS. PEPPER
TIMOTHY PEPPER
TRUDY PEPPER
HELEN PEPPER
MUSCLES MURRAY

TIME: *The present.*

SETTING: *The living room of the Pepper home. It has been transformed into a combination workshop and study.*

AT RISE: MRS. PEPPER *is seated at a table upstage working on an electric toaster which she is trying to repair according to instructions from a manual.* PAPA PEPPER, *in his shirt sleeves, is working at a drafting board center.* TIMOTHY *is working with some Pre-Flight tests.* HELEN *is seated at a card table piled high with textbooks on chemistry. There is a pause after the curtain opens, as everyone works at his appointed task. By facial expression and pantomime, each member of the cast should show that the going is a bit difficult. From offstage comes the sound of scales being practiced on a piano. The same exercise should be repeated several times, with the same*

——Reprinted by permission from *On Stage for Teen-Agers* by Helen Louise Miller; Plays, Inc., Boston, Mass., Copyright, 1944.

mistake being made at the same place each time.

TIMOTHY (*flinging down his book in despair*): For heaven's sake, cut out that racket. Mother, can't you make Trudy stop pounding on that piano?

MOTHER (*without raising her eyes from the toaster*): She's only practicing her music lesson, dear.

HELEN: Well, hasn't she practiced long enough? She's gone over that same exercise at least twenty-five times and is still making the same mistake. It's getting on my nerves.

MR. PEPPER: And on mine, too. It's bad enough I have to pay for her music lessons without having to listen to her practice. Why can't she do that when I'm not home?

MOTHER: But I always depend on you, dear, to make her stick with her practicing. I never did think Trudy was very musical; but just because you had a cousin who was a concert pianist, you have always been determined to give her piano lessons. Personally, I think she'd do better at elocution.

TIMOTHY: Electrocution would be more suitable, if you ask me.

MOTHER: You have no room to talk, Timothy, after what we've been through with your saxophone.

TIMOTHY: But at least I can play it. Besides, she's making it impossible for me to concentrate. I'll have you know these Pre-Flight courses are no cinch.

MR. PEPPER: Tim's right, Mother. If we're all going to take these Home Study courses this winter, we'll have to have peace and quiet in the evenings. Trudy must find another hour for her practice.

MOTHER: Very well. I'll call her. (*Calling*) Trudy, Trudy . . . you may stop now.

TRUDY (*offstage*): But the hour isn't up. I have fifteen minutes to go.

HELEN: Can you beat it? Any other time she'd be dying to quit before the hour was up.

MOTHER: It's all right, dear. Father says you may skip those last fifteen minutes.

TRUDY (*with a final bang on the piano*): Whoopee! That's swell! (*Runs into the room*) Thanks a lot, Dad. Come on, Tim, let's play some table tennis.

TIMOTHY: Nothing doing. I have to plug away at this engine material.

TRUDY: O.K. We'll play later. Come on, Sis, let's make some fudge.

HELEN: Not tonight, Trudy. I have a long assignment in my chemistry course, and it's going to keep me busy.

TRUDY: I never knew you were such a plugger. Well, Dad, it looks as if you and I were going to be partners. How about a game of rummy?

Bet I can trim you. (*Hangs over the back of his chair.*)

MR. PEPPER: Not tonight, Trudy. And don't joggle me when I'm drawing.

TRUDY: Sorry. I guess this is no place for me. Mother, will you show me how to set the sleeve in that sweater I'm knitting?

MOTHER: Some other time, dear. Not now. I'm too busy with this toaster.

TRUDY: What's the matter with it?

MOTHER: Oh, it's just an old one I found down in the cellar. It hasn't worked for years.

TRUDY: But there's nothing the matter with our good one. Why don't you use that?

MOTHER: We do. I'm just experimenting with this for my assignment in Home Repairing.

TRUDY: Phew! This is the busiest family I ever saw. Do you care if I go to the movies?

MOTHER: You went to the movies last night, Trudy. You know I don't like you to go on school nights. Why don't you do your homework?

MR. PEPPER: Yes, for mercy's sake. Go get a book and settle yourself. It's high time you were doing your lessons.

TRUDY: They're all done.

TIMOTHY (*incredulously*): Ha! A likely story!

TRUDY (*indignant*): They are so! I had three study periods in school today, and I finished everything.

HELEN: Three study periods! That's the limit! We never had more than one a week when I was in junior high school.

TRUDY: Oh, but that was years ago. Things are more modern now. Say, do you want to hear a good joke I heard today?

MR. PEPPER: No, we don't want to hear any jokes. Can't you see we're all working? Clear out of here or keep quiet so we can think.

TRUDY: But my goodness, I'm not doing anything because I don't have anything to do . . . unless I play the radio.

HELEN: Heaven forbid! That's all we need! . . .

MOTHER: Can't you read a book?

TRUDY: Nope. I owe a fine at the library, and I can't get any more books till I pay it, and I can't pay it till I get my allowance, and I won't get my allowance till next week, so I can't get any more books till then.

TIMOTHY: Ye gods! Mother, can't you make her get out of here? I've read this paragraph three times, and I still don't know what it means. (*Mutters to himself as he rereads a paragraph.*)

MR. PEPPER: Keep quiet. First thing I'll be doing your problems instead of my own. Trudy, I'll give you exactly three seconds to find yourself something to do or go to bed.

MOTHER: Oh, now, James, don't be so impatient. Listen, Trudy, you can see we're all busy tonight. Now be a good girl and go upstairs to your room.

TRUDY: But, Mother, it's too cold up there. How about letting me go over to Louise Anderson's?

MOTHER: The Andersons are having company tonight. I met Mrs. Anderson at market today. She's entertaining her bridge club.

TRUDY: Then that's out. (*Phone rings*) I hope that's for me.

MR. PEPPER: Well, if it is, make it snappy. Don't hang on the wire the rest of the evening.

TRUDY (*at phone*): Hello . . . Yes, yes . . . this is Trudy Pepper. Who? (*Pleased*) Oh, it's you, Muscles. (*In a stage whisper*) It's Muscles Murray. (*Into phone*) Yeah . . . No, I'm not doing a thing. What? Well, just a minute . . . I'll have to ask. (*Putting hand over the mouthpiece of phone and speaking to her mother.*) Mother, it's Muscles Murray. He wants me to go to the movies with him. May I, Mother, please?

HELEN: Forever more! Don't tell me you're beginning to have dates at your age!

TRUDY (*to* HELEN): Oh, be quiet. (*To* MRS. PEPPER) Please, Mother, can't I go?

MOTHER: Of course not. I just finished telling you I don't like you to go to the movies on school nights. Besides, I don't know this Murray boy.

TRUDY: Oh, he's nice. Honest, he's swell. Please, Mother. We'll be home early.

MR. PEPPER: You heard what your mother said.

TRUDY: But, Dad . . . Please! If I don't go, he might never ask me again.

MR. PEPPER: That would be a good thing. Now tell him you can't go and hang up. (*To himself*) A man can't have a minute's peace in his own house.

TRUDY (*almost in tears*): Hello . . . I'm awful sorry, Muscles, but I can't go this evening. Yeah . . . Yeah . . . Me, too . . . I'm devastated. Maybe some other time? What? What's that? You want to come over? Well, wait a minute. I'll have to ask again. (*With hand over mouthpiece*) Mother, now he wants to come over here. Is it all right?

MR. PEPPER: It certainly is not all right. I don't want any more people around this house tonight. Tell him no. He can't come.

TRUDY: Oh, Dad, he'll think we're terrible. He doesn't know very many people. He just moved here from Chicago.

MR. PEPPER: Well, let him move back again. He can't come over here tonight.

TRUDY: Oh, Mother, can't you make Dad understand? I just can't tell him you don't want him.

MOTHER: But, Trudy, you heard what your father said. Just tell him some other time.

TRUDY (*desperate*): I can't. I simply can't. (*Hangs up receiver.*) I'll just hang up on him. There! Maybe he'll think we were cut off. (*Begins to cry.*) I don't see why he couldn't come over. He's the nicest boy in our room. Nobody around this house even cares if I turn out to be an old maid. You're all too busy improving your minds to care what becomes of me.

TIMOTHY: Good grief! Now she's bawling. You should have let her go to the movies. Then she'd have been out of the house.

MOTHER: You keep out of this, Timothy. Trudy is too young to be running around with boys.

TRUDY: It was only one boy, and we wouldn't be running around. We'd be right here at home. I didn't care about the movies, but I don't see why he couldn't come over here. (*Crying harder*) Now he'll never call me again . . . never!

MOTHER: Now don't cry about it, dear. You have plenty of time for boys to call you up. Oh, my! This is a distressing evening. Please, Trudy, control yourself.

HELEN: I was never allowed to go out with boys when I was her age.

TIMOTHY: Muscles! What a beautiful name! What is he! Champion prize fighter or something?

TRUDY: You keep quiet, Timothy Pepper. All you care about is airplanes, and you don't know as much about them as you think you do. Muscles knows twice as much now as you'll ever know about engines.

TIMOTHY: Pardon me! I thought his name was Muscles . . . not Brains.

TRUDY: Some people can have both; and then again, other people have neither.

HELEN: This is childish. Mother, can't you do something with her? I'll never get anywhere with all this confusion.

TRUDY: I suppose you think everybody will keep perfectly quiet whenever you want to do something.

HELEN: After this, I'll study in my

own room even if the furnace is broken.

TRUDY: You won't have to. I'll go up to my room where I won't disturb you . . . even if I freeze.

MOTHER: Maybe it would be a good idea to cool off your temper a bit. (*Doorbell rings*) Answer the door, dear. I do hope we're not getting company. (TRUDY *starts towards door.*)

TRUDY (*at door*): Well, for goodness' sake! Where did you come from?

MUSCLES (*offstage*): Hy'a, Trudy! Something must be wrong with that telephone of ours. I came over to find out if it's O.K. for me to spend the evening. We were cut off before you ever had a chance to tell me.

TRUDY (*flustered*): Well, my goodness! Oh, dear! Well . . . I certainly wasn't expecting you. I . . . You . . . I guess you'd better go home.

MUSCLES: What's the matter? Isn't it all right? Of course, if you have company, I'll shove off.

TRUDY: Oh, we don't exactly have company, but . . .

MR. PEPPER: Tell whoever that is to come in or get out; and get that door shut. You're wasting the heat.

MUSCLES (*entering*): Gee, that's good news, Mr. Pepper. I'm sure glad to come inside. It's cold over at our house, too. Every time my folks go out for the evening they turn the oil burner down so low that I practically get chilblains. I guess you never met me, did you? I'm Muscles Murray, your new neighbor. I guess you're Trudy's Dad.

MR. PEPPER: That's who I am, all right, and I suppose you're the young man that called on the phone a few moments ago.

MUSCLES (*laughing*): Yeah, wasn't that the limit? Central cut us off before Trudy got a chance to give me the go signal . . . or I guess I should say the come-ahead signal. But, thinks I, I'll just hop over there and find out for myself; if it's not O.K., if they have company or something, I'll just hop back again. I sure am glad it's all right.

MRS. PEPPER (*looking doubtfully at* MR. PEPPER): Well, I guess it's all right, now that you're here . . . but . . .

MUSCLES: Thanks, Mrs. Pepper. Thanks a lot. You *are* Mrs. Pepper, aren't you?

TRUDY: Sure, sure, she's Mrs. Pepper. And this is my brother, Timothy, and this my sister, Helen.

MUSCLES (*in response to nods from* TIM *and* HELEN): Glad to know you! By golly, this looks like a study hall, doesn't it, Trudy? I should have brought my homework . . . only . . .

TIMOTHY (*with sarcasm*): Only it's all done . . . like Trudy's.

MUSCLES: Right. With all those study periods, we kids get a break for once.

HELEN (*grimly*): What a break!

MUSCLES: I'll say! It's swell. Nothing to do in the evenings but visit the neighbors. It's a great life.

MRS. PEPPER: I'm sorry we don't seem more hospitable, Muscles, but we're each taking a Home Study course this winter and we're taking our work pretty seriously, so we have to have things quiet for our study hour.

MUSCLES: Sure. I understand that. What are you studying, Mrs. Pepper? You seem to be having an awful struggle with that toaster.

MRS. PEPPER: Yes, I'm afraid I don't have a mechanical mind. I'm taking a course in Household Repairs, and this toaster is my assignment. I think I could do better with a wire hairpin and the touch system than following the instructions in this manual.

MUSCLES: Maybe I could help you.

TRUDY: Muscles is awfully smart in shopwork and things like that.

MRS. PEPPER: Well . . . you see . . . here is the diagram in the manual . . . But I don't know if this wire here . . . gets twisted around this thingamabob or whether it should tie up with this long dangly thing on the other end.

MUSCLES: Well, I tell you, Mrs. Pepper, I think you have your wires crossed somewhere . . . but let's have a look at it. Oh, this is going to be easy. If you tighten this connection here . . . like this . . . and scrape off the end of this wire, I believe everything will be O.K. There . . . that looks better. I believe you'll have a first-rate toaster here in no time.

MRS. PEPPER: For mercy's sake, is that all it needed?

MUSCLES: Just a simple twist of the wrist apparently.

MRS. PEPPER: And do you really think it will work now?

MUSCLES: You'll have toast before you can say "zippety-doo-dah." Let's go plug it in and give it a try.

MRS. PEPPER (rising): I can hardly wait to see if it works. Come along, Trudy. We'll try it out. (TRUDY, MRS. PEPPER, and MUSCLES exit.)

TIMOTHY: Good night, Dad! Can't you get rid of that drip? He'll drive us crazy. The nerve of him coming here to see if he could come over.

MR. PEPPER: The minute he sets foot in this room again, I'm going to send him home. For the past hour I've been trying to get some sense out of this diagram, and I can't figure it out at all.

TIMOTHY (sarcastically): No doubt, Muscles, the Mental Giant, could clear it up for you in nothing flat. Trudy seems to think he's Superman.

HELEN: Maybe he was a chemist when he was a baby. I might ask him to help me with this.

TIMOTHY: Just for fun, I'll ask him a question or two about airplane engines when he comes back.

MR. PEPPER: Make it snappy because he won't be here long.

TRUDY (as they re-enter): You sure fixed that toaster in a hurry.

MRS. PEPPER: You certainly did. Now come along, Muscles, and explain just exactly what you did, so I can write up the experiment.

MUSCLES: Oh, it was as easy as ABC. It was just a matter of . . .

TIMOTHY (interrupting): They tell me you're quite the boy with airplanes, Muscles. Know anything about engines?

MUSCLES: Oh, not very much. Are you taking a Pre-Flight course?

TIMOTHY: Yeah. And I'm boning up on engines right now.

MUSCLES: That ought to be interesting. I used to be keen on engines. What type are you studying? Radial engines?

TIMOTHY (*blankly*): Radial?

MUSCLES: Yes . . . the kind in which the cylinders are equally spaced around a single crank of a crankshaft.

TIMOTHY (*showing surprise*): No . . . er . . . no . . . the question that I'm working on right now wants to know the advantages of the V or inverted type of engine.

MUSCLES (*leaning over his shoulder to look at his book*): Well . . . let me see. Of course one advantage of the V-type is that it improves the visibility for the pilot. And then, of course, the V-type gives better streamlining and at the same times lowers the center of gravity. Then you might also mention that it increases propeller clearance over the ground. That's about all I can think of offhand, but that should cover the advantages.

TIMOTHY (*in admiration*): Yeah! Gosh, it sure ought to cover everything. Say, while you're here, you might take a look at that first question. I wasn't quite sure of that one.

MUSCLES (*reading*): "In a four-stroke cycle engine, how many strokes really produce power?" Oh, no. This is wrong. You see, the answer would be only one out of four, because the power stroke is produced by the ignition and expansion of the gas within the cylinder.

TIMOTHY: That's right. Well, thanks, Muscles. Thanks a lot.

MUSCLES: Maybe I could help you with some of those other questions. Airplanes are one of my hobbies.

TIMOTHY: You sure do seem to understand them.

TRUDY: I told you he knew all about engines.

HELEN: So you did. But you didn't tell us if he knows anything about chemistry.

TRUDY: That's what Helen's taking up. I think she's crazy. And besides, chemicals have such awful smells. I'd rather study tap dancing.

MUSCLES: I'm a little rusty on chemistry, Miss Pepper, but I'll help you all I can.

HELEN: I'm not very advanced. We're just working on the molecular theory, and I get atoms and molecules all mixed up.

MUSCLES: I think I can help you with that. You see, an atom is the smallest particle which enters into a chemical equation. When two or more atoms unite chemically, they form a molecule. We'll say one atom of carbon unites with 2 atoms of oxygen and forms one molecule of what, Miss Pepper?

HELEN: Umm! I guess that would be one molecule of carbon dioxide.

MUSCLES: That's right. And the equation for that would be

$$C + O_2 = CO_2$$

HELEN: I see. Thanks a lot.

TRUDY: My goodness, Muscles! You're turning out to be a big help to my family. Maybe you **could** even help Dad.

MR. PEPPER: I hardly think so. Electronics is college stuff.

MUSCLES: Electronics, eh? Yes, I guess you're right. I wouldn't be much help in that department. Just what are you working on, Mr. Pepper? A diagram?

MR. PEPPER: Yes. I'm showing the potential distribution in a two-electrode tube in a vacuum.

MUSCLES: Ummmm. Pretty difficult, isn't it?

MR. PEPPER: It's not easy.

MUSCLES: Mind if I give it a try?

MR. PEPPER: Think you could?

MUSCLES: I don't know. I'm a little rusty on this sort of thing. . . . But I'll see what I can do. (*Sits at table*) Now let me see . . . (*Draws for a few moments in silence*)

MR. PEPPER (*looking over his shoulder*): By jiminy! I believe you've got it!

MRS. PEPPER: How marvelous, Muscles!

TIMOTHY: Some kid, I'd say!

HELEN: We should get you to be our instructor, Muscles.

MR. PEPPER: Yes, sir . . . my boy . . . that does the trick.

MUSCLES: Yes, I think you'll find that O.K. Now you'll want to jot down the explanation for your notes.

MR. PEPPER: This is great. Here I've been struggling with that blasted thing all evening. Let me have another look at it.

MUSCLES: Shall I go over the explanation step by step?

MR. PEPPER: O.K. Shoot. (*Writes as* MUSCLES *dictates.*)

MUSCLES: Well, first you draw a two-electrode tube having electrode F and B with a difference of a potential 100 volts between them. Obviously, the potential at F is zero or around potential, and as the point of view moves from F to B, the potential must rise from zero to one hundred volts. Got that straight?

MR. PEPPER: Yep. Go ahead.

MUSCLES: Well, then, the manner of the rise of the potential from F to B is shown by curves. If F and B consist of cold parallel plates, the change of potential along a line near the center of the plates will be uniform; and we've represented that by a straight line. If F is a small round wire (cold) and B is a hollow concentric cylinder surrounding F, the potential gradient near the wire will be high, owing to a strong electrostatic field, and then fall off as B is approached. Such a case may be represented, as we did here, by a curve.

MR. PEPPER: Well, that puts it all in fine shape. Thanks a million, my boy.

MUSCLES: You're certainly welcome. That was fun. I haven't had a problem like that in a long time.

TIMOTHY: Holy smokes! How old are you?

MUSCLES: Fourteen my next birthday. Why?

TIMOTHY: Well, I must say, I never met anybody like you. How in the world do you know all this stuff?

HELEN: Trudy didn't tell us you were a child prodigy.

MUSCLES: If she had, I'd have cut her up in little pieces. I'm not a child prodigy.

MR. PEPPER: Well, you must be something special to work out my diagram and help Tim with his engines.

HELEN: And straighten me out with my chemistry.

MRS. PEPPER: To say nothing of my toaster.

MUSCLES: Aw, heck! I didn't want to tell anybody, but you folks have been so nice about letting me come over tonight. You see, I was . . . well . . . my real name is Myron Murray. Maybe you've heard of me or something.

TIM: Not Myron Murray the Boy Wizard! Not the kid who won the National Radio Prizes on the Science Quiz programs!

MUSCLES: I'm afraid that's me.

TIM: Well, what do you know!

MR. PEPPER: Small wonder you know your way around in the electronics field!

HELEN: Trudy, why didn't you tell us he was a celebrity?

MUSCLES: I'm no celebrity in Trudy's eyes. She corrects my spelling papers at school and sees me as I really am.

MRS. PEPPER: I was about to ask you why you were attending junior high school.

MUSCLES: Well, you see . . . science just comes easy to me . . . but gosh! What a struggle I do have with spelling and English! And I'm not any too strong on history, either. It keeps me stepping to make the grade in some of those subjects, as Trudy can tell you.

HELEN: Well, you sure helped me make the grade with my assign-ment. Now I'll have time to go down to the library for a while. (*Packing up her books.*)

MUSCLES: Glad I could help you.

HELEN: Maybe tomorrow night you'd help me work out my next set of questions.

MUSCLES: I sure will.

HELEN: So long, everybody. I'll not be out late, Mother.

MOTHER: Oh, we'll be up when you come home. (HELEN *exits.*)

TRUDY: Well, Muscles, how about a game of table tennis?

MUSCLES: All right, but you play with me at your own risk.

TIMOTHY: Not so fast, Trudy. I'd like to show Muscles that motor down in the cellar. I've been tinkering around with it for six months, and it's not right yet. How about taking a look at it, Muscles?

MUSCLES (*with a smile and a shrug of his shoulders at* TRUDY): Sure . . . I'll look it over.

MR. PEPPER: I'll go along. I'd like to ask Muscles a few questions about the Kenetron tube and the Klystron tube.

MUSCLES: Well, they are both pretty important. The Kenetron is a tube used in the Precipitron. That's a new device designed to wash and cleanse the air of dust, smoke, and germs. The Klystron tube is the one used in radar. (*As they exit*)

TIM: Radar . . . That's the old super-sleuth all right.

MR. PEPPER (*as they leave stage*): Then it must be the Ignitron tube that changes A.C. into D.C., isn't it, Muscles?

MUSCLES: Yes . . . They're used in the

new resistance welding of aluminum. (TRUDY *and her mother are left alone.*)

TRUDY: Well, how do you like that? Off he goes with Dad and Tim, leaving me high and dry! Of all the nerve!

MOTHER (*smiling*): Well, aren't you pleased Muscles was such a success with the family?

TRUDY: I didn't want him to be this much of a success. My goodness, I want him to pay some attention to me. I'm going down in that cellar and drag him back! After all, he came to see me!

MOTHER: Oh, no, Trudy. That would be a fatal mistake. I can see you need to take a Home Study course in how to influence your boy friends.

TRUDY: You mean I shouldn't go after him.

MOTHER: Certainly not. They'll be coming back after a while . . . and in the meantime you and I can stir up a batch of Peanut Delights . . . Never forget, my child, that no matter how scientific he might be . . . the road to a man's heart is still . . .

TRUDY: Sure, sure, I know . . . is still through his stomach. Well, come on, Mother, you lead the way . . . I'll follow.

❖❖❖

SOMETHING TO THINK ABOUT

1. In what ways does this play "sound like home"?
2. Does Trudy say things you have heard yourself say? Read the lines that tell you.
3. Why is the ending exactly right?
4. Why are the names of the characters good?
5. In acting out the play, can you point out some lines which should be read in these different ways: slowly, rapidly and excitedly, happily, disgustedly?
6. What costumes should be used? What properties are needed?

CLEAR AS A BELL—OR FUZZY?

Here are some words which appear in the play. Is your enunciation of them crystal-clear?

Try saying these words that end in *ing*:

pounding	dying	beginning	running
practicing	doing	improving	distressing
making	entertaining	bawling	something

Do you say the endings of these words clearly?

practiced	first	swell	with
worked	assignment	will	both
finished	market	tell	truth

There are some words that sound almost alike—but not quite. Incorrect enunciation may cause an audience to misunderstand an actor. Try saying these:

our — are	affect — effect	lose — loose
accept — except	formerly — formally	quite — quiet
conscious — conscience	seize — siege	diseased — deceased

◀ ROBERT D. HENRY
AND JAMES M. LYNCH, JR.

The Boy Patriot

Here is a radio play about a young man who, because of his courage, became one of our great American heroes.

Characters
ANNOUNCER
VOICES 1 AND 2
READER
WASHINGTON
NATHAN HALE
STEPHEN JONES
GUARD
SERGEANT
BRITISH GUARD
DRIVER
OFFICER

MUSIC: *Some patriotic air of American origin. Up and fade.*

ANNOUNCER: Heroes! American heroes! What would this great country of America have done without her Revolutionary War heroes? Her star-studded past would have been drab indeed, if it weren't for the names of such men and women as:

VOICE 1: James Otis, who first dared to dub King George III a tyrant.

VOICE 2: Samuel Adams, the firebrand of the American Revolution.

VOICE 1: Patrick Henry, whose "Give

——From *History Makers*, a book of radio plays by Robert D. Henry and James M. Lynch, Jr. Reprinted with the special permission of the publisher and copyright holder, Row, Peterson and Company, Evanston, Ill.

me liberty or give me death" was the rally cry for thousands of patriots.

VOICE 2: John Paul Jones, the father of the United States Navy.

VOICE 1: George Rogers Clark, the conqueror of the British in the Northwest.

VOICE 2: Mollie Pitcher, the heroine of the Battle of Monmouth.

ANNOUNCER: And on and on. One might name hundreds more if one took the time. But high on every list of American heroes, the name of Nathan Hale appears. Why is he so honored? Why is he alone enshrined as the Boy Patriot, when he failed? Because he died? Because his task was so great? Yes, but mainly because he had the true American spirit and courage. The courage to try against impossible odds, and thus point the way for others to follow. . . . (*Pause.*)

MUSIC: *Up and cut.*

Fanfare.

ANNOUNCER: The year is 1776. The Declaration of Independence has just been signed. The thirteen colonies are now free and independent states, though they are finding it difficult to convince *themselves* of this, to say nothing of the rest of the world. The new country has an army, composed mostly of hardy farmers. It has an able Commander-in-Chief, too. But it lacks, most of all, knowledge of the enemy's strength and condition; for an army cannot fight intelligently if it knows nothing of its opponents.

BIZ:[1] *Hubbub. Fades as gavel knocks three times.*

WASHINGTON: Gentlemen, we are at war with the British Empire. Of its army we know nothing. As soon as possible we must find out how many troops they have on hand and what war materials are available. We can get this information only through undercover workers . . . an espionage system, as it were. Gentlemen, we must have spies if we are to win this war.

BIZ: *Hubbub.*

HALE (*his voice gradually drowning out the others*): General Washington, I would like to volunteer for such service.

BIZ: *Applause.*

WASHINGTON: Captain Hale, your country and its army, to say nothing of myself, are deeply indebted to you. Your display of courage and loyalty, I trust, will be of great inspiration to others.

MUSIC: *Up and fade.*

BIZ: *Horse and wagon moving slowly.*

GUARD: Halt! Who goes there?

HALE (*off mike*): Whoa! . . . A friend.

BIZ: *Horse snorts as horse and wagon stop.*

GUARD: Come down off that wagon till we search you.

BIZ: *Squeak of wheel as man descends.*

GUARD: What's your name?

HALE (*on mike*): Farmer Harrington, sir. I have some produce I'd like to sell.

GUARD: All right. Everything's in order. You may proceed.

HALE: Thank you.

BIZ: *Squeak of wheel as he climbs back into wagon.*

HALE: Giddap.

BIZ: *Horse and wagon up and under.*

HALE (*to himself over sound*): Let's see now. . . . Over there are five mounted cannon . . . a storehouse for grain . . . a corral with—let's see—two, four, six, eight, ten, eleven, fourteen horses . . . probably for the officers.

BIZ: *Troops marching in the distance. Cut horse and wagon.*

SERGEANT (*off mike*): Company halt! . . . Left face! . . . (*Angrily*) What's the matter with *you*, Martin? Don't you know your left hand from your right yet? (*Fades out until barely audible but continues to shout.*) You're fighting a war. If you can't follow orders, those blithering Yankees will have an easy time of it, take it from me.

HALE (*to himself*): Four, eight, twelve, sixteen men in that squad. . . . That makes 250. . . . Guess I'd better get over to those tents . . . (*Fade*) . . . and see how many men are quartered there.

BIZ: *Horse and wagon up and under.*

STEPHEN JONES: Well, what do you know about that? Why, that's

---

[1] Biz—Stage business; sounds, noise, etc.

Cousin Nathan Hale over there on that farm wagon. What's he doing in a British camp? I thought he was a rebel. . . . Well, maybe he's changed his mind. (*Shouts*) Nathan! . . . Nathan Hale! . . . Hey, Nathan! Wait a minute. . . . (*Quietly*) That's funny. He kept on as if he didn't hear me. . . . But I'm sure he did. . . . (*Fade*) . . . I'd better go see the General at once.

MUSIC: *Atmospheric. Up and fade.*

BIZ: *Door opens and shuts immediately. Footsteps cross room and stop.*

CAPTAIN: Well? What do you want? Out with it. Can't you see I'm busy?

JONES: Yes, sir. . . . You see, sir, I'm Stephen Jones, and I have a cousin named Nathan Hale, who is a captain in the Colonial Army.

CAPTAIN: What about your cousin? We'll have the whole crew of your Yankees wiped out in a few days anyhow. . . . I'm sorry, Mr. Jones, but there's nothing I can do about your cousin. He'll have to suffer along with the others.

JONES: But you don't understand, sir. He's here . . . in this camp.

CAPTAIN (*laughing*): Ho-Ho! In *this* camp? Why, the whole Yankee army couldn't get through our lines, let alone one American captain.

JONES: But that's just it, sir. He isn't in uniform.

CAPTAIN (*excited*): What? You mean he's disguised? He's a spy then. By Godfrey, these Yankees have more nerve than a pack of wolves!

JONES (*fade*): Yes, sir. That's what I've been trying to tell you, sir, for the last five minutes.

MUSIC: *Atmospheric. Up and fade.*

CAPTAIN: All right, Captain Hale. We caught you with these papers in your possession. They condemn you as a spy. What have you to say for yourself?

HALE: Well, sir, I am an officer in the American Army. It is true that I've been visiting your camp in search of information.

CAPTAIN (*angrily*): Then you'll hang, Hale. You'll hang. We'll show you young rebel whippersnappers what it means to spy on a British camp. Nobody can get away with that out here. . . . (*Fade*) . . . Take him away.

ANNOUNCER: The fate of a spy—conviction without trial. The penalty—death. Hale, his doom sealed, was again locked in the jail. As he awaited the dawn of his last day on earth; a friendly guard who liked the courageous youth despite his being an enemy . . . (*Fade*) . . . gave him a few sheets of paper and a pencil.

BIZ: *Scratching of pen up and under.*

HALE (*low to himself*): Dear Mother: Don't cry when you read this, Mother. I'm dying the way I've always wanted to, you know, for my country. They have probably told you why. I was captured by the British while getting military information for General Washington. I came here of my own accord. . . .

MUSIC: *Atmospheric. Up and under.*

HALE: Dear Sister: You too would do the same thing . . . give your life for your country . . . if your country needed you. Please take good care of Mother, and don't worry. It won't be long; and I shall face it bravely knowing that you will pray for me.

MUSIC: *Up and under.*

HALE: Dearest: We planned so much . . . you and I—where we would live, what we were going to do— that this letter is indeed difficult to write. I won't see you ever again . . . but I shall carry a picture of you in my heart as I give my life for my country.

MUSIC: *Up and fade.*

BIZ: *Pounding on door.*

HALE: Guard! . . . Guard!

GUARD (*off mike*): Quiet in there! Quiet! (*on mike*) What's the matter with you?

HALE: I have some letters that the other guard said you would deliver for me.

GUARD (*angrily*): All right. Let's have them. . . . Hmmm. . . . Dear Mother: Don't——

HALE: But you aren't supposed to read them. The other guard said——

GUARD (*interrupting*): Oh, I'm not supposed to read them, eh? Well, here!

BIZ: *Tearing of paper.*

GUARD: Maybe you'd like the pieces. Only a fool would let a spy write letters. . . . (*Fade*) . . . How do we know whether they're in code or not? . . .

BIZ: *Single drum beaten slowly. Marching men.*

OFFICER: Halt.

BIZ: *Marchers stop on second beat.*

OFFICER: Are you ready, driver? You know what to do, of course?

DRIVER: All ready. Just put the mask on his head, and I'll whip up the horses.

HALE: The mask isn't necessary. I'm not afraid to die.

OFFICER: All right, Captain Hale. Climb up on the tailboard of the wagon, please. Have you anything to say before you are hanged as a spy?

HALE: Yes. . . . I only regret that I have but one life to lose for my country.

OFFICER: Are you ready, Captain Hale?

HALE: I am ready.

OFFICER: May God have mercy on your soul.

BIZ: *Roll of drums increasing to maximum.*

BIZ: *Sound of whip striking horse. Horse and wagon start up quickly and fade out.*

BIZ: *Drums break off sharply.*

ANNOUNCER: Thus, Nathan Hale was hanged as a spy. He was heartlessly denied the services of a minister, and even a copy of the Bible was refused him. That is the fate of a captured spy—death without mercy. But Nathan Hale died willingly—just as willingly as he accepted his country's order to spy on the British. He died like a gentleman and a soldier, his bravery making even his executioners bow their heads in respect.

MUSIC: *Taps up to finish.*

READER:
"To every man upon this earth
Death cometh soon or late.
And how can man die better

Than facing fearful odds
For the ashes of his fathers
And the temples of his Gods?"
MUSIC: *Theme up and under.*

❧❦❧

INTERPRETING CHARACTERS WITH YOUR VOICE

Since, in a radio play, characters cannot be seen, voices are very important. Decide how each of the characters in the play should speak.

Choose a number of persons to say the following lines. Determine which voice best interprets meaning and character.

1. ANNOUNCER: . . . high on every list of American heroes, the name of Nathan Hale appears. Why is he so honored? Why is he alone enshrined as the Boy Patriot, when he failed? Because he died? Because his task was so great? Yes, but mainly because he had the true American spirit and courage. The courage to try against impossible odds, and thus point the way for others to follow. . . .

2. WASHINGTON: Captain Hale, your country and its army, to say nothing of myself, are deeply indebted to you. Your display of courage and loyalty, I trust, will be of great inspiration to others.

3. STEPHEN JONES: Well, what do you know about that? Why, that's Cousin Nathan Hale over there on that farm wagon. What's he doing in a British camp? I thought he was a rebel. . . . Well, maybe he's changed his mind. (*Shouts*) Nathan! . . . Nathan Hale! . . . Hey, Nathan! Wait a minute. . . . (*Quietly*) That's funny. He kept on as if he didn't hear me. . . . But I'm sure he did. . . . (*Fade*) . . . I'd better go see the General at once.

4. CAPTAIN (*excited*): What! You mean he's disguised? He's a spy then. By Godfrey, these Yankees have more nerve than a pack of wolves!

5. ANNOUNCER: The fate of a spy—conviction without trial. The penalty—death.

6. OFFICER: All right, Captain Hale. Climb up on the tailboard of the wagon, please. Have you anything to say before you are hanged as a spy?

7. HALE: Yes. . . . I only regret that I have but one life to lose for my country.

"ON THE BEAM" WITH WORDS

1. What radio terms are used in the play?
2. What do these words mean?

origin	espionage	accord
odds	conviction	executioners

COMPARING AND CONTRASTING

You have just read a play version of the story of Nathan Hale. It will be interesting to see whether the facts as given in the play agree with the historical facts. On the next page you will see first what *Britannica Junior* has to say about Nathan Hale. Next you will see what two historians, Wilson and Lamb, have to say in their book, *American History*. How do the three versions agree? How do the three versions differ? Why do playwrights often change basic facts?

1. **HALE, NATHAN** *(nā'thăn)* (1756–1776). While standing upon the scaffold awaiting death Nathan Hale declared: "I only regret that I have but one life to lose for my country." And it is because of his courage and patriotism that Hale, who was put to death at the age of 20, is regarded as one of America's national heroes.

His birthplace was Coventry, Connecticut, and in 1773 he was graduated with honors from Yale. Shortly after the Revolutionary War opened he gave up his position of schoolteacher and entered the American army as first lieutenant of a Connecticut regiment. Having served successfully at the siege of Boston, he was made captain lieutenant and in 1776 received the formal commission of captain. Shortly thereafter he volunteered to break through the British lines to secure some highly valued information about enemy fortifications in Long Island and New York. Disguised as a Dutch schoolteacher, Hale succeeded in his mission; but just as he was about to leave the enemy's territory, he was captured and condemned to death as a spy. The following morning he was hanged. Statues in his honor have been made by Karl Gerhardt and by Frederick MacMonnies.*

2. It was in 1776 that Nathan Hale was executed as a spy. He was a young Connecticut schoolteacher seeking to obtain information for Washington behind the British lines on Long Island. Just as he was about to escape with sketches of some of the British positions he was caught. When facing death he had the courage to say, "I only regret that I have but one life to give for my country."**

*——Reprinted from *Britannica Junior* (1950) by permission of Encyclopædia Britannica, Inc.
**——Reprinted from *American History* by Howard E. Wilson and Wallace E. Lamb, by permission of American Book Company.

◄ᴄ CHARLES DICKENS

A Christmas Carol

Adapted for Radio by Walter Hackett

Probably you have already heard "A Christmas Carol" dramatized over the radio or seen it in the movies. It is undoubtedly one of the best known and best loved of all Christmas stories. The story as it is given here is adapted for radio presentation. Surely you will want to act it out. If you have the facilities, you might broadcast it to another class.

SOUND: *Church clock striking three times.*

CHORUS (*young voices*): *They sing a chorus of "God Rest Ye Merry, Gentlemen." At its climax:*

——Reprinted by permission from *Plays, The Drama Magazine for Young People,* 8 Arlington St., Boston, Mass., Copyright, 1947.

SOUND: *Door opens.*

SCROOGE (*barks*): Stop it! Stop it, I say! (*Singing stops*) Get away from here. We'll have no singing around here. Understand me! No singing!

BOY: A Merry Christmas, sir.

SCROOGE: Get away, I say.

SECOND BOY: No need to wish 'im a Merry Christmas. That's Old Scrooge.

MUSIC: A *contemporary Christmas ballad. Forte*[1] *and fade under.*

NARRATOR: Yes, that is Old Scrooge . . . Ebenezer Scrooge. It is the afternoon before Christmas Day in the year of our Lord 1844. Despite the bitterly cold weather, all of London is in a festive mood. But there is no happy expression on Ebenezer Scrooge's lined face as he closes the front door of his warehouse and returns to his office. (*Music out*) He throws a glowering look at his clerk, Bob Cratchit. Satisfied that the poor wretch is hard at work, Scrooge adjusts his spectacles. Then without warning . . .

SOUND: *Door* (*away*) *opens.*

FRED: A Merry Christmas, Uncle. God save you!

SCROOGE: Bah! Humbug!

FRED: Christmas a humbug? Surely, you don't mean that, Uncle.

SCROOGE: Merry Christmas, indeed! What right have you to be merry? You're poor enough.

FRED: What right have you to be dismal? You're rich enough.

SCROOGE: What's Christmas time to you but a time for paying bills without money; a time for finding yourself a year older and not an hour richer. If I had my way, every idiot who goes about with "Merry Christmas" on his lips should be boiled with his own pudding and buried with a stake of holly through his heart. You keep Christmas in

[1] *forte* (fôr'tā). Loud.

your own way, and let me keep it in mine.

FRED: I came here to ask you to spend Christmas Day with Peg and me.

SCROOGE (*flatly*): No!

FRED: But we want nothing from you, Uncle, other than your company. (*Pause*) Won't you change your mind and have dinner with us?

SCROOGE: Good afternoon, Fred.

FRED: A Merry Christmas.

SCROOGE: Good afternoon.

FRED: And a Happy New Year.

SCROOGE: Bah! Humbug!

MUSIC: A *brief bridge, up and out.*

CRATCHIT: Er, pardon me, Mr. Scrooge, but there is a gentleman here to see you.

SCROOGE: What about, Cratchit?

CRATCHIT: He didn't say, sir.

GENTLEMAN: Ah, good afternoon, sir. Have I the pleasure of addressing Mr. Scrooge or Mr. Marley?

SCROOGE: Mr. Marley, my former partner, has been dead these seven years. He died seven years ago this very night.

GENTLEMAN: Then I have no doubt his liberality is well represented by his surviving partner.

SCROOGE: What do you want?

GENTLEMAN: At this festive season, Mr. Scrooge, we try and make some slight provision for the poor and destitute. Many thousands are in want of common necessities.

SCROOGE: Are there no prisons?

GENTLEMAN: Oh, plenty of prisons.

SCROOGE: And the workhouses, are they still in operation?

GENTLEMAN: I wish I could say they

were not. How much shall I put you down for, Mr. Scrooge?

SCROOGE: Nothing!

GENTLEMAN (*puzzled*): Nothing!

SCROOGE: Exactly! Let these deserving people of yours go to the establishments I have mentioned.

GENTLEMAN: Most of them would rather die than do that.

SCROOGE: Then let them do that and help decrease the surplus population. I'm busy. Good afternoon to you.

GENTLEMAN (*quietly*): Very good, Mr. Scrooge. Merry Christmas to you.

SOUND: *Door (off) open and close.*

SCROOGE (*grumbles*): Charity! Pah! Humbug!

CRATCHIT: Er, Mr. Scrooge, sir.

SCROOGE: Well, what is it, Cratchit?

CRATCHIT: I was wondering—

SCROOGE: You were wondering if you could go home.

CRATCHIT: Yes, sir. It's getting late.

SCROOGE: Yes, go on. You'll want all day tomorrow, I suppose?

CRATCHIT: If quite convenient, sir.

SCROOGE: It's not convenient, and it's not fair.

CRATCHIT: It's only once a year, sir.

SCROOGE: A poor excuse for picking a man's pocket every twenty-fifth day of December. I suppose you must have the whole day. But be here all the earlier the next day. Understand?

CRATCHIT: Yes, sir. And Merry Christmas.

SCROOGE: Christmas! Humbug!

MUSIC: A *Christmas theme, up and under.*

NARRATOR: A few minutes later Scrooge leaves his warehouse and makes his way to his melancholy chambers, a gloomy suite of rooms. By the light of a single flickering candle, he eats his cold supper. And then to save lighting his stove, Ebenezer Scrooge retires for the night. (*Music out*) The minutes tick away. Scrooge sleeps uneasily, tossing from side to side.

SOUND: *Chains being dragged across the floor.*

NARRATOR: Suddenly he awakes with a start. Walking toward him, and dragging a heavy chain, is a gray, dim figure of a man. It stops at the foot of the bed.

SCROOGE (*frightened*): Who are you? What do you want with me? (*Pause*) Who are you?

MARLEY: Ask me who I *was*.

SCROOGE: You're . . . you're . . .

MARLEY: Yes, in life I was your partner, Jacob Marley.

SCROOGE: But it cannot be so. You're dead.

MARLEY: You don't believe in me.

SCROOGE: No. You're nothing but an undigested bit of beef, a blot of mustard, a crumb of cheese.

MARLEY: You are wrong, Ebenezer. I am the ghost of Jacob Marley.

SCROOGE: Why do you come to me?

MARLEY: It is required of every man that the spirit within him should walk abroad among his fellow men and travel far and wide; and if that spirit goes not forth in life, it is condemned to do so after death.

SCROOGE: No, no, I don't believe it.

MARLEY: It is then doomed to wander through the world.

SCROOGE: You are chained, Jacob. Tell me why?

MARLEY: I wear the chain I forged in life. I made it link by link, and yard by yard. I wore it of my own free will. Is its pattern strange to you?

SCROOGE (*trembling*): I don't understand.

MARLEY: This chain I wear is as heavy as the one you are now forging.

SCROOGE: You talk strangely, Jacob.

MARLEY: For seven years I have been dead—traveling the whole time. No rest, no peace. Only remorse.

SCROOGE: But you were always shrewd, Jacob.

MARLEY: Aye, too shrewd.

SCROOGE: A good man of business.

MARLEY: Business! Mankind was my business. The common welfare was my business; charity, mercy, forbearance, and benevolence were all my business. But I heeded none of these. Instead, I thought only of money.

SCROOGE: And what is wrong with making money?

MARLEY: That is your fault, Ebenezer, as it was mine. That is why I am here tonight. That is part of my penance.[2] I am here to warn you . . . to help you escape my fate. You have one chance left.

SCROOGE: Tell me how this chance will come!

MARLEY: My time draws near. I must go. Tonight you will be haunted by three spirits. The first will appear when the bell strikes one; expect the second at the stroke of two,

² *penance.* An act to show repentance.

and the third as the bell tolls three.

SCROOGE: Couldn't I take 'em all at once, and have it over with?

MARLEY: No. And heed them when they appear. (*Fading*) Remember, it is your last chance to escape my miserable fate.

MUSIC: A bit ominous.[3] *Forte and fade out under* NARRATOR.

NARRATOR: As Scrooge stares in frightened silence, the wraithlike figure of his deceased partner dissolves into space. Then, exhausted by the ordeal, Scrooge drops off to sleep. Twelve o'clock comes. Time passes. Then:

SOUND: *Off in the distance, steeple clock strikes once.*

NARRATOR: The curtains of Scrooge's bed are drawn aside, but by no visible hand. There by the bed stands an unearthly visitor . . . a strange figure—like a child. Its hair is white, and in its hand it holds a sprig of fresh green holly. Scrooge stares and then speaks.

SCROOGE: Are you the spirit whose coming was told me by Jacob Marley?

FIRST GHOST (*a gentle voice*): I am.

SCROOGE: Who and what are you?

FIRST GHOST: I am the Ghost of Christmas Past.

SCROOGE: Long past?

FIRST GHOST: No. Your Past. Rise and walk with me.

SCROOGE: Where?

FIRST GHOST: Out through the window.

³ *ominous.* Foreshadowing something frightful to come.

SCROOGE: But we are three stories above ground. I am only a mortal.

FIRST GHOST: Bear but a touch of my hand upon your heart, and you shall be upheld in more than this.

SCROOGE: What are we to do?

FIRST GHOST: I am going to help reclaim you. Come! Walk with me out into the night . . . into the past.

SOUND: *Wind. It sweeps in; hold and then fade out.*

SCROOGE: Tell me, Ghost of Christmas Past, where are we?

FIRST GHOST: Look down, Ebenezer, and remember back.

SCROOGE (*amazed*): Why . . . why, of course. The river . . . the meadows . . . and—why, there's my old school. I went there as a lad. But there is no one about.

FIRST GHOST: It is Christmas holiday. Let us look into this study hall.

SCROOGE: Empty, except for a young boy sitting at a desk, his head in his hands. Left behind. He . . . he's crying. Poor chap! No place to go at Christmas. Ah, now he's looking up.

FIRST GHOST: Do you recognize him?

SCROOGE (*stunned*): Why, it's—

FIRST GHOST: What is his name?

SCROOGE (*slowly*): Ebenezer Scrooge. (*Pause*) I wish—But it's too late now.

FIRST GHOST: What is the matter?

SCROOGE: Nothing, nothing. There were some boys singing Christmas carols outside my warehouse door yesterday afternoon. I drove them away.

FIRST GHOST: Let us see another Christmas.

SOUND: *Wind up briefly and out.*

FIRST GHOST: It is a year later . . . another Christmas.

SCROOGE: And again there is the school.

FIRST GHOST: That boy standing in the driveway, pacing up and down.

SCROOGE: It is I.

FIRST GHOST: And what do you see?

SCROOGE: A coach coming up the driveway. Now it has stopped, and a little girl gets out. Look, she is hugging me. It's Fan, my sister.

FIRST GHOST: Listen to what she says.

FAN: I've come to bring you home, dear brother. Father's not mean any more, and he says you're never coming back here, and from now on we'll always be together. (*Fading*) Just think, together for the first time in four years.

FIRST GHOST: Your sister was a delicate creature . . . kind . . . big-hearted.

SCROOGE: So she was, so she was. She died comparatively young.

FIRST GHOST: She left one child behind her.

SCROOGE: Yes. Fred, my nephew.

FIRST GHOST (*mildly*): He was in to wish you a Merry Christmas yesterday.

SCROOGE: Yes. Yes, he did so. Please take me back.

FIRST GHOST: Not yet. There is one more shadow.

SCROOGE: No more. I do not wish to see it.

FIRST GHOST: You must.

SOUND: *The wind sweeps in full again, then out.*

FIRST GHOST: The years have passed. In this house below. Look, there sits a young girl, a beautiful girl.

SCROOGE: It's Belle.

FIRST GHOST: The girl you were to marry. And there you sit next to her, a young man in your prime. Only now your face begins to show the signs of avarice. There is a greedy, restless motion in your eyes. Listen to what she is saying to you.

BELLE (*she is about* 18): It matters very little to you. Another idol has displaced me, a golden one. You hold money more important than me or anything else, for that matter. And I'm going to grant your wish: free you from marrying me. (*Fading*) That is the way you wish it, Ebenezer. I feel sorry for you.

SCROOGE: Spirit, show me no more.

FIRST GHOST: Today, Belle is a happy woman, surrounded with her fine children. Those children might have been yours if you hadn't been so selfish.

SCROOGE: Take me back. Haunt me no more! I beg of you, don't!

MUSIC: *Ethereal*[4] *theme. Forte and fade under for narrator.*

NARRATOR: The steeple clock has just finished striking the second hour of Christmas Day. Scrooge finds himself back in his bedroom. Slowly his door, though bolted, swings open.

MUSIC: *Out.*

SECOND GHOST (*a big, booming voice*): Good morning, Ebenezer. Welcome me. I am the Ghost of Christmas Present. Look upon me.

SCROOGE: You're practically a giant. Yet you have a young face.

SECOND GHOST: Have you never seen the like of me before?

4 *ethereal. Airy; spiritlike.*

SCROOGE: Never.

SECOND GHOST: I have many brothers, over eighteen hundred of them, one for each Christmas since the very first.

SCROOGE: And you are here to take me with you?

SECOND GHOST: Yes. I trust you will profit by your journey. Touch my robe, Ebenezer.

SOUND: W*ind. Up full and out into:*

CHORUS (*mixed voices*): *Singing a chorus of a Christmas hymn. As they near conclusion, fade them under for:*

SCROOGE: Those people in this church, they seem very happy.

SECOND GHOST: They are, for they are giving thanks for all the joys brought to them during the year.

SCROOGE: And the crew of that ship over there. . . . Look, they are shaking hands with the captain.

CHORUS: *Out.*

SECOND GHOST: Wishing him a Merry Christmas. But come! We have not much time left, and there is still another place we must visit. It is a very poor house in a very poor section of London. This one directly below us.

SCROOGE: Indeed it is. Who, may I ask, lives here?

SECOND GHOST: An underpaid clerk named Bob Cratchit.

SCROOGE: The Bob Cratchit who is employed by me?

SECOND GHOST: The very same.

SCROOGE: That woman . . . those four children.

SECOND GHOST: His wife and family.

SCROOGE: Coming up the stairs right

now. That's Cratchit. He's carrying a young boy.

SECOND GHOST: His fifth child . . . Tiny Tim.

SCROOGE: He carries a crutch.

SECOND GHOST: Because he is crippled.

SCROOGE: But the doctors ——

SECOND GHOST: Cratchit cannot afford a doctor, not on fifteen shillings a week.

SCROOGE: But—

SECOND GHOST: Sshhh! Listen.

SOUND: *Door opens.*

CRATCHIT (*heartily*): Good afternoon, everyone.

TIM: And a most Merry Christmas.

MRS. CRATCHIT: Father . . . Tiny Tim.

THE OTHER CRATCHITS (*they ad lib*[5]): "Merry Christmas," "Welcome," "Tiny Tim, sit next to me," "Father, let me take your muffler."

MRS. CRATCHIT: And how did Tiny Tim behave at church?

CRATCHIT: As good as gold, and better.

TIM: I was glad to be able to go to church. That's because I wanted the people to see that I'm a cripple.

MRS. CRATCHIT: Now that's a peculiar thing to say, Tiny Tim.

TIM (*eagerly*): No, it isn't. That's because I was in God's House, and it was God who made the blind able to see and the lame able to walk. And when the people at church saw me and my crutch, I was hoping they would think of what God can do, and that they would say a prayer for me.

MRS. CRATCHIT: I . . . I'm certain they must have prayed for you.

5 *ad lib.* Make up sayings.

TIM: And one of these days I'm going to get well, and that'll mean I can throw away this crutch, and run and play like the other boys.

CRATCHIT (*softly*): You will, Tim— one of these days. (*Heartily*) And now, Mother, the big question. When will dinner be ready?

SOUND: *Ad libs from the children.*

MRS. CRATCHIT: It's ready right now: just about the finest goose you have ever seen. Martha, you carry it in. Tom, you fetch the potatoes and turnips. Dick, Peter, set the chairs around the table.

TIM: And I'll sit between Father and Mother.

CRATCHIT: This is going to be the best Christmas dinner anyone could hope for. (*Fading*) And I'm the luckiest man in the world, having such a fine family.

SCROOGE: It isn't a very big goose, is it? I could eat the whole bird myself, I believe.

SECOND GHOST: It is all Bob Cratchit can afford. His family doesn't complain. To them, that meager goose is a sumptuous banquet. And more important, much more important, Ebenezer.

SCROOGE: Go on.

SECOND GHOST: They are a happy and united group. Look at their shining faces. Listen to them.

SOUND: *The* CRATCHITS *ad libbing in happy fashion.*

CRATCHIT: What a superb dinner we have had . . . the tempting meat, the delicious dressing.

TIM: And the plum pudding, Father. Don't forget that.

CRATCHIT: That pudding was the greatest success achieved by Mrs. Cratchit since her marriage.

SOUND: *The children laugh.*

MRS. CRATCHIT: Thank you for the compliment. I must confess it was good.

CRATCHIT: And now for the crowning touch. The punch!

SOUNDS (*ad libs of*): "The punch!" "Good!" "Oh!"

CRATCHIT: Here we are. Get your glasses. You, Peter . . . Dick . . . Tom . . . Martha . . . Tiny Tim . . . and last, but far from least you, Mother. And not to forget myself. (*With finality*) There!

TIM: A toast!

CRATCHIT: First the founder of this feast, the man who has made it possible. I give you Mr. Scrooge.

MRS. CRATCHIT (*bristling*): Mr. Scrooge, indeed. I wish I had him here. I'd give him a piece of my mind to feast upon, and I hope he'd have a good appetite for it.

CRATCHIT (*warningly*): My dear, the children! Christmas Day.

MRS. CRATCHIT: He's a hard, stingy, unfeeling man. You know he is, Robert, better than anybody else.

CRATCHIT (*mildly*): My dear. Remember, Christmas Day.

MRS. CRATCHIT: I'm sorry. Very well, I'll drink his health. Long life to him! A Merry Christmas to him! To Mr. Scrooge.

FAMILY (*chorusing*): To Mr. Scrooge!

CRATCHIT: And now a toast to us: A Merry Christmas to us all. God bless us!

FAMILY: God bless us.

TIM: God bless us every one.

MUSIC: *"Noel"—Forte and fade under.*

SCROOGE: Spirit, tell me if Tiny Tim will live.

SECOND GHOST: I see a vacant seat in the chimney corner, and a crutch without an owner, carefully preserved. If these shadows remain unaltered by the Future, the child will die.

SCROOGE: No, no. Oh, no, kind Spirit! Say he will live, that he will be spared.

SECOND GHOST: Why concern yourself about him? Isn't it better that he die and decrease the surplus population?

SCROOGE: But these poor people must be helped.

SECOND GHOST: Are there no prisons? And the workhouses, are they still in operation?

SCROOGE: Do not taunt me.

SECOND GHOST: It is time for us to go.

SCROOGE: No, I wish to remain.

SECOND GHOST: I can remain no longer. Touch my robe, and we shall go.

SCROOGE: No! No, I say! Spirit, don't desert me. I need your help.

MUSIC: *Up briefly and under.*

NARRATOR: As Ebenezer Scrooge comes to his senses, he discovers himself standing on the street, outside of his lodgings. A heavy snow is falling, blanketing a sleeping London. The wind has died down. It is still early Christmas morning.

MUSIC: *Out into:*

SOUND: *Steeple bell off in distance striking three times.*

THIRD GHOST (*warningly*): Ebenezer . . . Ebenezer Scrooge.

SCROOGE: You are the third and last.

THIRD GHOST: I am the Ghost of Christmas Yet to Come.

SCROOGE: You are about to show me shadows of the things that have not happened, but will happen in the time before us. Is that so, Spirit?

THIRD GHOST: Yes, Ebenezer, that is correct.

SCROOGE: I tremble at going with you. I fear what I am to see.

THIRD GHOST: Come, Ebenezer.

SOUND: *Wind up full and out.*

SCROOGE: Why do we stop here on this street corner, Spirit?

THIRD GHOST: Those two men standing there, do you know them?

SCROOGE: Why, yes, I do business with them.

THIRD GHOST: Their conversation is interesting.

MAN 1: When did he die?

MAN 2: Last night, I believe.

MAN 1: I thought he'd never die.

MAN 2: What has he done with his money?

MAN 1: I haven't heard. Left it to his company, perhaps. Well, one thing is certain, he didn't leave it to charity.

MAN 2: Are you going to his funeral?

MAN 1: Not unless a free lunch is provided.

MAN 2 (*fading*): A very good point. Can't say that I blame you.

SCROOGE: Spirit, this dead man they were discussing, who is he?

THIRD GHOST: I will show you.

SOUND: *Wind up briefly and out.*

SCROOGE: This room, it's too dark to see.

THIRD GHOST: In front of you is a bed. On it lies a man—the body of the man those men on the street were discussing.

SCROOGE: And no one has come to claim this body?

THIRD GHOST: No one, for he left not a friend behind him. Come closer and look into his face.

SCROOGE: No.

THIRD GHOST: Look!

SCROOGE: Spirit, this is a fearful place. Let us go.

THIRD GHOST: Look at the face of this unclaimed man.

SCROOGE: I would do it if I could. But I haven't the power. Let me see some tenderness connected with a death. If I don't, that lonely body in this dark room will ever haunt me.

THIRD GHOST: Yes, I know of such a home, one where there is tenderness connected with death. Over here on this poor street and in this dismal house.

SCROOGE: But this house—Why, yes, I've been here before. Bob Cratchit, my clerk, lives here. There is Mrs. Cratchit and her eldest daughter, Martha.

MARTHA: Your eyes, Mother, you'll strain them working in this bad light.

MRS. CRATCHIT: I'll stop for a while. I wouldn't show weak eyes to your father when he comes home. It's time he was here.

MARTHA: Past it, rather. But these days he walks slower than he used to, Mother.

MRS. CRATCHIT: I have known him to walk with Tiny Tim upon his shoulder very fast, indeed. He was very light to carry; and your father loved him so, it was no trouble.

SOUND: *Door handle.*

MRS. CRATCHIT: There is your father now at the door.

SOUND: *Door opens and shuts.*

MRS. CRATCHIT: You're late tonight, Robert.

CRATCHIT: Yes, I'm late.

MARTHA: I'll get some tea for you, Father.

CRATCHIT: Thank you, Martha.

MRS. CRATCHIT: You went there today, Robert?

CRATCHIT: Yes. I wish you could have gone. It would have done you good to see how green a place it is.

MRS. CRATCHIT: I'll see it soon.

CRATCHIT: I promised him I would walk there every Sunday. My poor Tiny Tim. At last he got rid of his crutch.

MRS. CRATCHIT (*fading*): Yes, at last he did. Our poor Tiny Tim.

SCROOGE: Tell me, Spirit, why did Tiny Tim have to die?

THIRD GHOST: Come, there is still another place to visit.

SOUND: *Wind. Up and out.*

SCROOGE: A graveyard. Why do we pause here?

THIRD GHOST: That tombstone . . . read the name on it.

SCROOGE: Before I do, answer me one question. Are these the shadows of the things that *will* be, or are they the shadows of the things that *may* be, only?

THIRD GHOST: The inscription on the tombstone.

SCROOGE: It reads . . . (*slowly*) "Ebenezer Scrooge." No, Spirit. Oh, no, no! Hear me! I am not the man I was. I will not be the man I must have been but for this les-

son. I will honor Christmas in my heart.

THIRD GHOST: But will you?

SCROOGE: Oh, yes. I will try and keep it alive all the year. I will live in the Past, the Present, and the Future. I will not shut out the lesson that all three Spirits have taught me. Oh, tell me there is hope, that I may sponge away the writing on this stone.

SOUND: *Wind up strong. Hold and out into: Joyous church bells, tolling Christmas Day. Hold under.*

SCROOGE (*moans, as though coming out of a dream*): Tell me there is hope, that I may sponge away the writing on this stone. (*Coming to*) Eh, what am I holding on to? The bedpost. I am in my own bed . . . home. Those bells! It must be Christmas Day. Christmas Day—I wonder if it really is. We shall see. Open the window.

SOUND: *Window being raised.*

SCROOGE: You boy, down there.

BOY (*away*):Eh?

SCROOGE: What day is today, my fine lad?

BOY: Today! Why, Christmas Day, of course.

SCROOGE: And to think the Spirits have done it all in one night.

BOY: What did you say, sir?

SCROOGE: Do you know the poulterer's in the next street?

BOY: I should hope I did.

SCROOGE: An intelligent boy! A remarkable boy! Do you know whether they've sold the prize turkey that was hanging in the window?

BOY: The one as big as me?

SCROOGE: What a delightful boy! Yes, the one as big as you.

BOY: It's hanging there now.

SCROOGE: Go and buy it. I am in earnest. Here is the money. Catch. (*Pause*) Deliver it to Bob Cratchit, who lives on Golden Street in Camden Town.

BOY: But, sir, there will be considerable change left over.

SCROOGE (*chuckling*): Keep it, my boy. Keep it.

BOY (*delighted*): Oh, thank you, sir.

SCROOGE: And, boy.

BOY: Yes, sir.

SCROOGE: Don't let Mr. Cratchit know who sent the turkey. It's something of a surprise. And something else.

BOY: Yes, sir.

SCROOGE: A very Merry Christmas to you.

MUSIC: *A Christmas hymn. Up and under.*

SOUND: *Knock on door. Repeated. Door opens.*

FRED: What is it? (*Pause*) Why, bless my soul!

SCROOGE (*heartily*): Yes, yes, it is I—your Uncle Scrooge. I've come for dinner. Now let me in. I have a present for your good wife. From now on I'm going to be one of your most persistent guests. I've changed, my boy: you'll see!

MUSIC: *Up and under for* NARRATOR.

NARRATOR: Scrooge was better than his word. He did everything he promised, and infinitely more. He became a persistent visitor to his nephew's home, and even took Fred into business with him. He raised Bob Cratchit's salary to a figure that left that bewildered gentleman gasping; and to Tiny Tim, who did not die, he was a second father. He provided doctors for the little lad, and very soon Tiny Tim will have his wish: he will be able to throw away his crutch and run and play like the other boys. As for the three Spirits, Ebenezer Scrooge never saw them again. That was due to the unchallengeable fact that Scrooge, for the rest of his days, helped keep alive the spirit of Christmas. And so, as Tiny Tim observed, God bless us every one.

MUSIC: *Up full to close.*

✦❧✦

TO THINK ABOUT

1. Why could this story be called "The Reformation of Ebenezer Scrooge"?

2. What different details at the beginning of the story show Scrooge's miserliness? What details show his change at the end?

3. Who were the three Spirits of Christmas? What did each show Scrooge?

4. Who was Jacob Marley? Why did he come to Scrooge? Read the lines that tell.

5. What is the most appealing scene? Who is the most lovable character? Which line of the story do you think is widely remembered?

WORDS TO KNOW

Did you understand the meaning of all the words in the story? The italicized words below are all key words. What do they mean? Use your dictionary for those you are not sure of.

1. a *festive* mood
2. his *liberality*
3. poor and *destitute*
4. *surplus* population
5. the chain I *forged*
6. part of my *penance*
7. *wraithlike* figure
8. young man in your *prime*
9. *meager* goose
10. *sumptuous* banquet
11. remain *unaltered*
12. *persistent* guests
13. *bewildered* gentlemen
14. *unchallengeable* fact

WORDS TO SAY CLEARLY AND CORRECTLY

Say correctly each of these words, all of which are spoken in the play. Use your dictionary if you are in any doubt about the correct pronunciation.

poor	comparatively	meager	haunt
suite	superb	sumptuous	infinitely

INTERPRETING LINES

Choose key lines in the play, and practice saying them to give the right meanings. For example, how would you say these?

1. Bah! Humbug!
2. A poor excuse for picking a man's pocket every twenty-fifth day of December.
3. God bless us every one.

LOOKING BACKWARD THROUGH THE CHAPTER

1. The three plays which you have just read are quite different. What sort of play is each, and how is it different from the other two?
2. Which characters will you remember?
3. What truths about life and people do you find in the three plays?

A TEST FOR YOUR WITS

Can you identify by name each of these characters?

1. A man who gave his life for his country
2. A man who, through three visions, learned Christian love and charity
3. A boy whose nickname did not indicate his mental qualities
4. A girl who learned how to treat her boy friends
5. A little crippled boy who was cured by the kindness of his father's employer

SOMETHING TO TRY

1. Choose a scene from a book, and write it in play form. Act it out.
2. Write a radio play based on a book scene or on an event in history. Broadcast it to your class.
3. Hold an oral-reading clinic. Take turns reading short passages aloud, preferably passages containing conversation. Listen carefully to one another for pro-

nunciation, enunciation, phrasing of words according to meaning, inflection, and variety of tone. Offer suggestions to one another.

If you have a public-address system in your school, or if you have a microphone, and if it is available for class use, listen to one another by that means.

Moreover, if your school has phonograph records in which the spoken voice is heard, you can learn much by listening to the ways others use their voices.

4. If you would like to read other plays, the list below will be helpful.

PLAYS TO READ AND ACT

Du Bois, Graham, *Plays for Great Occasions*, 1951 (Plays, Inc.).
Twenty-four one-act plays for holidays.

Hackett, Walter, *Radio Plays for Young People*, 1950 (Plays, Inc.).
Dramatized classics for either radio or schoolroom.

Hark, Mildred, and McQueen, Noel, *Twenty-five Plays for Holidays*, 1952 (Plays, Inc.).
Plays for Christmas, Thanksgiving, and other holidays.

MacAlvay, Nora, and Comer, Virginia Lee (editors), *First Performance*, 1952 (Harcourt).
Five excellent three-act plays for junior--high school.

MacIsaac, Frederick J., *Tony Sarg Marionette Book*, 1921 (Viking).
Instructions for giving marionette plays, and the scripts for two plays.

Major, Clare Tree, *Playing Theatre; Six Plays for Children*, 1920 (Oxford).
Plays made from such old favorites as "Cinderella" and "Robin Hood."

Marsh, Florence A. (editor), *Plays for Young People* 1931 (Allyn).
Dramatized versions of historical events and scenes from literature.

Paradis, Marjorie, *One-act Plays for All-girl Casts*, 1952 (Plays, Inc.).
All kinds for all girls.

Robinson, Marvin G. (editor), *From Story to Stage*, 1946 (W. H. Baker).
Eleven short plays of well-known stories.

Portraits
of Americans

Three Kidnaped Daughters

Even girls had to be brave in the early days of America. Everyone knows how fearless Daniel Boone was, but not everyone knows the thrilling story of Jemima Boone and her two friends.

The story of their experience took place in 1776. Only a year before, Daniel Boone had directed the building of the stockade fort at Boonesborough (now spelled Boonesboro) on the bank of the Kentucky River. With this assurance, the settlers had flocked to Caintuck, as Kentucky was then called. One Sunday afternoon Jemima Boone and two of her friends started out on a calm little canoe ride. They did not know that there were Indians lying in wait.
(Note the time when you begin reading.)

I**N SPITE** of all the talk about Indian wars and in spite of the December murders, Boonesborough had begun to feel fairly secure again in the early summer of 1776. Further to the north, a few settlers had been killed; but Daniel and Squire Boone had come home from their surveying at the Falls of the Ohio without hint of danger. Daniel himself lived in an unfortified cabin by the river, and it is said that a few other settlers had even built cabins on the other side.

Everything seemed so safe that on Sunday, July 7, after the usual Bible reading, a party of three young girls went for a paddle on the river. Jemima Boone was suffering from a "cane stab" in the foot. It was not an infrequent injury, since the stubble of broken cane was sharp, and young

girls and even grown women rarely wore shoes in the summertime. Jemima wanted to soak the wound in the cool water of the river, and Betsey and Fanny Callaway went with her to paddle the canoe.

These three were the belles of Boonesborough. Betsey, sixteen, was engaged to marry Samuel Henderson. Jemima and Fanny, though only fourteen, already had serious suitors eager to marry them.

Daniel Boone himself is said to have seen them on their way and then to have strolled off on one of his solitary rambles. If that is so, he did not go far, for it is quite certain that he was soon back in the cabin with his moccasins off, taking a quiet Sunday afternoon nap.

The two Callaway girls paddled about safely enough, with Jemima Boone steering and dangling her bare foot in the river. The current car-

———From *Fighting Frontiersman* by John Bakeless, copyright 1948 by John Bakeless, by permission of William Morrow and Company, Inc.

ried them slowly downstream until they were about a quarter of a mile below the fort, and then drew them toward a steep cliff on the other side of the river.

Not being very skillful or very strong, they had trouble with the canoe and, according to some stories, got stuck on a sandbar. Struggle as they might, they could not control the canoe; and "it would go to the other shore despite of their hearts."

The cane came down so close to the water's edge here that its branches hung over into the river. It was an ideal hiding place for five warriors, who had been watching the fort and who, observing the girls' struggles, had quietly waited to see if they might not drift within reach.

The band included some Shawnees, who seem to have met the Cherokee chief, Hanging Maw, in the forest. He had come north along the Warriors' Path[1] to stir up the northern tribes against the white men who were encroaching on the common hunting grounds. Apparently they had come down to reconnoiter Boonesborough, more or less under Hanging Maw's leadership, before going back to Ohio to hold a council and discuss plans for attacking it. There was no war as yet and no special reason for taking prisoners. The tribes had not formally cast their lot with the British. But no Indian was going to neglect a chance like this.

As they silently waited, the boat drifted nearer and nearer. The girls'

[1] Warriors' Path. A route used by Indians, which Boone and his followers also used in their trek from North Carolina to Kentucky; it came to be known as Wilderness Road.

futile struggles with the paddles only brought it closer. When they had drifted into shallow water a few yards from shore, the Indians pounced on them. One ran waist-deep into the water and, seizing the canoe, tried to haul it to shore. Little Fanny Callaway, the smallest of the three, whacked him over the head with the paddle until it broke. Betsey, too, struck out with her paddle as hard as she could, until the other Indians made signs that they would upset the canoe unless they stopped.

The little white squaws were then easily overpowered, dragged through the shallow water to shore, and then, under cover of a densely wooded ravine, rushed to the hills which edge that side of the river. Their screams were instantly silenced by the threatening flourish of knives and tomahawks. One warrior seized Betsey Callaway by the hair and threatened to scalp her if she made another sound. After that, the mute threat of the tomahawks was enough to keep them quiet.

When the Indians reached the hilltop, Jemima Boone, who was not Daniel Boone's daughter for nothing, announced that she would not go another step. They could kill her if they wanted to, but her bare and wounded foot was a good deal worse than death. The Indians at first threatened, but the fourteen-year-old girl was stubborn. Refractory prisoners were casually tomahawked in most cases; but the American Indian has a gentle way with children always, and these girls were little more than children. Besides, Hanging Maw when not upon the warpath was a kindly soul, indulgently inclined. Bowing to the inevitable, he and his braves provided moccasins for Jemima and for Fanny Callaway, both of whom were barefoot. Then they cut off the long skirts of all three at the knees, so that they could travel more easily, and let them make wrapped leggings out of the scraps as protection against the underbrush and brambles through which they would have to go.

Recognizing Hanging Maw, whom she had seen at her father's cabin, probably in the Watauga country, Jemima Boone told him who she was.

The Cherokee chief was mildly amused. Rare was the Cherokee who got the better of the white hunter, "Wide Mouth."

"We have done pretty well for old Boone this time," said he, laughing.

The wily savages as usual divided their party going through canebrakes, so that the trail would be hard to follow. They forced their captives to do the same thing, and even to walk down little streams to hide the trail completely. Where possible, the Indians traveled on the barren tops of ridges, where they left less "sign" than in the lush vegetation of the lowlands.

The Indians treated the girl captives well enough. They shared the hard, dry, smoked buffalo tongue which was their only ration, chatted freely, and explained that they were going to the Shawnee towns.

The war party camped that night not far from the present city of Winchester, Kentucky, after covering some ten or twelve miles. Each girl was pinioned for the night with thongs at the elbows and set against a tree, since it was impossible to lie down when bound in this way. One end of the thong was tied to the tree and the other held by a sleeping Indian. The three were placed far enough apart so that they could not reach each other, while the Indians sprawled on the ground in a circle around them. Jemima Boone, who had a penknife in her pocket, tried to reach it and cut herself and the others loose while the Indians slept; but it was no use. All night long they sat there, each girl lashed to her tree, wondering what the morning would bring.

As soon as it was light, Hanging Maw started his band off northward as fast as he could, the girls still full of confidence they would be rescued— a confidence that dwindled as the day passed with no sign that rescuers had found the trail.

By leaving as much evidence of their passing as they could, the quick-witted daughters of the pioneers aided the pursuit which they knew would do its best to follow them. Betsey Callaway, the only one with shoes, managed to dig her high wooden heels into any damp earth, and especially into the mud at buffalo wallows, as plain evidence that a white woman had passed that way. They managed to lag behind the Indians whenever possible and contrived to break a good many twigs. When the warriors asked suspiciously what they were doing, the girls replied innocently that they were tired and were helping themselves along by grasping the bushes. The explanation was not a conspicuous success, but in spite of the Indians' vigilance they broke enough twigs to leave marks on their hands.

Once the Indians detected Betsey Callaway in the act of breaking a twig. They threatened her with their tomahawks, but they never noticed that she was slyly tearing off bits of her clothing and dropping them on the trail. One fragment of her white linen handkerchief even had the name "Callaway" marked on it. Eventually, the Indians knocked the wooden heels off her shoes to keep her from leaving marks; but the dauntless little sixteen-year-old continued to leave the imprint of her shoe sole.

Jemima Boone made her sore foot the excuse for frequent falls, accompanied by loud screams intended for any white ears that might be listening in the forest. The Indians hushed her by waving their knives and tomahawks, but it was not long before the girl prisoners found another way of disturbing their captors. Encountering a stray pony in the woods, the Indians put Jemima Boone on it, hoping to hurry up their march. Sometimes the other two also rode.

Children of the frontier, these young girls knew all about horses. They did what they could to make the pony troublesome and then tumbled off at every possible excuse. Laughing heartily, the warriors would pick them up and put them back. When they continued to fall off, the joke rather wore out. An Indian mounted and gravely tried to teach them to ride. It was no use. They fell off almost as frequently as before.

They were, of course, taking desperate chances when they annoyed the Indians in this way. If the good-natured Hanging Maw had not been the most tolerant Cherokee ever heard of, the three of them would have been tomahawked a dozen times over. Except for bruises, however, no one was hurt except Betsey Callaway, who was justifiably bitten by the outraged pony. Finally the harassed Indians decided that since the "pretty squaws" were still falling off the pony nearly as fast as they could be put back, the party would make better time without a mount. They turned the horse loose again and went ahead with their captives on foot.

The Indian kidnapers had been so quick and clever that, according to one story, the girls were not even missed until milking time. Then a hunter, probably one of their suitors, who had gone out to meet them, gave the alarm. According to other stories, their screams were heard at once, but they were too far down the river for help to reach them, as they had taken the only boat.

There was intense excitement in Boonesborough. Daniel Boone leaped from the bed in his cabin, seized his rifle, and raced for the river bank, without even waiting for his moccasins. No one had ever seen him betray so much agitation.

Efforts at rescue were delayed at the very start, because the Indians had been careful to set the canoe adrift, and the riflemen had no way of getting across the Kentucky River without wetting their powder. The intrepid John Gass had to swim over for the canoe, expecting invisible Indians to begin sniping at him from the bushes at any moment. No one had any idea how strong the raiding band was nor where they were. While Gass swam, the rest of the Kentuckians lined the bank and covered the other shore with their rifles. But there was no need of precaution. The Indians had long since gone.

When Gass towed the canoe back, Boone took five men over the river and examined the other shore. A mounted party had already ridden downstream, crossed by the ford, and were working upstream from there. Boone divided his men so as to find the trail as soon as possible. With John Gass and Samuel Henderson, he himself started downstream toward the horsemen. John Floyd led another party upstream. As Boone, finding no tracks, was turning back, Colonel Callaway rode up with his mounted party. It was John Floyd and his men who actually picked up the Indians' trail.

Callaway wanted to ride straight after them, feeling sure that his mounted men could ride them down easily enough. He was probably right. But Daniel Boone pointed out that the Indians would certainly keep one warrior traveling well in their rear to give the alarm if the pursuit got close. He would hear the approach of horsemen, and the Indians would instantly tomahawk their prisoners to prevent recapture. This actually did happen to another woman prisoner in that very year. They agreed that Callaway should disregard the trail entirely and ride off at full speed for the ford across Licking River, where he would lie in ambush. Meantime, Boone's party would

follow the Indians' trail, or its general direction, with the utmost caution.

It was now so late that there was little hope of following more than a few miles. Floyd's men went as far as they could, and Boone soon overtook them. As they consulted, a dog began barking in the woods. Slipping silently toward the sound, they came upon nine strange white men building a cabin. The Indians had passed without molesting them and apparently without even noticing their presence. Boone and his party halted here for the night, ready to start early Monday morning.

They had rushed after the Indians so hastily that they were still wearing their long, Sunday-go-to-meeting pantaloons, precious garments reserved strictly for the Sabbath and exceedingly awkward for wilderness travel. Worse still, they had no food; and it began to look as if there would be a long chase. John Gass, the man who swam the river for the canoe, made his way back to Boonesborough in the black night of the forest and returned before morning with breechclouts, leggings, hunting shirts, and more ammunition, as well as a supply of jerked venison, which was the only provender the housewives of Boonesborough could supply. He also brought moccasins for Daniel Boone, who had been dashing about the woods in his bare feet for hours and by this time needed them badly.

Three of the cabin builders now joined the pursuit, and they pushed on as soon as there was daylight enough to see the trail. For a time it was easy to follow, and they even noted the exact spot where the Indians had camped. Beyond their camp, however, the warriors had slipped by separate paths through the thickest canebrake they could find. The trail had simply vanished.

Boone soon gave up the attempt to find it again. He knew that every minute counted, and he felt sure that the Indians were making for the Shawnee camps on the Scioto. Remarking that it was no use to follow the trail very closely, anyway, until the Indians had gone farther and become less cautious, he led his men swiftly and silently for thirty miles northward along the general route the kidnapers were taking, and then turned at right angles until he crossed the trail itself. Boone and his men knew they were going in the right direction. Even though they were not trying to follow the Indian trail, they frequently crossed it and recognized the "sign" the girls had left. Betsey Callaway's lover could look down in the mud and see her foot-prints. The suitors of the other two girls could catch similar "signs" that their intended wives had passed that way, en route to become squaws in some smoky wigwam in a squalid village.

After resting for the night when there was no more hope of following the trail, the pursuers were up and away at dawn. Knowing the country of old, Daniel Boone remarked that he was sure the Indians would cross a stream which they were then approaching, only a short distance ahead. They found the crossing within two hundred yards. The moccasin prints were still fresh, the water still muddy. Boone had been right again!

Since the Indians had now covered thirty-five miles without any sign of white pursuers, Boone believed they would be less cautious. It was time to stick doggedly to their trail. The band was still making some effort to evade pursuit, for though they followed the Warriors' Path most of the time, they broke off every now and then for a little while into one of the numerous buffalo traces running parallel with it.

Their precaution was useless. Boone was by this time too close to be shaken off. In a little while his party passed the freshly slaughtered carcass of a buffalo from which only the hump had been cut. It was so fresh that blood was still oozing. Again Daniel ventured a prophecy: The Indians, he said, would halt and cook at the next water. Again Daniel was right. The Indians did exactly what he had expected.

Moving silently ahead, Boone's men came on a small snake the Indians had paused to kill. It was still wriggling. Ten miles farther on the white men came to a small stream. The trail did not cross. Instead, it disappeared entirely. There was no "sign" of any kind on the other bank. This meant that the Indians had taken the precaution of wading along the stream for a while to break the trail before halting. Their trail did not go on. They must be very near, probably within earshot.

It was about noon. Boone was sure the raiders were concealed somewhere near at hand cooking a meal. For the third time he was right.

Now came the ticklish part of the rescue. As they went along, Boone and his men had discussed the danger that he had already pointed out to Callaway. The prisoners might be tomahawked the moment the Indians saw the rescuers. The Boonesborough men made ready for quick action at the finish. In the lightest whisper, Daniel Boone gave his orders. They must exercise the utmost caution. They must approach in dead silence. When they came up with the Indians, no one was to fire until he got Boone's signal. The surest way to save the captives was to pour in a sudden volley and then charge into the camp.

The party divided. Samuel Henderson and one group went downstream. Daniel Boone and another group went upstream. Within two or three hundred yards, they found the Indians, "up a little creek that puts into Licking River just above Parker's Ferry," not far from the Blue Licks.

The raiders believed that they had by this time distanced any possible pursuit. Even the prisoners had begun to agree with them and had nearly given up hope of rescue. Actually, however, the pursuit had been much swifter than the Indians dreamed. While Boone's men were closing in from the south, Colonel Callaway's band were already lying in wait, some miles ahead to the north. The Indians could not escape unpunished. Saving the girls was the real problem.

As Boone's men crept up to the outskirts of the camp, the warriors had just kindled a fire and were getting ready to cook. Betsey Callaway sat leaning against a tree. The two younger girls lay with their heads in her lap. Only one Indian—the guard lounging near the girls—had his rifle with him.

The other Indians were all busy. One was gathering wood. One was forcing a spit through the buffalo hump to get it ready for cooking. Hanging Maw had gone to the stream to fill the kettle. They had posted a sentry on a small mound in the rear, exactly as Daniel Boone had predicted; but the brave had just strolled down to the fire to light his pipe and get materials for mending his moccasins. He had left his rifle behind him. The unhappy warrior had chosen the worst possible moment to do it, for within a few seconds John Floyd's rifle was drawing a bead on him from the underbrush.

The leading white man was within thirty yards of the Indians before he saw them. He turned silently to wave the others on. As he did so, the Indians caught sight of him. The two sides had seen each other at almost the same moment, but only Boone's men were armed and ready. Seeing that Boone's plan for surprising the Indians with a sudden volley was now impossible, the leading rifleman fired instantly, hoping to drive the Indians away from the girls. Boone and Floyd fired also, and one other man got a shot in before the Indians vanished. Floyd's shot knocked the sentry sprawling into the fire; but Indians build small fires, and he was not too badly hurt to reach the canebrake.

Fanny Callaway was idly watching the warrior who was putting the buffalo meat on the broiling stick. There was not a sound in the woods around her. Suddenly, she saw blood burst from a shot wound in the Indian's breast, and then heard a sudden sputter of shots.

"That's Daddy," cried Jemima Boone, as the rifles cracked.

"Run, gals, run!" yelled the rescuers.

The three girls jumped up, screaming with joy. One Indian paused in his sprint for the canebrake to throw a tomahawk which just missed Betsey Callaway's head, and it is said that the others threw knives. Seeing what might happen, Daniel Boone roared an order to the girls:

"Fall down!"

They threw themselves on the ground obediently, but were too agitated to stay there, and bounced up as the white men rushed yelling into the camp.

Boone and Floyd felt sure their shots had gone home, but the canebrake was too thick around them for certainty. There was a hasty crashing and rustling in it as the Indians fled. Then silence. It was practically impossible to find an Indian in a canebrake, and the white men let them go.

Since the kidnapers had told their prisoners that there was an Indian band at the Blue Licks and another on the Kentucky River, it was desirable to get back to Boonesborough as soon as possible. But everyone was exhausted, the girls by the discomfort of two nights tied up to trees and the speed with which the Indians had forced them along; the rescuers by the even greater speed with which they had followed. Boone therefore made

camp for the night after covering a relatively short distance.

Next day, entirely unmolested, they set out for home. Encountering the stray pony again, they stopped to catch it, and the girls who had pretended to so much trouble in staying on its back rode home to Boonesborough with no difficulty at all.

It all ended happily. The cane stab in Jemima Boone's foot, the original cause of the fatal canoe ride, had miraculously healed during her captivity. The Indian band at the Blue Licks which Hanging Maw had mentioned never appeared. The other band along the Kentucky River did little damage. Boonesborough gave itself up to rejoicing.

The anxious fiancés of the rescuing party made sure of their brides by getting married as soon as they could. Betsey Callaway had been kidnaped on July 7. She was married to Samuel Henderson on August 6. The other two girls, being only fourteen, were married to their admirers the following year, Jemima Boone to Flanders Callaway; Fanny Callaway to John Holder. Both bridegrooms had assisted in the rescue. Daniel Boone had had his own doubts about Jemima's suitor, but he withdrew them all after the share Flanders Callaway had taken in the pursuit of Hanging Maw. That worthy chief, quite unintentionally, had helped the course of true love on its way.

Hardly had Boonesborough settled down to the routine of everyday frontier life once more, when startling news arrived from the East. The Colonies had declared their independence. America was a nation, and Kentucky was part of it. A traveler brought with him a copy of the *Virginia Gazette*. The Declaration of Independence was read aloud from its pages, cheered, and celebrated with a bonfire. Soon there was a new flag fluttering in the forest.

(Stop. Note the time; and check your speed with the Reading Score Board, page 221.)

TO CONSIDER

1. In what ways were the girls able to leave signs for their rescuers?
2. How did Daniel Boone show his knowledge of the woods and of Indians?
3. What do you discover about the way the settlers lived in Boonesborough?
4. How do the first and last paragraphs of the story give a time setting?

ORGANIZED THINKING

To find out more about Daniel Boone himself, you undoubtedly would go to an encyclopedia. You would notice immediately that the material was organized for easy reading. For practice, consult your encyclopedia and find what is said on each of the following topics. On your paper, list the important details for each.

  I. Early life of Daniel Boone
  II. Building the Wilderness Road
  III. Boonsboro
  IV. Daniel Boone's later years

CHOOSING WORDS

Which word should be used in each of these sentences? What meaning does it give?

1. Daniel had strolled off on one of his (solemn, solitary) rambles.
2. The canoe became stuck on (an island, a sandbar).
3. The girls' struggles with the canoe were (futile, senile).
4. (Reformatory, Refractory) prisoners were usually tomahawked.
5. Each girl was (pinioned, beaten) at night with thongs at her elbows.
6. In spite of the Indians' (vigorous, vigilance) the girls broke many twigs.
7. The (intrepid, intrinsic) John Gass swam for the canoe.
8. The Indians took the (premonition, precaution) of wading along the stream.
9. One Indian paused in his (spirit, sprint) for the canebrake.
10. The anxious (finances, fiancés) made sure of their brides by marrying them.

WORDS OF THE WOODS

What do the following mean?

cane stab	canebrake	sniping	ambush
moccasins	thongs	the ford	a spit

READING SCORE BOARD

Number of Words in Story: 3430.

Number of Minutes	34	17	14	11 1/2	8 1/2	7
Reading Rate	100 w.p.m.	200 w.p.m.	250 w.p.m.	300 w.p.m.	400 w.p.m.	500 w.p.m.

⊰⊱ ARTHUR GUITERMAN

Daniel Boone

Here is the story of the great Daniel himself.

Daniel Boone at twenty-one
Came with his tomahawk, knife, and gun
Home from the French and Indian War
To North Carolina and the Yadkin shore.
He married his maid with a golden band,
Builded his house and cleared his land;
But the deep woods claimed their son again
And he turned his face from the homes of men.
Over the Blue Ridge, dark and lone,
The Mountains of Iron, the Hills of Stone,
Braving the Shawnee's jealous wrath,
He made his way on the Warrior's Path.
Alone he trod the shadowed trails;
But he was lord of a thousand vales
As he roved Kentucky, far and near,
Hunting the buffalo, elk, and deer.
What joy to see, what joy to win
So fair a land for his kith and kin,
Of streams unstained and woods unhewn!
"Elbowroom!" laughed Daniel Boone.

On the Wilderness Road that his axmen made
The settlers flocked to the first stockade;
The deerskin shirts and the coonskin caps

——Taken from *I Sing the Pioneer* by Arthur Guiterman, published and copyright 1926 by E. P. Dutton & Co., Inc., New York.

Filed through the glens and the mountain gaps;
And hearts were high in the fateful spring
When the land said, "Nay!" to the stubborn king.
While the men of the East of farm and town
Strove with the troops of the British Crown,
Daniel Boone from a surge of hate
Guarded a nation's westward gate.
Down on the fort in a wave of flame
The Shawnee horde and the Mingo came,
And the stout logs shook in a storm of lead;
But Boone stood firm, and the savage fled.
Peace! And the settlers flocked anew,
The farm lands spread, the town lands grew;
But Daniel Boone was ill at ease
When he saw smoke in his forest trees.
"There'll be no game in the country soon.
Elbowroom!" cried Daniel Boone.

Straight as a pine at sixty-five—
Time enough for a man to thrive—
He launched his bateau[1] on Ohio's breast
And his heart was glad as he oared it west;
There was kindly folk and his own true blood
Where great Missouri rolls his flood;
New woods, new streams, and room to spare,
And Daniel Boone found comfort there.
Yet far he ranged toward the sunset still
Where the Kansas runs and the Smoky Hill,
And the prairies toss, by the south wind blown;
And he killed his bear on the Yellowstone.
But ever he dreamed of new domains
With vaster woods and wider plains;
Ever he dreamed of a world-to-be
Where there are no bounds and the soul is free.
At fourscore-five, still stout and hale,
He heard a call to a farther trail;
So he turned his face where the stars are strewn;
"Elbowroom!" sighed Daniel Boone.

Down the Milky Way in its banks of blue
Far he has paddled his white canoe
To the splendid quest of the tameless soul—

_____
[1] *bateau.* A flat-bottomed boat.

He has reached the goal where there is no goal.
Now he rides and rides an endless trail
On the hippogriff[2] of the flaming tail
Or the horse of the stars with the golden mane,
As he rode the first of the blue-grass strain.
The joy that lies in the search he seeks
On breathless hills with crystal peaks;
He makes his camp on heights untrod,
The steps of the shrine, alone with God.
Through the woods of the vast, on the plains of space
He hunts the pride of the mammoth race
And the dinosaur of the triple horn,
The manticore[3] and the unicorn,
As once by the broad Missouri's flow
He followed the elk and the buffalo.
East of the sun and west of the moon,
"Elbowroom!" laughs Daniel Boone.

Biography in a Nutshell

1. How do the four stanzas give the outline of Daniel Boone's career? Can you give a title to each? Can you summarize each in a single sentence?

2. What are some of the facts you learn about Boone's life in each of the first three stanzas? Are these facts historically true? Check with your history book or with an encyclopedia.

3. How is the last stanza an excellent conclusion to the poem?

Meaning in Every Line

What do these lines mean?

1. He married his maid with a golden band,
2. Braving the Shawnee's jealous wrath,
3. When the land said, "Nay!" to the stubborn king.
4. Guarded a nation's westward gate.
5. He has reached the goal where there is no goal.

Look at the last line of each stanza. Why did Guiterman use the verbs *laughed*, *cried*, *sighed*, and *laughs*.

[2] *hippogriff*. A winged animal, part horse.
[3] *manticore*. A monster described in ancient fables.

◀◀ ROBERT HAVEN SCHAUFFLER

Washington

Sometimes we think of our great men of history as being stuffed shirts. Schauffler shows that George Washington was a real flesh-and-blood person.

Off with the ruffle!
Away with the wig!
No more shall they muffle
The soul of our big
Father of men.
Stockings of silk—
All of that ilk—
Strip them away
Swift as we may!
Joyously then
Burn the false reams
Of the Reverend Weems[1]—
Myth of the hatchet—
Others to match it.
Now see a man
Young for his age,
With a hearty laugh,
Lips that could quaff,
Lips that could rage,
An eye for the stage,
Or a fishing rod,
A close-run race,
Or a charming face.
No statue, he!
Look, and we see
No carefully shod
Gray demigod
Carved by smug preachers
And treacherous teachers.

——Reprinted by permission of Dodd, Mead & Company from *New and Selected Poems* by Robert Haven Schauffler. Copyright, 1942, by Robert Haven Schauffler.

[1] *Reverend Weems*, The early biographer of Washington; one who started the cherry-tree myth.

Down with the wig
And the mask of the prig!
Do what they can
To smooth and conceal it,
They're forced to reveal it—
He was a *man!*

⋖⋐⋗

OFF WITH THE RUFFLE!

1. Why are so many of our historical figures painted as stuffed shirts?
2. What details does Schauffler give to show that Washington was a real person?
3. What do you think of the short lines of the poem? Why are they effective?

⋖⋐ HENRY WADSWORTH LONGFELLOW

Paul Revere's Ride

Because of Longfellow's poem, Paul Revere is remembered chiefly for a famous ride he took one night in April of 1775 to warn the country folk around Lexington of the British plans to attack. Today we scarcely think of Paul Revere as a real man at all but, as his biographer says, more as "a symbol of preparedness, awareness of danger."
But it *was* an exciting ride, as you will see.

Listen, my children, and you shall hear
Of the midnight ride of Paul Revere,
On the eighteenth of April, in Seventy-five;
Hardly a man is now alive
Who remembers that famous day and year.

He said to his friend, "If the British march
By land or sea from the town tonight,
Hang a lantern aloft in the belfry arch
Of the North Church tower as a signal light—
One, if by land, and two, if by sea;
And I on the opposite shore will be,
Ready to ride and spread the alarm
Through every Middlesex village and farm,
For the country folk to be up and to arm."

——Used by permission of and arrangement with Houghton Mifflin Company, the authorized publishers.

Then he said, "Good night!" and with muffled oar
Silently rowed to the Charlestown shore,
Just as the moon rose over the bay,
Where swinging wide at her moorings lay
The *Somerset*, British man-of-war;
A phantom ship, with each mast and spar
Across the moon like a prison bar,
And a huge black hulk, that was magnified
By its own reflection in the tide.

Meanwhile, his friend, through alley and street,
Wanders and watches with eager ears,
Till in the silence around him he hears
The muster of men at the barrack door,
The sound of arms, and the tramp of feet,
And the measured tread of the grenadiers,
Marching down to their boats on the shore.

Then he climbed the tower of the Old North Church,
By the wooden stairs, with stealthy tread,
To the belfry-chamber overhead,
And startled the pigeons from their perch
On the somber rafters, that round him made
Masses and moving shapes of shade—
By the trembling ladder, steep and tall,
To the highest window in the wall,
Where he paused to listen and look down
A moment on the roofs of the town,
And the moonlight flowing over all.

Beneath, in the churchyard, lay the dead,
In their night-encampment on the hill,
Wrapped in silence so deep and still
That he could hear, like a sentinel's tread,
The watchful night-wind, as it went
Creeping along from tent to tent,
And seeming to whisper, "All is well!"
A moment only he feels the spell
Of the place and the hour, and the secret dread
Of the lonely belfry and the dead;
For suddenly all his thoughts are bent
On a shadowy something far away,
Where the river widens to meet the bay—

A line of black that bends and floats
On the rising tide, like a bridge of boats.

Meanwhile, impatient to mount and ride,
Booted and spurred, with a heavy stride
On the opposite shore walked Paul Revere.
Now he patted his horse's side,
Now gazed at the landscape far and near,
Then, impetuous, stamped the earth,
And turned and tightened his saddle-girth;
But mostly he watched with eager search
The belfry-tower of the Old North Church,
As it rose above the graves on the hill,
Lonely and spectral and somber and still.
And lo! as he looks, on the belfry's height
A glimmer, and then a gleam of light!
He springs to the saddle, the bridle he turns,
But lingers and gazes, till full on his sight
A second lamp in the belfry burns!

A hurry of hoofs in a village street,
A shape in the moonlight, a bulk in the dark,
And beneath, from the pebbles, in passing, a spark
Struck out by a steed flying fearless and fleet:
That was all! And yet, through the gloom and the light,
The fate of a nation was riding that night;
And the spark struck out by that steed, in his flight,
Kindled the land into flame with its heat.
He has left the village and mounted the steep,
And beneath him, tranquil and broad and deep,
Is the Mystic, meeting the ocean tides;
And under the alders that skirt its edge,
Now soft on the sand, now loud on the ledge,
Is heard the tramp of his steed as he rides.

It was twelve by the village clock
When he crossed the bridge into Medford town.
He heard the crowing of the cock,
And the barking of the farmer's dog,
And felt the damp of the river fog,
That rises after the sun goes down.

It was one by the village clock
When he galloped into Lexington.
He saw the gilded weathercock
Swim in the moonlight as he passed,
And the meeting-house windows, blank and bare,
Gaze at him with a spectral glare,
As if they already stood aghast
At the bloody work they would look upon.

It was two by the village clock,
When he came to the bridge in Concord town.
He heard the bleating of the flock,
And the twitter of birds among the trees,
And felt the breath of the morning breeze
Blowing over the meadows brown.
And one was safe and asleep in his bed
Who at the bridge would be first to fall,
Who that day would be lying dead,
Pierced by a British musket-ball.

You know the rest. In the books you have read,
How the British Regulars fired and fled—
How the farmers gave them ball for ball,
From behind each fence and farmyard wall,
Chasing the redcoats down the lane,
Then crossing the fields to emerge again
Under the trees at the turn of the road,
And only pausing to fire and load.

So through the night rode Paul Revere;
And so through the night went his cry of alarm
To every Middlesex village and farm—
A cry of defiance and not of fear,
A voice in the darkness, a knock at the door,
And a word that shall echo forevermore!
For, borne on the night-wind of the Past,
Through all our history, to the last,
In the hour of darkness and peril and need,
The people will waken and listen to hear
The hurrying hoofbeats of that steed,
And the midnight message of Paul Revere.

A Front-page News Story

1. A reporter, in writing the story of this famous ride, would have to answer these questions: Who? What? When? Where? How? Why? Can you answer them?

2. Can you trace what Paul Revere did, hour by hour?

3. How would the last six lines be more appropriate for an editorial than for a news story?

The Right Words Give Television

What pictures flash into your mind when you read these groups of words?

belfry arch	phantom ship	night-encampment
country folk	measured tread	booted and spurred
muffled oar	trembling ladder	gilded weathercock

The Whole Story about Paul Revere

Paul Revere's famous ride has completely overshadowed all the other interesting facts of his life. Consult an encyclopedia or a good biography of him, and find out the whole story. What facts do you find that should go under these two headings?

I. Paul Revere, the patriot

II. Paul Revere, the craftsman

How does the organization of ideas help you to understand and remember what you read?

ᐁ Douglas Southall Freeman

General Lee at the Surrender

The greatness of Robert E. Lee's character was seen in the bitterest moment of his life—the defeat of the Confederate Army. Here is the story of Lee's meeting with Grant on April 9, 1865.

Douglas Southall Freeman is a colorful and exact writer. It is said that in the anxious days before D-Day of World War II, General Omar Bradley spent much of his time reading one of Freeman's volumes about Lee.

(Note the time when you begin reading.)

As the little cavalcade passed toward the village of Appomattox, Lee had to arouse himself and arrange the details: Grant had left it to him to select the place of meeting. Would

——Reprinted from *R. E. Lee*, *Vol. IV* by Douglas Southall Freeman; copyright 1935 by Charles Scribner's Sons; used by permission of the publishers.

Marshall go ahead and find a suitable house? Obediently, the colonel trotted off. Lee remained with Babcock. They did not talk—how could they?

After a while the orderly returned to say that Colonel Marshall had found a room for the conference. Lee went on and, under the soldier's guidance, drew rein beyond the court-house in the yard of a house on the left-hand side of the road to Lynch-burg.

Lee dismounted in the yard; and after the orderly took Traveller [his famous horse], he walked toward the wide steps that led to the covered porch which ran the whole width of the house. Entering the central hall, at the top of the steps, he turned into the front room on his left, a typical parlor of a middle-class Virginia home.

Half an hour passed, perhaps the longest half hour in Lee's whole life. If there was any conversation, it was in snatches and was slow, labored, and vague. About 1:30 o'clock there was a clatter in the road, the sound of the approach of a large body of mounted men. They drew nearer, they halted, they dismounted. Some of them climbed the steps. Babcock went to the door and opened it. A man of middle height, slightly stooped and heavily bearded, came in alone. He was dressed for the field, with boots and breeches mud-bespattered. He took off his yellow thread gloves as he stepped forward. Lee had never seen him to remember him, but he knew who he was and, rising with Marshall, he started across the room to meet General Grant. They shook hands quietly with brief greetings. Then Grant sat down at the table in the middle of the room, and Lee returned to his place.

The conversation began: "I met you once before, General Lee," Grant said in his normal tones, "while we were serving in Mexico, when you came over from General Scott's head-quarters to visit Garland's brigade, to which I then belonged. I have always remembered your appearance, and I think I should have recognized you anywhere."

"Yes," answered Lee quietly, "I know I met you on that occasion, and I have often thought of it and tried to recollect how you looked, but I have never been able to recall a single feature."

Mention of Mexico aroused many memories. Grant pursued them with so much interest and talked of them so readily that the conversation went easily on until the Federal was almost forgetting what he was about. Lee felt the weight of every moment and brought Grant back with words that seemed to come naturally, yet must have cost him anguish that cannot be measured.

"I suppose, General Grant," he said, "that the object of our present meeting is fully understood. I asked to see you to ascertain upon what terms you would receive the surrender of my army."

Grant did not change countenance or exhibit the slightest note of exul-tation in his reply. "The terms I pro-pose are those stated substantially in my letter of yesterday—that is, the offi-cers and men surrendered are to be paroled and disqualified from taking up arms again until properly ex-changed, and all arms, ammunition and supplies to be delivered up as captured property."

Lee nodded an assent that meant more than his adversary realized. The phantom of a proud army being marched away to prison disappeared as Grant spoke, and the hope Lee had first expressed to Taylor that morning was confirmed. "Those," said he, "are about the conditions I expected would be proposed."

"Yes," Grant answered, "I think our correspondence indicated pretty clearly the action that would be taken at our meeting; and I hope it may lead to a general suspension of hostilities and be the means of preventing any further loss of life."

Grant talked on of peace and its prospects. Lee waited and then, courteously, but in a manifest desire to finish the business in hand, he said: "I presume, General Grant, we have both carefully considered the proper steps to be taken, and I would suggest that you commit to writing the terms you have proposed, so that they may be formally acted upon."

"Very well, I will write them out."

Lee sat in silence and looked straight ahead as Grant called for his manifold order book, opened it, lit his pipe, puffed furiously, wrote steadily for a while with his pencil, paused, reflected, wrote two sentences, and then quickly completed the text. Grant went over it in an undertone with one of his military secretaries, who interlined a few words. Lee did not follow any of this. He sat as he was until Grant rose, crossed to him, and put the manifold book in his hands, with the request that he read over the letter.

Lee probably was at his tensest then, for he busied himself with little mechanical acts as though to master his nerves. He placed the book on the table. He took his spectacles from his pocket. He pulled out his handkerchief. He wiped off the glasses, he crossed his legs, he set his glasses very carefully on his nose, and then he took up the order book for a slow, careful reading:

> Appomattox C. H. Va.
> Apr. 9th, 1865.

Gen. R. E. Lee,
  Comd. C. S. A.
Gen.

In accordance with the substance of my letter to you of the 8th instant I propose to receive the surrender of the Army of N. Va. on the following terms, to-wit:

Rolls of all the officers and men to be made in duplicate, one copy to be given to an officer designated by me, the other to be retained by such officer or officers as you may designate. The officers to give their individual paroles not to take up arms against the

—At this point, Lee turned the page and read on——

Government of the United States until properly and each company or regimental sign a like parole for the men of their command.

Lee stopped in his reading, looked up, and said to Grant: "After the words 'until properly,' the word 'exchanged' seems to be omitted. You doubtless intended to use that word."

"Why, yes," answered Grant, "I thought I had put in the word 'exchanged.'"

"I presumed it had been omitted inadvertently, and with your permission

I will mark where it should be inserted."

"Certainly."

Lee felt for a pencil but could not find one. Colonel Horace Porter stepped forward and offered his. Lee took it, thanked him, placed the book on the table, inserted the caret, and resumed his reading:

The arms, artillery, and public property to be parked and stacked and turned over to the officer appointed by me to receive them.

This will not embrace the side arms of the officers, nor their private horses or baggage. This done each officer and man will be allowed to return to their homes not to be disturbed by United States authority so long as they observe their paroles and the laws in force where they may reside.

Very respectfully,

U. S. GRANT, Lt Gl.

There was a slight change in Lee's expression as he read the closing sentences, and his tone was not without warmth as now he looked up at Grant and said: "This will have a very happy effect on my army."

"Unless you have some suggestions to make in regard to the form in which I have stated the terms," Grant resumed, "I will have a copy of the letter made in ink and sign it."

Lee hesitated: "There is one thing I would like to mention. The cavalrymen and artillerists own their own horses in our army. Its organization in this respect differs from that of the United States. I would like to understand whether these men will be permitted to retain their horses."

"You will find," answered Grant, "that the terms as written do not allow this. Only the officers are allowed to take their private property."

Lee read over the second page of the letter again. For months he had agonized over his field transportation and cavalry mounts. He knew what the army's horses would mean to the South, stripped as it had been of all draft animals, and he wanted those of his men who owned mounts to have them for the spring ploughing. His face showed his wish. His tongue would not go beyond a regretful "No, I see the terms do not allow it; that is clear."

Grant read his opponent's wish, and, with the fine consideration that prevailed throughout the conversation—one of the noblest of his qualities, and one of the surest evidences of his greatness—he did not humiliate Lee by forcing him to make a direct plea for a modification of terms that were generous. "Well, the subject is quite new to me. Of course, I did not know that any private soldiers owned their animals, but I think this will be the last battle of the war—I sincerely hope so—and that the surrender of this army will be followed soon by that of all the others, and I take it that most of the men in the ranks are small farmers, and as the country has been so raided by the two armies, it is doubtful whether they will be able to put in a crop to carry themselves and their families through the next winter without the aid of the horses they are now riding, and I will arrange it this way: I will not change the terms as now written, but I will instruct the officers I shall appoint to receive the paroles to let all the men who claim to own a horse or mule to take the animals home with them to work their little farms."

It could not have been put more understandingly or more generously. Lee showed manifest relief and appreciation. "This will have the best possible effect upon the men," he said; "it will be very gratifying and will do much toward conciliating our people."

While Grant set about having his letter copied, Lee directed Marshall to draft a reply.

The finished letter was soon brought Lee and was read over by him:

Lieut-Gen. U. S. Grant,
    Commanding Armies of the United
        States.
    General: I have received your letter of this date containing the terms of surrender of the Army of Northern Virginia as proposed by you. As they are substantially the same as those expressed in your letter of the 8th instant, they are accepted. I will proceed to designate the proper officers to carry the stipulations into effect.
Very respectfully, your obedient servant.

Lee put his signature to this without a quiver. Marshall sealed it and went over to Parker, who already had Grant's letter waiting for him, duly signed and in an addressed envelope. They made the exchange and the surrender was complete. It was then about 3:45 P.M.

The rest was casual and brief. Grant explained why he was without his sword. Lee is said to have remarked that he usually wore his when with the army in the field. Then Lee requested that Grant notify Meade of the surrender, so that firing might not break out and men be slain to no purpose. He requested also, that pending the actual surrender, the two armies be kept separate, so that personal encounters would be avoided. Grant acquiesced immediately and suggested that time might be saved if two of his officers rode to Meade through the Confederate lines.

Lee thereupon rose, shook hands with General Grant, bowed to the spectators and passed from the room. He went through the hall to the porch, where several Federal officers at once sprang to their feet and saluted. Putting on his hat, Lee mechanically but with manifest courtesy returned their salute and with measured tread crossed the porch. At the head of the steps he drew on his gauntlets, and absently smote his hands together several times as he looked into space—across the valley to the hillside where his faithful little army lay. In a moment he aroused himself and, not seeing his mount, called in a voice that was hoarse and half-choked, "Orderly! Orderly!" Quickly Tucker answered from the corner of the house, where he was holding Traveller's rein as the steed grazed. Lee walked down the steps and stood in front of the animal while the man replaced the bridle. Lee himself drew the forelock from under the brow band and parted and smoothed it. Then, as Tucker stepped aside, Lee mounted slowly and with an audible sigh. At that moment General Grant stepped down from the porch on his way to the gate, where his horse was waiting. Stopping suddenly, Grant took off his hat but did not speak. The other Federalists followed the courteous example of their chief. Lee raised his hat, without a word, turned his horse and rode away to an ordeal worse than a meeting with Grant— the ordeal of breaking the news to his soldiers and of telling them farewell.

By no means all the men were prepared for the surrender. The rapidity of the retreat, the failure of rations, and the dwindling of brigades to companies had spelled disaster in the minds of the intelligent. The circle of fire reflected on the clouds the night of the 8th had convinced the discerning that the army was virtually surrounded. The halt of the morning and the frequent passage of flags of truce had confirmed their fears of capitulation.[1] Yet such was the faith of the army in itself and in its commander that many were unwilling to believe the end had come.

Lee came toward them, down from the ridge, across the little valley, up the hillside through the pickets, and into the line. He was as erect as ever, but he was staring straight ahead of him, with none of the cheerfulness and composure that usually marked his countenance even in the most dreadful moments of his hardest battles. The men started to cheer him, as they often did when he rode among them; but somehow their cheers froze in their throats at the sight of him. They hesitated a moment as he rode

fixedly on, and then without a word they broke ranks and rushed toward him.

"General," they began to cry, "are we surrendered?"

The question was like a blow in the face. He tried to go on; but they crowded about him, bareheaded. He removed his hat in acknowledgment and attempted once more to proceed. The road was too full of frenzied, famished faces. He had to halt and answer his loyal old soldiers. "Men," he said, "we have fought the war together, and I have done the best I could for you. You will all be paroled and go to your homes until exchanged." Tears came into his eyes as he spoke. He attempted to say more but even his amazing self-mastery failed him. Moving his lips in a choking "good-by," he again essayed to ride on to the orchard from which he had come.

"General, we'll fight 'em yet," they answered.

"General, say the word and we'll go in and fight 'em yet."

Everywhere as the news spread, each soldier reacted to it in his own fashion. Some wept, openly and without abashment. Others were dazed, as though they did not understand how the Army of Northern Virginia, Lee's army, could surrender. To Field's division, which had suffered little on the retreat, it seemed incomprehensible. To others, it was as the very end of the world. "Blow, Gabriel, blow!" cried one man, and threw down his musket as General Grimes told him what had happened. "My God, let him blow, I am ready to die!"

[1] *capitulation.* Surrender.

Some blasphemed and some babbled, but all who could do so crowded to say farewell to Lee. Catching hold of his hands, they looked up at him and cried the more. They touched his uniform or his bridle rein, if they could not grasp his hand; and if they could not reach him, they smoothed Traveller's flanks or patted his neck. And in a confused roar, half-sob, half-acclamation, they voiced their love for him, their faith in him, their goodby to him as their commander.

The sun was now near its setting. The immediate duties were done. Lee started toward his headquarters, which were under a large white oak, about a mile to the rear. As he went, the scenes of his return from the interview with General Grant were repeated in heightened pathos. For now the whole army knew that the surrender had occurred, and most of the intelligent men had been given time to reflect what that act meant to him who was, in their eyes, both cause and country. "There was," Blackford wrote, "a general rush from each side of the road to greet him as he passed, and two solid walls of men were formed along the whole distance. Their officers followed, and behind the lines of men were groups of them, mounted and dismounted, awaiting his coming. . . . As soon as he entered this avenue of these old soldiers, the flower of the army, the men who had stood to their duty through thick and thin in so many battles, wild, heartfelt cheers arose which so touched General Lee that tears filled his eyes and trickled down his cheeks as he rode his splendid charger, hat in hand, bowing his acknowledgments. This exhibition of feeling on his part found quick response from the men whose cheers changed to choking sobs as, with streaming eyes and many evidences of affection, they waved their hats as he passed. Each group began in the same way, with cheers, and ended in the same way, with sobs, all along the route to his quarters. Grim, bearded men threw themselves on the ground, covering their faces with their hands and wept like children. Officers of all ranks made no attempt to conceal their feelings, but sat on their horses and cried aloud. Traveller took as much pleasure in applause as a human being, and acknowledged the cheers of the troops by tosses of his head and the men frequently cheered him for it, to which he would answer back as often as they did. On this, Traveller's last appearance before them, his head was tossing a return to the salutes all along the line. One man extended his arms, and with an emphatic gesture said, "I love you just as well as ever, General Lee!"

They thronged about him when he reached his headquarters; and when he dismounted, all who were in sight of his camp hastened up.

"Let me get in," they began to cry. "Let me bid him farewell."

Lee stood with Long and Stevens and a few other old personal friends, and he sought to keep his composure; but as man after man crowded around him, each with warm words, his eyes filled anew with tears. In broken phrases he told his veterans to go home, to plant a crop and to obey the law, and again and again he tried to say farewell. But they would not have it so. One handsome private, a gentleman in bearing, for all his dirt and rags, shook hands and said, "General, I have had the honor of serving in this army since you took command. If I thought I were to blame for what has occurred today, I could not look you in the face, but I always try to do my duty. I hope I have the honor of serving under you again. Good-by, General; God bless you."

Lee lifted his hat once more in salute and went into his tent . . . to be alone.

(Note the time; and check your reading rate with the Reading Score Board, page 237.)

❧❦❧

TRIBUTE TO A GREAT HERO

1. Again and again in the selection General Lee's greatness is seen. Point out passages which prove his heroism.

2. In moments of crisis the greatness or the meanness of a person can be seen. How is this selection proof of that statement?

3. How is Grant's fineness of spirit also shown?

4. In what ways are the last two pages of the story sad?

KEY WORDS

How are these words important to the story? What does each mean?

Nouns

cavalcade	hostilities	capitulation
adversary	mounts	abashment
suspension	modification	pathos

Verbs

dismounted	agonized	confirmed
ascertain	humiliate	blasphemed
paroled	acquiesced	acknowledged

SHINING RECORDS

1. If you can find a good biography of Grant, compare the story of the surrender as it is told there with the story by Freeman that you have just read.

2. The account of General Lee at the surrender is only one part of the fascinating story of his life. Using a reference book, complete and add to the following outline:

   I. Lee's record as a young soldier
      A. At eighteen was sent to West Point
      B. =?=
      C. =?=
      D. =?=
   II. Lee's life after the conclusion of the War between the States

READING SCORE BOARD

Number of Words in Story: 3330.

Number of Minutes	33	16 1/2	13 1/3	11	8 1/4	6 2/3
Reading Rate	100 w.p.m.	200 w.p.m.	250 w.p.m.	300 w.p.m.	400 w.p.m.	500 w.p.m.

✧ ABRAHAM LINCOLN

The Gettysburg Address

Lincoln gave the following address after a two-hour oration delivered by the brilliant Edward Everett. There may have been some doubts when Abraham Lincoln rose to speak; but after the first few words, there could be no doubts. A hush fell upon the people. At the conclusion, there was no applause, for they were too moved. They felt it would be like applauding a prayer.

"The Gettysburg Address" is recognized everywhere as one of the masterpieces of all literature.

FOURSCORE and seven years ago our fathers brought forth on this continent a new nation, conceived in liberty, and dedicated to the proposition that all men are created equal.

Now we are engaged in a great civil war, testing whether that nation, or any nation so conceived and so dedicated, can long endure. We are met on a great battlefield of that war. We have come to dedicate a portion of that field as a final resting place for those who here gave their lives that that nation might live. It is altogether fitting and proper that we should do this.

But, in a larger sense, we cannot dedicate—we cannot consecrate—we cannot hallow—this ground. The brave men, living and dead, who struggled here, have consecrated it far above our poor power to add or detract. The world will little note nor long remember what we say here, but it can never forget what they did here. It is for us, the living, rather, to be dedicated here to the unfinished work which they who fought here have thus far so nobly advanced. It is rather for us to be here dedicated to the great task remaining before us—that from these honored dead we take increased devotion to that cause for which they gave the last full measure of devotion; that we here highly resolve that these dead shall not have died in vain; that this nation, under God, shall have a new birth of freedom; and that government of the people, by the people, for the people, shall not perish from the earth.

November 19, 1863

❖❖❖

AN ADDRESS OF THE AGES—"THE GETTYSBURG ADDRESS"

Write in a single sentence why, in your opinion, this brief address is considered one of the greatest pieces of writing in the English language. Discuss your sentences.

LINCOLN STILL SPEAKS

1. In what ways are Lincoln's words as fitting today as they were in 1863?
2. How did Lincoln's theme, expressed in the first sentence and repeated in the last, help to bind the wounds of war? How is that theme a world issue today?
3. Do you find any feeling of hatred in the address? any sentimentality?

A BIBLICAL ROLL OF WORDS

One of the few books that Lincoln had in his boyhood years was the Bible. Its influence can be seen in his vocabulary. What word or words might another speaker, without this influence, have used for each of these?

fourscore and seven years ago	hallow
proposition	devotion
consecrate	perish

❖❖ WALT WHITMAN

O Captain! My Captain!

In figurative language, Walt Whitman is writing of the death of Abraham Lincoln. He refers to Lincoln as "my Captain" and to the country as "the ship." This is one of the most beloved poems in American literature.

O Captain! my Captain! our fearful trip is done,
The ship has weather'd every rack, the prize we sought is won,
The port is near, the bells I hear, the people all exulting,
While follow eyes the steady keel, the vessel grim and daring;
　　But O heart! heart! heart!
　　　　O the bleeding drops of red,

Where on the deck my Captain lies,
    Fallen cold and dead.

O Captain! my Captain! rise up and hear the bells;
Rise up—for you the flag is flung—for you the bugle trills,
For you bouquets and ribbon'd wreaths—for you the shores a-crowding
For you they call, the swaying mass, their eager faces turning;
    Here Captain! dear father!
        This arm beneath your head!
            It is some dream that on the deck,
                You've fallen cold and dead.

My Captain does not answer, his lips are pale and still,
My father does not feel my arm, he has no pulse nor will,
The ship is anchor'd safe and sound, its voyage closed and done,
From fearful trip the victor ship comes in with object won;
    Exult O shores, and ring O bells!
        But I with mournful tread
            Walk the deck my Captain lies,
                Fallen cold and dead.

❖❰❖

Meanings within Meanings

Can you complete each of these statements?
1. The "Captain" is really =?=.
2. The "fearful trip is done" refers to =?=.
3. The "prize we sought is won" refers to =?=.
4. The phrase "bleeding drops of red" indicates =?=.
5. The "ship is anchored safe and sound" means =?=.

Words and Rhythms

As you have already seen, the words of the poem help to create its dignity and its emotion. What do these phrases mean?

1. weather'd every rack   4. vessel grim
2. people all exulting   5. ribbon'd wreaths
3. steady keel   6. mournful tread

Rhythm has been used for a similar purpose.
1. How and why does each stanza change in length of line?
2. How does the last stanza differ from the first two?

❧ ROSEMARY AND STEPHEN VINCENT BENÉT

Nancy Hanks

Here is a poem that shows a mother's love for her son. The mother happens to be Nancy Hanks; and the son, Abraham Lincoln. Much of the meaning of the poem hinges on the first four lines; don't miss them.

If Nancy Hanks
Came back as a ghost,
Seeking news
Of what she loved most,
She'd ask first,
"Where's my son?
What's happened to Abe?
What's he done?

"Poor little Abe,
Left all alone
Except for Tom,
Who's a rolling stone;
He was only nine
The year I died.
I remember still
How hard he cried.

"Scraping along
In a little shack,
With hardly a shirt
To cover his back,
And a prairie wind
To blow him down,
Or pinching times
If he went to town.

"You wouldn't know
About my son?
Did he grow tall?
Did he have fun?

Did he learn to read?
Did he get to town?
Do you know his name?
Did he get on?"

❖❖❖

The Meaning

1. Why are the first four lines important to an understanding of the poem?
2. What are the details that make this a pathetic little poem?

❖❖ Donald Culross Peattie

Heart's Blood

Sometimes, perhaps, we take the Red Cross for granted. We forget that it was born in blood and tears. We forget the frail little woman—Clara Barton —who risked her life to care for the wounded and dying.
(Note the time when you begin reading.)

Upon the darkening battlefield at Fredericksburg, his right arm mangled, lay a boy not long out of school. If he had any hopes of survival, they were that the enemy stretcher bearers might find him; then, if he lived that long, he would meet the surgeon's knife dripping bacterial filth. After that, if he escaped gangrene, he would be transferred to a Confederate prison camp, there to battle typhoid, typhus, pneumonia, and tuberculosis. As he lay on the field of agony, the best he could hope to see was the old yellow hospital flag coming, with its associations of quarantine and death. For in

——From *Journey into America* by Donald Culross Peattie. Reprinted by permission of and arrangement with Houghton Mifflin Company, the authorized publishers.

1862 no one had yet looked upon the blood-bright emblem of the Red Cross.

A woman's face appeared above him, a human angel with dark compassionate eyes, long tender mouth, and hands like his mother's. Save his own mother there was no person in the world he would have been so glad to see. For he recognized his old teacher, Miss Barton, Clara Barton of the low, sweet voice, who had never punished a child, in an age of plentiful school thrashings; Miss Barton who by sheer comradeship had conquered the hobbledehoy toughs taller than she. Clara Barton, whom everybody loved.

With a sob the boy flung his left

arm around her neck, and buried his face in the cloak of the pitying woman. "Do you know me?" he cried. "I am Charley Hamilton, who used to carry your satchel home from school!" Charley's right arm, she saw, would never carry a satchel again.

At Clara Barton's call, stretcher bearers came for Charley. Across the field a surgeon's lantern wavered toward them. There was just one woman on that field, and hundreds of men needed her.

So this little woman—she was exactly five feet tall and forty years of age, slender, nervous, almost morbidly responsive to suffering—daily and hourly met with her womanhood the man-made agonies of war. She was great enough for the encounter. In Civil War times no mere lady even dreamed of nursing at the front; husband-hunting ninnies were turned back every day. The army nurses, who had to qualify first through personal selection by aged and overworked Dorothea Dix,[1] seldom left the walls of the base hospital, where only a small fraction of the wounded ever arrived.

Clara Barton, the future founder of the American Red Cross, went out on the field. She belonged to no organization, had no official standing, and reached the desperately wounded only by battling for passes through the naturally preoccupied resistance of generals, surgeons, the Sanitary Commission, quartermasters, and supply-train drivers. She was simply a compassionate woman who, sometimes as-sisted by a few other women, sometimes hindered even by her friends, fought the pitched battle of mercy against Mars.[2]

Clara Barton was born near Worcester, Massachusetts, in 1821, on Christmas Day. To me it seems that she was one of the few persons in the history of the human race not miserably unworthy of the comparison which that anniversary invites.

From her father, an old Indian-fighter, she had gained a precocious mastery of military affairs. She knew a major from a colonel when she could hardly see his uniform for mud or darkness; she remembered regimental numbers, listened without a blush to the blue swearing of army muleteers beside her on the wagon trains, and she comprehended the respective duties of the Sanitary Commission, the army surgeon, and the quartermaster. Unlike most women in wartime, she never considered herself an exception to the rule; she went where she was told, and troubled to obtain the right sort of passport. Military men quickly came to perceive all this; regiments recognized her, and cheered her as she trudged past them in the rain, going up to the front with clothes, bandages, fruits, jellies, sweets, wines, messages from home.

It was after the first battle of Bull Run that Clara Barton, then a clerk in the Patent Office at the capital, had begun to realize that every hour that elapses between a wound and arrival at a base hospital increases in geometrical ratio the likelihood of death. Men who might have been

[1] *Dorothea Dix.* American social reformer, superintendent of women nurses during the War between the States.

[2] *Mars.* God of war.

saved if their forces had been rallied at the start were hopeless cases before they reached the operating tents. She saw men who had been waiting so long in the stretcher queues that their feet had rotted off from gangrene, and she fought that fatal delay.

Surgeons sometimes opposed her. Regulation army nurses often looked coldly upon her. But Clara Barton knew that Ladies' Aid Societies at home were not enough, nor was the Sanitary Commission; and by sheer force of accomplishment slowly she won her way. When a doctor shaking with fatigue staggered from the operating tent where his last candle had guttered out, through the darkness a small cloaked figure came toward him, behind her a man bearing a whole chest of candles. When the anesthetics gave out, Clara Barton was there with stimulants. She soon learned that "missing" was the most ominous word in the ghastly reports of the battles. She found thousands of missing men for their families.

Behind her she had only two slim organizations, a group of women in Worcester and another in Bordentown, New Jersey—little towns, that's all, but with big-hearted people in them. They helped, and Clara Barton used her own money without thought. For herself, dainty and feminine though she was, she spent practically nothing, like a nun, a lay Sister of Charity. In spite of the opposition of Secretary of War Stanton, she found army friends who helped her; they would tell her when a big battle was coming on. "Follow the cannon" was her motto. And when the soldiers saw her, they joked, "Here comes the stormy petrel!"[3]

At Fredericksburg, with the troops, she crossed the Rappahannock under that murderous fire, ahead of all the army doctors and nurses. In the streets a man to whom she stopped to give a drink was shot dead in her arms; the bullet went through her sleeve. It was a rent she never mended.

At Chatham, those days after the battle, the stormy petrel—in truth a dark dove of mercy—found that "twelve hundred men were crowded into the Lacy House, which contained but twelve rooms. They covered every foot of the floors and porticoes and even lay on the stair landings!" Through that crowd, unknown to each other, moved Clara Barton and Walt Whitman,[4] who had come to seek his brother the captain. The man with the brushy beard and rubicund face, with the sombrero cocked over a heavy-lidded, pitying, and too-knowing eye, must have remarked the quick, prim, trim woman with the bit of red at her throat. Miss Barton had a passion for red; there was always a fleck of it about her frugal dress. Though it had not yet taken the shape of a cross, it seemed to symbolize for her the heart's blood which she put into her work. She saw Walt, no doubt, but her business was with the broken and dying; as for him, he found his brother, wounded, but now he found, too, that these were all his brothers. Those walls echoed with

[3] *stormy petrel.* A bird that is always active just before a storm; hence, it is thought of as a harbinger of trouble.

[4] *Walt Whitman.* American poet; see page 493.

agony, and outside, Walt writes, "I notice a heap of amputated feet, legs, arms, hands, etc., about a load for a one-horse cart." Into that vintage trampled from the grapes of wrath, two of the amplest souls our nation ever bore distilled a Godlike love that sanctifies the wine.

(How long did it take you to read this story? Check your reading rate with the Reading Score Board, page 245.)

❖❖❖

A FAMOUS WOMAN

1. In what ways was Clara Barton's work of mercy hard for her?
2. In what ways was she suited for the work?
3. What medical aid was given wounded soldiers? Contrast the conditions then with those of World War II.
4. What hint is given concerning the selection of the symbol of the Red Cross?
5. Who was Walt Whitman?

PARAGRAPHS WITH DESIGN

Several paragraphs of the story explain important points. A topic sentence is given, and it is followed by a number of details for proof. List the details which prove each of these topic sentences:

1. Clara Barton, the future founder of the American Red Cross, went out on the field. (page 242)
2. From her father, an old Indian-fighter, she had gained a precocious mastery of military affairs. (page 242)

Some paragraphs contain excellent description. Can you find the passages which describe Clara Barton and Walt Whitman?

WORDS RICH IN MEANING

What does each of these mean?
1. the surgeon's knife dripping *bacterial filth*
2. conquered the *hobbledehoy toughs* taller than she
3. in the stretcher *queues*
4. "missing" was the most *ominous* word
5. Here comes the *stormy petrel!*
6. the man with the brushy beard and the *rubicund* face
7. a *fleck* of it about her *frugal* dress

INFORMATION WELL ORGANIZED

There is much more to the story of Clara Barton than what you have read in this chapter. Mr. Peattie has only pulled aside the curtain. Consult a reference book for interesting facts about each of the following. Notice especially the organization of facts in each of the articles.

1. Clara Barton   2. The Red Cross   3. Walt Whitman

READING SCORE BOARD

Number of Words in Story: 1240.

Number of Minutes	12	6	5	4	3	2 1/2
Reading Rate	100 w.p.m.	200 w.p.m.	250 w.p.m.	300 w.p.m.	400 w.p.m.	500 w.p.m.

PHRASES, NOT WORDS

Analyze several paragraphs of the story about Clara Barton, deciding on the natural phrases that the eyes should make to pick up meaning rapidly.

◆C ARTHUR HUFF FAUSET

Booker T. Washington

Here is the story of a Negro boy who took the name of the father of his country for his own name. Everyone knows that he lived to become the leader of his race and an honored American.
(Note the time when you begin reading.)

LITTLE BOOKER did not know either the time of his birth or who his father was. He judged that he was born about 1858 or 1859. Later in life he celebrated his birthday on Easter Sunday. He *did* know that he had been born a slave and that the place of his birth was a plantation near Hale's Ford, Franklin County, Virginia.

Think of having to live in an old shack which was used as the plantation kitchen, in which the only windows were openings in the sides through which the sickening hot sun poured in the summer, and icy cold blasts of wind blew in the winter!

——From *For Freedom* by Arthur Huff Fauset, copyright 1927. Used by permission of the Publishers, Franklin Publishing and Supply Company.

His bed was a bundle of old rags. His clothing was scanty. The food he received was meager and unwholesome, consisting usually of a scrap of bread with a piece of meat, and occasionally a few potatoes or a cup of milk.

Booker frequently got so hungry that he would eat the corn meal and other scraps of food placed in a trough for the pigs and cows to eat!

Sunday was glad day. Then his mother was permitted to serve a bit of molasses to her children. While the syrup was being poured on his little tin plate, Booker would close his eyes so that he might have the surprise of his life on opening them to see how much of the precious goodie he had received. Then he would tip his plate in one direction and another in order to make the molasses spread, and make himself believe that in this way he had more.

One day Booker's family was aroused by a slave woman who rushed breathlessly into the plantation quarters and thrust her head inside the door of the cabin where Booker lived, shouting, "Praise God! We're all sent for to come to the big house!"

"The big house" was the home of the owner of the slaves. Booker could not understand why there should be so much excitement, but he trundled along with his mother and the crowd of slaves who were hurrying to find out what was the matter.

A white man was reading a paper to the slaves gathered around him. Suddenly the slaves leaped into the air, raising their arms heavenward and shouting, "Praise the Lord! Glory Hallelujah!"

Then his mother leaned over and kissed him and his sister and brother, and with tears running down her cheeks she explained as clearly as she could that Lincoln had signed a paper which made every slave free at last.

Booker's family did not remain much longer in Virginia. They moved to a mining town in West Virginia, called Malden.

Booker was only a little boy, but he was put right to work in the salt mines of Malden. The work was very hard and long, beginning frequently at four o'clock in the morning.

How Booker disliked the heavy tasks! Still he did not grumble, for he realized that his mother and stepfather needed all the money they could get.

One thing worried Booker even as a little boy. He could not read or write, and he had observed wherever he went that people who did the important things were those who could read and write.

Booker often wished that he might go to school like the white boys and girls of the town; but since this was not possible, he started out to be his own teacher. He noticed that there was a number on each barrel of salt which his stepfather packed, and that the number always was "18." Booker soon understood what this number meant and learned to write it also.

The days passed. Slowly, slowly, he learned one thing after another. It was a difficult task. If only he could go to school! If only his mother or his father knew enough to teach him something! These things bothered him, but they failed to check his search for knowledge. All by himself he managed to master the alphabet.

He was just about ready to begin his own reading instructions when word got about that a school for colored children was to be opened in Malden. Booker was happier than a prince when he learned about this.

But the poor boy was doomed to further disappointment. His stepfather said to him, "Booker, I'm sorry as can be; but we simply cannot get along without your help in the mines. You'll have to forget about school and keep on with your work."

Booker was almost heartbroken.

"All right," he said to himself as he braced himself to one last effort,

"I learned my a, b, c's all by myself, I guess I can keep on learning things. School or no school, they're not going to keep me from learning."

He kept on trying. Day after day he toiled early and late in the dark, damp salt mine; and while he worked he made numerous observations and notes. Each day found him a little farther advanced in his reading and writing even though he had to instruct himself altogether.

One day his stepfather said to him, "Booker, it is a shame to keep you out of school entirely. Do you think you could work in the morning and after school if we let you go to school?"

Booker promised gladly to do this. So he was permitted to go to school. Under the arrangement he worked from four o'clock in the morning until nine, then he attended school, after which he worked several hours in the evening.

Ah, but he was a proud little fellow that first day in school! He had one exciting experience, however. It came about in this way:

The teacher always called the roll early in the morning. Each child in answering would give his name. As this was taking place, Booker noticed that each pupil gave two names. But Booker had only the one name! All his life he had been known simply as Booker. He felt very much ashamed.

At any moment he might be called upon to give his name.

"What shall I say?" he asked himself.

Like a flash the answer came to him: "Make up a name. And when you make one, use a good one!"

What better name could he take than that of the father of his country? Therefore, when the teacher called for his name, Booker answered, "Booker Washington."

Booker Washington kept that name through life. Later he added Taliferro as his middle name because he learned that the probable name of his father was Taliferro.

One day he was working in the mines when he heard two of the miners talking about a school for colored people somewhere in Virginia at a place called Hampton. Their remarks burned into his mind like a searing firebrand. He could not rid himself of one idea: "I must go to Hampton."

From that day his mind gave him no peace until he got his chance to go to Hampton Institute.

He did not go immediately, however. After a few months longer in the mines he was employed as house boy by Mrs. Viola Ruffner, from Vermont. She was a hard person to get along with because she was so particular. Everything that was done for her had to be "just-so." No one had stayed with her long.

But Booker was no ordinary worker. He learned her ways and patiently did the work as she desired to have it done. A whole year and a half he stayed with her. In the meantime he learned lessons of cleanliness, thrift, and orderliness which he never forgot.

At last Booker was ready to start out for Hampton Institute. He was only fourteen years of age. The school was more than five hundred miles away, and much of the journey was over mountains. Since he had very little money, he decided to travel by foot as much as necessary and trust to good fortune for "lifts" on the way.

When he arrived at Hampton he had just fifty cents in his pockets. He was tired and very hungry. His clothes were very much soiled and wrinkled, and he was grimy from the dust of travel. His appearance was more like that of a tramp than of an applicant to a school.

Naturally, he made a very unfavorable impression upon the headmistress of the school as he presented himself before her. For a long while she pretended not to see him, and attended to the needs of other more promising students. Booker waited until at last she was compelled to ask him what he wished. He told her, simply, that he was anxious to become a student in Hampton Institute.

She looked at him and wondered what she might say in order to test him and perhaps to discourage him. She knew that many Negroes imagined that when they entered school they would start right away studying Latin and Greek. If there was one thing they did not wish, it was to be given some menial task.

She struck upon a plan to test him. "The adjoining recitation room needs sweeping," she said quietly. "Take the broom and sweep it."

Did that teacher hope to discourage Booker Washington by such an examination? She could not have asked him anything more to his liking. Had he not learned from Mrs. Ruffner that labor could be as dignified as any other form of activity if only it were performed with dignity?

Booker went into that recitation room and began cleaning. He was so anxious to make a good impression that he went over each part of the room at least four times, paying especial attention to the corners.

Finally the headmistress came in to inspect the work. She was not able to find a particle of dust. She said simply, "I guess you will do to enter this institution."

Needless to say, Booker Washington made an enviable record at Hampton Institute. He worked as janitor most of the time he was a student; but when he was graduated, he was on the list of honor students.

In 1880 he received a request to assist the work at Hampton among the Indian students. He accepted the offer. The task required great tact and much patience, but Washington succeeded admirably. All the while he continued to devote his nights to study and cherished the idea that burned in his breast.

It was just at this time that General Armstrong, president of Hampton, received a message from some gentlemen in Alabama stating that they desired to begin a normal school for colored people, and requesting that he recommend someone to take charge of the work. They did not have a colored man in mind; but when General Armstrong suggested Booker Washington and told them about his early struggles and successes, the reply was almost immediate: *"Booker Washington will suit us. Send him at once."*

Booker Washington left the scenes which he had known all his life and journeyed many hundreds of miles to the town of Tuskegee, Alabama, where the new school was to be located.

Naturally, the first thing he looked for when he arrived in Tuskegee was the school building. To his disappointment he found that the school was nothing more than a name plus "hundreds of hungry, earnest souls who wanted to secure knowledge."

Washington lost no time in selecting a building.

He found a broken-down shanty and an old Methodist church which could serve the purpose for a while. The buildings were in wretched condition. Whenever it rained, the students had to hold umbrellas over their heads to keep from being drenched by the water!

Many persons in Washington's position would have turned back as soon as they arrived at Tuskegee. But Washington was more determined now than ever that his mission should succeed.

First of all, he studied the conditions.

He got a mule and buggy and traveled over the state of Alabama in order to see how the people lived.

He found many disheartening situations. In many places the Negroes lived hardly any better than cattle. If they had schools, they were the worst imaginable.

Booker Washington laid the foundation of all his educational work in the future at this very point.

"My people," he said to himself, "must be trained to work out their own salvation. Before they can do this, they must learn the value of labor and the dignity of doing anything well. The idea they have that learning Latin and Greek is going to raise them out of their difficulties is entirely wrong. Their only hope lies in dignified labor, whether that be on the farm, in the mill, or about the home."

When Booker Washington returned to Tuskegee, his mind was made up to establish a school for industrial education rather than for academic training.

Many pupils answered his first call for scholars. They varied in age from very young students to old men and women. Many of them carried books of mathematics, philosophy, and other high-sounding subjects. The bigger the books were, the more important the owners felt themselves to be.

How shocked they were when Booker Washington dealt with them almost in the same way in which the headmistress at Hampton had dealt with him on his first day at that school!

Instead of beginning by teaching them Latin or trigonometry, Washington started out by telling them what a fine thing it was to be able to work, and to make things.

The pupils were amazed.

Work? Why, that was all they had learned to do for more than two hundred years! Must a teacher come from hundreds of miles away to teach them to work!

"Indeed!" the pupils remonstrated.

"So this is the reason for calling us to school. As if we have not had enough of work already. We want to learn how to become doctors, lawyers, and bankers, or other kinds of great men and women. What has work got to do with this?"

Quite a few of the pupils deserted him in the beginning. Booker Washington was saddened by the fact, but he did not give way an inch.

"Anyone who stays in this school must work," he said. "The cornerstone of all our efforts will be labor and the joy that can come from doing a thing well."

Gradually Washington's ideas began to impress the students. They noticed that he never asked them to do anything which he himself would not help to do. They observed also that as long as they followed his directions they prospered and the school flourished.

After a time Booker Washington had developed a working atmosphere which people all over that section of Alabama called "Tuskegee Spirit."

Tuskegee Institute won the sympathy of all classes of citizens. The students conducted themselves in such a way that one could not help but be proud of them. They not only worked diligently in the school, but whenever it was necessary they went out into the neighborhood and spread "Tuskegee Spirit" by assisting the poor people who lived near the school in whatever way they might be of service.

The students learned to work thoroughly. They also came to appreciate the fact that any job could be dignified, and that a laborer was just as important to his community as any other citizen.

Tuskegee Institute became one of the most famous schools in America and in the world. Booker Washington, its founder, was looked up to not only as the president of this institution, but as the leader of his race as well. For he was such a far-seeing and thoughtful man that whenever he said anything, men and women all over the country were eager to learn about it.

Before Booker Washington's arrival in Tuskegee, people used to refer to the three R's of education. Washington introduced the three H's—education of the head, the heart, and the hand.

Today the graduates of Tuskegee Institute may be found in all parts of the country. Each one is equipped to perform a worth-while service to his community. Each one is further equipped with a cultural training which enables him to enjoy the artistic and social life of the community.

Booker Washington never gave up hard work. If he was not at Tuskegee directing the affairs of his great institution, he could be observed traveling over the country or in Europe in the interest of his school. For this reason he was one of the most respected men of his time.

Many great institutions of learning honored him in various ways. Of all Negroes he was most welcome everywhere. It was rumored during the presidency of Theodore Roosevelt that he was being considered for an office in his cabinet. Few men of his day were better known or more generally admired.

Unfortunately, Booker T. Washington toiled harder than was good for his physical strength. The dignity of labor impressed him so forcibly that he never knew when to stop working.

He practically never took a vacation, and he tried to oblige everybody by doing things which were requested of him. The result was what one might expect: he broke down under the strain.

In November, 1915, the entire country was surprised to learn that he was dangerously ill. A few days later the nation was shocked to hear of his death.

He was a great man in life. Few, however, appreciated what a truly great leader he was until he had passed away. Since his death his loss has been felt very keenly by the Negroes of America. One often hears a Negro say, "What would Booker Washington have done in this case?"

Perhaps no one has so admirably expressed the exalted place which Booker T. Washington attained in the history of our land as a wealthy friend of his, Andrew Carnegie, who remarked at his passing, "History will tell of two Washingtons—the white and the black—one the father of his country, the other the leader of his race."

(Stop. Note the time; and check your speed of reading with the Reading Score Board, page 252.)

❖❰❖

REASONS FOR LEADERSHIP

1. Why was Booker T. Washington's rise to greatness especially hard?
2. How did Booker T. Washington learn to read?
3. How did he get his name?
4. What other great Negro leaders can you name? What has each contributed?

ORGANIZING INFORMATION

Here are a number of facts about Booker T. Washington. On your paper, can you put them in order under two major headings?

I. Early life of Booker T. Washington

II. Booker T. Washington's contribution as an educator

Had 40 buildings erected in first 19 years

Was born in 1856 on plantation in Virginia

Was graduated in 1875

While working, went to school at night

Became one of America's great educators

Worked his way through Hampton

Worked in saltworks and coal mines

Walked 500 miles to go to Hampton Institute

Was chosen to organize school for Negroes at Tuskegee, Alabama

Opened school in an old church with only 30 pupils

READING SCORE BOARD

Number of Words in Story: 3010.

Number of Minutes	30	15	12	10	7 1/2	6
Reading Rate	100 w.p.m.	200 w.p.m.	250 w.p.m.	300 w.p.m.	400 w.p.m.	500 w.p.m.

◄ᴵᴄ ISABEL PROUDFIT

"Mark Twain!"

Samuel Clemens found that piloting a steamer down the Mississippi River was hard enough in the daytime. But when nights were as dark as the inside of a cow, it was terrible. The following story tells about his experiences. Perhaps, too, you will find how he received his pen name Mark Twain.
(Note the time when you begin reading.)

APRIL of the year 1857! A barefoot boy by the name of Sam Clemens sat on a mud levee in Missouri, watching a steamboat come in.

Eleven years later it was a young man who waited, a young man with shoes on his feet, a steamship ticket in his pocket, and an ambitious plan to go to South America.

The boat which he boarded presently was the *Paul Jones,* a fine, fresh steamer. It churned the Ohio River confidently. The young man, too, went his way with confidence, exploring first the accommodations given over to the passengers, then making his way on the third day to the pilothouse on the hurricane deck.

——Reprinted by permission of Julian Messner, Inc. from *River Boy . . . The Story of Mark Twain,* by Isabel Proudfit. Copyright dated Oct. 19, 1940 by Isabel Proudfit.

Here he found a small, neat man behind the big wheel, a man who controlled the steamboat resolutely, although he was nursing a sore foot at the time. Sam Clemens, who had scraped acquaintance with a watchman on his first river trip, now entered the pilothouse quietly.

"Good morning," he said, in his slow drawl. Meanwhile his quick eye took in the luxurious appointments of the pilothouse. Red and gold curtains at the windows, brass instruments polished until they shone, a comfortable leather sofa, a stove with a good fire in it, a brass cuspidor instead of a mere box of sand to spit in!

"Good morning," answered the pilot without taking his eyes off the river.

This man, Sam knew, was in complete command of the steamboat. Even the captain spoke to him respectfully. His salary was nothing short of magnificent—two hundred and fifty dollars a month, while preachers in the towns they visited often received that much only twice a year.

A sudden impulse swept over Sam.

"How," he said in his mildest voice in order to make his suggestion more dramatic, "would you like to teach a young man the river?"

By teaching him the river, he meant teaching him the art of piloting. Sam made the suggestion half-humorously, for he still intended to hunt coca[1] in South America.

The man at the wheel turned for the first time to look at his caller. He was not unduly impressed with what he saw.

"I would not like it at all," he said. "Cub pilots are more trouble than they are worth."

It was an unexpected answer, but Sam parried it smoothly. He said that he was a printer by trade, that he did not care much for the work, that he was thinking of going to South America. He asked the pilot, whose name was Horace Bixby, if he knew the three Bowen boys from his home town of Hannibal. All three of the Bowens had gone on the river as pilots. Mr. Bixby knew them well; he told a story or two about them. But when Sam asked him again if he would like to teach him piloting, he still said no emphatically.

This refusal piqued[2] Sam's interest.

Every morning now he dropped up to the pilothouse, seeking to ingratiate[3] himself with Bixby. After talking about a number of other subjects, he inquired innocently one day,

"What do you charge for teaching a young man the river?"

"Five hundred dollars."

Sam had no such sum of money. The fact that he did not have it made him perversely stick to the subject.

"I haven't got five hundred dollars," he said. "But I have a lot of land in Tennessee worth twenty-five cents an acre. I'll give you two thousand acres of that."

Mr. Bixby was not at all interested.

Sam thought of Pamela's[4] husband in St. Louis, a successful businessman, and wondered if he could borrow from him.

"I'll give you one hundred dollars," he said, "and the rest when I earn it."

Mr. Bixby was weakening. He liked this young man, and besides his sore foot hurt him considerably. Standing behind the big wheel for hours at a time did not help it to get well. With a cub pilot at his elbow he could sit down more often on the leather sofa.

"All right," he said unexpectedly. "Take the wheel and see what you can do with it. Keep her pointed as she is—toward that lower cottonwood snag. Keep your eyes always on the river."

With a sigh of relief, he sank down on the sofa. Sam, who had sprung forward eagerly when Bixby said to take the wheel, took a spoke in either

---

[1] coca. A plant having leaves which yield a pain-killing drug.

[2] piqued. Aroused.

[3] ingratiate. To work oneself into the favor of another.

[4] Pamela. Sister of Sam Clemens.

hand. The wheel was taller than he was. If it had not been sunk into the floor a foot or two, he could not have seen over the top of it. Yet here he was in this glass temple, guiding the floating palace serenely down the river.

With the wheel in his hands, his plan to go to South America shrank rapidly in importance. Besides, if the truth were told, he did not have enough money to get him to the Amazon. Perhaps after all the Mississippi was his river.

When the *Paul Jones* reached New Orleans, Sam inquired half-heartedly for the next boat to South America. They told him that none had sailed from there in years. Thus relieved of the possibility of carrying out his original plan, he went back happily to the *Paul Jones* and Mr. Bixby.

Mr. Bixby sent him below to stow away his belongings, then received him matter-of-factly in the pilot-house. The time was late afternoon. The boat was still tied up at the wharf, where piles of freight were waiting to be put on board. Presently, however, the freight was loaded, a bell rang, and Mr. Bixby backed the boat expertly out into the river, pointing her nose upstream with a minimum of effort.

Several hours went by. The "texas-tender"[5] in his white apron came up with food and hot coffee. The last glow faded from the sky. The boat began to nose her way gently through

[5] *texas-tender*. The steward in charge of the officers' quarters. On a Mississippi steamer the staterooms were named after states, and the officers' quarters were the largest rooms.

the soft darkness, following the bank on one side for a time, then mysteriously crossing over.

Sam knew in a way why this was necessary. In mid-stream the current was strong. The art of steering consisted in knowing where the channel was deep and the water still—"easy water" they called it. The channel changed from time to time, and there were twelve hundred miles of river between New Orleans and St. Louis. Still, the best way for him to learn, he thought, would be to take the wheel and begin.

Mr. Bixby, however, made no move to hand over the wheel. He merely smoked his pipe in silence, mentioned the name of a point or two in passing, shifted his weight occasionally from his sore foot to his good one.

Off the bow of the boat a sailor, called a "leadsman," was throwing a weighted rope into the water. When the lead touched bottom, he could tell how deep the water was. After each throw he spoke in a droning voice, and another sailor on the hurricane deck repeated his words. In this way the man in the pilothouse learned the depth of the water.

"M-a-r-k three!" came the cry.

Another throw.

"Quarter-less-three!" The water was getting shallower.

"Half twain! Quarter twain! M-a-r-k twain!" Only twelve feet of water here. Better not crowd in much closer to shore. It took twelve feet of water for the boat to pass safely over.

Each "mark," or fathom, was six feet. "Quarter twain" meant two and a quarter fathoms, or thirteen and a half feet. "Mark twain"—the phrase that was to echo down the years as the name of a famous author—meant two fathoms, the depth needed for safe passage.

At eight o'clock another pilot came up from below, exchanged a few words with Mr. Bixby, put on gloves so that his hands would not slip on the wheel, lighted a cigar, and took over the wheel. Sam, the humble "cub," and Mr. Bixby, the glorious expert, went below for supper and bed.

At midnight, when he was fast asleep in his berth, Sam had a rude shock. The watchman wakened him with a lighted lantern.

"Come, turn out!" he said.

Sam listened for sounds of shipwreck, and, hearing none, dozed off to sleep again. In a few minutes the watchman was back, speaking this time more roughly.

"You," he said. "Turn out, I tell ye."

Was this some kind of practical joke? If so, it was growing tiresome. To waken a young man in the middle of the night for no reason twice was carrying a joke too far. It was Sam's turn to speak gruffly.

"What do you want to come bothering around me in the middle of the night for?" he demanded. "Like as not, I'll not get back to sleep again."

It was the watchman's turn to be surprised. A young man so green that he did not know that the pilots changed every four hours! Did he think then that one man worked all night, while the other lolled in his berth? Other men in other berths broke into guffaws of laughter at Sam's ignorance.

The next moment Mr. Bixby was in the cabin, his words crackling around Sam's head. Never in his life had Sam dressed so fast. Indeed, he did not wait to get on all his clothes, but dashed out of the cabin and up the steps to the pilothouse, with his shirt and shoes in his hands.

Mr. Bixby took the wheel, and Sam peered out of the window. It was "as dark as the inside of a cow" out there, "a solid wall of black cats," as he described it later. Impossible to see where they were going.

"We're going to land at Jones' plantation," said Mr. Bixby calmly. "Lower end this time. The stumps are sticking out of the water at the upper end now. Until we get more rain, we don't dare put in there."

Holy mackerel, thought Sam! Twelve hundred miles of river, the night as black as pitch, and this man knows not only that we're at Jones' plantation, but how far the stumps are sticking out of the water at the upper end! No wonder a pilot is paid $250. a month and his board. I shall have to go back to printing soon at ten dollars a week.

Mr. Bixby began to question him.

"What's the name of the first point I told you above New Orleans?" he asked.

"I don't remember."

"You don't remember! Well, then, what's the name of the next one?"

"I don't remember that one either."

"Well this beats anything. Tell me the name of *any* point or place I told you."

By this time Sam was so rattled he could remember none of the names Mr. Bixby had mentioned so casually during the afternoon.

"Well," said Mr. Bixby. "By the ghost of great Caesar! You don't know enough to pilot a cow down a lane, let alone a steamboat on the river!"

That second four hours or "watch," in the pilothouse, Sam's skin prickled practically all the time.

The first time they landed at a town the next morning Sam rushed off the boat and bought a notebook. In this he wrote down everything Mr. Bixby said. No one but a riverman could interpret these notes. Sam himself struggled to remember what they meant. Here is a sample:

Meriweather's Bend

¼ less 3'—run shape of upper bar and go into the low place in willows about 200 (ft.) lower down than last year.

The sandbars, it seemed, increased or decreased periodically, shifted their position from time to time, moving nearer or farther from the shore. A pilot could not tear the bottom out of an expensive steamboat guessing about them. He must learn their position from the face of the river, the tilt of drowned cottonwood trees along the bank, the word of the leadsman droning out the depth of the water, the ripples that broke along the shore. Was the water two fathoms or two and a quarter deep at their point last week? Sam searched his notebook for the answer.

The familiar cry of "mark twain" took on new meaning for him. He learned to listen anxiously for it—"mark twain": safe water. Then if a snag did not detain him—but Bixby had told him on their last trip that the trees at that point were about to fall in the water—he would be all right. Was this the place where the cottonwoods leaned so drunkenly last week? Eagerly he searched his notebook for the answer. Twelve hundred miles of river, and Bixby had said that he must know every foot as well as he knew the upstairs hall at home, when he crept up to bed at night without a candle.

One more shock awaited him. When they had covered the entire length of the river from New Orleans to St. Louis, and he had written faithfully in his notebook everything Bixby had said about it, he discovered that he still knew only half the river. The four hours that he was off duty! Here was a whole new wilderness of facts about which he knew nothing. The bluff reefs, wind reefs, shoals and shallows, bends and banks and snags and stumps along full half of the river were not in his notebook at all. Moistening his lips, Sam undertook to get the whole story of the river into his notebook.

Nevertheless, in spite of all this unlearned lesson which was the river, Sam enjoyed his hours on the steamboat as he had never enjoyed anything before. The pilots were a fine group of men, some of them in polished silk hats and kid gloves, others in loose, jaunty clothes of good quality. On shore they were treated like princes. In St. Louis and New Orleans they had their own club rooms, where they might lounge and smoke together. As a cub pilot Sam did not go to these club rooms, excepting on errands, but the time was coming when he would. The time was coming, too, when he would dress well in blue serge and fancy shirts, with patent-leather shoes on his feet. With his thin face and mop of reddish hair, he made a striking appearance.

As a cub pilot, of course, earning nothing a week, he did not make any such impression. People liked him, however. He was young and energetic. Usually at the tip of his tongue there was a funny story. He even wrote these tales down and sent them to newspapers in New Orleans, where they were sometimes published. An odd young man, but agreeable. That was what most people thought of him.

(Note the time; and check your speed of reading with the Reading Score Board, page 258.)

❦

EASY WATER

1. Do you find signs of Mark Twain's humor in this selection? Where?
2. Why is the job of a river pilot a hard one? Why did Mark Twain find it an interesting one?
3. How did Mark Twain get his pen name?
4. Which of his stories show his interest in the Mississippi River?

PICTURES FOR THE MIND'S EYE

What do the words in italics mean?

Adjectives

ambitious plan
hurricane deck
luxurious appointments
weighted rope

familiar cry
polished silk hats
jaunty clothes
striking appearance

Adverbs

said *emphatically*
inquired *innocently*
backed the boat *expertly*
speak *gruffly*

mentioned *casually*
decreased *periodically*
listen *anxiously*
had written *faithfully*

MORE TO BE KNOWN

Consult an encyclopedia or a reference book like *American Authors* to find out the rest of the story about Mark Twain. Find facts about the following:

I. Mark Twain's next adventure after he left the Mississippi River
II. His rise to fame as a literary figure
III. His financial misfortune and his sorrows

Perhaps you can find out more about steamboating on the Mississippi in the middle of the last century. Exchange your findings in class.

READING SCORE BOARD

Number of Words in Story: 2430.

Number of Minutes	24	12	10	8	6	5
Reading Rate	100 w.p.m.	200 w.p.m.	250 w.p.m.	300 w.p.m.	400 w.p.m.	500 w.p.m.

◀ CLAIRE LEE PURDY

"By 'n' By Hard Times"

In this chapter you have been reading about a number of great Americans. As you have seen, each made a distinct contribution to American life. This last story is about one of America's great musicians—Stephen Foster. It tells the last sad chapter of his life, covering the years 1852 to 1864.
(Note the time that you begin reading.)

STEPHEN AND JANE, his wife, returned home to Allegheny[1] from their trip to the deep South and found the troubles from which they had run away waiting for them. They had now to face their difficulties.

Stephen wrote many songs in the months that followed. Though his music brought him a modest income, his expenses were often greater than his earnings. He had to borrow money —from his brother Mit, from Jane's mother, from his brother William. He began the sad business of robbing Peter to pay Paul. These loans began to claim most of the money he received from the New York publishers.

1 *Allegheny.* Now Pittsburgh.

——Reprinted by permission of Julian Messner, Inc., from *He Heard America Sing, The Story of Stephen Foster.* Copyright dated May 2, 1940 by Julian Messner, Inc.

Jane worried and fretted. Stephen became nervous and cross. When he worked, he demanded quiet. If Jane swept the floor while he was composing, he was annoyed. If a dog howled in the night, he could not sleep. At a concert, if one of the musicians played poorly, Stephen immediately rose and left the hall angrily, to the embarrassment of his wife and friends. He began to smoke constantly—so much that once his throat swelled almost shut, and he nearly lost his life. He began also to drink a great deal.

Friends shook their heads over the change in the happy dreamer they had known. His family worried. They tried to jolly him into good humor, but it was not often that he broke from his moody thoughts to laugh with them.

Some of Stephen's suffering went into the writing of the famous song "Old Dog Tray." This tender, melancholy song about a faithful old dog was inspired by a handsome setter which had been given the composer by a friend.

One day Stephen sat watching the dog playing with children on the East Common. The sad young man was thinking gloomily of his troubles. Because he could not be the gay companion of former days, many of his "boon companions" no longer welcomed him with the old warmth. His dog would not desert him merely because his thoughts had grown serious and his soul troubled.

"Old Dog Tray's ever faithful,
 Grief cannot drive him away,
 He's gentle, he is kind;
 I'll never, never find
 A better friend than Old Dog Tray."

Stephen dashed to the piano. Feverishly he composed, his cheeks and his eyes burning with some inner fire. When he had done, he had written a great tribute in song to a faithful pet.

The composer's erratic[2] moods grew upon him. There is a story that not long after he had written "Old Dog Tray," Stephen was disturbed one night by the barking of a stray dog near the house. Furious because his rest was disturbed, he dashed out of the house in his night clothes and drove the animal away. Muttering angrily, the composer returned to the house to find Ma and Pa and Mit

and Henry and Jane sitting in the kitchen, singing "Old Dog Tray." It was their way of chiding him.

Stephen had to laugh. How funny and ridiculous he must have looked, he thought, running wildly after a poor old dog!

The years 1851 to 1856 were productive years for the composer. Some of his best songs were written during that period, and the sales of his published compositions mounted steadily. Stephen was recognized in America as a great man. His publishers welcomed his songs and suggested that he move nearer their offices. So it was that Stephen and Jane and little Marion[3] moved to New York.

All went well for a while, but the old homesicknesses that Stephen never in his life conquered came to him again. Mit has told us how it was:

After his marriage, Stephen received very flattering offers from the publishers in New York, and strong inducements to make that city his home. He removed there and had every favorable prospect that a young man could hope for. . . .

He went to housekeeping and liked New York very much. But after a year the old fondness for home and Mother began to be too strong for him to overcome. One day he suddenly proposed to his wife that they return to Pittsburgh. He brought a dealer to the house, sold out everything in the way of furniture, and within twenty-four hours was on the road to the home of his father in Allegheny. He arrived late at night and was not expected. When he rang the bell, his mother was awakened and knew his footsteps on the porch. She arose

---

[2] *erratic.* Strange; changeable.

[3] *Marion.* Stephen and Jane's daughter.

immediately and went down herself to let him in. As she passed through the hall, she called out, "Is that my dear son come back again?" Her voice so affected him that when she opened the door she found him sitting on the little porch bench weeping like a child.

Stephen was at home again. For a few moments Jane was forgotten. Standing with little Marion in the shadows of the porch, she may have cried a little, too. No one knows. Perhaps Jane realized at last that love of home would always be the dominating emotion of Stephen's life—not his and Jane's home but that of his beloved parents. Bitter knowledge for the young wife.

One day Jane left the Allegheny household, taking little Marion with her to live with sister Agnes. Who knows what misunderstandings came between Jane and her husband? All that is certain is that one day she went away, with tears in her eyes. And Stephen, with tears in his eyes, stayed at home with Ma and Pa and Mit.

Stephen, restless and at odds with himself, went back to New York. The publishers of his songs welcomed him. Firth, Pond & Company agreed to take all the songs he wrote and to pay him more money.

During the lonely months in New York, Stephen went often to the theater. The conductor Louis Antoine Jullien was giving concerts at Castle Garden. Each night the orchestra presented an overture, a movement from a symphony, and selections from operas. Anna Zerr usually appeared as soloist, with a song or two.

Sitting with his eyes closed, Stephen would give himself up to the enjoyment of melody. One night he clapped loudly with the rest of the audience to call Anna Zerr back to the stage for an encore. The orchestra played a brief introduction. Stephen sat forward in his chair. Was it possible? Anna Zerr began to sing, and her song was his own "Old Folks at Home." No one in the theater knew that the shy man who sat listening attentively with the rest was the composer of the beautiful melody.

"Way down upon the Swanee River—" sang Anna Zerr. Stephen was remembering how he happened to choose the name Swanee. His song had been written and was complete before he could settle on the name of the river. One day he burst into Mit's office to ask for a suggestion. It had to be a southern river, he explained, and the name had to be a word of two syllables. Mit took down an atlas from a shelf.

"What about Pedee?" he suggested. "That's a river in the Carolinas."

Stephen considered the name. It was hardly a poetic word. He shook his head.

Suddenly Mit's finger stopped in Florida. "What about Swanee?"

"That's it!" Stephen cried, and the song was done.

Tears came to Stephen's eyes. Homesickness for Ma and Pa, the old folks at home, made his throat ache.

The audience applauded Anna Zerr. The critics writing in the newspapers the next day were not so kind. "We don't," said one of them, "like Mlle. Zerr's singing of 'Old Folks at Home.'

True, she sings it only on an *encore*, but we think she sings it in bad taste; and we think, moreover, that it is bad taste for her to sing it at all."

There was an ill-natured comment in *Dwight's Journal of Music:*

We wish to say that such tunes (Old Folks at Home), although whistled and sung by everybody, are erroneously supposed to have taken a deep hold of the popular mind; that the charm is only skin deep; that they are hummed and whistled *without musical emotion*, whistled "for lack of thought"; that they persecute and haunt the morbidly sensitive nerves of deeply musical persons, so that they too hum and whistle them involuntarily, hating them even while they hum them; that such melodies become catching, idle habits, and are not popular in the sense of musically inspiring, but that such and such a melody *breaks out* every now and then, like a morbid irritation of the skin.

The critics were mistaken. The songs they attacked have lived on as beautiful and authentic expressions of deep emotion. They were mistaken; yet they had the power to hurt a great and sensitive spirit.

One critic, it is true, defended Foster: "I see," he wrote, "Miss Augusta Browne sneers at Negro melodies. Let her compose one which, like 'Old Folks at Home,' shall be sung, played, and whistled from Maine to California, in four months after it is published, and I will concede her the right to ridicule them if she likes."

One evening as Stephen sat alone he thought longingly of Jane. He remembered her as she had been in the days when Old Black Joe carried bouquets down the hall to "Miss Jinny." Thinking of her beautiful laughing eyes and her soft brown hair, he began to scribble words and music. For his wife he wrote "Jeanie With the Light Brown Hair," a graceful little song of yearning and regret:

Jeanie with the Light Brown Hair

I dream of Jeanie with the light brown hair,
Borne, like a vapor, on the summer air;
I see her tripping where the bright streams play,
Happy as the daisies that dance on her way.
Many were the wild notes her merry voice would pour,
Many were the blithe birds that warbled them o'er:
Oh! I dream of Jeanie with the light brown hair,
Floating, like a vapor, on the soft summer air.

One of the few friends and companions of his last years was George Cooper, who wrote the words for many of the later songs. They lived from hand to mouth, writing a song in the morning, selling it in the evening for enough money to buy a few meals. With a pathetic attempt at brightening a gloomy situation with humor, Foster called Cooper the "left wing of the song factory."

One raw winter day they set out in a snowstorm to find a publisher for the song "Willie Has Gone to the War." Stephen had no overcoat. His shoes were old and cracked, and the slushy snow soon soaked through the thin leather. As he and Cooper passed Wood's Music Hall, the proprietor hailed them from the lobby.

"What have you got there, Steve?" he asked, noticing the rolled paper under his arm.

Stephen showed him the song. It was sold as he and Cooper stood shivering in the wintry slush and cold for ten dollars cash, fifteen dollars more to be paid at the box office that evening.

Stephen did not complain. Mechanically he wrote more songs. He cared nothing for food. Often he ate only an apple for his dinner. He lost interest in his appearance. Alcohol alone sustained him, after a fashion.

Because Stephen had not learned in his youth to struggle in the face of disappointment, he shrank from making the effort in those last years when his heart had grown weary. Because he was gentle and trusting and modest, he often did not receive the reward his genius deserved. Because he was lonely, he sought more and more to forget his melancholy life in drink. So it was that, as Edgar Allan Poe had done before him, he destroyed himself. His granddaughter wrote in years to come: "He suffered much and died for his fault."

Mit once came to see him. Shocked at Stephen's shabby appearance, the patched coat and cheap glazed cap, he said: "Steve, why do you go around looking so careless and unkempt? If I went around like that, I should be afraid of being insulted."

Stephen answered, "Mitty, don't worry so about me. No gentleman will insult me, and no other can."

One day George Cooper found Stephen lying very ill in the dingy basement room that he had been allowed to occupy rent-free. Stephen had fallen and had cut himself badly on a broken water pitcher. He must have been ill for many days, lying alone and neglected.

Cooper made arrangements to take him to Bellevue Hospital. There Stephen was placed in a charity ward; and there he died on January 13, 1864, in his thirty-eighth year.

Trains and boats and coaches could not bring Mit and Jane to him in time. Before they arrived, death had come a-knocking at the door.

The lovable, kindly, gentle writer of songs left to America and the world a wealth of rich melody and graceful lyric poetry. As for worldly goods, he left only a shabby purse containing thirty-eight cents—a penny for every year of his brief life. There was also a scrap of paper on which he had written, "Dear friends and gentle hearts." With those affectionate words, Stephen Foster, dear friend to all and gentle heart of song, bade his family, his friends, and the world good-by.

(Note the time now. Check your reading speed with the Reading Score Board, page 263.)

DEAR FRIENDS—

1. Why is Stephen Foster's music enjoyed by almost everyone? How can it usually be recognized?
2. In what ways was Stephen Foster his own worst enemy?
3. How was he inspired to write some of his songs?
4. How can many of his poor songs be explained?
5. Which of his songs do you know?

IMPORTANT STATEMENTS

How is each of the following important to the story of Stephen Foster's life?
1. "left wing of the song factory"
2. "He suffered much and died for his fault."
3. "No gentleman will insult me, and no other can."
4. "Dear friends and gentle hearts"

INTERESTING WAYS OF SAYING THINGS

Can you explain the meaning of each of the following?
1. robbing Peter to pay Paul
2. boon companions
3. the charm is only skin deep
4. melodies become catching
5. death had come a-knocking at the door

STEPHEN FOSTER'S PLACE IN AMERICAN MUSIC

Do you know how musicians look upon Stephen Foster's songs? What is his place in American music? Consult an encyclopedia or a reference book on music, and find out how he is regarded. Summarize your findings in a brief paragraph.

READING SCORE BOARD

Number of Words in Story: 2240.

Number of Minutes	22 1/2	11 1/5	9	7 1/2	5 3/5	4 1/2
Reading Rate	100 w.p.m.	200 w.p.m.	250 w.p.m.	300 w.p.m.	400 w.p.m.	500 w.p.m.

LOOKING BACKWARD THROUGH THE CHAPTER

From your reading in this chapter, what details concerning each of the following persons do you remember vividly? What contribution to American life did each make?

Daniel Boone
George Washington
Paul Revere
Robert E. Lee

Abraham Lincoln
Clara Barton
Booker T. Washington
Stephen Foster

How Much Do You Remember?

About Whom?

Who is referred to in each of these statements?

1. A voice in the darkness, a knock at the door,
   And a word that shall echo forevermore!
2. Rare was the Cherokee who got the better of the white hunter, "Wide Mouth."
3. A woman's face appeared above him, a human angel with dark compassionate eyes, long tender mouth, and hands like his mother's.
4. What better name could he take than that of the father of his country?
5. "Men," he said, "we have fought the war together, and I have done the best I could for you."

By Whom?

Who wrote each of the following?

1. Nancy Hanks
2. Paul Revere's Ride
3. The Gettysburg Address
4. O Captain! My Captain!
5. General Lee at the Surrender

Meaning What?

Choose the word or phrase in each line that most nearly gives the meaning of the word in italics:

1. *futile:* (a) fertile (b) useless (c) useful
2. *inevitable:* (a) unavoidable (b) ineffectual (c) infallible
3. *consecrate:* (a) hallow (b) hollow (c) conscript
4. *ominous:* (a) omnipotent (b) seeing goodness (c) foretelling evil
5. *rubicund:* (a) rudiment (b) ruble (c) ruddy

Other Things to Do

1. Read in the encyclopedia or in another reference book about one of your favorite American heroes. Choose one that is not included in this chapter. Write a sketch of the life, and try to make it show the person as a real human being.
2. Put in verse form the story of some event in the life of any American hero you choose.
3. Listen to a few Stephen Foster recordings, and discuss their characteristics.

A Reading Skill—Seeing Organization

Look for the author's plan. (1) Sometimes the plan may be chronological; the author tells you what happened first, what happened next, and so on. (2) Often the plan is a step-by-step organization of ideas (remember the major heads and sub-heads in your outlines). Whatever the plan is, look for it and follow it. And when you have finished reading, review the blueprint in your mind.

STORIES ABOUT GREAT AMERICANS

Brown, John Mason, *Daniel Boone*, 1952 (Random House).
Boone and the Kentucky pioneers.

Commager, Henry Steele, *America's Robert E. Lee*, 1951 (Houghton).
The great Confederate general's choice between a united country and his beloved Southern traditions.

Daugherty, James H., *Abraham Lincoln*, 1943 (Viking).
Emphasizes the greatness in spirit of the man.

Daugherty, James H., *Of Courage Undaunted*, 1951 (Viking).
Lewis and Clark, who followed the spirit of adventure westward.

Daugherty, Sonia, *Ten Brave Women*, 1953 (Lippincott).
Biographical sketches of ten heroic American women, past to present.

Eaton, Jeanette, *That Lively Man, Ben Franklin*, 1948 (Morrow).
Inspiring and quick-moving biography of Benjamin Franklin.

Ellsberg, Edward, *"I Have Just Begun to Fight!" The Story of John Paul Jones*, 1942 (Dodd).

Forbes, Esther, *Johnny Tremain*, 1943 (Houghton).
Young apprentice to Paul Revere during the year of the Tea Party and the Battle of Lexington.

Gray, Elizabeth Janet, *Penn*, 1938 (Viking).
A lively portrait of the founder of Pennsylvania.

La Farge, Oliver, *Cochise of Arizona*, 1953 (Aladdin).
Two great Americans: the Indian, Cochise, and General Howard.

Lawson, Robert, *Mr. Revere and I*, 1953 (Little).
The story of Paul Revere "as recently revealed by his horse."

Lenski, Lois, *Indian Captive; the Story of Mary Jemison*, 1941 (Lippincott).
The "White Woman of the Genesee," who lived with the Indians.

Nolan, Jeannette C., *The Story of Clara Barton of the Red Cross*, 1941 (Messner).
One of America's most famous women—a nurse.

Sandburg, Carl, *Abe Lincoln Grows Up*, 1928 (Harcourt).
Lincoln's boyhood and youth.

Spencer, Philip, *Day of Glory*, 1955 (Aladdin).
Joseph Warren, Samuel Adams, Paul Revere and John Hancock in the "most important twenty-four hours in American history"—April 19, 1775.

Vance, Marguerite, *The Jacksons of Tennessee*, 1953 (Dutton).
Perceptive, warm dual biography of Rachel and Andrew Jackson.

A Treasury
of Verse

America for Me

Love of country is an emotion that is hard for many of us to put into words. Often poets can say the things we think but cannot express. In the following six poems you will find how poets describe their love of country—and ours.

Henry van Dyke spent four years as Minister to Holland. During that time he grew homesick for his native country. The following poem was written to show his happiness when he knew that he was returning to America.

'Tis fine to see the Old World, and travel up and down
Among the famous palaces and cities of renown,
To admire the crumbly castles and the statues of the kings,
But now I think I've had enough of antiquated things.

So it's home again, and home again, America for me!
My heart is turning home again, and there I long to be,
In the land of youth and freedom beyond the ocean bars,
Where the air is full of sunlight and the flag is full of stars.

Oh, London is a man's town, there's power in the air;
And Paris is a woman's town, with flowers in her hair;
And it's sweet to dream in Venice, and it's great to study Rome;
But when it comes to living, there is no place like home.

I like the German fir woods, in green battalions drilled;
I like the garden of Versailles with flashing fountains filled;
But, oh, to take your hand, my dear, and ramble for a day
In the friendly western woodland where Nature has her way!

I know that Europe's wonderful, yet something seems to lack;
The Past is too much with her, and her people looking back.
But the glory of the Present is to make the Future free—
We love our land for what she is and what she is to be.

Oh, it's home again, and home again, America for me!
I want a ship that's westward bound to plow the rolling sea,
To the blessed Land of Room Enough beyond the ocean bars,
Where the air is full of sunlight and the flag is full of stars.

❖❖❖

BEAUTY AND MEANING IN RHYME

1. Why does Van Dyke say that it's "America for Me"?
2. Why do you suppose the second and last stanzas are printed in italics?
3. What words and phrases are used to make us see each of these?

castles	German fir woods
London	Versailles
Paris	America

❖❖ HENRY HOLCOMB BENNETT

The Flag Goes By

Everyone thrills at the sight of the American flag as it
is carried in a military parade. But what does the flag
really mean? This poem gives the answer.

Hats off!
Along the street there comes
A blare of bugles, a ruffle of drums,
A flash of color beneath the sky:
    Hats off!
The flag is passing by!

Blue and crimson and white it shines,
Over the steel-tipped, ordered lines.
    Hats off!
The colors before us fly;
But more than the flag is passing by.

Sea fights and land fights, grim and great,
Fought to make and to save the state:
Weary marches and sinking ships;
Cheers of victory on dying lips;

Days of plenty and years of peace;
March of a strong land's swift increase;
Equal justice, right, and law;
Stately honor and reverend awe;
Sign of a nation, great and strong
To ward her people from foreign wrong:
Pride and glory and honor—all
Live in the colors to stand or fall.

Hats off!
Along the streets there comes
A blare of bugles, a ruffle of drums;
And loyal hearts are beating high:
Hats off!
The flag is passing by!

❖❖❖

SIGN OF A NATION

1. What does Bennett mean when he says: *But more than the flag is passing by?*
Read the lines which give the meaning of the flag.

2. How do you know that in stanzas 1, 2, and 4 the poet is *looking* at the flag,
and in stanza 3 he is *thinking* about the flag?

3. What line tells you that the flag is being carried in a military parade?

4. What words does Bennett use to make us see the flag? What words give the
sound of bugles and of drums?

◄ KATHARINE LEE BATES

America the Beautiful

There are some who believe that this poem, as a song, should replace "The Star-Spangled Banner" as our national anthem. Surely it is one of our most beautiful patriotic poems and songs. The author was inspired to write it in 1893 after having seen the breath-taking view from the top of Pikes Peak.

O beautiful for spacious skies,
　　For amber waves of grain,
For purple mountain majesties
　　Above the fruited plain!
　　　　America! America!
　　God shed His grace on thee
And crown thy good with brotherhood
　　From sea to shining sea!

O beautiful for pilgrim feet,
　　Whose stern, impassioned stress
A thoroughfare for freedom beat
　　Across the wilderness!
　　　　America! America!
　　God mend thine every flaw,
Confirm thy soul in self-control,
　　Thy liberty in law!

O beautiful for heroes proved
　　In liberating strife,
Who more than self their country loved,
　　And mercy more than life!
　　　　America! America!
　　May God thy gold refine
Till all success be nobleness
　　And every gain divine!

O beautiful for patriot dream
　　That sees beyond the years

——"America the Beautiful," reprinted by permission of Mrs. George Sargent Burgess.

Thine alabaster cities gleam
Undimmed by human tears!
America! America!
God shed His grace on thee
And crown thy good with brotherhood
From sea to shining sea.

◆◀【◆▶

Long May Our Land Be Bright

1. Look carefully now at the first three poems. How do the poets' purposes seem to differ?

2. What scenes in America are we shown in Katharine Lee Bates's poem?

3. Why do you think some persons feel that this should be our national anthem? What do you think about it?

◀【 Samuel Francis Smith

America

Here is the first stanza of one of our best-loved songs.

My country, 'tis of thee,
Sweet land of liberty,
    Of thee I sing;
Land where my fathers died,
Land of the pilgrims' pride,
From every mountainside
    Let freedom ring.

✦❰ RALPH WALDO EMERSON

Concord Hymn

The following poem was written to commemorate the
completion of a statue honoring the gallant defense
made by the minutemen at a bridge in Concord,
Massachusetts. It was they who "fired the shot heard
round the world," since the skirmish at the bridge
announced the beginning of the Revolutionary War.

By the rude bridge that arched the flood,
    Their flag to April's breeze unfurled,
Here once the embattled farmers stood
    And fired the shot heard round the world.

The foe long since in silence slept;
    Alike the conqueror silent sleeps;
And Time the ruined bridge has swept
    Down the dark stream which seaward creeps.

On this green bank, by this soft stream,
    We set today a votive[1] stone;
That memory may their deeds redeem,
    When, like our sires, our sons are gone.

Spirit, that made those heroes dare
    To die, and leave their children free,
Bid Time and Nature gently spare
    The shaft we raise to them and thee.

❖❰❖

GREATNESS IN SIMPLICITY

1. How is the simplicity of the poem appropriate to the deed it was honoring?
2. What meaning lies behind these lines?
    a. Here once the embattled farmers stood
        And fired the shot heard round the world.
    b. That memory may their deeds redeem,
        When, like our sires, our sons are gone.

——"Concord Hymn," used by permission of and arrangement with Houghton Mifflin Company, the authorized publishers.
[1] *votive.* Given in devotion.

⁌ OLIVER WENDELL HOLMES

Old Ironsides

In the War of 1812, the *Constitution* was a great fighting frigate aptly nicknamed "Old Ironsides." After the war, the ship gradually fell into disrepair; and finally it was ordered dismantled. Holmes wrote a flaming denouncement in the poem "Old Ironsides," which was published in the newspapers. As a result, the ship was saved. It was reconditioned in 1930.

Ay, tear her tattered ensign down!
    Long has it waved on high,
And many an eye has danced to see
    That banner in the sky;
Beneath it rung the battle shout
    And burst the cannon's roar;—
The meteor of the ocean air
    Shall sweep the clouds no more.

Her deck, once red with heroes' blood,
    Where knelt the vanquished foe,
When winds were hurrying o'er the flood,
    And waves were white below,
No more shall feel the victor's tread,
    Or know the conquered knee;—
The harpies[1] of the shore shall pluck
    The eagle of the sea!

Oh, better that her shattered hulk
    Should sink beneath the wave;
Her thunders shook the mighty deep,
    And there should be her grave:
Nail to the mast her holy flag,
    Set every threadbare sail;
And give her to the god of storms,
    The lightning, and the gale!

———"Old Ironsides," used by permission of and arrangement with Houghton Mifflin Company, the authorized publishers.

[1] *harpies.* Mythological creatures, part woman and part bird, that were supposed to seize the souls of the dead.

An Appeal to the Heart

1. What lines in the poem show you that Holmes was appealing to the emotions of the people even more than to their minds?
2. What was Holmes's suggestion if the ship had to be destroyed?

Poetic Words

Holmes has used some words in unusual meanings. For example, notice the words *flood* and *deep*. What meanings do you usually associate with them?

1. When winds were hurrying o'er the flood.
2. Her thunders shook the mighty deep.

Sometimes, too, he uses personification (see page 297) to heighten meaning. Who are the *harpies* and the *eagle* in these lines?

> The harpies of the shore shall pluck
>   The eagle of the sea!

Moreover, Holmes's use of adjectives is fine. You see pictures in such phrases as *tattered ensign* and *battle shout*. What other excellent examples do you find?

◄ Richard Hovey

The Sea Gypsy

The next eight poems have to do with people's love of nature and the great wide world. "The Sea Gypsy" catches the feeling, which everyone has at some time, of wanting to see the world beyond the horizon.

> I am fevered with the sunset,
>   I am fretful with the bay,
> For the wander-thirst is on me
>   And my soul is in Cathay.
>
> There's a schooner in the offing,
>   With her topsails shot with fire,
> And my heart has gone aboard her
>   For the Islands of Desire.
>
> I must forth again tomorrow.
>   With the sunset I must be
> Hull down on the trail of rapture
>   In the wonder of the sea.

PROSE VERSUS POETRY

Write a sentence giving the thought in each of the following. Then notice how much more effective is the thought as it is given in poetry.

1. For the wander-thirst is on me
   And my soul is in Cathay.
2. There's a schooner in the offing,
   With her topsails shot with fire.

WORDS OF POETRY

Substitute a synonym for each of these words and phrases from the poem. Whose words are more effective, yours or Hovey's?

fevered	offing
fretful	forth
wander-thirst	hull down

« RICHARD LE GALLIENNE

"I Meant to Do My Work Today"

Why didn't we do our work today? Perhaps we blamed spring fever. Le Gallienne blamed a brown bird that sang in an apple tree.

I meant to do my work today,
But a brown bird sang in the apple tree,
And a butterfly flitted across the field,
And all the leaves were calling me.

And the wind went sighing over the land,
Tossing the grasses to and fro,
And a rainbow held out its shining hand—
So what could I do but laugh and go?

——"I Meant to Do My Work Today," from *The Lonely Dancer and Other Poems,* by Richard Le Gallienne. Copyright 1913 by Richard Le Gallienne. Used by permission of Dodd, Mead & Co., Inc.

◄**◄ JOYCE KILMER**

Trees

This poem is probably the most popular poem ever written about trees. It has been set to music, and the last two lines are quoted by thousands.

I think that I shall never see
A poem lovely as a tree.

A tree whose hungry mouth is pressed
Against the earth's sweet flowing breast;

A tree that looks at God all day
And lifts her leafy arms to pray;

A tree that may in summer wear
A nest of robins in her hair;

Upon whose bosom snow has lain;
Who intimately lives with rain.

Poems are made by fools like me,
But only God can make a tree.

◄**◄◆**

A POET'S WAY

Poets have special ways of saying things. Sometimes they give the characteristics of human beings to things which do not possess them. For example, in "I Meant to Do My Work Today" you find that "leaves were calling me" and "a rainbow held out its shining hand." Both the leaves and the rainbow were given human qualities, and the reader accepts these poetic ideas. Study "Trees" for the same poetic style of writing.

——"Trees," from *Trees and Other Poems* by Joyce Kilmer. Copyright 1914 by Doubleday & Company, Inc.

◀ ROBERT FROST

Stopping by Woods on a Snowy Evening

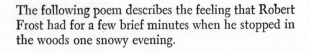

The following poem describes the feeling that Robert Frost had for a few brief minutes when he stopped in the woods one snowy evening.

Whose woods these are I think I know.
His house is in the village, though;
He will not see me stopping here
To watch his woods fill up with snow.

My little horse must think it queer
To stop without a farmhouse near
Between the woods and frozen lake
The darkest evening of the year.

He gives his harness bells a shake
To ask if there is some mistake.
The only other sound's the sweep
Of easy wind and downy flake.

The woods are lovely, dark and deep,
But I have promises to keep,
And miles to go before I sleep,
And miles to go before I sleep.

◆◖◗◆

STOPPING A MOMENT

Is this poem an expression of an idea or of a feeling? Is "I" thinking or simply enjoying a quiet moment in the woods? Notice the different little things which his eyes and ears take in.

Have you experienced a single moment which you remembered a long time afterward? That experience can probably be the basis of a poem.

⊀ CHRISTINA GEORGINA ROSSETTI

Who Has Seen the Wind?

*The next two poems give two poets' feelings toward
the wind. Can you find their different points of view?*

Who has seen the wind?
    Neither I nor you:
But when the leaves hang trembling,
    The wind is passing through.

Who has seen the wind?
    Neither you nor I:
But when the trees bow down their heads,
    The wind is passing by.

⊀ HAMLIN GARLAND

Do You Fear the Wind?

Do you fear the force of the wind,
The slash of the rain?
Go face them and fight them,
Be savage again.
Go hungry and cold like the wolf,
    Go wade like the crane:
The palms of your hands will thicken,
The skin of your cheek will tan;
You'll grow ragged and weary and swarthy,
    But you'll walk like a man!

TWO POEMS ABOUT THE WIND

Study carefully "Who Has Seen the Wind?" and "Do You Fear the Wind?"
How do the two poems differ? Which is gentle, and which is rugged? Which contains lines that could help to guide your way of living? Which catches a single
impression, and which translates an impression into a challenge?

——"Do You Fear the Wind?" used by permission of Constance Garland Doyle and Isabel
Garland Lord.

◄◄ RACHEL FIELD

A Summer Morning

In this short poem is a picture of a summer morning.
Notice each of the details used to give the picture.

I saw dawn creep across the sky,
And all the gulls go flying by.
I saw the sea put on its dress
Of blue midsummer loveliness,
And heard the trees begin to stir
Green arms of pine and juniper.
I heard the wind call out and say:
"Get up, my dear, it is today!"

◄◄◄

THROUGH A POET'S EYES

1. What details has Rachel Field used to make us see the summer morning?
2. At what time of the day is the morning described?
3. How does a summer morning look to *you*? What details would *you* use?
4. In what way does the poem remind you of Kilmer's "Trees" (page 277)?

NOT TRUE, BUT BEAUTIFUL

Rachel Field says that the sea put on its dress, the trees stirred their arms (not branches), and the wind called out to her. A literal-minded person might say, "That's silly. Such things don't happen." Actually they don't, but this trick of poets helps us to see vividly the pictures they paint.

Look through the poems in this chapter. Can you find other examples in which nature is given human characteristics?

——From *The Pointed People*. Reprinted by permission of Arthur Pederson.

◄I◄ JOHN GREENLEAF WHITTIER

The Barefoot Boy

Although Whittier wrote his poem about a barefoot
boy about one hundred years ago, the barefoot boy
today is practically unchanged.

Blessings on thee, little man,
Barefoot boy, with cheek of tan!
With thy turned-up pantaloons,
And thy merry whistled tunes;
With thy red lip, redder still
Kissed by strawberries on the hill;
With the sunshine on thy face,
Through thy torn brim's jaunty grace;
From my heart I give thee joy—
I was once a barefoot boy!
Prince thou art—the grown-up man
Only is republican.[1]
Let the million-dollared ride!
Barefoot, trudging at his side,
Thou hast more than he can buy
In the reach of ear and eye—
Outward sunshine, inward joy:
Blessings on thee, barefoot boy!

Oh, for boyhood's painless play,
Sleep that wakes in laughing day,
Health that mocks the doctor's rules,
Knowledge never learned of schools,
Of the wild bee's morning chase,
Of the wild flower's time and place,
Flight of fowl and habitude
Of the tenants of the wood;
How the tortoise bears his shell,
How the woodchuck digs his cell,
And the ground mole sinks his well;

[1] *republican.* One who must share the responsibility for the management of the government.
——"The Barefoot Boy," used by permission of and arrangement with Houghton Mifflin
Company, the authorized publishers.

How the robin feeds her young,
How the oriole's nest is hung;
Where the whitest lilies blow,
Where the freshest berries grow,
Where the ground nut trails its vine,
Where the wood grape's clusters shine;
Of the black wasp's cunning way,
Mason of his walls of clay,
And the architectural plans
Of gray hornet artisans!
For, eschewing books and tasks,
Nature answers all he asks;
Hand in hand with her he walks,
Face to face with her he talks,
Part and parcel of her joy—
Blessings on the barefoot boy!

⟡⟨⟨⟡

Blessings on Thee!

1. What does Whittier mean when he says, *"Thou hast more than he can buy"*?
Read aloud the lines which show all the things the barefoot boy has.
2. What could be said about what the city boy has?

⟨⟨ Eugene Field

Little Boy Blue

The next five poems show poets thinking on serious
and even tragic subjects.
Eugene Field is known as "the child's poet." In
poems such as this, he shows his love and appreciation of children as well as an understanding of the
feelings and emotions of parents.

The little toy dog is covered with dust,
But sturdy and stanch he stands;
And the little toy soldier is red with rust,
And his musket molds in his hands.

—"Little Boy Blue," published by Charles Scribner's Sons.

Time was when the little toy dog was new,
And the soldier was passing fair;
And that was the time when our Little Boy Blue
Kissed them and put them there.

"Now, don't you go till I come," he said,
"And don't you make any noise!"
So, toddling off to his trundle bed,
He dreamt of the pretty toys;
And, as he was dreaming, an angel song
Awakened our Little Boy Blue—
Oh! The years are many, the years are long,
But the little toy friends are true!

Ay, faithful to Little Boy Blue they stand,
Each in the same old place—
Awaiting the touch of a little hand,
The smile of a little face;
And they wonder, as waiting the long years through
In the dust of that little chair,
What has become of our Little Boy Blue
Since he kissed them and put them there.

◄ℂ HENRY WADSWORTH LONGFELLOW

The Wreck of the Hesperus

Death sometimes comes in violent ways. Here is the story of what happened when a schooner could not survive a hurricane. The skipper of the schooner was given sufficient warning, but he was certain—too certain—that he could outride the storm.

It was the schooner *Hesperus*,
    That sailed the wintry sea;
And the skipper had taken his little daughtèr,
    To bear him company.

——"The Wreck of the *Hesperus*," used by permission of and arrangement with Houghton Mifflin Company, the authorized publishers.

Blue were her eyes as the fairy flax,
    Her cheeks like the dawn of day,
And her bosom white as the hawthorn buds,
    That ope in the month of May.

The skipper he stood beside the helm,
    His pipe was in his mouth,
And he watched how the veering flaw did blow
    The smoke now west, now south.

Then up and spake an old Sailòr,
    Had sailed to the Spanish Main,
"I pray thee, put into yonder port,
    For I fear a hurricane.

"Last night the moon had a golden ring,
    And tonight no moon we see!"
The skipper, he blew a whiff from his pipe,
    And a scornful laugh laughed he.

Colder and louder blew the wind,
    A gale from the Northeast,
The snow fell hissing in the brine,
    And the billows frothed like yeast.

Down came the storm, and smote amain
    The vessel in its strength;
She shuddered and paused, like a frightened steed,
    Then leaped her cable's length.

"Come hither! come hither! my little daughtèr,
    And do not tremble so;
For I can weather the roughest gale
    That ever wind did blow."

He wrapped her warm in his seaman's coat
    Against the stinging blast;
He cut a rope from a broken spar
    And bound her to the mast.

"O Father! I hear the churchbells ring,
    Oh say, what may it be?"
" 'Tis a fog bell on a rock-bound coast!"—
    And he steered for the open sea.

"O Father! I hear the sound of guns,
  Oh say, what may it be?"
"Some ship in distress, that cannot live
  In such an angry sea!"

"O Father! I see a gleaming light,
  Oh say, what may it be?"
But the father answered never a word,
  A frozen corpse was he.

Lashed to the helm, all stiff and stark,
  With his face turned to the skies,
The lantern gleamed through the gleaming snow
  On his fixed and glassy eyes.

Then the maiden clasped her hands and prayed
  That savèd she might be;
And she thought of Christ, who stilled the wave,
  On the Lake of Galilee.

And fast through the midnight dark and drear,
  Through the whistling sleet and snow,
Like a sheeted ghost, the vessel swept
  Tow'rds the reef of Norman's Woe.

And ever the fitful gusts between
  A sound came from the land;
It was the sound of the trampling surf
  On the rocks and the hard sea sand.

The breakers were right beneath her bows,
  She drifted a dreary wreck,
And a whooping billow swept the crew
  Like icicles from her deck.

She struck where the white and fleecy waves
  Looked soft as carded wool,
But the cruel rocks, they gored her side
  Like the horns of an angry bull.

Her rattling shrouds, all sheathed in ice,
  With the masts went by the board;
Like a vessel of glass, she stove and sank,
  Ho! ho! the breakers roared!

At daybreak, on the bleak sea beach,
  A fisherman stood aghast,
To see the form of a maiden fair
  Lashed close to a drifting mast.

The salt sea was frozen on her breast,
  The salt tears in her eyes;
And he saw her hair, like the brown seaweed,
  On the billows fall and rise.

Such was the wreck of the *Hesperus*,
  In the midnight and the snow!
Christ save us all from a death like this,
  On the reef of Norman's Woe!

❖❖❖❖

POEMS ABOUT THE DEATH OF CHILDREN

1. The death of children always pulls at the heartstrings. Can you point out lines in "Little Boy Blue" and in "The Wreck of the *Hesperus*" which are especially pathetic?

2. In "The Wreck of the *Hesperus*" Longfellow has used a number of similes (see page 297) to make us see the people and the events. For example:

> Blue were her eyes *as the fairy flax,*
> Her cheeks *like the dawn of day.*

Can you find nine other similes in the poem?

3. In "The Wreck of the *Hesperus*" why do you think an accent mark is placed over the words *daughtèr, Sailòr,* and *savèd?*

◂◖ JOHN MCCRAE

In Flanders Fields

The following is a poem which came out of World
War I. During that war Flanders came to be regarded
as the "battleground of Europe." There the graves are
marked by white crosses and brilliant red poppies.
McCrae, a Canadian medical corps officer, was deeply
moved by the sight of the crosses; and this poem
came as a result. McCrae died in a hospital in France
during the war of which he wrote.

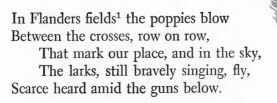

In Flanders fields[1] the poppies blow
Between the crosses, row on row,
    That mark our place, and in the sky,
    The larks, still bravely singing, fly,
Scarce heard amid the guns below.

We are the dead; short days ago
    We lived, felt dawn, saw sunset glow,
Loved and were loved, and now we lie
    In Flanders fields.

Take up our quarrel with the foe!
To you from failing hands we throw
    The torch: be yours to hold it high!
    If ye break faith with us who die,
We shall not sleep, though poppies grow
    In Flanders fields.

◂◖◆

A GREAT WAR POEM

1. Why is "In Flanders Fields" as popular now as it was when it was first written?
What emotions are expressed which belong to all times rather than to any one
period?

2. In the poem beauty is contrasted with death. Which lines show the poet's love
of the beauty of the earth?

3. Why is this poem easy to memorize?

[1] *Flanders fields.* Location in France, of an American military cemetery.
——"In Flanders Fields," used by permission of Dr. J. M. Kilgour.

◀︎ Emily Dickinson

I'm Nobody! Who Are You?

Most people have ambitions to be a "Somebody."
How refreshing it is to find one person who feels different!

I'm nobody! Who are you?
Are you nobody, too?
Then there's a pair of us—don't tell!
They'd banish us, you know.

How dreary to be somebody!
How public, like a frog
To tell your name the livelong day
To an admiring bog!

◀︎ Robert Browning

Song from "Pippa Passes"

Some days we know in our very heart of hearts
that all's right with the world.

The year's at the spring,
And day's at the morn;
Morning's at seven;
The hillside's dew-pearled;
The lark's on the wing;
The snail's on the thorn;
God's in his heaven—
All's right with the world!

——"I'm Nobody! Who Are You?" from *The Complete Poems of Emily Dickinson*, by permission of Little, Brown & Co.

◄◄ HENRY WADSWORTH LONGFELLOW

The Arrow and the Song

"Hitch your wagon to a star" was the advice of one poet. It is good advice, for surely everyone needs ways by which to guide his life. The next four selections are ladders to better and happier living.

I shot an arrow into the air;
It fell to earth, I know not where;
For, so swiftly it flew, the sight
Could not follow it in its flight.

I breathed a song into the air;
It fell to earth, I knew not where;
For who has sight so keen and strong,
That it can follow the flight of song?

Long, long afterward, in an oak
I found the arrow, still unbroke;
And the song, from beginning to end,
I found again in the heart of a friend.

◄◄ SAADI

Friendship

He is no friend who in thine hour of pride
Brags of his love and calls himself thy kin.
He is a friend who hales his fellow in,
And clangs the door upon the wolf outside.

——"The Arrow and the Song," used by permission of and arrangement with Houghton Mifflin Company, the authorized publishers.

◄ HENRY VAN DYKE

Four Things

> Four things a man must learn to do
> If he would make his record true:
> To think without confusion clearly;
> To love his fellow men sincerely;
> To act from honest motives purely;
> To trust in God and Heaven securely.

◄ THE BIBLE

Psalm 23

> The Lord is my shepherd; I shall not want.
> He maketh me to lie down in green pastures:
> He leadeth me beside the still waters.
> He restoreth my soul:
> He leadeth me in the paths of righteousness for his name's sake.

> Yea, though I walk through the valley of the shadow of death,
> I will fear no evil—for thou art with me;
> Thy rod and thy staff they comfort me.

> Thou preparest a table before me in the presence of mine enemies:
> Thou anointest my head with oil; my cup runneth over.

> Surely goodness and mercy shall follow me all the days of my life:
> And I will dwell in the house of the Lord forever.

Cowboy's Meditation

This last group of poems is made up of American folk
songs. They are the music of the people. Cowboys,
mountaineers, Negroes, Indians, railroad and canal
workers, all have had their songs. They have made
them up and passed them on from father to son for
generations. To get the most enjoyment from these
poems, they should be sung or read in a speaking
choir. For use in class, they have been arranged as
speaking-choir selections.

   The first poem belongs to the cowboy. John A.
Lomax, a famous collector of cowboy songs, has said,
"The broad sky under which he [the cowboy] slept,
the limitless plains over which he rode, the big, open
free life he lived near to Nature's breast, taught him
simplicity, calm, directness. He spoke out plainly the
impulses of his heart."

One boy: At night when the cattle are sleeping
                 On my saddle I pillow my head,
            And up at the heavens lie peeping
                 From out of my soft grassy bed.
            How often and often I've wonder'd
                 At night, when lying alone
            If ev'ry bright star up in heaven
                 Is a big peopled world like our own.

All: Roll on, roll on,
                 Roll on, little dogies,[1] roll on, roll on,
            Roll on, roll on,
                 Roll on, little dogies, roll on.

One boy: At night in the bright stars up yonder
                 Do the cowboys lie down to their rest?
            Do they gaze at this old world and wonder
                 If rough riders dash over its breast?
            Do they listen to the wolves in the canyons?
                 Do they watch the night owl in its flight?
            With their horse as their only companion
                 While guarding the herd through the night?

[1] *dogies.* Small, unbranded calves on the range.

All: Roll on, roll on,
               Roll on, little dogies, roll on, roll on,
          Roll on, roll on,
               Roll on, little dogies, roll on.

One boy: Are they worlds with their names and ranches?
               Do they ring with rough rider refrains?
          Do the cowboys scrap there with Comanches
               And other red men of the plains?
          Are the hills covered over with cattle
               In those mystic worlds far, far away?
          Do the ranch houses sing with the prattle
               Of sweet little children at play
          —until sleep comes in the sweet prairie night?

All: Roll on, roll on,
               Roll on, little dogies, roll on, roll on,
          Roll on, roll on,
               Roll on, little dogies, roll on.

Sourwood Mountain

"Sourwood Mountain" is one of the most popular of the Southern mountaineer ballads. It should surely be accompanied by banjo playing and a certain amount of foot tapping.

One boy: Rooster crowin' on the sourwood mountain,
All: Hay didy um didy idy um day;
One boy: So many pretty girls I can't count 'em,
All: Hay didy um didy idy um day.

One boy: I got a gal at the head of the holler,
All: Hay didy um didy idy um day;
One boy: She won't come, and I won't foller,
All: Hay didy um didy idy um day.

One boy: Old man, old man, I want your daughter,
All: Hay didy um didy idy um day;
One boy: To bake my bread and carry the water,
All: Hay didy um didy idy um day.

Nobody Knows the Trouble I've Seen

Mark Twain spoke of the Negro spiritual as the finest flower of American music. Surely it is one of the most popular types of folk music. The following song shows the characteristic religious faith, the melancholy, and the simplicity of rhyme and rhythm.

One girl:	Nobody knows the trouble I've seen,
All:	Nobody knows my sorrow;
One girl:	Nobody knows the trouble I've seen;
All:	Glory hallelujah!
One girl:	Sometimes I'm up, sometimes I'm down,
All:	Oh, yes, Lord!
One girl:	Sometimes I'm almost to the groun',
All:	Oh, yes, Lord!
One girl:	Although you see me goin' long so,
All:	Oh, yes, Lord!
One girl:	I have my troubles here below,
All:	Oh, yes, Lord!
One girl:	What makes old Satan hate me so?
All:	Oh, yes, Lord!
One girl:	He got me once, and let me go!
All:	Oh, yes, Lord!
One girl:	Nobody knows the trouble I've seen,
All:	Nobody knows my sorrow;
One girl:	Nobody knows the trouble I've seen;
All:	Glory hallelujah!

The Erie Canal

Boats on the Erie Canal were pulled by mules or horses which followed a towpath along the bank. Often the drivers sang songs to relieve the monotony of their work. Here is one of the songs which they liked to sing. As you will see, it is about their work.

One boy: I've got a mule, her name is Sal,
Fifteen years on the Erie Canal.
She's a good old worker and a good old pal,
Fifteen years on the Erie Canal.
We've hauled some barges in our day,
Filled with lumber, coal, and hay.
And every inch of the way I know
From Albany to Buffalo.

All: Low bridge, everybody down!
Low bridge, for we're comin' to a town!
You can always tell your neighbor, can always tell your pal,
If you've ever navigated on the Erie Canal.

One boy: We'd better look for a job, old gal,
Fifteen years on the Erie Canal.
You bet your life I wouldn't part with Sal,
Fifteen years on the Erie Canal.
Giddap there, Sal, we've passed that lock,
We'll make Rome 'fore six o'clock,
So one more trip and then we'll go
Right straight back to Buffalo.

All: Low bridge, everybody down!
Low bridge, for we're comin' to a town!
You can always tell your neighbor, can always tell your pal,
If you've ever navigated on the Erie Canal.

One boy: Where would I be if I lost my pal?
Fifteen years on the Erie Canal.
Oh, I'd like to see a mule as good as Sal,
Fifteen years on the Erie Canal.
A friend of mine once got her sore,
Now he's got a broken jaw,

'Cause she let fly with her iron toe
And kicked him into Buffalo.

All: Low bridge, everybody down!
            Low bridge, for we're comin' to a town!
            You can always tell your neighbor, can always tell your pal,
            If you've ever navigated on the Erie Canal.

❖❖❖

❖❖ NATALIE CURTIS

Song of the Rain Chant

Because the Indian, to a very large extent, depended upon nature for his existence, many of his
songs were about nature. The need of rain and sun
and gentle winds was very real to him. Here is a
Navaho chant about the rain which had come to aid
the growing maize.

Solo Voice: Far as man can see,
Chorus: Comes the rain,
                        Comes the rain with me.

Solo Voice: From the Rain-Mount,
                    Rain-Mount far away,
Chorus: Comes the rain,
                        Comes the rain with me.

Solo Voice: 'Mid the lightnings,
                    'Mid the lightning zigzag,
                    'Mid the lightning flashing,
Chorus: Comes the rain,
                        Comes the rain with me.

Solo Voice: 'Mid the swallows,
                    'Mid the swallows blue,
                    Chirping glad together,
Chorus: Comes the rain,
                        Comes the rain with me.

——From *The Indians' Book*, translated by Natalie Curtis. Used by permission of Paul
Burlin, copyright owner.

Solo Voice:	Through the pollen,
	Through the pollen blest.
	All in pollen hidden
Chorus:	Comes the rain,
	Comes the rain with me.
Solo Voice:	Far as man can see,
Chorus:	Comes the rain,
	Comes the rain with me.

❖❖❖

Looking Backward through the Chapter

1. What five broad types of subject matter are dealt with in this chapter?
2. What poem in each group do you like best? Why?
3. Do you know other poems that might be added to each group?
4. From your reading in this chapter, what do you think constitutes good poetry?
5. Which of the poems in this chapter would you like to memorize?

A Poetry Quiz

Who Wrote What?

Can you match these authors and titles?

1. America the Beautiful	a. John McCrae
2. The Barefoot Boy	b. Eugene Field
3. In Flanders Fields	c. Henry W. Longfellow
4. Trees	d. Ralph W. Emerson
5. Little Boy Blue	e. Katharine Lee Bates
6. Do You Fear the Wind?	f. Oliver W. Holmes
7. The Arrow and the Song	g. John Greanleaf Whittier
8. Concord Hymn	h. Hamlin Garland
9. Old Ironsides	i. Robert Frost
10. Stopping by Woods on a Snowy	j. Joyce Kilmer
Evening	

In What Poem?

Name the poem in which each of these appears:

1.   Hats off!
   Along the street there comes
   A blare of bugles, a ruffle of drums.
2. I heard the wind call out and say:
   "Get up, my dear, it is today!"
3. And they wonder, as waiting the long years through
   In the dust of that little chair.
4. I am fevered with the sunset,
      I am fretful with the bay.
5. Blessings on thee, little man.

What Are the Lines of Poetry?

Can you quote the lines of poetry which express each of these ideas?
1. A person may sing a song and later find it in the heart of a friend.
2. Though we are dying, we give you the torch to carry on.
3. Face the elements of life fearlessly, and you'll walk like a man.
4. The song of a bird in an apple tree kept me from doing my work today.
5. The present and the future of America make me prefer this country to Europe, bowed by the weight of the past.

Many Ways of Enjoying Poetry

1. Spend several periods reading aloud your favorite poems.
2. Broadcast to another class, or to your own, a poetry-appreciation program.
3. Collect information about your favorite poets.
4. Make a class booklet of the verse written by your class. Later present the booklet to your school library.
5. Arrange a number of poems for your speaking choir, and then try them out. If you will turn to page 502, you will notice a number of poems marked with asterisks. The poems so marked can be adapted for speaking-choir selections.
6. Make a study of folk poetry.

Some Facts about Figures of Speech

Poets have ways by which they make us see things clearly. Three of the devices that they use are (1) similes, (2) metaphors, and (3) personification.

A **simile** is a comparison of two unrelated things through some common point of resemblance. The objects being compared are linked by the word *like* or *as*.

> Blue were her eyes as the fairy-flax,
> Her cheeks like the dawn of day.
> *Henry W. Longfellow*

A **metaphor** is a direct comparison. As such, the words *like* and *as* are omitted.

> The silver birch is a dainty lady,
> She wears a satin gown.
> *E. Nesbit*

Personification is the figure of speech that occurs when we speak of things that are not persons as though they were. Objects take on the characteristics of human beings.

> I saw the sea put on its dress
> Of blue midsummer loveliness.
> *Rachel Field*

What figures of speech do you see in the following?
1. Old Woman Rain
   Is coming down the street.
   Louise Driscoll
2. I wander'd lonely as a cloud
   That floats on high o'er vales and hills.
   William Wordsworth

3. I like to see it [train] lap the miles,
   And lick the valleys up.
                              Emily Dickinson

4. Who knocks? That April!
   Lock the door!
                              Emily Dickinson

5. Like an army defeated
   The snow hath retreated.
                         William Wordsworth

6. Candles divine are you and I.
                           Morris Abel Beer

7. Teach me, Father, how to go
   Softly as the grasses grow.
                            Edwin Markham

8. You are a tulip seen today.
                            Robert Herrick

9. The muscles of his brawny arms
   Are strong as iron bands.
                        Henry W. Longfellow

10. The old moon laughed and sang a song.
                              Eugene Field

11. While from my path the hare
    Fled like a shadow.
                       Henry W. Longfellow

12. At last she came to his hermitage,
    Like the bird from the woodlands to the cage.
                           Ralph W. Emerson

13. Majestic Liberty, serene
    Thou frontest on the chaste white sea!
                          Charles H. Phelps

14. I heard the trailing garments of the Night.
                        Henry W. Longfellow

15. Death, thou'rt a cordial old and rare.
                             Sidney Lanier

Poetry

Adshead, Gladys, and Duff, Annis (editors), *An Inheritance of Poetry*, 1948 (Houghton).
   Outstanding collection of great poetry.

Arbuthnot, May Hill (compiler), *Time for Poetry*, 1951 (Scott, Foresman).
   Excellent anthology of varied verse.

Benét, Rosemary C., and Benét, Stephen Vincent, *A Book of Americans*, 1933 (Rinehart).
   Famous American historical portraits in verse.

Benét, William Rose (compiler), *Poems for Youth*, 1925 (Dutton).
    Outstanding poems of American poets, selected for young people.

Brewton, John E. (compiler), *Under the Tent of the Sky*, 1937 (Macmillan).
    A collection of poetry about animals.

Daringer, Helen F., and Eaton, Anne T. (compilers), *Poet's Craft*, 1935 (World Book).
    Attractive collection of verse, with aids to appreciation and understanding.

Field, Eugene, *Poems of Childhood*, 1925 (Scribner).
    "Wynken, Blynken, and Nod" and other favorites.

Lear, Edward, *The Complete Nonsense Book*, 1942 (Dodd).
    Humorous verse and limericks, all "nonsense."

Nash, Ogden (editor), *The Moon Is Shining Bright as Day*, 1953 (Lippincott).
    One of the best collections of lighter poems.

Parker, Elinor M. (compiler), *100 Story Poems*, 1951 (Crowell).
    From ballad to modern—for every taste and mood.

Richards, Laura E., *Tirra Lirra*, 1932 (Little).
    A collection of humorous verse.

Sechrist, Elizabeth H. (compiler), *Poems for Red Letter Days*, 1951 (Macrae).
    A large collection of poems for patriotic and religious holidays.

Thompson, Blanche J. (compiler), *Silver Pennies*, 1925 (Macmillan).
    Favorite modern poems for young people.

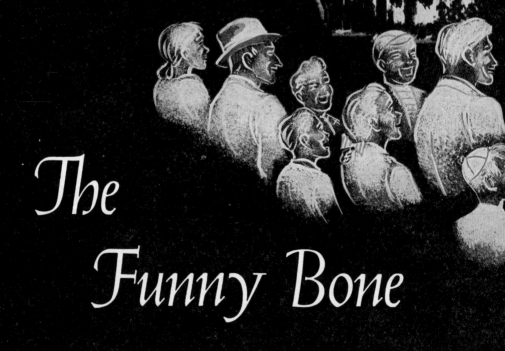

The Funny Bone

The Doughnuts

Homer Price belongs in the same all-boy class as Henry Aldrich, Tom Sawyer, Huck Finn, and Penrod Schofield. In this story Homer, a doughnut machine, an advertising man, and a rich lady have a sidesplitting adventure.
(Note the time when you begin reading.)

ONE Friday night in November Homer overheard his mother talking on the telephone to Aunt Agnes over in Centerburg. "I'll stop by with the car in about half an hour, and we can go to the meeting together," she said, because tonight was the night the Ladies' Club was meeting to discuss plans for a box social and to knit and sew for the Red Cross.

"I think I'll come along and keep Uncle Ulysses company while you and Aunt Agnes are at the meeting," said Homer.

So after Homer had combed his hair and his mother had looked to see if she had her knitting instructions and the right size needles, they started for town.

Homer's Uncle Ulysses and Aunt Agnes have a very up-and-coming lunchroom over in Centerburg, just across from the courthouse on the town square. Uncle Ulysses is a man with advanced ideas and a weakness for laborsaving devices. He equipped the lunchroom with automatic toasters, automatic coffee maker, auto-

——From *Homer Price* by Robert McCloskey. Copyright 1943 by Robert McCloskey. Reprinted by permission of The Viking Press, Inc., New York.

matic dish washer, and an automatic doughnut maker. All just the latest thing in laborsaving devices. Aunt Agnes would throw up her hands and sigh every time Uncle Ulysses bought a new laborsaving device. Sometimes she became unkindly disposed toward him for days and days. She was of the opinion that Uncle Ulysses just frittered away his spare time over at the barbershop with the sheriff and the boys, so, what was the good of a laborsaving device that gave you more time to fritter?

When Homer and his mother got to Centerburg, they stopped at the lunchroom; and after Aunt Agnes had come out and said, "My, how that boy does grow!" which was what she always said, she went off with Homer's mother in the car. Homer went into the lunchroom and said, "Howdy, Uncle Ulysses!"

"Oh, hello, Homer. You're just in time," said Uncle Ulysses. "I've been going over this automatic doughnut machine, oiling the machinery and cleaning the works . . . wonderful things, these laborsaving devices."

"Yep," agreed Homer, and he picked up a cloth and started polishing the metal trimmings while Uncle Ulysses tinkered with the inside workings.

"Opfwo-oof!!" sighed Uncle Ulysses and, "Look here, Homer, you've got a mechanical mind. See if you can find where these two pieces fit in. I'm going across to the barbershop for a spell, 'cause there's somethin' I've got to talk to the sheriff about. There won't be much business here until the double feature is over, and I'll be back before then."

Then as Uncle Ulysses went out the door he said, "Uh, Homer, after you get the pieces in place, would you mind mixing up a batch of doughnut batter and put it in the machine? You could turn the switch and make a few doughnuts to have on hand for the crowd after the movie . . . if you don't mind."

"O.K." said Homer, "I'll take care of everything."

A few minutes later a customer came in and said, "Good evening, Bud."

Homer looked up from putting the last piece in the doughnut machine and said, "Good evening, Sir, what can I do for you?"

"Well, young feller, I'd like a cup o' coffee and some doughnuts," said the customer.

"I'm sorry, Mister, but we won't have any doughnuts for about half an hour, until I can mix some dough and start this machine. I could give you some very fine sugar rolls instead."

"Well, Bud, I'm in no real hurry, so I'll just have a cup o' coffee and wait around a bit for the doughnuts. Fresh doughnuts are always worth waiting for is what I always say."

"O.K.," said Homer, and he drew a cup of coffee from Uncle Ulysses' super automatic coffee maker.

"Nice place you've got here," said the customer.

"Oh, yes," replied Homer, "this is a very up-and-coming lunchroom with all the latest improvements."

"Yes," said the stranger, "must be a good business. I'm in business, too. A traveling man in outdoor advertising. I'm a sandwich man, Mr. Gabby's my name."

"My name is Homer. I'm glad to meet you, Mr. Gabby. It must be a fine profession, traveling and advertising sandwiches."

"Oh, no," said Mr. Gabby, "I don't advertise sandwiches, I just wear any kind of an ad, one sign on front and one sign on behind, this way . . . Like a sandwich. Ya know what I mean?"

"Oh, I see. That must be fun; and you travel, too?" asked Homer as he got out the flour and the baking powder.

"Yeah, I ride the rods between jobs, on freight trains, ya know what I mean?"

"Yes, but isn't that dangerous?" asked Homer.

"Of course there's a certain amount a risk; but you take any method a travel these days, it's all dangerous. Ya know what I mean? Now take airplanes, for instance . . ."

Just then a large shiny black car stopped in front of the lunchroom, and a chauffeur helped a lady out of the rear door. They both came inside, and the lady smiled at Homer and said, "We've stopped for a light snack. Some doughnuts and coffee would be simply marvelous."

Then Homer said, "I'm sorry, Ma'm, but the doughnuts won't be ready until I make this batter and start Uncle Ulysses' doughnut machine."

"Well, now, aren't *you* a clever young man to know how to make *doughnuts!*"

"Well," blushed Homer, "I've really never done it before, but I've got a receipt to follow."

"Now, young man, you simply must allow me to help. You know, I haven't made doughnuts for years; but I know the best receipt for doughnuts. It's marvelous, and we really must use it."

"But, Ma'm . . ." said Homer.

"Now just *wait* till you taste these doughnuts," said the lady. "Do you have an apron?" she asked, as she took off her fur coat and her rings and her jewelry and rolled up her sleeves. "Charles," she said to the chauffeur, "hand me that baking powder, that's right, and, young man, we'll need some nutmeg."

So Homer and the chauffeur stood by and handed things and cracked the eggs while the lady mixed and stirred. Mr. Gabby sat on his stool, sipped his coffee, and looked on with great interest.

"There!" said the lady when all of the ingredients were mixed. "Just *wait* till you taste these doughnuts!"

"It looks like an awful lot of batter," said Homer as he stood on a chair and poured it into the doughnut machine with the help of the chauffeur. "It's about *ten* times as much as Uncle Ulysses ever makes."

"But wait till you taste them!" said the lady with an eager look and a smile.

Homer got down from the chair and pushed a button on the machine marked, *"Start."* Rings of batter started dropping into the hot fat. After a ring of batter was cooked on one side, an automatic gadget turned it over, and the other side would cook. Then another automatic gadget gave the doughnut a little push; and it rolled neatly down a little chute, all ready to eat.

"That's a simply *fascinating* machine," said the lady as she waited for the first doughnut to roll out.

"Here, young man, you must have the first one. Now isn't that just *too* delicious!? Isn't it simply marvelous?"

"Yes, Ma'm, it's very good," replied Homer as the lady handed doughnuts to Charles and to Mr. Gabby and asked if they didn't think they were simply divine doughnuts.

"It's an old family receipt!" said the lady with pride.

Homer poured some coffee for the lady and her chauffeur and for Mr. Gabby, and a glass of milk for himself. Then they all sat down at the lunch counter to enjoy another few doughnuts apiece.

"I'm so glad you enjoy my doughnuts," said the lady. "But now, Charles, we really must be going. If you will just take this apron, Homer, and put two dozen doughnuts in a bag to take along, we'll be on our way. And, Charles, don't forget to pay the young man." She rolled down her sleeves and put on her jewelry; then Charles managed to get her into her big fur coat.

"Good night, young man, I haven't had so much fun in years. I *really* haven't!" said the lady, as she went out the door and into the big shiny car.

"Those are sure good doughnuts," said Mr. Gabby as the car moved off.

"You bet!" said Homer. Then he and Mr. Gabby stood and watched the automatic doughnut machine make doughnuts.

After a few dozen more doughnuts had rolled down the little chute, Homer said, "I guess that's about enough doughnuts to sell to the after theater customers. I'd better turn the machine off for a while."

Homer pushed the button marked "*Stop*," and there was a little click, but nothing happened. The rings of batter kept right on dropping into the hot fat, and an automatic gadget kept right on turning them over, and another automatic gadget kept right on giving them a little push, and the doughnuts kept right on rolling down the little chute, all ready to eat.

"That's funny," said Homer, "I'm sure that's the right button!" He pushed it again, but the automatic doughnut maker kept right on making doughnuts.

"Well, I guess I must have put one of those pieces in backwards," said Homer.

"Then it might stop if you pushed the button marked '*Start*,'" said Mr. Gabby.

Homer did, and the doughnuts still kept rolling down the little chute, just as regular as a clock can tick.

"I guess we could sell a few more doughnuts," said Homer, "but I'd better telephone Uncle Ulysses over at the barbershop." Homer gave the number; and while he waited for someone to answer, he counted thirty-seven doughnuts roll down the little chute.

Finally someone answered, "Hello! This is the sarber bhop, I mean the barber shop."

"Oh, hello, sheriff. This is Homer. Could I speak to Uncle Ulysses?"

"Well, he's playing pinochle right now," said the sheriff. "Anythin' I can tell 'im?"

"Yes," said Homer. "I pushed the button marked *Stop* on the doughnut machine, but the rings of batter keep right on dropping into the hot fat, and an automatic gadget keeps right on turning them over, and another automatic gadget keeps giving them a little push, and the doughnuts keep right on rolling down the little chute! It won't stop!"

"O.K. Wold the hire, I mean, hold the wire, and I'll tell 'im." Then Homer looked over his shoulder and counted another twenty-one doughnuts roll down the little chute, all ready to eat. Then the sheriff said, "He'll be right over. . . . Just gotta finish this hand."

"That's good," said Homer. "G'by, sheriff."

The window was full of doughnuts by now, so Homer and Mr. Gabby had to hustle around and start stacking them on plates and trays and lining them up on the counter.

"Sure are a lot of doughnuts!" said Homer.

"You bet!" said Mr. Gabby. "I lost count at twelve hundred and two, and that was quite a while back."

People had begun to gather outside the lunchroom window, and someone was saying, "There are almost as many doughnuts as there are people in Centerburg, and I wonder how in tarnation Ulysses thinks he can sell all of 'em!"

Every once in a while somebody would come inside and buy some; but while somebody bought two to eat and a dozen to take home, the machine made three dozen more.

By the time Uncle Ulysses and the sheriff arrived and pushed through the crowd, the lunchroom was a calamity of doughnuts! Doughnuts in the window, doughnuts piled high on the shelves, doughnuts stacked on plates, doughnuts lined up twelve deep all along the counter, and doughnuts still rolling down the little chute, just as regular as a clock can tick.

"Hello, sheriff, hello, Uncle Ulysses, we're having a little trouble here," said Homer.

"Well, I'll be dunked!!" said Uncle Ulysses.

"Dernd ef you won't be when Aggy gits home," said the sheriff.

"Mighty fine doughnuts, though. What'll you do with 'em all, Ulysses?"

Uncle Ulysses groaned and said, "What will Aggy say? We'll never sell 'em all."

Then Mr. Gabby, who hadn't said anything for a long time, stopped piling doughnuts and said, "What you need is an advertising man. Ya know what I mean? You got the doughnuts, ya gotta create a market . . . Understand? . . . It's balancing the demand with the supply . . . That sort of thing."

"Yep!" said Homer. "Mr. Gabby's right. We have to enlarge our market. He's an advertising sandwich man; so if we hire him, he can walk up and down in front of the theater and get the customers."

"You're hired, Mr. Gabby!" said Uncle Ulysses.

Then everybody pitched in to paint the signs and to get Mr. Gabby sandwiched between. They painted "SALE ON DOUGHNUTS" in big letters on the window, too.

Meanwhile the rings of batter kept right on dropping into the hot fat, and an automatic gadget kept right on turning them over, and another automatic gadget kept right on giving them a little push, and the doughnuts kept right on rolling down the little chute, just as regular as a clock can tick.

"I certainly hope this advertising works," said Uncle Ulysses, wagging his head. "Aggy'll certainly throw a fit if it don't."

The sheriff went outside to keep order, because there was quite a crowd by now—all looking at the doughnuts and guessing how many thousands there were, and watching new ones roll down the little chute, just as regular as a clock can tick. Homer and Uncle Ulysses kept stacking doughnuts. Once in a while somebody bought a few, but not very often.

Then Mr. Gabby came back and said, "Say, you know there's not much use o' me advertisin' at the theater.

The show's all over, and besides almost everybody in town is out front watching that machine make doughnuts!"

"Zeus!" said Uncle Ulysses. "We must get rid of these doughnuts before Aggy gets here!"

"Looks like you will have ta hire a truck ta waul 'em ahay, I mean haul 'em away!!" said the sheriff, who had just come in. Just then there was a noise and a shoving out front, and the lady from the shiny black car and her chauffeur came pushing through the crowd and into the lunchroom.

"Oh, gracious!" she gasped, ignoring the doughnuts, "I've lost my diamond bracelet, and I know I left it here on the counter," she said, pointing to a place where the doughnuts were piled in stacks of two dozen.

"Yes, Ma'm, I guess you forgot it when you helped make the batter," said Homer.

Then they moved all the doughnuts around and looked for the diamond bracelet, but they couldn't find it anywhere. Meanwhile the doughnuts kept rolling down the little chute, just as regular as a clock can tick.

After they had looked all around, the sheriff cast a suspicious eye on Mr. Gabby; but Homer said, "He's all right, sheriff, he didn't take it. He's a friend of mine."

Then the lady said, "I'll offer a reward of one hundred dollars for that bracelet! It really *must* be found! . . . it *really* must!"

"Now don't you worry, lady," said the sheriff. "I'll get your bracelet back!"

"Zeus! This is terrible!" said Uncle Ulysses. "First all of these doughnuts, and then on top of all that, a lost diamond bracelet . . ."

Mr. Gabby tried to comfort him, and he said, "There's always a bright side. That machine'll probably run outta batter in an hour or two."

If Mr. Gabby hadn't been quick on his feet, Uncle Ulysses would have knocked him down, sure as fate.

Then while the lady wrung her hands and said, "We must find it, we *must!*" and Uncle Ulysses was moaning about what Aunt Agnes would say, and the sheriff was eyeing Mr. Gabby, Homer sat down and thought hard.

Before twenty more doughnuts could roll down the little chute, he shouted, "SAY I know where the bracelet is! It was lying here on the counter and got mixed up in the batter by mistake! The bracelet is cooked inside one of those doughnuts!"

"Why . . . I really believe you're right," said the lady through her tears. "Isn't that *amazing?* Simply *amazing!*"

"I'll be durn'd!" said the sheriff.

"OhH-h!" moaned Uncle Ulysses. "Now we have to break up all of these doughnuts to find it. Think of the *pieces!* Think of the *crumbs!* Think of what *Aggy* will say!"

"Nope," said Homer. "We won't have to break them up. I've got a plan."

So Homer and the advertising man took some cardboard and some paint and printed another sign. They put this sign in the window, and the sandwich man wore two more signs that said the same thing and walked around in the crowd out front.

FRESH DOUGHNUTS
2 FOR 5¢
WHILE THEY LAST
$100.⁰⁰ PRIZE
FOR FINDING
A BRACELET
INSIDE A DOUGHNUT
P.S. YOU HAVE TO GIVE THE
BRACELET BACK

THEN . . . The doughnuts began to sell! *Everybody* wanted to buy doughnuts, *dozens* of doughnuts!

And that's not all. Everybody bought coffee to dunk the doughnuts in, too. Those that didn't buy coffee bought milk or soda. It kept Homer and the lady and the chauffeur and Uncle Ulysses and the sheriff busy waiting on the people who wanted to buy doughnuts.

When all but the last couple of hundred doughnuts had been sold, Rupert Black shouted, "I GAWT IT!!" and sure enough . . . there was the diamond bracelet inside of his doughnut!

Then Rupert went home with a hundred dollars, the citizens of Centerburg went home full of doughnuts, the lady and her chauffeur drove off with the diamond bracelet, and Homer went home with his mother when she stopped by with Aunt Aggy.

As Homer went out of the door, he heard Mr. Gabby say, "Neatest trick of merchandising I ever seen," and Aunt Aggy was looking sceptical while Uncle Ulysses was saying, "The rings of batter kept right on dropping into the hot fat, and the automatic gadget kept right on turning them over, and the other automatic gadget kept right on giving them a little push, and the doughnuts kept right on rolling down the little chute just as regular as a clock can tick—they just kept right on a comin', an' a comin', an' a comin', an' a comin'."

(Note the time. Then check your speed of reading with the Reading Score Board.)

◈❊❊◈

READING TO GET A POINT

Someone has said that there are two kinds of readers: one, the kind that goes through ideas; and two, the kind that lets ideas go through him. The second kind of reader sounds very much like a sieve: the best ideas in the world run through him, but nothing sticks.

Surely a chapter called "The Funny Bone" has entertainment as its chief purpose. However, even in humor there are certain underlying ideas. We may laugh and know why we are laughing. We may laugh at both reality and exaggeration and recognize the cause of our laughter. So, throughout this chapter, enjoy the foolishness; but at the same time keep the thinking machine well oiled.

1. Homer never tries to be funny. What is it that makes him funny?
2. Which other characters in the story amuse you? Why?
3. Which parts of the story make you stretch your imagination?
4. What do you think of the names of the characters?
5. Do you know any of Homer's other adventures? Tell them to the class.

THE RIGHT WORDS

Can you explain the meaning of the words in italics?
1. plans for a *box social*
2. Uncle Ulysses just *frittered away* his spare time.
3. you've got a *mechanical mind*
4. I *ride the rods* between jobs
5. he's playing *pinochle* right now
6. the lunchroom was a *calamity of doughnuts*
7. Neatest trick of *merchandising*
8. Aunt Aggy was looking *sceptical*

READING SCORE BOARD

Number of Words in Story: 3060.

Number of Minutes	31	15 1/2	12 1/4	10 1/5	7 1/2	6
Reading Rate	100 w.p.m.	200 w.p.m.	250 w.p.m.	300 w.p.m.	400 w.p.m.	500 w.p.m.

⋘ BOB DAVIS

Jackknives from Heaven

The distance from earth to heaven may be great; but three boys believed that if their prayers were loud enough, they would be heard. You will discover in this story whether they were heard—and by whom.

(Note the time when you begin reading.)

MOTHER, true to the principles upon which her whole life was founded, never permitted us boys to drop the curtain on the day without hearing something from the Bible or the Book of Common Prayer. The "five-foot shelf" of President Eliot of Harvard had not yet come into existence, but the books of the church served always to strike the harmonic chords

——Reprinted from *Tree Toad* by Bob Davis. Used by permission of Jacques Chambrun, Inc.

of her soft singing voice and the strings of her heart. Soothing, even to children, were the intonations. After all these years I can still see her seated in the rocking chair, turning the pages of holy writ and directing her words to Brother Bill and to me.

She had a genius for selection in the matter of theme. What there was of drama and romance in the Old Testament she sought out and imparted with all its ancient glamour. This was especially the case when the sacred word pointed a moral that could be instilled into the juvenile mind. To me Genesis was not far removed from a gigantic circus parade in which the Lord summoned all living things out of the void and set the life of the world in motion.

Bill had a passion for the achievements of Samson, the soldiery conquests of Joshua before the walls of Jericho, the accuracy of David in his combat with Goliath. The boy craved action, which was always interpreted to suit himself. At intervals something or other turned up that he converted to his own original and sometimes twisted psychology. It was my lot to receive the sum total of his reflections, being a year and a half his junior, though ages behind him in swift reasoning.

On the night that I now summon out of the past it was the New Testament that lay upon Mother's knee. At random, apparently, but with deeper motives if the truth were known, she made her selections and conveyed the lessons to us. She came at last to Matthew vii:

"For where two or three are gathered together in My name, there am I in the midst of them. . . ."

The words struck a responsive chord in the deep recesses of Bill's intellect. Out of the corner of his eye I caught a swift flash of decision.

"What does that mean, Mother?" he asked with all the fervor of a sincere acolyte.

"Just what it says," was her response, stroking his offered hand.

"We unite in the congregation of the Lord. We have faith in his desire to help us. Remember the Sermon on the Mount:

"'Ask, and it shall be given you; seek and ye shall find. . . .'"

The word "given" seemed to coalesce the loose thoughts in his intelligence. Knowing all the outward manifestations of his inward reactions, I refrained from asking for an expression from Bill himself; but at the same time I knew that the evening's lesson had set a flood of ideas in motion, all of which would be conveyed to me at the proper time.

The stately grandfather's clock in the wide hallway broke into discordant clangings. That day, so far as we were concerned, was ended. Bidding her an affectionate good night, we passed down the corridor to the study where Father was completing the final draft of his next Sunday's sermon. Bill assured him that we were both much entertained by Mother's reading from the book of Matthew, and furthermore that he was just beginning to understand the power of the Lord.

And so to bed in the large square room containing upon either side our separate cots. Bill, after donning his canton-flannel homemade pajamas, took an unusually long time upon his knees, from which he arose with a fervent amen and seated himself upon my bunk. Familiar with the process of his meditations, I waited for him to put his thoughts into words. There was no doubt in my mind that something gigantic was formulating under Bill's hair.

"Bob, I gotta trust you with sump-in'," was his opening sentence in the crude speech into which boys fall when alone. "But nobody must know what we are goin' to do."

"All right, Bill. I won't tell nobody."

"Well," he hesitated, "you and me is goin' to ask the Lord for sumpin' and get it." The end of the sentence was whispered in my ear. It was a thrilling announcement.

"Gee, Bill. How?"

"Don't it say in the Book that when two or three ask for sumpin'—they—git—it. That's what Mother says, anyhow; and she *knows*."

"I'm willin' to try. What'll we ask for?"

"I ain't thought that out yet, but it'll be sumpin' we need bad. I'll tell you tomorrow mornin' what it is. Don't say a word to nobody."

I was still crossing my heart as Bill blew out the community candle and jumped into his own bed. Just how far he intended to go with his experiment was beyond my powers of reason. It was enough to know that an original thinker was bending his mind to the great problem and would report on the morrow. With that assurance I punched the pillow and passed into the fourth dimension.

I awoke at daybreak and found Bill sitting wide-eyed beside me. The conversation of the previous night came back with a rush.

"What are we goin' to ask for, Bill?" was my first question.

He replied with deliberation: "Two —white-handled—knives."

"Where'll they come from?"

"Heaven. Where else do you suppose?"

"Out of the sky?"

"Yes, sir. Out of the sky."

"Who'll send em?"

"Doesn't it say in the Bible, 'Ask and it shall be given you'? Ain't that enough? Besides, what do you care who sends 'em so long as they come. Gee, you're partic'lar."

The argument ebbed and flowed without advancing. We went into the pros and cons of the scheme and were finally brought down to earth by the cheerful voice of Mother announcing breakfast. Into our clothes we tumbled with the agreement that the demand for the gifts from on high would be made back of the barn the moment we could escape from the house. The morning's meal was a perfunctory affair from which we hastened out to the proving ground.

Desiring privacy, we drove all the chickens out of the barnyard and shut the gate. Bill climbed up on the roof of a granary and inspected the landscape for intruders. None was astir.

"You and me are the only two people in sight," was his comment, as he slid down a pillar, "and they ain't a cloud in the sky. Come on, and let's start. We better take hold of hands and look up while we are askin' for this favor. What we want to say is: 'O Lord, send down two white-handled knives. Amen!' Now both together:

"*O Lord, send down two white-handled knives. Amen!*"

Into the empyrean[1] we gazed for

[1] *empyrean*. The heavens.

some sign that the petition had been heard. Once again. Louder:

"O Lord, send down two white-handled knives"—Bill added, "to thy servants. Amen!"

"It's a long way to Heaven," said Bill. "I don't s'pose a prayer could get there right off. Give the Lord a chance." All the time we kept our eyes on space, hoping for some indication of a material sort.

"Don't think he heard it. Come on, let's yell it."

Again the two voices appealing in unison were lifted on high, the formula unchanged after we added the words "to thy servants." We were not aware of it at the time; but the demand was so far-reaching that it penetrated the barn and reached the ears of Father, who was out in the garden. Amazed at the clamor, he entered the barn from the kitchen and gave attention to the invocation of his two sons. Lacking a solution for the performance, he tiptoed back to the house and laid the matter before Mother. Two problems were presented: a—Was the appeal to be answered? b—How?

In the meantime two vociferous youngsters back of the barn, hand in hand, were bawling to high heaven for a pair of white-handled knives from the Giver of Every Good and Perfect Gift.

We released our prayers at three-minute intervals, scanning the blue sky for returns. Having no information as to just the direction from which the heavenly tokens would come, we did considerable revolving about the barnyard. A passer-by might

have concluded that we were indulging in that quaint pastime called "crack the whip," with our eyes fixed on the zenith. Regardless of the belief that hope springs eternal in the human breast, our patience was finally exhausted.

"Don't look like we was goin' to git the knives," remarked Bill as he made a final survey of the upper regions. "Mebby we got the prayer mixed up. S'pose we go in and ask Mother to tell us that part out of the Prayer Book again. We mustn't act like we was excited or anything like that. Just ask her to talk about it once more."

We opened the barnyard gate, let the chickens in to forage, and returned to the kitchen, where we found both our parents in conversation.

Bill put the question bluntly:

"Mother, when you want something and ask the Lord for it, how long does it take for him to make up his mind when he is goin' to give it to you?"

"That depends upon what you ask for, and also whether or not it is good for you," she responded, glancing at Father, who appeared to show some interest in the query.

"Moreover, you must have patience," our sire interposed, "and faith. The Lord moves in mysterious ways."

"What does it say about getting together?" I asked boldly, fearful that the issue would become fogged in a theological technicality.

Mother out of her perfect memory quoted the line in full: "For where *two or three are gathered together in My name, there am I in the midst of them."*

"If you want anything, boys," said Father, "ask for it with the feeling that the Lord will provide. But don't be in a hurry. All in good time. Come, now, get to your lessons. You can make your requests of the Lord after lunch."

That seemed perfectly fair to both of us, so we agreed through the medium of the sign language to postpone operations until the afternoon. Father got out of his dressing gown, donned a linen duster, and made some casual excuse for going downtown.

"I shall be back for lunch," he announced as he departed with his stout oak cane, which was understood by the whole family as having come from the deck of the *Kearsarge* of Civil War fame.

Bill did considerable slacking at his books that morning, his mind the more occupied with the immediate business of acquiring two white-handled knives. "The Book says, 'When *two* or *three* are gathered together,'" he soliloquized. "Mebby two boys like us ain't powerful enough. Don't you think we need help? Who else can we get? Ain't you got some ideas?"

I suggested one Dave Rickey, a neighbor's boy who was permitted to mingle with us on a basis of social equality. He was two years Bill's senior, but agreeable to any suggestion that smacked of mystery.

"You get Dave over here after lunch," said Bill, "and I'll talk him into helpin' us. If we get the knives,

mebby we can fix it for Dave to come in on sumpin' later."

Shortly before the lunch hour Father strolled up the garden path, set his Civil War relic in the cane rack, hung up his linen duster, and assumed an air of unusual importance. An enigmatical smile played around his lips during the simple repast. Mother hummed a few folk songs while serving the victuals and bestowed unusually large helpings upon us kids.

After the bread pudding, we excused ourselves and immediately legged it for the barnyard, where Dave Rickey was parked pending further particulars from Bill.

"Bob says you got a scheme for us fellers to get together on," he began; "and if it works, I'm in for my share. What's it, Bill?"

The cards were laid on the table face up. Dave made a wry face and set up a doubter's argument without delay. "You can't do it, Bill," he announced. "Whadda you mean askin' for knives and the like of that? Who ever heard of knives comin' from Heaven? You gotta gettum in the hardware store; four bits a knife and more'n that sometimes."

"Well, it don't cost nothin' to try it," was Bill's flat rejoinder, "and if we gettum we'll make up a list of the things we need and pile up a whole lot of stuff. It may be a great discovery, and we'll git the credit of bein' the first fellers to do it. Will you or won't you help? Foolin' around and talkin' won't do no good, Dave. We just gotta pray right now and pray hard. Well?"

Dave wavered a few moments and finally decided to come in. We joined hands and set up the refrain:

"*O Lord, send down two white-handled knives for thy servants. Amen!*"

"What's the matter with sendin' down three?" broke in the Rickey boy, withdrawing from the trio. "You fellers gotta gall leavin' me standin' here without a knife."

"Don't be crazy, Dave," said Bill, grabbing his hand again. "We must do this gradual. Come on and see what happens."

We won him over for another test. On the third appeal he lifted his voice and joined in the fervent request. As a matter of fact, he must have felt some of the spirit of faith that inspired us and finally launched into an elocutionary demand that smacked of hysteria. In the midst of the demonstration, which was primarily vocal, two glistening objects suddenly appeared over the peak of the barn and came hurtling downward. One of them hit Bill squarely on the forehead and bounced off on the ground. The other fell into the dust at my feet. The gifts came for all the world like a pair of mallard ducks dropping into a blind. Stunned by the accuracy and violence with which Bill's token arrived, the great originator was, to say the least, mildly bewildered. To his credit he made a quick recovery and became the active center of a commotion that beggars description.

"Hands off!" he shouted. "The knives are here, right from the Lord! Stand back, you fellers! This was my idea, and you'll have to lemme look 'em over first." Gathering both souvenirs up from the dirt, he made a careful inspection of each, opening the blades, snapping them shut, weighing one, then the other, separately in the palm of his hand.

"You orter have asked for three, Bill," remarked Dave after recovering from the shock. "We could have had 'em just's well. Now, for all we know, that's the last he'll send. I bet Bob'll get the worst of them two knives when you are ready to split 'em. That's the way with some people; holler for help and then don't do nothin' for the helpers."

"What's the use of talkin' like that, Dave," said Bill, rubbing the welt on his forehead. "I thought of this scheme, and see what I got for it. This is the first time anybody ever had a plan like this. You'll git yours when I'm ready to take it up with the Lord. And, besides, both these knives are exactly alike, and Bob can have his pick. That's the kind of a feller I am."

"Leavin' me— ?" inquired Dave with a hungry look.

"Nothin'," retorted Bill with vehement finality. "But that ain't sayin' that we ain't willin' to try. Here, Bob, which one of these knives do you want?"

They were identical in every particular. We took it for granted that the Lord distributed only the very best to "*his servants.*" I chose the one in my right hand and bowed respectfully to the blue sky. "Thank you, O Lord."

Bill voiced his appreciation with

equal fervor and then turned to Dave with a set expression on his mouth. "Now if you will tell us what you want, we'll try to git it. Don't be a pig."

A thin sneer spread over Dave's features. "Well, you got what you wanted, didn't you? What's the matter with me gettin' what I want? Why do you fellers have the pick; 'cause you're preacher's sons, I guess. Yes. You betcha. And I'll tell you sumpin' else: If I don't get just what I ask for, this is the last prayin' anybody'll ever hear out of me. And I'll quit goin' to Sunday school. Tell that to your father!"

Despite the exasperating circumstances, Bill kept his temper, wholly disregarding my gesture that we leave Dave flat and retire to the house. Bill seemed cocksure that he had the power to launch another fruitful petition.

"All right, Dave," he said with praiseworthy calm. "Whadda you want? 'Ask and ye shall receive,' as it says in the Book."

"Well," began the unrewarded, "I been wantin' a certain thing for a long time. I don't need it now; but when the winter comes, I will. Bet you couldn't get it for me."

"If you don't need it till winter, Dave," I suggested, "why don't you wait?"

"Nawsir! I want it right this afternoon! And you better keep your mouth shut, Bob. Me and Bill is doin' this. Ain't we, Bill?"

"That ain't polite, Dave; tellin' me to keep my mouth shut," I interposed.

"I know 'tain't. But that's what I want you to do, all the same. The time for you to put in your talk is when it comes to prayin'."

"Supposin' I won't?"

"Yes, you will, Bob," interrupted Bill. "We gotta help Dave get what he wants." Subservient to the demands of the Director General, I withdrew all opposition. Bill had the situation well in hand.

"Now, Dave," he continued in a cheerful and encouraging tone of voice, "what can we git for you?"

Dave braced himself and fired the shot: "A sled."

"W-h-a-t?"

"That's what I said: A—sled."

"To come down," said Bill, blanching, "and hit me in the eye? No, sir. Ask for something soft, Dave: A pair of mittens, or a tippet, or mebby a suit of clothes. We don't want to have no sled come at us. See what the knife did. Lookit." Thereupon Bill laid a finger on the bruised forehead.

"All — right," snorted the Rickey boy. "If you fellers can't get me a sled inside the next ten minutes, I ain't goin' to have nothin' more to do with religion."

Christianity was not to topple for the lack of one test. The offspring of a distinguished cleric dared not hesitate in such a crisis. I saw from Bill's determined expression that Dave Rickey could only be snatched from the burning by one more heroic demonstration. Our iron of inheritance was again to be thrust in the forge.

"We—will—get—the—sled—for—you —Dave, even if it knocks our brains out."

"Let's see you."

"But we gotta get under the eaves when we ask the Lord for it, so as not to take any chances. We can't do no more 'an protect ourselves. Git together."

"Now, all together: *O Lord, send down one sled for Dave Rickey, thy servant. Amen.*"

Furtively the trinity of hopefuls glanced upward with the full conviction, at least on the part of two of us, that a hand-painted sled with half-round runners and iron braces would come clipping from the shingles and crash into the barnyard. But there was something wrong with the schedule. Once again we lifted our voices and waited all atremble. More delay.

"'Tain't comin'," muttered Dave, glued against the barn fearful of the consequences. "You orter have asked for them three knives, Bill. What'll we do?"

"Keep prayin'," was the logical response from the boy in the middle. "It took us a long time to git what we asked for. What's your hurry?"

"And you can't use the sled till winter," I reminded Dave for the second time.

"Will you shut up, Bob!" said Dave, taking a kick at me behind Bill, who immediately rebuked us both with a demand for less talk and more faith.

The plea was repeated time and time again with varying elocutionary effect, three pairs of eyes searching the tip of the eaves for the first sign that we had been heard on high. The hot westering sun brought the per-spiration out as we hugged the barn and increased our efforts. Dave soon lost interest and tried to escape from Bill's clutch.

"Three more times, Dave; and if nothin' happens, we'll start again to-morrow morning."

"Nawsir. I'm through."

Bill released him, and we emerged from the protecting eaves. It was a sad admission of failure, made the more depressing by Dave's recanting of faith. "I-says-can-you-do-it-and-you-says-yes-and-you-didn't" was his farewell compound hyphenated mouthful. To all intents and purposes the great appeal had come to an unsuccessful conclusion; and because of that failure, a lamb was about to stray from the fold. I expected Bill to maneuver the drifting ship into peaceful waters and drop the anchor before the squall broke. . . . Not so. Dave, in a manner of speaking, had deserted. There was a hurt look in his eyes and a slight tremor about the chin.

"Won't you please wait till tomorrow morning, Dave?" I pleaded in sincere effort to give the Lord another chance.

To this invitation he responded, "Yes!" but seemed to look down upon me patronizingly. He then turned upon his heels and left the premises, throwing rocks at the chickens on the way out just to show us minister's sons that he was yet in possession of all his faculties.

Bill and I, still holding hands, walked into the sitting room. Mother was darning socks; and Father was deep in the pages of the Boston

Transcript, which followed him into the fastness of the Far West.

"We had faith, Father," Bill announced, "and patience, too. Didn't we, Bob?"

"And were you rewarded?" asked the soft-voiced woman at the darning needles, without missing a stitch.

"You tell Mother, Bob, how I did it," answered Bill for both of us. In the midst of the narrative, which was full of local color, Bill brought me to a halt with the demand that I be more specific. "Tell how the Lord picked me out and hit me with my knife right on the forehead."

"It can't be .possible," exclaimed Father, jumping up, "that I struck the boy."

"No, Father, it wasn't you. It was the Lord. He could see me standing right there beside the barn," Bill hastened to explain. "He made a fine shot."

Father's efforts at dissembling surprised me at the time. I never saw that otherwise tactful individual so completely at a loss for words. Mother went right on darning but appeared to be greatly amused at what amounted almost to a betrayal of the governor's nonsectarian secret.

"We had to get some help," Bill continued.

"What kind of help?" asked Father, glad of a new trend in the conversation.

"Well, we needed more power to get the prayer to heaven, so we asked Dave Rickey to join in. He didn't like it because we got a knife apiece. So I asked him what he wanted and he said a sled. But we couldn't get him

one, and he went home mad. We're gonna make one more try tomorrow mornin'."

"That's a fine predicament," or something like that, said Father, getting out from behind the *Transcript* and making for the hatrack and his linen duster. "I've got some business to attend to but will be back for supper. Boys, if you should see Dave Rickey again, tell him not to be discouraged."

With that cryptic remark he hurried out of the gate and disappeared down the street swinging the cane that emanated from the deck of the *Kearsarge*.

Mother cajoled us to remain in the balance of that afternoon and evening, to hear fascinating stories from the Old Testament. She was never more entertaining. Father appeared to be occupied on some secret mission, the precise nature of which was not imparted to his offspring. Little did we know as we crawled between the sheets in our youthful ignorance and passed into a sleep peopled with the most foolish dreams that the same kindly man who had released a flight of jackknives over the peak of the barn was moving heaven and earth to locate a sled before morning in a certain place where it would do the most good.

Under the influence of the placid night Dave had partly recovered his composure and appeared the next morning at the kitchen door. Bill and I greeted him with sincere warmth. Again, the hopeful trio would assail the distant gates with supplication, and mayhap all would yet be well.

Around the corner of the building and into the now historic barnyard we hurried, eager to begin the ceremonies. The spectacle that greeted our eyes paralyzed us completely. A miracle born of the darkness.

There in the barnyard, in about the same spot where the knives had fallen from the sky, rested a sled, striped in red and yellow and glistening with varnish. The jargon that arose from the Tower of Babel was pure English in comparison with the chaotic babble that broke loose behind that barn. It was too incoherent to be recorded. After the tumult and the shouting and the oft-repeated expressions of gratitude to the Most High for the nocturnal favor, Dave turned the sled over and found underneath the "belly board" something printed with a stencil.

"It says here," he read with boyish effort, " 'Buy of Charley Bell, the Hardware Man. Main Street.' I thought this here sled came from heaven."

"That don't mean nothin', Dave," broke in Bill, caressing the half-round steel runners. "For all we know, it may be at Charley Bell's store that the Lord trades. It ain't for us to ask."

"All right, Bill," answered Dave with a faraway look in his eyes, clutching the sled tightly to him, "I guess everythin' is gonna be all hunky if the danged winter ever comes."

With that incautious acknowledgment of my previously expressed suggestion, Dave bolted for his own humble domicile to prove to his widowed mother the efficacy of prayer.

(Stop. Note the time, and check your reading rate with the Reading Score Board.)

❖❆❖

READING SCORE BOARD

Number of Words in Story: 4440.

Number of Minutes	44	22	18	15	11	9
Reading Rate	100 w.p.m.	200 w.p.m.	250 w.p.m.	300 w.p.m.	400 w.p.m.	500 w.p.m.

COMPREHENSION CHECK

On your paper, write *True* or *False* for each of these statements:
1. Bill got his big idea from listening to his mother read the Bible.
2. He took his brother Bob into his confidence.
3. Bob did not want to co-operate.
4. Bill decided that they would ask for three white-handled knives.
5. The proving ground was behind the barn.
6. Dave Rickey asked to join in the experiment.

7. Their father heard them and answered with two white-handled knives.

8. Dave wanted a sled from heaven.

9. Father answered that prayer, too.

10. Then Father told the boys to stop praying for material things.

Getting Little Points of Humor

What is the humor in each of the following? What do the words in italics mean?

1. To me Genesis was not far removed from a *gigantic* circus parade.

2. "What does that mean, Mother?" he asked with all of the *fervor* of a sincere *acolyte*.

3. The word "given" seemed to *coalesce* loose thoughts in his intelligence.

4. Desiring *privacy*, we drove all the chickens out of the barnyard and shut the gate.

5. We released our prayers at three-minute intervals, *scanning* the blue sky for returns.

6. The Lord moves in *mysterious* ways.

7. After the *tumult* and the shouting and the oft-repeated expressions to the Most High for the *nocturnal* favor . . .

8. Dave bolted for his own humble *domicile* to prove to his widowed mother the *efficacy* of prayer.

Thinking It Over

1. What seems to you to be the basis of the humor of this story?

2. What does the word *sacrilegious* mean? Is this story sacrilegious?

❦❮ O. Henry

The Ransom of Red Chief

Kidnaping is a serious crime, and kidnapers should be severely punished. The kidnapers in this story received the worst kind of punishment and in the most *surprising* way.
(Note the time when you begin reading.)

I<small>T</small> looked like a good thing; but wait till I tell you. We were down south, in Alabama—Bill Driscoll and myself—when this kidnaping idea struck us. It was, as Bill afterwards expressed it, "during a moment of temporary men-tal apparition[1]"; but we didn't find that out till later.

There was a town down there, as flat as a flannel cake, and called Summit, of course. It contained inhabitants of as undeleterious and self-sat-

——From *Whirligigs* by O. Henry. Copyright 1910 by Doubleday & Company, Inc.

[1] *apparition.* Misused word; the speaker really meant *aberration* or mental wandering.

isfied a class of peasantry as ever clustered around a Maypole.

Bill and me had a joint capital of about six hundred dollars, and we needed just two thousand dollars more to pull off a town-lot scheme in western Illinois. We talked it over on the front steps of the hotel. Philoprogenitiveness,[2] says we, is strong in semirural communities; therefore, and for other reasons, a kidnaping project ought to do better there than in the radius of newspapers that send reporters out in plain clothes to stir up talk about such things. We knew that Summit couldn't get after us with anything stronger than constables and, maybe, some lackadaisical bloodhounds and a diatribe[3] or two in the *Weekly Farmers' Budget*. So it looked good.

We selected for our victim the only child of a prominent citizen named Ebenezer Dorset. The father was respectable and tight, a mortgage fancier and a stern, upright collection-plate passer and forecloser. The kid was a boy of ten, with bas-relief[4] freckles, and hair the color of the cover of the magazine you buy at the newsstand when you want to catch a train. Bill and me figured that Ebenezer would melt down for a ransom of two thousand dollars to a cent. But wait till I tell you.

About two miles from Summit was a little mountain covered with a dense cedar brake. On the rear elevation of this mountain was a cave. There we stored provisions.

[2] *philoprogenitiveness.* Love of children.
[3] *diatribe.* A bitter discussion.
[4] *bas-relief.* Sculpture in which the figures stand out only a little from the background.

One evening after sundown, we drove in a buggy past old Dorset's house. The kid was in the street, throwing rocks at a kitten on the opposite fence.

"Hey, little boy!" says Bill. "Would you like to have a bag of candy and a nice ride?"

The boy catches Bill neatly in the eye with a piece of brick.

That boy put up a fight like a welterweight cinnamon bear; but at last we got him down in the bottom of the buggy and drove away. We took him up to the cave, and I hitched the horse in the cedar brake. After dark I drove the buggy to the little village three miles away, where we had hired it, and walked back to the mountain.

Bill was pasting court plaster over the scratches and bruises on his features. There was a fire burning behind the big rock at the entrance of the cave; and the boy was watching a pot of boiling coffee, with two buzzard tail feathers stuck in his red hair. He points a stick at me when I come up, and says:

"Ha! Cursed paleface, do you dare to enter the camp of Red Chief, the terror of the plains?"

"He's all right now," says Bill, rolling up his trousers and examining some bruises on his shins. "We're playing Indian. We're making Buffalo Bill's show look like magic-lantern views of Palestine in the town hall. I'm Old Hank the Trapper, Red Chief's captive; and I'm to be scalped at daybreak. By Geronimo! That kid can kick hard."

Yes, sir, that boy seemed to be

having the time of his life. The fun of camping out in a cave had made him forget that he was a captive himself. He immediately christened me Snake-eye the Spy and announced that when his braves returned from the warpath, I was to be broiled at the stake at the rising of the sun.

Then we had supper and he filled his mouth full of bacon and bread and gravy and began to talk. He made a during-dinner speech something like this:

"I like this fine. I never camped out before; but I had a pet 'possum once, and I was nine last birthday. I hate to go to school. Rats ate up sixteen of Jimmy Talbot's aunt's speckled hen's eggs. Are there any real Indians in these woods? I want some more gravy. Does the trees' moving make the wind blow? We had five puppies. What makes your nose so red, Hank? My father has lots of money. Are the stars hot? I whipped Ed Walker twice, Saturday. I don't like girls. You dassent catch toads unless with a string. Do oxen make any noise? Why are oranges round? Have you got beds to sleep on in this cave? Amos Murray has got six toes. A parrot can talk, but a monkey or a fish can't. How many does it take to make twelve?"

Every few minutes he would remember that he was a pesky redskin, and pick up his stick rifle and tiptoe to the mouth of the cave to rubber for the scouts of the hated paleface. Now and then he would let out a war whoop that made Old Hank the Trapper shiver. That boy had Bill terrorized from the start.

"Red Chief," says I to the kid, "would you like to go home?"

"Aw, what for?" says he. "I don't have any fun at home. I hate to go to school. I like to camp out. You won't take me back home again, Snake-eye, will you?"

"Not right away," says I. "We'll stay here in the cave awhile."

"All right!" says he. "That'll be fine. I never had such fun in all my life."

We went to bed about eleven o'clock. We spread down some wide blankets and quilts and put Red Chief between us. We weren't afraid he'd run away. He kept us awake for three hours, jumping up and reaching for his rifle and screeching: "Hist! Pard," in mine and Bill's ears, as the fancied crackle of a twig or the rustle of a leaf revealed to his young imagination the stealthy approach of the outlaw band. At last I fell into a troubled sleep and dreamed that I had been kidnaped and chained to a tree by a ferocious pirate with red hair.

Just at daybreak, I was awakened by a series of awful screams from Bill. They weren't yells, or howls, or shouts, or whoops, or yawps, such as you'd expect from a manly set of vocal organs—they were simply indecent, terrifying, humiliating screams, such as women emit when they see ghosts or caterpillars. It's an awful thing to hear a strong, desperate, fat man scream incontinently[5] in a cave at daybreak.

I jumped up to see what the matter was. Red Chief was sitting on Bill's chest, with one hand twined

[5] *incontinently.* Unrestrainedly.

in Bill's hair. In the other he had the sharp case knife we used for slicing bacon; and he was industriously and realistically trying to take Bill's scalp, according to the sentence that had been pronounced upon him the evening before.

I got the knife away from the kid and made him lie down again. But, from that moment, Bill's spirit was broken. He lay down on his side of the bed, but he never closed an eye again in sleep as long as that boy was with us. I dozed off for a while, but along toward sunup I remembered that Red Chief had said I was to be burned at the stake at the rising of the sun. I wasn't nervous or afraid; but I sat up and lit my pipe and leaned against a rock.

"What you getting up so soon for, Sam?" asked Bill.

"Me?" says I. "Oh, I got a kind of a pain in my shoulder. I thought sitting up would rest it."

"You're a liar!" says Bill. "You're afraid. You was to be burned at sunrise, and you was afraid he'd do it. And he would, too, if he could find a match. Ain't it awful, Sam? Do you think anybody will pay out money to get a little imp like that back home?"

"Sure," said I. "A rowdy kid like that is just the kind that parents dote on. Now, you and the Chief get up and cook breakfast while I go up on the top of this mountain and reconnoiter."[6]

I went up on the peak of the little mountain and ran my eye over the contiguous[7] vicinity. Over toward Summit I expected to see the sturdy yeomanry of the village armed with scythes and pitchforks beating the countryside for the dastardly kidnapers. But what I saw was a peaceful landscape dotted with one man plowing with a dun mule. Nobody was dragging the creek, no couriers[8] dashed hither and yon, bringing tidings of no news to the distracted parents. There was a sylvan attitude of somnolent sleepiness pervading that section of the external outward surface of Alabama that lay exposed to my view. "Perhaps," says I to myself, "it has not yet been discovered that the wolves have borne away the tender lambkin from the fold. Heaven help the wolves!" says I, and I went down the mountain to breakfast.

When I got to the cave, I found Bill backed up against the side of it, breathing hard, and the boy threatening to smash him with a rock half as big as a coconut.

"He put a red-hot boiled potato down my back," explained Bill, "and then mashed it with his foot; and I boxed his ears. Have you got a gun about you, Sam?"

I took the rock away from the boy and kind of patched up the argument. "I'll fix you," says the kid to Bill. "No man ever yet struck the Red Chief but what he got paid for it. You better beware!"

After breakfast the kid takes a piece of leather with strings wrapped around it out of his pocket and goes outside the cave unwinding it.

"What's he up to now?" says Bill

---

[6] *reconnoiter.* To make a survey.

[7] *contiguous.* Adjoining.

[8] *couriers.* Messengers.

anxiously. "You don't think he'll run away, do you, Sam?"

"No fear of it," says I. "He don't seem to be much of a home body. But we've got to fix up some plan about the ransom. There don't seem to be much excitement around Summit on account of his disappearance, but maybe they haven't realized yet that he's gone. His folks may think he's spending the night with Aunt Jane or one of the neighbors. Anyhow, he'll be missed today. Tonight we must get a message to his father, demanding the two thousand dollars for his return."

Just then we heard a kind of war whoop, such as David might have emitted when he knocked out the champion Goliath. It was a sling that Red Chief had pulled out of his pocket, and he was whirling it around his head.

I dodged, and heard a heavy thud and a kind of a sigh from Bill, like one a horse gives out when you take his saddle off. A niggerhead rock the size of an egg had caught Bill just behind his left ear. He loosened himself all over and fell in the fire across the frying pan of hot water for washing the dishes. I dragged him out and poured cold water on his head for half an hour.

By and by, Bill sits up and feels behind his ear and says, "Sam, do you know who my favorite Biblical character is?"

"Take it easy," says I. "You'll come to your senses presently."

"King Herod,[9]" says he. "You won't

go away and leave me here alone, will you, Sam?"

I went out and caught that boy and shook him until his freckles rattled.

"If you don't behave," says I, "I'll take you straight home. Now, are you going to be good, or not?"

"I was only funning," says he sullenly. "I didn't mean to hurt Old Hank. But what did he hit me for? I'll behave, Snake-eye, if you won't send me home, and if you'll let me play the Black Scout today."

"I don't know the game," says I. "That's for you and Mr. Bill to decide. He's your playmate for the day. I'm going away for a while, on business. Now, you come in and make friends with him and say you are sorry for hurting him, or home you go, at once."

I made him and Bill shake hands, and then I took Bill aside and told him I was going to Poplar Cove, a little village three miles from the cave, and find out what I could about how the kidnaping had been regarded in Summit. Also, I thought it best to send a peremptory[10] letter to old man Dorset that day, demanding the ransom and dictating how it should be paid.

"You know, Sam," says Bill, "I've stood by you without batting an eye in earthquake, fire, and flood — in poker games, dynamite outrages, police raids, train robberies, and cyclones. I never lost my nerve yet till we kidnaped that two-legged skyrocket of a kid. He's got me going. You won't leave me long with him, will you, Sam?"

[9] *King Herod*. Herod the Great, the character in the Bible who ordered that all boy babies be killed.

[10] *peremptory*. Positive; giving no chance of denial.

"I'll be back some time this afternoon," says I. "You must keep the boy amused and quiet till I return. And now we'll write the letter to old Dorset."

Bill and I got paper and pencil and worked on the letter while Red Chief, with a blanket wrapped around him, strutted up and down, guarding the mouth of the cave. Bill begged me tearfully to make the ransom fifteen hundred dollars instead of two thousand. "I ain't attempting," says he, "to decry the celebrated moral aspect of parental affection; but we're dealing with humans, and it ain't human for anybody to give up two thousand dollars for that forty-pound chunk of freckled wildcat. I'm willing to take a chance at fifteen hundred dollars. You can charge the difference up to me."

So, to relieve Bill, I acceded; and we collaborated a letter that ran this way:

Ebenezer Dorset, Esq.:

We have your boy concealed in a place far from Summit. It is useless for you or the most skillful detectives to attempt to find him. Absolutely the only terms on which you can have him restored to you are these: We demand fifteen hundred dollars in large bills for his return; the money to be left at midnight tonight at the same spot and in the same box as your reply—as hereinafter described. If you agree to these terms, send your answer in writing by a solitary messenger tonight at half-past eight o'clock. After crossing Owl Creek, on the road to Poplar Cove, there are three large trees about a hundred yards apart, close to the fence of the wheat field on the right-hand side. At the bottom of the fence post, opposite the third tree, will be found a small pasteboard box.

The messenger will place the answer in this box and return immediately to Summit.

If you attempt any treachery or fail to comply with our demand as stated, you will never see your boy again.

If you pay the money as demanded, he will be returned to you safe and well within three hours. These terms are final; and if you do not accede to them, no further communication will be attempted.

Two Desperate Men

I addressed this letter to Dorset and put it in my pocket. As I was about to start, the kid comes up to me and says:

"Aw, Snake-eye, you said I could play the Black Scout while you was gone."

"Play it, of course," says I. "Mr. Bill will play with you. What kind of a game is it?"

"I'm the Black Scout," says Red Chief, "and I have to ride to the stockade to warn the settlers that the Indians are coming. I'm tired of playing Indian myself. I want to be the Black Scout."

"All right," says I. "It sounds harmless to me. I guess Mr. Bill will help you foil the pesky savages."

"What am I to do?" asks Bill, looking at the kid suspiciously.

"You are the hoss," says Black Scout. "Get down on your hands and knees. How can I ride to the stockade without a hoss?"

"You'd better keep him interested," said I, "till we get the scheme going. Loosen up."

Bill gets down on his all fours, and a look comes in his eyes like a rabbit's when you catch it in a trap.

"How far is it to the stockade, kid?" he asks in a husky manner of voice.

"Ninety miles," says the Black Scout. "And you have to hump yourself to get there on time. Whoa, now!"

The Black Scout jumps on Bill's back and digs his heels in his side.

"For heaven's sake," says Bill, "hurry back, Sam, as soon as you can. I wish we hadn't made the ransom more than a thousand. Say, you quit kicking me; or I'll get up and warm you good."

I walked over to Poplar Cove and sat around the post office and store, talking with the chawbacons that come in to trade. One whiskerando says that he hears Summit is all upset on account of Elder Ebenezer Dorset's boy having been lost or stolen. That was all I wanted to know. I bought some smoking tobacco, referred casually to the price of black-eyed peas, posted my letter surreptitiously,[11] and came away. The postmaster said the mail carrier would come by in an hour to take the mail on to Summit.

When I got back to the cave, Bill and the boy were not to be found. I explored the vicinity of the cave, and risked a yodel or two, but there was no response. So I lighted my pipe and sat down on a mossy bank to await developments.

In about half an hour I heard the bushes rustle, and Bill wabbled out into the little glade in front of the cave. Behind him was the kid, stepping softly like a scout, with a broad grin on his face. Bill stopped, took off his hat, and wiped his face with a red handkerchief. The kid stopped about eight feet behind him.

"Sam," says Bill, "I suppose you'll think I'm a renegade,[12] but I couldn't help it. I'm a grown person with masculine proclivities[13] and habits of self-defense, but there is a time when all systems of egotism and predominance fail. The boy is gone. I have sent him home. All is off. There was martyrs in old times," goes on Bill, "that suffered death rather than give up the particular graft they enjoyed. None of 'em ever was subjugated[14] to such supernatural tortures as I have been. I tried to be faithful to our articles of depredation; but there came a limit."

"What's the trouble, Bill?" I asks him.

"I was rode," says Bill, "the ninety miles to the stockade, not barring an inch. Then when the settlers was rescued, I was given oats. Sand ain't a palatable substitute. And then, for an hour I had to try to explain to him why there was nothin' in holes, how a road can run both ways, and what makes the grass green. I tell you, Sam, a human can only stand so much. I takes him by the neck of his clothes and drags him down the mountain. On the way he kicks my legs black-and-blue from the knees down; and I've got two or three bites on my thumb and hand cauterized.

[11] *surreptitiously.* Secretly.

[12] *renegade.* Traitor; deserter.
[13] *proclivities.* Inclinations.
[14] *subjugated.* Reduced to subjection.

"But he's gone"—continues Bill—"gone home. I showed him the road to Summit and kicked him about eight feet nearer there at one kick. I'm sorry we lose the ransom; but it was either that or Bill Driscoll to the madhouse."

"Bill," says I, "there isn't any heart disease in your family, is there?"

"No," says Bill, "nothing chronic except malaria and accidents. Why?"

"Then you might turn around," says I, "and have a look behind you."

Bill turns and sees the boy, and loses his complexion and sits down plump on the ground and begins to pluck aimlessly at grass and little sticks. For an hour I was afraid for his mind. And then I told him that my scheme was to put the whole job through immediately and that we would get the ransom and be off with it by midnight if old Dorset fell in with our proposition. So Bill braced up enough to give the kid a weak sort of a smile and a promise to play Russian in a Japanese war with him as soon as he felt a little better.

I had a scheme for collecting that ransom without danger of being caught by counterplots that ought to commend itself to professional kidnapers. The tree under which the answer was to be left—and the money later on—was close to the road fence with big bare fields on all sides. If a gang of constables should be watching for anyone to come for the note, they could see him a long way off crossing the fields or in the road. But no, siree! At half-past eight I was up in that tree as well hidden as a tree toad, waiting for the messenger to arrive.

Exactly on time, a half-grown boy rides up the road on a bicycle, locates the pasteboard box at the foot of the fence post, slips a folded piece of paper into it, and pedals away again back toward Summit.

I waited an hour and then concluded the thing was square. I slid down the tree, got the note, slipped along the fence till I struck the woods, and was back at the cave in another half an hour. I opened the note, got near the lantern, and read it to Bill. It was written with a pen in a crabbed hand, and the sum and substance of it was this:

Two Desperate Men

Gentlemen: I received your letter to-day by post, in regard to the ransom you ask for the return of my son. I think you are a little high in your demands, and I hereby make you a counter-proposition, which I am inclined to believe you will accept. You bring Johnny home and pay me two hundred and fifty dollars in cash, and I agree to take him off your hands. You had better come at night, for the neighbors believe he is lost, and I couldn't be responsible for what they would do to anybody they saw bringing him back.

Very respectfully,
Ebenezer Dorset

"Great pirates of Penzance!" says I, "of all the impudent—"

But I glanced at Bill and hesitated. He had the most appealing look in his eyes I ever saw on the face of a dumb or a talking brute.

"Sam," says he, "what's two hundred and fifty dollars, after all? We've got the money. One more night of this kid will send me to a bed in Bedlam.[15] Besides being a thorough gentleman, I think Mr. Dorset is a spendthrift for making us such a liberal offer. You ain't going to let the chance go, are you?"

"Tell you the truth, Bill," says I, "this little he ewe lamb has somewhat got on my nerves, too. We'll take him home, pay the ransom, and make our getaway."

We took him home that night. We got him to go by telling him that his father had bought a silver-mounted rifle and a pair of moccasins for him, and we were going to hunt bears the next day.

It was just twelve o'clock when we knocked at Ebenezer's front door. Just at the moment when I should have been abstracting the fifteen hundred dollars from the box under the tree, according to the original proposition, Bill was counting out two hundred and fifty dollars into Dorset's hand.

When the kid found out we were going to leave him at home, he started up a howl like a calliope and fastened him as tight as a leech to Bill's leg. His father peeled him away gradually, like a porous plaster.

"How long can you hold him?" asks Bill.

"I'm not so strong as I used to be," says old Dorset, "but I think I can promise you ten minutes."

"Enough," says Bill. "In ten minutes I shall cross the Central, Southern, and Middle Western States, and be legging it trippingly for the Canadian border."

And, as dark as it was, and as fat as Bill was, and as good a runner as I am, he was a good mile and a half out of Summit before I could catch up with him.

[15] *Bedlam.* A corruption of *Bethlehem,* the name of the first British lunatic asylum.

(What time is it? Check your reading time with the Reading Score Board, page 328.)

❖

SEEING THE POINTS OF HUMOR

1. How is this story the reverse of the usual story about kidnaping?
2. How is the ending typical of O. Henry's surprise endings?
3. What horrible tortures did the kidnapers have to suffer?

HUMOR IN BIG WORDS

Use your dictionary to check the meaning of the words in italics. Then notice the humor in the phrase.

1. *Philoprogenitiveness,* says we, is strong in semirural communities.
2. a mortgage *fancier*
3. *bas-relief* freckles
4. no *couriers* dashed *hither* and *yon*
5. posted my letter *surreptitiously*
6. None of 'em ever was *subjugated* to such *supernatural* tortures.
7. nothing *chronic* except malaria and accidents

8. send me to a bed in *Bedlam*
9. started up a howl like a *calliope*
10. peeled him away gradually, like a *porous* plaster

TIME TO EVALUATE

1. Wherein does O. Henry's humor lie?
2. How does this kind of humor satisfy American readers to a T?

READING SCORE BOARD

Number of Words in Story: 4140.

Number of Minutes	41	20 1/2	16 1/2	14	10 1/3	8 1/3
Reading Rate	100 w.p.m.	200 w.p.m.	250 w.p.m.	300 w.p.m.	400 w.p.m.	500 w.p.m.

SPEEDING UP

Choose several pages of "The Ransom of Red Chief," and make yourself read them more rapidly than your usual reading speed. Try to do the following:

1. Make your eyes pick up phrases rather than individual words.
2. Force yourself to read forward. Do not allow any backtracking.
3. Keep following the steps of the story.
4. Do "intelligent guessing" of the meaning of words you do not understand. Check with your dictionary later.
5. Do not allow yourself to daydream while reading.

◄◄ NATHALIA CRANE

The Janitor's Boy

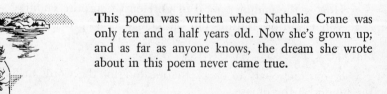

This poem was written when Nathalia Crane was only ten and a half years old. Now she's grown up; and as far as anyone knows, the dream she wrote about in this poem never came true.

Oh, I'm in love with the janitor's boy,
    And the janitor's boy loves me;
He's going to hunt for a desert isle
    In our geography.

——From *The Janitor's Boy* by Nathalia Crane. Used by permission of The Haddon Craftsmen, Inc.

A desert isle with spicy trees
 Somewhere near Sheepshead Bay;
A right nice place, just fit for two,
 Where we can live alway.

Oh, I'm in love with the janitor's boy,
 He's busy as he can be;
And down in the cellar he's making a raft
 Out of an old settee.

He'll carry me off, I know that he will,
 For his hair is exceedingly red,
And the only thing that occurs to me
 Is to dutifully shiver in bed.

The day that we sail, I shall leave this brief note,
 For my parents I hate to annoy:
"I have flown away to an isle in the bay
 With the janitor's red-haired boy."

So Can You

In addition to the clever idea of the poem, notice Nathalia Crane's use of exact rhyming words and of regular rhythm.

Perhaps you would like to write a composite class poem. Decide upon an idea and perhaps a first line. Then together work out the rest of the poem.

FRANK B. GILBRETH, JR., AND ERNESTINE GILBRETH CAREY

Aunt Anne

There were twelve children in the Gilbreth family —six boys and six girls. It is no wonder, therefore, that Aunt Anne had her hands full when she went to the Gilbreths to take charge of things for a few days while the father and mother were away. (Note the time when you begin reading.)

AUNT ANNE was good to us and we loved her and her family, but like

——From *Cheaper by the Dozen*, copyright 1948 by Frank B. Gilbreth, Jr., and Ernestine Gilbreth Carey. Reprinted by permission of the publisher, Thomas Y. Crowell Company.

Dad she insisted on having her own way. While we reluctantly accepted Dad's bossing as one of the privileges of his rank as head of the family, we had no intention of accepting it from anybody else, including his oldest sister.

After we moved to Montclair, Aunt Anne came to stay with us for several days while Mother and Dad were away on a lecture tour. She made it plain from the start that she was not a guest, but the temporary commander-in-chief. She even used the front stairs, leading from the front hall to the second floor, instead of the back stairs, which led from the kitchen to a hallway near the girls' bathroom. None of us was allowed to use the front stairs, because Dad wanted to keep the varnish on them looking nice.

"Daddy will be furious if he comes home and finds you've been using his front stairs," we told Aunt Anne.

"Nonsense," she cut us off. "The back stairs are narrow and steep, and I for one don't propose to use them. As long as I'm here, I'll use any stairs I have a mind to. Now rest your features and mind your business."

She sat at Dad's place at the foot of the table, and we resented this, too. Ordinarily, Frank, as the oldest boy, sat in Dad's place, and Anne, as the oldest girl, sat at Mother's. We also disapproved of Aunt Anne's blunt criticism of how we kept our bedrooms, and some of the changes she made in the family routine.

"What do you do, keep pigeons in here?" she'd say when she walked into the bedroom shared by Frank and Bill. "I'm coming back in fifteen minutes, and I want to find this room in apple-pie order."

And: "I don't care what time your regular bedtime is. As long as I'm in charge, we'll do things my way. Off with you now."

Experience has established the fact that a person cannot move from a small, peaceful home into a family of a dozen without having something finally snap. We saw this happen time after time with Dad's stenographers and with the cooks. In order to reside with a family of a dozen it is necessary either (1) to be brought up from birth in such a family, as we were; or (2) to become accustomed to it as it grew, as Dad and Mother did.

It was at the dinner table that something finally snapped in Aunt Anne.

We had spent the entire meal purposely making things miserable for her. Bill had hidden under the table, and we had removed his place and chair so she wouldn't realize he was missing. While we ate, Billy thumped Aunt Anne's legs with the side of his hand.

"Who's kicking me?" she complained. "Saints alive!"

We said no one.

"Well, you don't have a dog, do you?"

We didn't, and we told her so. Our collie had died some time before this.

"Well, somebody's certainly kicking me. Hard."

She insisted that the child sitting on each side of her slide his chair toward the head of the table, so that no legs could possibly reach her. Bill thumped again.

"Somebody *is* kicking me," Aunt Anne said, "and I intend to get to the bottom of it. Literally."

Bill thumped again. Aunt Anne picked up the table cloth and looked under the table, but Bill had anticipated her and retreated to the other end. The table was so long you couldn't see that far underneath without getting down on your hands and knees, and Aunt Anne was much too dignified to stoop to any such level. When she put the table cloth down again, Bill crawled forward and licked her hand.

"You do too have a dog," Aunt Anne said accusingly, while she dried her hand on a napkin. "Speak up now! Who brought that miserable cur into the house?"

Bill thumped her again and retreated. She picked up the table cloth and looked. She put it down again, and he licked her hand. She looked again, and then dangled her hand temptingly between her knees. Bill couldn't resist this trap, and this time Aunt Anne was ready for him. When he started to lick, she snapped her knees together like a vice, trapped his head in the folds of her skirt, and reached down and grabbed him by the hair.

"Come out of there, you scamp you," she shouted. "I've got you. You can't get away this time. Come out, I say."

She didn't give Bill a chance to come out under his own power. She yanked, and he came out by the hair of his head, screaming and kicking.

In those days, Bill was not a snappy dresser. He liked old clothes, preferably held together with safety pins, and held up by old neckties. When he wore a necktie around his neck, which was as seldom as possible, he sometimes evened up the ends by trimming the longer with a pair of scissors. His knickers were completely unfastened at the legs and hung down to his ankles. During the course of a day, his stockings rode gradually down his legs and, by dinner, had partially disappeared into his sneakers. When Mother was at home, she made him wear such appurtenances as a coat and a belt. In her absence, he had grown slack.

When Aunt Anne jerked him out, a piece of string connecting a buttonhole in his shirt with a buttonhole in the front of his trousers suddenly broke. Bill grabbed for his pants, but it was too late.

"Go to your room, you scamp you," Aunt Anne said, shaking him. "Just wait until your father comes home. He'll know how to take care of you."

Bill picked up his knickers and did as he was told. He had a new respect for Aunt Anne, and the whole top of his head was smarting from the hair-pulling.

Aunt Anne sat down with deceptive calm, and gave us a disarming smile.

"I want you children to listen carefully to me," she almost whispered. "There's not a living soul here, including the baby, who is co-operative. I've never seen a more spoiled crowd of children."

As she went on, her voice grew louder. Much louder.

"For those of you who like to believe that an only child is a selfish child, let me say you are one hundred per cent wrong. From what I have seen, this is the most completely selfish household in the entire world."

She was roaring now, wide open, and it was the first time we had ever seen her that way. Except that her voice was an octave higher, it might have been Dad, sitting there in his own chair.

"From this minute on, pipe down every last one of you, or I'll lambaste the hides off you. I'll fix you so you can't sit down for a month. Do you understand? Does everybody understand? In case you don't realize it, *I've had enough!*"

There was no doubt after that about who was boss, and Aunt Anne had no further trouble with us. When Dad and Mother returned home, all of us expected to be disciplined. But we had misjudged Aunt Anne.

"You look like you've lost weight," Dad said to her. "The children didn't give you any trouble, did they?"

"Not a bit," said Aunt Anne. "They behaved beautifully, once we got to understand each other. We got along just fine, didn't we, children?"

She reached out fondly and rumpled Billy's hair, which didn't need rumpling.

"Ouch," Billy whispered to her, grinning in relief. "It still hurts. Have a heart."

(Note the time, and check your rate of reading with the Reading Score Board.)

❦

A ROUND DOZEN

1. What kind of person was Aunt Anne? What kind of person was Bill? Read the parts that tell.

2. How were the children able to fool Aunt Anne so well?

3. Have you ever had a similar experience with a relative? Write or tell what happened. Perhaps it would be wise to change names so that no feelings could be hurt.

NOT A DOZEN WORDS

Choose the word or phrase in each line that gives the meaning of the word in italics:

1. *reluctantly:* (a) reliably   (b) willingly   (c) unwillingly
2. *resented:* (a) was displeased at   (b) was reserved   (c) resembled
3. *blunt:* (a) benign   (b) brusque   (c) bluster
4. *routine:* (a) routed   (b) regular procedure   (c) temporary plans
5. *accustomed:* (a) familiar with   (b) accredited   (c) costumed
6. *insisted:* (a) persisted   (b) resisted   (c) consisted
7. *dignified:* (a) dignitary   (b) stately   (c) petrified
8. *appurtenances:* (a) things unneeded (b) things disliked (c) things belonging to
9. *slack:* (a) careful   (b) careless   (c) sleazy
10. *lambaste:* (a) beat   (b) lampoon   (c) cook

CONSIDERING THE ELEMENTS OF HUMOR

1. Which kind of humor do you enjoy more: that which is based on a real situation or that which is based on exaggeration? Why?
2. On what kind of humor is the story about the Gilbreths based?
3. Were the children disrespectful to Aunt Anne?

READING SCORE BOARD

Number of Words in Story: **1300**

Number of Minutes	13	6 1/2	5 1/5	4 1/3	3 1/4	2 3/5
Reading Rate	100 w.p.m.	200 w.p.m.	250 w.p.m.	300 w.p.m.	400 w.p.m.	500 w.p.m.

◄ WILLIAM SAROYAN

"Locomotive 38"

Saroyan, like the Aram of this story, is Armenian. In "Locomotive 38" fourteen-year-old Aram has an extraordinary experience with an Ojibway Indian. You can decide for yourself whether the Indian was crazy.

(Note the time when you begin reading.)

ONE DAY a man came to town on a donkey and began loafing around in the public library where I used to spend most of my time in those days. He was a tall young Indian of the Ojibway tribe. He told me his name was Locomotive 38. Everybody in town believed he had escaped from an asylum.

Six days after he arrived in town his animal was struck by the Tulare Street trolley and seriously injured. The following day the animal passed

——From *My Name Is Aram,* copyright, 1937, 1938, 1939, 1940, by William Saroyan. Reprinted by permission of Harcourt, Brace and Company, Inc.

away, most likely of internal injuries, on the corner of Mariposa and Fulton streets. The animal sank to the pavement, fell on the Indian's leg, groaned, and died. When the Indian got his leg free, he got up and limped into the drugstore on the corner and made a long-distance telephone call. He telephoned his brother in Oklahoma. The call cost him a lot of money, which he dropped into the slot as requested by the operator as if he were in the habit of making such calls every day.

I was in the drugstore at the time, eating a Royal Banana Special, with crushed walnuts.

When he came out of the telephone booth, he saw me sitting at the soda fountain eating this fancy dish.

Hello, Willie, he said.

He knew my name wasn't Willie—he just liked to call me that.

He limped to the front of the store where the gum was and bought three packages of Juicy Fruit. Then he limped back to me and said, What's that you're eating, Willie? It looks good.

This is what they call a Royal Banana Special, I said.

The Indian got up on the stool next to me.

Give me the same, he said to the soda-fountain girl.

That's too bad about your animal, I said.

There's no place for an animal in this world, he said. What kind of an automobile should I buy?

Are you going to buy an automobile? I said.

I've been thinking about it for several minutes now, he said.

I didn't think you had any money, I said. I thought you were poor.

That's the impression people get, he said. Another impression they get is that I'm crazy.

I didn't get the impression that you were crazy, I said, but I didn't get the impression that you were rich, either.

Well, I am, the Indian said.

I wish I was rich, I said.

What for? he said.

Well, I said, I've been wanting to go fishing at Mendota for three years in a row now. I need some equipment and some kind of an automobile to get out there in.

Can you drive an automobile? the Indian said.

I can drive anything, I said.

Have you ever driven an automobile? he said.

Not yet, I said. So far I haven't had any automobile to drive, and it's against my family religion to steal an automobile.

Do you mean to tell me you believe you could get into an automobile and start driving? he said.

That's right, I said.

Remember what I was telling you on the steps of the public library the other evening? he said.

You mean about the machine age? I said.

Yes, he said.

I remember, I said.

All right, he said, Indians are born with an instinct for riding, rowing, hunting, fishing, and swimming. Americans are born with an instinct for fooling around with machines.

I'm no American, I said.

I know, the Indian said. You're an Armenian. I remember. I asked you, and you told me. You're an Armenian born in America. You're fourteen years old, and already you know you'll be able to drive an automobile the minute you get into one. You're a typical American, although your complexion, like my own, is dark.

Driving a car is no trick, I said. There's nothing to it. It's easier than riding a donkey.

All right, the Indian said. Just as you say. If I go up the street and buy an automobile, will you drive for me?

Of course, I said.

How much in wages would you want? he said.

You mean you want to give me wages for driving an automobile? I said.

Of course, the Ojibway said.

Well, I said, that's very nice of you, but I don't want any money for driving an automobile.

Some of the journeys may be long ones, he said.

The longer the better, I said.

Are you restless? he said.

I was born in this little old town, I said.

Don't you like it? he said.

I like mountains and streams and mountain lakes, I said.

Have you ever been in the mountains? he said.

Not yet, I said, but I'm going to reach them some day.

I see, he said. What kind of an automobile do you think I ought to buy?

How about a Ford roadster? I said.

Is that the best automobile? he said.

Do you want the *best*? I said.

Shouldn't I have the best? he said.

I don't know, I said. The best costs a lot of money.

What is the best? he said.

Well, I said, some people think the Cadillac is the best. Others like the Packard. They're both pretty good. I wouldn't know which is best. The Packard is beautiful to see going down the highway, but so is the Cadillac. I've watched a lot of them fine cars going down the highway.

How much is a Packard? he said.

Around three thousand dollars, I said. Maybe a little more.

Can we get one right away? he said.

I got down off the stool. He sounded crazy, but I knew he wasn't.

Listen, Mr. Locomotive, I said, do you really want to buy a Packard right away?

You know my animal passed away a few minutes ago, he said.

I saw it happen, I said. They'll probably be arresting you any minute now for leaving the animal in the street.

They won't arrest me, he said.

They will if there's a law against leaving a dead donkey in the street, I said.

No, they won't, he said.

Why not? I said.

Well, he said, they won't after I show them a few papers I carry around with me all the time. The people of this country have a lot of respect for money, and I've got a lot of money.

I guess he is crazy after all, I thought.

Where'd you get all this money? I said.

I own some land in Oklahoma, he said. About fifty thousand acres.

Is it worth money? I said.

No, he said. All but about twenty acres of it is worthless. I've got some oil wells on them twenty acres. My brother and I.

How did you Ojibways ever get down to Oklahoma? I said. I always thought the Ojibways lived up north, up around the Great Lakes.

That's right, the Indian said. We used to live up around the Great Lakes, but my grandfather was a pioneer. He moved west when everybody else did.

Oh, I said. Well, I guess they won't bother you about the dead donkey at that.

They won't bother me about anything, he said. It won't be because I've got money. It'll be because they think I'm crazy. Nobody in this town but you knows I've got money. Do you know where we can get one of them automobiles right away?

The Packard agency is up on Broadway, two blocks beyond the public library, I said.

All right, he said. If you're sure you won't mind driving for me, let's go get one of them. Something bright in color, he said. Red, if they've got red. Where would you like to drive to first?

Would you care to go fishing at Mendota? I said.

I'll take the ride, he said. I'll watch you fish. Where can we get some equipment for you?

Right around the corner at Homan's, I said.

We went around the corner to Homan's and the Indian bought twenty-seven dollars' worth of fishing equipment for me. Then we went up to the Packard agency on Broadway. They didn't have a red Packard, but there was a beautiful green one. It was light green, the color of new grass. This was back there in 1922. The car was a beautiful sports touring model.

Do you think you could drive this great big car? the Indian said.

I *know* I can drive it, I said.

The police found us in the Packard agency and wanted to arrest the Indian for leaving the dead donkey in the street. He showed them the papers he had told me about, and the police apologized and went away. They said they'd removed the animal and were sorry they'd troubled him about it.

It's no trouble at all, he said.

He turned to the manager of the Packard agency, Jim Lewis, who used to run for Mayor every time election time came around.

I'll take this car, he said.

I'll draw up the papers immediately, Jim said.

What papers? the Indian said. I'm going to pay for it now.

You mean you want to pay three thousand two hundred seventeen dollars and sixty-five cents *cash?* Jim said.

Yes, the Indian said. It's ready to drive, isn't it?

Of course, Jim said. I'll have the boys go over it with a cloth to take off any dust on it. I'll have them check the motor, too, and fill the gasoline tank. It won't take more than ten minutes. If you'll step into the office, I'll close the transaction immediately.

Jim and the Indian stepped into Jim's office.

About three minutes later Jim came over to me, a man shaken to the roots.

Aram, he said, who is this guy? I thought he was a nut. I had Johnny telephone the Pacific-Southwest, and they said his bank account is being transferred from somewhere in Oklahoma. They said his account is something over a million dollars. I thought he was a nut. Do you know him?

He told me his name is Locomotive 38, I said. That's no name.

That's a translation of his Indian

name, Jim said. We've got his full name on the contract. Do you know him?

I've talked to him every day since he came to town on that donkey that died this morning, I said, but I never thought he had any money.

He says you're going to drive for him, Jim said. Are you sure you're the man to drive a great big car like this, son?

Wait a minute now, Mr. Lewis, I said. Don't try to push me out of this chance of a lifetime. I can drive this big Packard as well as anybody else in town.

I'm not trying to push you out of anything, Jim said. I just don't want you to drive out of here and run over six or seven innocent people and maybe smash the car. Get into the car, and I'll give you a few pointers. Do you know anything about the gear shift?

I don't know anything about anything yet, I said, but I'll soon find out.

All right, Jim said. Just let me help you.

I got into the car and sat down behind the wheel. Jim got in beside me.

From now on, son, he said, I want you to regard me as a friend who will give you the shirt off his back. I want to thank you for bringing me this fine Indian gentleman.

He told me he wanted the best car on the market, I said. You know I've always been crazy about driving a Packard. Now how do I do it?

Well, Jim said, let's see.

He looked down at my feet.

My gosh, son, he said, your feet don't reach the pedals.

Never mind that, I said. You just explain the gearshift.

Jim explained everything while the boys wiped the dust off the car and went over the motor and filled the gasoline tank. When the Indian came out and got into the car, in the back where I insisted he should sit, I had the motor going.

He says he knows how to drive, the Indian said to Jim Lewis. By instinct, he said. I believe him, too.

You needn't worry about Aram here, Jim said. He can drive all right. Clear the way there, boys, he shouted. Let him have all the room necessary.

I turned the big car around slowly, shifted, and shot out of the agency at about fifty miles an hour, with Jim Lewis running after the car and shouting, Take it easy, son. Don't open up until you get out on the highway. The speed limit in town is twenty-five miles an hour.

The Indian wasn't at all excited, even though I was throwing him around a good deal.

I wasn't doing it on purpose, though. It was simply that I wasn't very familiar with the manner in which the automobile worked.

You're an excellent driver, Willie, he said. It's like I said. You're an American, and you were born with an instinct for mechanical contraptions like this.

We'll be in Mendota in an hour, I said. You'll see some great fishing out there.

How far is Mendota? the Indian said.

About ninety miles, I said.

Ninety miles is too far to go in an

hour, the Indian said. Take two hours. We're passing a lot of interesting scenery I'd like to look at a little more closely.

All right, I said, but I sure am anxious to get out there and fish.

Well, all right then, the Indian said. Go as fast as you like this time, but some time I'll expect you to drive a little more slowly, so I can see some of the scenery. I'm missing everything. I don't even get a chance to read the signs.

I'll travel slowly *now* if you want me to, I said.

No, he insisted. Let her go. Let her go as fast as she'll go.

Well, we got out to Mendota in an hour and seventeen minutes. I would have made better time except for the long stretch of dirt road.

I drove the car right up to the river bank. The Indian asked if I knew how to get the top down, so he could sit in the open and watch me fish. I didn't know how to get the top down, but I got it down. It took me twenty minutes to do it.

I fished for about three hours, fell into the river twice, and finally landed a small one.

You don't know the first thing about fishing, the Indian said.

What am I doing wrong? I said.

Everything, he said. Have you ever fished before?

No, I said.

I didn't think so, he said.

What am I doing wrong? I said.

Well, he said, nothing in particular, only you're fishing at about the same rate of speed that you drive an automobile.

Is that wrong? I said.

It's not exactly wrong, he said, except that it'll keep you from getting anything to speak of, and you'll go on falling into the river.

I'm not falling, I said. They're pulling me in. They've got an awful pull. This grass is mighty slippery, too. There ain't nothing around here to grab hold of.

I reeled in one more little one, and then I asked if he'd like to go home. He said he would if I wanted to, too, so I put away the fishing equipment and the two fish and got in the car and started driving back to town.

I drove that big Packard for this Ojibway Indian, Locomotive 38, as long as he stayed in town, which was all summer. He stayed at the hotel all the time. I tried to get him to learn to drive, but he said it was out of the question. I drove that Packard all over the San Joaquín Valley that summer, with the Indian in the back, chewing eight or nine sticks of gum. He told me to drive anywhere I cared to go, so it was either to some place where I could fish, or some place where I could hunt. He claimed I didn't know anything about fishing or hunting, but he was glad to see me trying. As long as I knew him he never laughed, except once. That was the time I shot at a jack-rabbit with a 12-gauge shotgun that had a terrible kick, and killed a crow. He tried to tell me all the time that that was my average. To shoot at a jack-rabbit and kill a crow. You're an American, he said. Look at the way you took to this big automobile.

One day in November that year his

brother came to town from Oklahoma, and the next day when I went down to the hotel to get him, they told me he'd gone back to Oklahoma with his brother.

Where's the Packard? I said.

They took the Packard, the hotel clerk said.

Who drove? I said.

The Indian, the clerk said.

They're both Indians, I said. Which of the brothers drove the car?

The one who lived at this hotel, the clerk said.

Are you sure? I said.

Well, I only saw him get into the car out front and drive away, the clerk said. That's all.

Do you mean to tell me he knew how to shift gears? I said.

It *looked* as if he did, the clerk said. He looked like an expert driver to me.

Thanks, I said.

On the way home I figured he'd just wanted me to *believe* he couldn't drive, so *I* could drive all the time and feel good. He was just a young man who'd come to town on a donkey, bored to death or something, who'd taken advantage of the chance to be entertained by a small town kid who was bored to death, too. That's the only way I could figure it out without accepting the general theory that he was crazy.

(Note the time. Then check your rate of reading with the Reading Score Board.)

◆))◆

Points of Fun

1. How is exaggeration a part of the humor of this story?
2. What is your theory about the Indian? Was he crazy?
3. What kind of boy was Aram?
4. What strange tricks of writing do you find in the story?

Reading Signals

Did the omission of quotation marks bother you at first? Most writers use quotation marks when they want to tell the reader that someone is speaking. Saroyan does not use these reading signals. Suppose he did not use *any* signals. You might get something like this:

1. Caesar entered on his head his helmet on his feet his sandals in his hand his sword on his forehead a frown—and sat down
2. Every lady in our land
   Has twenty nails on each hand
   Five and twenty on hands and feet
   And this is true without deceit

Can you tell what signals should be used? How are reading signals simply common-sense means by which writers help readers to understand what they are saying?

READING SCORE BOARD

Number of Words in Story: 3020

Number of Minutes	30	15	12	10	7 1/2	6
Reading Rate	100 w.p.m.	200 w.p.m.	250 w.p.m.	300 w.p.m.	400 w.p.m.	500 w.p.m.

◀◉ DAVID McCORD

Big Chief Wotapotami

Big Chief Wotapotami
Sat in the sun
And said, "Me hot am I."
Sat in the shade
And said, "Me cooler."
Such is the life
Of an Indian ruler.

Big Chief Wotapotami
Said to his tribe
(The Potawatami):
"White man come,
You get-um earful;
Want-um you boys
Be kind o' keerful."

◆❰ CLARENCE DAY

Father Teaches Me to Be Prompt

Clarence Day's *Life with Father* was a best seller as a book, ran for years as a play, and was a smash hit as a movie. Here is the story of one of Clarence's experiences with Father.
(Jot down the time when you begin reading.)

FATHER made a great point of our getting down to breakfast on time. I meant to be prompt, but it never occurred to me that I had better try to be early. My idea was to slide into the room at the last moment. Consequently, I often was late.

My brothers were often late, too, with the exception of George. He was the only thoroughly reliable son Father had. George got down so early, Father pointed out to me, that he even had time to practice a few minutes on the piano.

The reason George was so prompt was that he was in a hurry to see the sporting page before Father got hold of the newspaper; and the reason he then played the piano was to signal to the rest of us, as we dressed, which team had won yesterday's ball game. He had made up a code for this purpose; and we leaned over the banisters, pulling on our stockings and shoes, to hear him announce the results. I don't remember now what the titles were of the airs he selected, but the general idea was that if he played a gay, lively air it meant that the Giants had won, and when the

——Reprinted from *Life with Father* by Clarence Day, by permission of Alfred A. Knopf, Inc. Copyright, 1934, 1935 by Clarence Day.

strains of a dirge or lament floated up to us, it meant that Pop Anson had beaten them.

As Father didn't approve of professional baseball, we said nothing to him about this arrangement. He led his life and we led ours, under his nose. He took the newspaper away from George the moment he entered the room, and George said good morning to him and stepped innocently into the parlor. Then, while Father watched him through the broad doorway and looked over the political headlines, George banged out the baseball news for us on the piano. Father used to admonish him with a chuckle not to thump it so hard, but George felt that he had to. We were at the top of the house, and he wanted to be sure that we'd hear him even if we were brushing our teeth. George always was thorough about things. He not only thumped the piano as hard as he could, but he hammered out the tune over and over besides, while Father impatiently muttered to himself, *"Trop de zèle."*[1]

Upstairs, there was usually some discussion as to what kind of news George was sending. He had not been

[1] *Trop de zèle.* Too much zeal.

allowed to learn popular tunes, which it would have been easy for us to recognize; and the few classic selections which were available in his little music book sounded pretty much alike at a distance. George rendered these with plenty of good will and muscle but not a great deal of sympathy. He regarded some of the rules of piano-playing as needlessly complicated.

The fact remained that he was the one boy who was always on time, and Father was so pleased by this that he bought a watch for him with "George Parmly Day, Always on Time" engraved on the back. He told me that as I was the eldest he had meant to give me a watch first, and he showed me the one he had bought for me. It was just like George's except that nothing had been engraved on it yet. Father explained that to his regret he would have to put it away for a while, until I had earned it by getting down early to breakfast.

Time went on, without much improvement on my part. Dawdling had got to be a habit with me. Sometimes my lateness was serious. One morning, when breakfast was half over and I had nothing on but a pair of long woolen drawers, Father called up from the front hall, napkin in hand, that he wouldn't stand it and that I was to come down that instant. When I shouted indignantly that I wasn't dressed yet, he said he didn't care. "Come down just as you are, confound it!" he roared. I was tempted to take him at his word, but thought there might be some catch in it and wouldn't, though I hurried, of course,

all I could. Father ate his usual hearty breakfast in a stormy mood, and I ate my usual hearty breakfast in a guilty and nervous one. Come what might, we always ate heartily. I sometimes wished afterward that I hadn't, but it never seemed to hurt Father.

Mother told Father that if he would give me the watch, she was sure I'd do better. He said that he didn't believe it and that that was a poor way to bring a boy up. To prove to him that he was wrong, Mother at last unlocked her jewel box and gave me a watch which had belonged to one of her elderly cousins. It was really too valuable a watch for a boy to wear, she said, and I must be very careful of it. I promised I would.

This watch, however, turned out to be painfully delicate. It was old, I was young. We were not exactly made for each other. It had a back and front of thin gold; and as Mother had had the former owner's monogram shaved off the front cover, that cover used to sink in the middle when pressed. Also, the lid fitted so closely that there was barely room for the glass crystal over the face. Such a very thin crystal had to be used that any pressure on the lid broke it.

I didn't press on the lid, naturally, after the first time this happened. I was careful; and everything would have gone well enough if other boys had been careful, too. It was not practicable, however, for me to make them be careful enough. When I had a fight, friendly or otherwise, I used to ask my opponent if he would be so kind as not to punch me on the left side of my stomach. He might or might not listen. If he and I were too excited and kept on long enough, the watch crystal broke anyway. There was never time to take off my watch first, and anyhow there was no place to put it. A watch that goes around the streets in a boy's pocket has to take life as it comes. This watch had never been designed for any such fate.

The first two crystals I broke Mother paid for, as Father disapproved of the whole business and would have nothing to do with it. Mother was always short of small change, however; and I hated to trouble her—and she hated to be troubled, too. "Oh, Clarence, dear! You haven't broken your watch again?" she cried when I opened the cover the second time, to show her the shattered fragments. She was so upset that I felt too guilty to tell her the next time it happened, and from then on I was reduced to the necessity of paying for the damage myself.

My pocket money never exceeded a dollar a month. Every new crystal cost twenty-five cents. It was a serious drain.

Wrestling and rolling around on the floor with Sam Willets, my watch quite forgotten, I would suddenly hear a faint tinkle and know that I was once more insolvent. I would pick out the broken glass and leave the watch with no crystal till I had twenty-five cents on hand, but these delays made me nervous. I knew that Mother wanted to feel sure I was taking good care of the watch, and that she might look at it any evening. As soon as I had the money, I hurried over to Sixth Avenue, where two old Germans kept a tiny watch shop, and left it there to be fixed. One of my most dismal memories is of that stuffy little shop's smell of sauerkraut, and how tall the glass counter then seemed, and the slowness of those two old Germans. When I got there late and they made me leave the watch overnight, I didn't have one easy moment until I got it back the next day. Again and again I argued with them that twenty-five cents was too much, especially for a regular customer, but they said it didn't pay them to do the work even for that because those thin old-fashioned crystals were hard to get.

I gave up at last. I told Mother I didn't want to wear the watch any more.

Then I found, to my amazement, that this way out of my troubles was barred. The watch was an heirloom. And an heirloom was a thing that its recipient must value and cherish. No good Chinese, I read later on in life, fails to honor his ancestors; and no good boy, I was told in my youth, fails to appreciate heirlooms.

I left Mother's room in low spirits. That night, as I wound up my watch with its slender key, I envied George. Father had selected the right kind for George; he knew what a boy needed. It had a thick nickel case, it had an almost unbreakable crystal, and it endured daily life imperturbably, even when dropped in the bathtub.

It seemed to me that I was facing a pretty dark future. The curse of great possessions became a living thought to me, instead of a mere phrase. The demands that such possessions made on their owners for upkeep were merciless. For months I had had no money for marbles. I couldn't even afford a new top. In some way that I didn't fully understand I was yoked to a watch I now hated—a delicate thing that would always make trouble unless I learned to live gingerly.

Then I saw a way out. All this time I had kept on being late for breakfast at least once a week, out of habit; but it now occurred to me that if I could reform, perhaps Father might relent and give me that reliable nickel watch he had bought. I reformed. I occasionally weakened in my new resolution at first; but every time that crystal got broken, I was spurred on to fresh efforts. When I had at length established a record for promptness

that satisfied Father, he had my name engraved on the watch he had bought, and presented it to me. He was a little surprised at the intense pleasure I showed on this occasion; and as he watched me hopping around the room in delight, he said, "There, there" several times. "Don't be so excited, confound it," he added. "You'll knock over that vase."

Mother said she couldn't see why Father should give me a nickel watch when I had a gold one already, but he laughed and told her that "that old thing" was no kind of a watch for a boy. She reluctantly laid it away again to rest in her jewel box.

Her parting shot at Father was that anyhow she had been right; she had said all along that a watch was what I needed to teach me how to be prompt.

(How long did it take you to read the story? Check your speed of reading with the Reading Score Board, page 345.)

◆❖

Enjoying Life with Father

1. From this sketch what kinds of persons do you think Father, Mother, Clarence, and George were? Give incidents to prove your opinions.
2. How was George able to signal the baseball news?
3. Why did Clarence feel that he had become yoked to a watch?
4. How did Clarence manage his finances? Have you ever had similar troubles?
5. Have you read any other stories by Clarence Day about his life with Father and Mother? Tell them to the class.

Interesting and Exact Words

What does each of these phrases mean? What synonym could you suggest for each word in italics? Which is more interesting and exact, your word or Clarence Day's?

1. *thoroughly* reliable
2. *needlessly* complicated
3. a *stormy* mood

4. *shattered* fragments
5. once more *insolvent*
6. endured daily life *imperturbably*
7. learned to live *gingerly*
8. *intense* pleasure
9. *reluctantly* laid it away
10. her *parting* shot

You, Too

Would you like to write or tell about an amusing experience you have had with your father or mother? Concentrate on a single experience, and choose all details to make your point of humor clear.

Reading Score Board

Number of Words in Story: 1860

Number of Minutes	19	9 1/2	7 1/2	6	4 5/8	3 3/4
Reading Rate	100 w.p.m.	200 w.p.m.	250 w.p.m.	300 w.p.m.	400 w.p.m.	500 w.p.m.

◀ Frances Eisenberg

Remember Mother

Giving Mother a handkerchief for Mother's Day would certainly have been easier on everyone's nerves than—. But let Frances Eisenberg tell what happened when she planned a special surprise. (Note the time when you begin reading.)

Father was in the front yard late one afternoon cutting the hedge and I was standing there watching him, and all of a sudden a lady came up our walk. She had on a big hat and she was carrying a black brief case.

"Hello, little girl," she said to me. "How do you do," she said to my father. She stood in the middle of the sidewalk and let out a long breath. "My goodness, what a beautiful, well-kept yard," she said, looking around. "How in the world do you keep your grass so green this dry weather?"

My father stopped cutting the hedge and straightened his shoulders. He looked very pleased.

"Well," he said, "this spring I sowed the yard with grass seed and

——Slightly adapted from *There's One in Every Family*, Copyright, 1941, by Frances Eisenberg, published by J. B. Lippincott Company.

I put a good thick layer of Wonder Worker fertilizer on top of it and in a few weeks it had come out green like it is now. My wife complained some of the smell, but I think it was worth it myself."

"I should say so!" The lady smiled all over. She spread out her handkerchief on the step and sat down on it, and laid her briefcase beside her. She started taking off her gloves. "You've got some nice rose bushes too. You must be quite a gardener."

My father looked even more pleased. "Well, I lived on a farm when I was a boy," he told her. "I guess it sort of stays in your blood. Some of these days I'm going to have a vegetable garden. Maybe this summer if I get around to it."

"We had one once before but it didn't come up," I told her. I sat down on the end of the step and watched her. My father gave me a sort of mad look but the lady didn't pay any attention to what I said. She was unzipping her brief case.

"I'm a farm girl myself," she said. "I always say there's nothing like spending your childhood in the great out of doors. Is this your little girl?"

"Yes," my father said, beginning to clip again.

"She's a pretty child," the lady said, looking kind at me. "What pretty hair!"

I felt surprised. Nobody had ever said that before.

"I've got a little brother too," I told her. "My mother took him to town this afternoon to get his teeth fixed."

"Well, isn't that nice!" she said. "That makes it even better." She began to take out some papers and cards and things. "They don't stay little long," she told my father. "First thing you know these kiddies of yours will be grown up with children of their own."

"I'm nine already," I said.

My father stopped clipping the hedge and looked at the grass. "It's a funny thing about fertilizer," he said. "Now you take bone meal. There's nothing in the world better for potatoes but it's not worth a hoot for grass. It seems to turn it brown. I'd just as soon put salt on grass as bone meal, for all the good it will do."

"Really?" the lady said looking polite. "Not changing the subject," she said, "but you know some day you're going to think back about your children the way they are today and a good photograph would mean the world to you."

"We had our picture in the paper once," I told her. "Did you see it?"

"I don't remember," she said.

"And when papa was interested in it he took a lot of pictures of us," I said. "Some of them had white streaks on them, and Joe nearly always hides his face, but you can tell who it is. Do you want me to go in the house and get them?"

"No, thank you," she said, looking at me not quite so kind. "I mean a large hand-tinted photograph that you'd be proud to keep in the living room. Of course kodak pictures are all very well but they don't catch the personality like a real photograph."

"Well," my father said, and he

started to talk about fertilizer again, but I went up close to him where he could see me.

"Papa," I said. "Can Joe and I have our pictures taken?"

My father looked at me. "What for?" he asked.

"So you can remember what we look like," I said. "And besides mother might like to have it for Mother's Day."

"Bless her little heart," the lady said. "We ought to encourage them in their little unselfish ideas, oughtn't we? And after all, what could they get their mother for a dollar that would mean so much in sentiment?"

My father opened his mouth to say something, but before he could say it she handed him a coupon in a hurry. "Just fill this out and bring it to the studio with you," she said. "It's not necessary to have an appointment, but I must have the dollar in advance because we have to have some idea of how many people are going to take advantage of this offer."

My father began to look in his pocket for a dollar and finally he found one. He looked at it a minute and handed it to her sort of slow. "I guess you're right," he said.

"I'm sure you'll never regret it," she told him, taking the money and zipping up her briefcase in a hurry. She started down the walk. "Are there any children next door?" she asked me as she went.

"No," I said. I watched her walking fast down the street and I was thinking about what she said, that I had pretty hair. Nobody ever said that, I thought.

I went in the house and looked in the bathroom mirror. I don't think I'm pretty, I thought looking at my face. I looked at my hair and it didn't seem to me to be very pretty. It's too long, I thought. It needs some of it cut off and then it would look better.

Just then I heard my mother and Joey coming on the porch and I went out there.

"Mother, can I have a haircut?" I asked her.

"No, not now," she said.

"I mean sometime before tomorrow afternoon," I told her. I opened my mouth to tell her why, then I remembered not to just in time. In a minute I would have told her about the surprise.

"Can I before then?" I asked her.

"We'll see," she said.

My mother went in the kitchen to start cooking supper, and Joe went upstairs to take his good clothes off and I went too. He took them off very slow, and every few minutes he would stop to feel of the new filling in his tooth.

"Joe, you're going to have a surprise tomorrow," I told him.

"What is it?" he asked, feeling of the filling.

"If I told you it wouldn't be a surprise, and besides you might tell Mother. But anyway, it's something good."

"Is it something to eat?" Joe said.

"You ought to be ashamed," I told him. "You're always thinking of yourself. You ought to think more about other people. You ought to think about your mother and all she does for you."

"Why ought I?"

"Because next Sunday's Mother's Day," I said.

Joe didn't say anything else, and I stood there for a minute wondering if I better tell him but I thought no, he's too little to keep a secret and besides he might be stubborn and say he wouldn't have his picture taken. So it would be better to wait till tomorrow and let him find out what it was when it was too late to do anything about it.

The next morning when I first got up I looked in the bathroom mirror, and I remembered that I needed a haircut before we had our pictures taken. We didn't have to go to school because of a teacher's meeting, so after breakfast I asked my mother if I could go down to the Peerless Barber Shop and have it cut.

My mother had her head tied up in a towel and she was climbing on a chair to clean out the pantry shelves.

"Not today," she said.

"I need one," I told her. "I can't go to my music lesson this afternoon without a haircut."

"Don't be silly," she said. "Run on upstairs and make up the beds. I'm not going to have time for them this morning."

I went, but I went pretty slow. I need a haircut, I thought. The way it is now it's not long and it's not short. It looks awful.

While I was making up the beds I kept looking in the mirror. Every time I looked my hair looked worse. My mother will feel bad when she sees a picture of me with my hair like this, I thought. If she knew why I wanted a haircut she would let me have one.

When I went in my mother and father's room my mother's sewing basket was on the table and the embroidery scissors were sticking out the top. I looked in their mirror. I thought I would cut a little off the edges. I cut a little off, and then a little more, but the scissors were dull and they would hardly cut at all. My hair was looking pretty jagged and I was feeling sort of nervous, and all of a sudden the scissors slipped and cut a big piece out of one side.

Now I've ruined it, I thought. Now the sides look different and it looks even worse than it did when it was too long.

I tried to cut the long side to match the short side, but the scissors made that side look worse than the other one.

I put the scissors back in the basket and I picked up all of the hair off the floor as quick as I could, and then I stood there and looked at my head to see if there was anything I could do about it. All I could think of to do was to hide it some way till the hair grew out again, because if my mother saw it she might feel bad or she might get mad.

I got a handkerchief out of my father's dresser drawer and tied it around my head. I finished the beds as quick as I could and went out in the yard. I was feeling pretty anxious about my hair. Joe was swinging in the swing and I went out where he was and sat down on the sidewalk. I wanted to tell him what I had done, but I thought I better not.

"What's that thing on your head for?" Joe asked me after a while.

"To keep the dust out," I told him.

I sat there and wondered how long it would take the hair to grow. I wish now I had left it alone, I thought. Or anyway I wish I hadn't cut off so much, or used sharper scissors. But it's too late to do anything about it now.

We had sandwiches for lunch because my mother was too busy to cook anything. We ate them on the back steps. My mother seemed to be thinking about the housecleaning she was doing, and she didn't seem to notice my head.

"Can Joey go to my music lesson today?" I asked her.

"Yes, I guess so if he'll behave himself," she said.

After lunch I got ready and I helped Joe get ready. Then I went in my room and shut the door and took off the handkerchief and put on my hat. You couldn't tell that there was anything wrong unless you looked close, because I pulled the hat down over my face as far as it would go.

I got the exercise book and "The Happy Huntsman" off the piano and Joe and I went down to the street car track and got on the car. Joe stood up by the motorman and he stared at everything the motorman did. He stuck his head almost under the motorman's arm to see how he ran the car.

"Move, boy!" the motorman would say every few minutes looking mad at Joe.

I sat on the end seat in the front of the car, and I thought I ought to try to make Joe sit down like he was supposed to do, but I felt too discouraged. I sat there and thought about my troubles. I thought how Mrs. Rainwater was going to be mad about the bad lesson I was going to have and whether Joe would act right when we had our pictures taken, and whether somebody would find out about my haircut before it had time to grow.

Finally we got downtown and we went to the second floor of the Lewis and Jones Music Store to Mrs. Rainwater's studio. It was called a studio but it was just a room with a piano in it and some chairs and some pictures on the walls of some of the children Mrs. Rainwater gave music lessons to. My picture wasn't there because I hadn't had one taken since I was little and even if I had Mrs. Rainwater wouldn't want to hang it up because nearly every time I took my music lesson she said I was the worst pupil she had.

After the lesson, we went over on Market Street to Henson's Hardware Store where my father worked. He was waiting on a customer, and he looked sort of surprised when he saw us coming.

"Don't you remember, papa?" I asked him. "We're supposed to have our picture taken for mother's Mother's Day present."

"Oh yes," he said. "You'll have to go by yourselves though. I'm too busy."

"We have to have the coupon," I said.

He took all the things out of his pocket and found the coupon, and after a long time I got Joe to come on and go with me and we went down the street to the People's Studio. The window was full of pictures and in one window there was a big picture of an old white-haired lady with a kind smile on her face looking at a picture of her children and underneath her a sign said, "Remember Mother. She Remembers You."

"What are we going in here for?" Joe asked when we started in the door. He pulled back a little.

"Come on, Joe," I told him. "We're going to have our picture taken. It's not going to hurt you. Come on now and act like you're supposed to."

Joe came but he came slow and he looked like he was about to be stubborn.

A girl came out of a back room chewing some gum and took the coupon. She told us to come with her and we went, and there was a big picture on the wall of some trees and bushes and a fountain. The girl told us to sit down on a bench in front of it.

I sat down and I pulled Joe down too.

"Don't you want to take off your hat, honey?" she asked me, going over to the camera.

"No," I told her. "I have to keep my hat on."

"You'd look better without it, honey. It's going to cast a shadow over your face."

"I have to keep it on anyway," I said.

"All right, suit yourself," she said. Her voice sounded a little mad. "Little boy, you'll have to sit up straighter than that. Get your head up now, and look into the camera."

But Joe kept letting his head droop down until it almost touched his knees. "Sit up, Joe," I told him, but he wouldn't mind me.

The girl started chewing her gum fast. "Listen, honey," she said after a while. "Let's you put your arm around him and sort of hold him up. I can't just stand here and wait for the spirit to move him."

So I put my arm around Joe's shoulder and held him up a little and the girl said, "Now look this way and smile, little boy," but Joe kept looking down at his feet and what you could see of his face was not smiling.

"Sometimes he gets shy," I told the girl. "But he's not as bad as he used to be."

"I'd hate to see him like he used to be," the girl said partly under her breath.

"All right, honey, you smile," she said out loud to me. "I'm going to have to take it now. I can't wait any longer." The camera gave a click. "That's all," she said.

"Joe, why didn't you sit up and look at the camera like that girl said?" I asked him when we were starting back to the store. "You always have to ruin everything. What do you want to do that way for?"

Joe didn't say anything. He kept walking slow, looking in the windows. There's no use talking to him, I thought.

When we got home that night I looked in the mirror to see if my hair had grown any, but if it had I couldn't tell it.

I tied the handkerchief back around my head and ate supper that way, and once my mother asked me why I had it on, but just then Joe turned over the gravy and she forgot to ask any more. And the next day was Friday and I wore my hat in school and everybody stared at me, but not as much as they would have stared if they saw how my hair looked.

All day Saturday I wore the handkerchief tied on my head and my mother was too busy housecleaning to ask me about it, so I stopped worrying so much.

Every time I had a chance that day I went to the telephone and called my father to remind him to bring the picture, but finally he told me to stop calling him because he was too busy to keep answering the telephone.

"All right," I said. But I hope he remembers, I thought. It would be awful for us not to have anything for her on Mother's Day.

That night when my father came home he had the picture. My mother was in the kitchen, so we looked at it.

"I don't think they did a very good job," my father said taking it out of the envelope. "The colors are too artificial looking, and besides, it's not posed right. It's not natural enough."

It didn't look so very good, like my father said. You couldn't see much of my face because of the hat, and all you could see of Joe was the top of his head and a piece of his blouse and his legs, because he was hiding his face on his knees almost.

"Well, anyway it's better than a handkerchief," I told my father. "And anyway you can sort of tell what we looked like."

"Yes," my father said. "Only you'd think they could do better than that. They're supposed to be professionals. I could do that well myself, and I'm only an amateur."

I took the picture upstairs to show to Joe before I wrapped it up.

"See, Joe," I told him. He was counting his cold drink bottle caps and he would hardly look at it.

"I see it," he said.

"It would look better if you had done what that girl said," I told him. "All you had to do was hold up your head and smile. You look sort of funny all bent over like that."

"I don't care," Joey said. He started crawling under the bed to find a bottle top.

The next morning just before breakfast when I was setting the table I put the package at my mother's place.

She didn't seem to notice it when she put the cereal around, but when we all sat down, then she saw it, and she looked surprised. "What's this?" she said.

"It's a Mother's Day present," I told her, "and it's not a handkerchief. It's something from Joe and me for you to keep in the living room."

"I can't imagine," she said, beginning to untie it.

"It's a picture," Joe said after a minute.

"Hush, Joe," I said.

But just then she got the paper off and she saw for herself that it was a picture.

"Mercy," she said.

"It's a picture of Joe and me," I

told her. "A lady came around with a coupon and papa gave us a dollar. That's why."

"They should have done better than that," my father said, looking at it. "It don't look like professional work to me."

"What happened to Joe?" my mother asked.

"He acted stubborn," I said. "He wouldn't do what the girl said. He just about ruined it, but I think it looks pretty good. Don't you?"

"Yes," my mother said. "Thank you very much."

"You're supposed to keep it in the living room," I told her. "And when we're grown up you're supposed to look at it and remember how we were."

"I see," my mother said. She kept looking at the picture. "What's your hat pulled down like this for, Helen, why didn't you push it back the way it belongs?"

For a minute I couldn't think of a good reason. "I just didn't," I said.

My mother looked hard at me. "I thought there was something funny about the way you've been going around with your head tied up," she said. "All right, let's see what you've done to your hair."

"I didn't mean to. The scissors slipped. I just wanted to look good to have my picture taken."

"Let's see it," she said.

I untied the handkerchief very slow. "I don't guess you'll like the way it looks," I told her. I took the handkerchief off.

My mother gave an awful groan. For a minute she didn't say anything. "What did you use, the hedge clippers?" she asked me after a while.

"You shouldn't have done that," my father said, starting to drink his coffee. "You're old enough to know better."

Joe looked at my head once, then he began to eat his biscuit and honey.

"You're going to be a pretty thing at Mrs. Rainwater's recital next week," my mother said, looking disgusted at me. "We'll certainly feel proud of you sitting up there looking like a picked chicken."

"I knew you'd be mad," I told her. "I thought you would be."

"Of course I'm mad!" my mother said. We ate the rest of our breakfast without anybody saying anything.

"I guess I better get ready for Sunday School," I said as soon as I had finished. I started to go toward the bathroom.

My mother got up and started scraping the plates. "Sometimes I feel almost like quitting," I heard her say partly to herself as I went out the door.

I felt sort of surprised. I thought everybody thought it was wonderful to be a mother, I thought. That's why we have Mother's Day.

"Sometimes I almost wish I'd kept on working and not done this," she said. "Sometimes I think it would have been better."

"You do?" my father said, stopping chewing and looking sort of shocked.

"Well, sometimes," my mother said.

(What time is it now? How long did it take you to read the story? Check your reading speed with the Reading Score Board.)

REMEMBERING POINTS OF HUMOR

1. What sales techniques did the lady with the coupons use?
2. Is there truth in the old expression "Children and fools speak the truth"?
3. What kind of little boy was Joe?
4. Why did Mother have a right to be discouraged sometimes?
5. Have you ever had an experience like this one? Exchange stories in class.

TO CONSIDER

What kind of English does the author use in this story? For what reason did she write the story as she did?

READING SCORE BOARD

Number of Words in Story: 3890

Number of Minutes	39	19 1/2	15 1/2	13	9 3/4	7 3/4
Reading Rate	100 w.p.m.	200 w.p.m.	250 w.p.m.	300 w.p.m.	400 w.p.m.	500 w.p.m.

"That was my thermos bottle you just shot off!"

"Anyway, Dad, I did improve in weight!"

Limericks

The limerick is one of the easiest forms of poetry to imitate. As you see, lines 1, 2, and 5 rhyme, as do lines 3 and 4. Which are the short lines?

Edward Lear is one of the most famous of the writers of limericks. His first limericks appeared in 1846 in *The Book of Nonsense*, and their immediate popularity started the ball rolling.

There was an Old Man of the Coast
Who placidly sat on a post;
  But when it grew cold
  He relinquished his hold,
And called for some hot buttered toast.

EDWARD LEAR

There was an Old Man, who said, "Well!
Will nobody answer this bell?
  I have pulled day and night,
  Till my hair has grown white,
But nobody answers this bell!"

EDWARD LEAR

There was an old man of Tarentum,
Who gnashed his false teeth till he bent 'em:
  And when asked for the cost
  Of what he had lost,
Said, "I really can't tell, for I rent 'em!"

ANONYMOUS

There was a young man of Devizes,
Whose ears were of different sizes;
  The one that was small
  Was of no use at all,
But the other won several prizes.

ANONYMOUS

There once was a man from Nantucket
Who kept all his cash in a bucket;
  But his daughter, named Nan,
  Ran away with a man,
And as for the bucket, Nantucket.

ANONYMOUS

A sleeper from the Amazon
Put nighties of his gra-mazon—
   The reason that
   He was too fat
To get his own pajamazon.

ANONYMOUS

There was an old lady of Steen,
Whose musical sense was not keen;
   She said, "Well, it's odd,
   But I cannot tell 'God
Save the Weasel' from 'Pop Goes the Queen.'"

ANONYMOUS

IF AT FIRST YOU DON'T SUCCEED . . .

Now plan to write some limericks of your own. Perhaps some of these first lines will help to get you started:

   There once was a young man from Maine
   There was an old man of the sea
   There was a young thing from Duluth
   The waiter who waited on Lizzie
   A cannibal chief and his wife

OLIVER WENDELL HOLMES

The Deacon's Masterpiece

Or the Wonderful "One-Hoss Shay"
A Logical Story

In this poem Oliver Wendell Holmes is making sly fun of any system of logic. Build your reasoning as carefully as you know how, and you will certainly find that there is a weak link somewhere. Like the "one-hoss shay," your reasoning will go to pieces all at once, "Just as bubbles do when they burst."

Have you heard of the wonderful one-hoss shay,[1]
That was built in such a logical way
It ran a hundred years to a day,

———Reprinted by permission of and arrangement with Houghton Mifflin Company, the authorized publishers.

[1] *shay.* Colloquial for *chaise,* a two-wheeled carriage.

And then, of a sudden, it—ah, but stay,
I'll tell you what happened without delay,
Scaring the parson into fits,
Frightening people out of their wits—
Have you ever heard of that, I say?

Seventeen hundred and fifty-five,
Georgius Secundus[2] was then alive—
Snuffy old drone from the German hive;
That was the year when Lisbon-town
Saw the earth open and gulp her down,
And Braddock's army was done so brown,
Left without a scalp to its crown.
It was on the terrible earthquake-day
That the Deacon finished the one-hoss shay.

Now in building of chaises, I tell you what,
There is always *somewhere* a weakest spot—
In hub, tire, felloe, in spring or thill,
In panel, or crossbar, or floor, or sill,
In screw, bolt, thoroughbrace—lurking still,
Find it somewhere you must and will—
Above or below, or within or without—
And that's the reason, beyond a doubt,
A chaise *breaks down* but doesn't *wear out*.

But the Deacon swore (as Deacons do,
With an "I dew vum" or an "I tell yeou")
He would build one shay to beat the taown
'N' the keounty 'n' all the kentry raoun';
It should be so built that it *couldn'* break daown
—"Fur," said the Deacon, " 't's mighty plain
Thut the weakes' place mus' stan' the strain;
'N' the way t' fix it, uz I maintain,
    Is only jest
T' make that place uz strong uz the rest."

So the Deacon inquired of the village folk
Where he could find the strongest oak,
That couldn't be split nor bent nor broke—
That was for spokes and floor and sills;
He sent for lancewood to make the thills;

---

[2] *Georgius Secundus.* George II, King of England.

The crossbars were ash, from the straightest trees,
The panels of white-wood, that cuts like cheese,
But lasts like iron for things like these;
The hubs of logs from the "Settler's ellum"—
Last of its timber—they couldn't sell 'em,
Never an ax had seen their chips,
And the wedges flew from between their lips,
Their blunt ends frizzled like celery-tips;
Step and prop-iron, bolt and screw,
Spring, tire, axel, and linchpin, too,
Steel of the finest, bright and blue;
Thoroughbrace bison-skin, thick and wide;
Boot, top, dasher, from tough old hide
Found in the pit when the tanner died.
That was the way he "put her through."
"There!" said the Deacon, "naow she'll dew."

Do! I tell you, I rather guess
She was a wonder, and nothing less!
Colts grew horses, beards turned gray,
Deacon and deaconess dropped away,
Children and grandchildren—where were they?
But there stood the stout old one-hoss shay
As fresh as on Lisbon-earthquake-day!

Eighteen Hundred—it came and found
The Deacon's Masterpiece strong and sound.
Eighteen hundred increased by ten—
"Hahnsum kerridge" they called it then.
Eighteen hundred and twenty came—
Running as usual; much the same.
Thirty and forty at last arrive,
And then come fifty, and FIFTY-FIVE.

Little of all we value here
Wakes on the morn of its hundredth year
Without both feeling and looking queer.
In fact, there's nothing that keeps its youth,
So far as I know, but a tree and truth.
(This is a moral that runs at large;
Take it.—You're welcome.—No extra charge.)

FIRST OF NOVEMBER—the Earthquake-day—
There are traces of age in the one-hoss shay,
A general flavor of mild decay,
But nothing local, as one may say.
There couldn't be—for the Deacon's art
Had made it so like in every part
That there wasn't a chance for one to start.
For the wheels were just as strong as the thills,
And the floor was just as strong as the sills,
And the panels just as strong as the floor,
And the whipple-tree neither less nor more,
And the back-crossbar as strong as the fore,
And spring and axle and hub *encore*.
And yet, *as a whole*, it is past a doubt
In another hour it will be *worn out!*

First of November, Fifty-five!
This morning the parson takes a drive.
Now, small boys, get out of the way!
Here comes the wonderful one-hoss shay,
Drawn by a rat-tailed, ewe-necked bay.
"Huddup!" said the parson.—Off went they.

The parson was working his Sunday's text—
Had got to *fifthly*, and stopped perplexed
At what the—Moses—was coming next.
All at once the horse stood still,
Close by the meet'n'-house on the hill.
—First a shiver, and then a thrill,
Then something decidedly like a spill—
And the parson was sitting upon a rock,
At half-past nine by the meet'n'-house clock—
Just the hour of the Earthquake shock!
—What do you think the parson found,
When he got up and stared around?
The poor old chaise in a heap or mound,
As if it had been to the mill and ground.
You see, of course, if you're not a dunce,
How it went to pieces all at once—
All at once, and nothing first—
Just as bubbles do when they burst.

End of the wonderful one-hoss shay.
Logic is logic. That's all I say.

The Logical Next Step

1. What does the word *logic* mean?
2. Holmes tells the story of the one-hoss shay to prove what point?
3. When the logic of an idea has been proved wrong, how is the result like Humpty Dumpty and the one-hoss shay?
4. What did the Deacon do in building the shay to avoid having a "weakest spot"? What similarity is there in building a foolproof argument?
5. Where is the "weakest spot" in this logic?

> All wild creatures are timid.
> Some timid creatures are bunnies.
> All bunnies are dumb.
> Seventh-graders are timid.
> Therefore, seventh-graders are dumb bunnies.

Yankee Dialect

List the words which Holmes uses to give the sound of Yankee dialect. How should they be pronounced according to the Yankee way?

Worth Remembering

What groups of lines in the poem do you think are worth remembering? Why are the last two lines especially important?

◀️ Paul Laurence Dunbar

Discovered

Paul Laurence Dunbar is one of America's beloved poets. The following poem is one of his most popular. It shows a beauty of rhythm, a sly humor, and a mastery of dialect.

> Seen you down at chu'ch las' night,
> Nevah min', Miss Lucy.
> What I mean? Oh, dat's all right,
> Nevah min', Miss Lucy.
> You was sma't ez sma't could be,
> But you couldn't hide f'om me.
> Ain't I got two eyes to see!
> Nevah min', Miss Lucy.

Guess you thought you's awful keen;
  Nevah min', Miss Lucy.
Evahthing you done, I seen;
  Nevah min', Miss Lucy.
Seen him tek yo' ahm jes' so,
When he got outside de do'—
Oh, I know dat man's yo' beau!
  Nevah min', Miss Lucy.

Say now, honey, wha'd he say?—
  Nevah min', Miss Lucy!
Keep yo' secrets—dat's yo' way—
  Nevah min', Miss Lucy.
Won't tell me an' I'm yo' pal—
I'm gwine tell his othah gal,—
Know huh, too, huh name is Sal;
  Nevah min', Miss Lucy!

❖❖❖

Never Underestimate the Power of a Woman

1. Who do you think is the speaker in this poem? What kind of person is he or she?

2. If you were to write one more stanza, how would you make the story end?

The Soft Sounds of Dialect

Notice carefully how Dunbar achieves the sound of the spoken word in his poem. Can you point out specific ways?

◄◄ T. A. DALY

Between Two Loves

T. A. Daly is a master in his handling of Italian dialect. Moreover, his delicious sense of humor and his sympathetic portrayal of characters make his poems topnotch entertainment. Here is a poem about a man who was trying to choose between two sweethearts.

I gotta lov' for Angela,
    I lov' Carlotta, too.
I no can marry both o' dem,
    So w'at I gonna do?

O! Angela ees pretta girl,
She gotta hair so black, so curl,
An' teeth so white as anytheeng.
An' O! she gotta voice to seeng,
Dat mak' your hearta feel eet must
Jump up an' dance or eet weel bust.
An' alla time she seeng, her eyes
Dey smila like Italia's skies,
An' makin' flirtin' looks at you—
But dat ees all w'at she can do.

Carlotta ees no gotta song,
But she ees twice so big an' strong
As Angela, an' she no look
So beautiful—but she can cook.
You oughta see her carry wood!
I tal you w'at, eet do you good.
When she ees be som'body's wife
She worka hard, you bat my life!
She never gattin' tired, too—
But dat ees all w'at she can do.

O! my! I weesh dat Angela
    Was strong for carry wood,

Or else Carlotta gotta song
     An' looka pretta good.
I gotta lov' for Angela,
     I lov' Carlotta, too.
I no can marry both o' dem,
     So w'at I gonna do?

❦❦❦

A PREDICAMENT

In what predicament was "I"? How do you think he will solve it?

MUSICAL SPEECH OF THE ITALIAN

How does Daly make you hear the speech of an Italian? Study the words which he respells in order to imitate the sounds.

❦ OGDEN NASH

I Will Arise and Go Now

When most people think of the verse of Ogden Nash, they think of good fun and unusual rhyme and rhythm. All the ingredients are to be found in this poem of his.

In far Tibet
There live a lama,[1]
He got no poppa,
Got no momma,

He got no wife,
He got no chillun,
Got no use
For penicillun,

He got no soap,
He got no opera,
He don't know Irium
From copra,

[1] *lama.* A priest.
——From *Versus* by Ogden Nash, by permission of Little, Brown & Co. Copyright 1949, by Ogden Nash

He got no songs,
He got no banter,
Don't know Jolson,
Don't know Cantor,

He use no lotions
For allurance,
He got no car
And no insurance,

Indeed, the
Ignorant Have-Not
Don't even know
What he don't got.

If you will mind
The Philco, comma,
I think I'll go
And join that lama.

DON'T GO YET

1. What do you know about a lama? Check with your encyclopedia.
2. What rhyme words does Nash use that particularly amuse you?
3. Why is the ending exactly right?

LOOKING BACKWARD THROUGH THE CHAPTER

1. Study the selections in this chapter for the different kinds of humor. What makes the selections funny? What is the point of humor of each?
2. Which selections do you like best? Why?
3. Which of the stories do you recognize as being based on true experience?
4. In which of the stories is exaggeration a major part of the fun? Point out specific examples of exaggeration.
5. Is there any laughing *at* people in the selections in this chapter? How do the authors direct their humor? How is their method a good lesson for all of us?

A QUIZZICAL QUIZ

Who Wrote about Them?

Who wrote about each of these?
1. Two youngsters plan a gift for Mother's Day.
2. A boy repairs a doughnut machine.
3. A man cannot decide which of two women he loves more.
4. A boy torments his kidnapers.

5. Two brothers decide to test a Bible quotation.
6. A boy is given a delicate gold watch.
7. A boy acts as chauffeur for a rich Indian.
8. A girl plans to elope with a red-haired boy.
9. A shay is built to last one hundred years.
10. A large family of children try to torment a relative.

Same or Opposite?

Number your paper from 1 to 10. Write S for those pairs of words that are alike in meaning and O for those that are opposite.

1. calamity — disaster
2. emerged — appeared
3. reconnoiter — survey
4. tumult — calm
5. insolvent — wealthy
6. chaise — carriage
7. logical — flighty
8. slack — careless
9. surreptitiously — stealthily
10. efficacy — effectiveness

YOUR OWN POINTS OF HUMOR

1. Everyone has had an experience or two which he *knows* is funny. Spend some time telling these stories in class or writing them and reading them aloud.

2. Practice telling about amusing experiences. This skill is one that everyone needs in informal conversation.

3. Perhaps you would like to put your story in verse form.

4. Keep a diary for one week, jotting down each day one humorous experience you have. Make your points of humor clear.

A READING CHECK

1. Do you feel that you are improving in your understanding of what you read?
2. Is your speed of reading increasing?
3. Are you forcing your eyes to pick up several words at a time?
4. Do you do "intelligent guessing" of the meaning of unknown words? And do you then check your guesses with the dictionary?
5. Do you try to draw your own conclusions from what you read?
6. Do you notice interesting and colorful ways of saying things?
7. Do you recognize in your reading sly points of humor?

JUST FOR FUN

Fenner, Phyllis (compiler), *Fun, Fun, Fun*, 1953 (F. Watts).
    Jolly stories for fun-loving readers.

Hale, Lucretia P., *The Peterkin Papers*, 1924 (Houghton).
    Humorous classic of the amusing difficulties of the Peterkin family and the Lady from Philadelphia.

Jackson, Jacqueline, *Julie's Secret Sloth*, 1953 (Little).
    Merry mishaps with a hidden pet.

Lawson, Robert, *Mr. Twigg's Mistake*, 1947 (Little).
"Squirt" and his pet mole—the effects of an amazing box of cereal.

Leaf, Munro, *Sam and the Superdroop*, 1948 (Viking).
A story to outlaw all comics.

Richardson, Myra R., *The Mule Skinners*, 1945 (Viking).
Chuckle-provoking antics of a young man and a donkey helping the army.

Scoggin, Margaret C. (editor), *Chucklebait*, 1945 (Knopf).
Anthology of funny stories appealing to young folk.

Scoggin, Margaret C. (editor), *More Chucklebait*, 1949 (Knopf).
More funny stories.

Smith, Elva S., and Hazeltine, Alice I. (compilers), *Just for Fun*, 1948 (Lothrop).
Varied collection of humorous tales, poetry, and plays.

Stong, Philip D., *Way Down Cellar*, 1942 (Dodd).
Mischievous fun dealing with three boys and a secret staircase.

Tarkington, Booth, *Penrod*, 1914 (Doubleday).
Troubles of a lively boy, his pals, and his dog.

Temple, Willard H., *Web Adams*, 1943 (Scribner).
Tricks and mishaps of a fun-loving lad.

Twain, Mark, *The Adventures of Huckleberry Finn*, 1912 (Harper).
———, *The Adventures of Tom Sawyer*, 1917 (Harper).
American classics of boy life.

From Microbes
to Atoms

◄◄ Paul de Kruif

Leeuwenhoek,
First of the Microbe Hunters

It is always interesting to see the beginnings of developments and then the results. Back in the seventeenth century Leeuwenhoek saw microbes for the first time. In the nineteenth century Pasteur carried the discovery forward, and in our own century many of the remarkable medical discoveries are based on the original work done by Leeuwenhoek. The next two articles will show something of the development.

Leeuwenhoek (1632–1723) was a real explorer. True, he did not go anywhere. He simply peered through his lenses at such things as a bee's sting, a louse's leg, and drops of water. But what he discovered was the beginning of a new chapter in science.

(Note the time when you begin reading.)

Two hundred and fifty years ago an obscure man named Leeuwenhoek looked for the first time into a mysterious new world peopled with a thousand different kinds of tiny beings. Some were ferocious and deadly, others friendly and useful, many of them more important to mankind than any continent or archipelago.

Today it is respectable to be a man of science. Those who go by the name of scientist form an important element of the population. Their laboratories are in every city; their achievements are on the front pages of the newspapers, often before they are fully achieved. But take yourself back to Leeuwenhoek's day, two hundred and fifty years ago, and imagine your-self just through high school, getting ready to choose a career, wanting to know—

You have lately recovered from an attack of mumps. You ask your father what is the cause of mumps, and he tells you a mumpish evil spirit has got into you. His theory may not impress you much, but you decide to make believe you believe him and not to wonder any more about what is mumps. If you publicly don't believe him, you are in for a beating and may even be turned out of the house. Your father is Authority.

That was the world three hundred years ago, when Leeuwenhoek was born. It had hardly begun to shake itself free from superstitions; it was barely beginning to blush for its ignorance. It was a world where science (which only means trying to find

——Abridged from *Microbe Hunters*, copyright, 1926, by Paul de Kruif. Reprinted by permission of Harcourt, Brace and Company, Inc.

truth by careful observation and clear thinking) was just learning to toddle on vague and wobbly legs. It was a world where Servetus was burned to death for daring to cut up and examine the body of a dead man, where Galileo was shut up for life for daring to prove that the earth moved around the sun.

Antony Leeuwenhoek was born in 1632 amid the blue windmills and low streets and high canals of Delft, in Holland. His family were burghers of an intensely respectable kind. I say intensely respectable because they were basketmakers and brewers, and brewers are respectable and highly honored in Holland. Leeuwenhoek's father died early and his mother sent him to school to learn to be a government official; but he left school at sixteen to be an apprentice in a dry-goods store in Amsterdam. That was his university. Think of a present-day scientist getting his training for experiment among bolts of gingham, listening to the tinkle of the bell on the cash drawer, being polite to an eternal succession of Dutch housewives who shopped with a penny-pinching dreadful exhaustiveness. But that was Leeuwenhoek's university, for six years!

At the age of twenty-one he left the dry-goods store, went back to Delft, married, set up a dry-goods store of his own there. For twenty years after that very little is known about him, except that he had two wives (in succession) and several children, most of whom died. There is no doubt that during this time he was appointed janitor of the city hall of Delft, and that he developed a most

idiotic love for grinding lenses. He had heard that if you very carefully ground very little lenses out of clear glass, you would see things look much bigger than they appeared to the naked eye.

It would be great fun to look through a lens and see things bigger than your naked eye showed them to you! But *buy* lenses? Not Leeuwenhoek! There never was a more suspicious man. Buy lenses? He would make them himself! During these twenty years of his obscurity he went to spectaclemakers and got the rudiments of lens-grinding. He visited alchemists and apothecaries and put his nose into their secret ways of getting metals from ores. He began fumblingly to learn the craft of the gold- and silversmiths. He was a most pernickety man and was not satisfied with grinding lenses as good as those of the best lens-grinder in Holland. They had to be better than the best, and then he still fussed over them for long hours. Next he mounted these lenses in little oblongs of copper or silver or gold, which he had extracted himself, over hot fires, among strange smells and fumes. Today searchers pay seventy-five dollars for a fine shining microscope, turn the screws, peer through it, make discoveries—without knowing anything about how it is built. But Leeuwenhoek—

Now this self-satisfied dry-goods dealer began to turn his lenses onto everything he could get hold of. He looked through them at the muscle fibers of a whale and the scales of his own skin. He went to the butcher shop and begged or bought ox eyes and was amazed at how prettily the crystalline lens of the eye of the ox is put together. He peered for hours at the build of the hairs of a sheep, of a beaver, of an elk, that were transformed from their fineness into great rough logs under his bit of glass. He delicately dissected the head of a fly; he stuck its brain on the fine needle of his microscope. How he admired the clear details of the marvelous big brain of that fly! He examined the cross sections of the wood of a dozen different trees and squinted at the seeds of plants. He grunted "Impossible!" when he first spied the outlandish large perfection of the sting of a flea and the legs of a louse.

There never was a less sure man than Leeuwenhoek. He looked at this bee's sting or that louse's leg again and again and again. He left his specimens sticking on the point of his strange microscope for months. In order to look at other things, he made more microscopes till he had hundreds of them! Then he came back to those first specimens to correct his first mistakes. He never set down a word about anything he peeped at, he never made a drawing until hundreds of peeps showed him that, under given conditions, he would always see exactly the same thing. And then he was not sure!

You have read that he made better and better lenses with the fanatical persistence of a lunatic; that he examined everything with the silly curiosity of a puppy. Yes, and all this squinting at bee stings and mustache hairs and what-not were needful to prepare him for that sudden day when he looked through his toy of a gold-mounted lens at a fraction of a small drop of clear rain water to discover—

What he saw that day starts this history. Leeuwenhoek was a maniac observer; and who but such a strange man would have thought to turn his lens on clear, pure water, just come down from the sky? What could there be in water but just—water? You can imagine his daughter Maria—she was nineteen, and she took such care of her slightly insane father!—watching him take a little tube of glass, heat it red-hot in a flame, draw it out to the thinness of a hair. . . . Maria was devoted to her father. Let any of those stupid neighbors dare to snigger at him! But what in the world was he up to now, with that hair-fine glass pipe?

You can see her watch that absent-minded wide-eyed man break the tube into little pieces, go out into the garden to bend over an earthen pot kept there to measure the fall of the rain. He bends over that pot. He goes back into his study. He sticks the little glass pipe onto the needle of his microscope. . . .

What can that dear silly father be up to?

He squints through his lens. He mutters guttural words under his breath. . . .

Then suddenly the excited voice of Leeuwenhoek: "Come here! Hurry! There are little animals in this rain water. . . . they swim! They play around! They are a thousand times smaller than any creature we can see with our eyes alone. . . . Look! See what I have discovered!"

Leeuwenhoek's day of days had come. Alexander had gone to India and discovered huge elephants that no Greek had ever seen before—but those elephants were as commonplace to Hindus as horses were to Alexander. Caesar had gone to England and come upon savages that opened his eyes with wonder—but these Britons were as ordinary to each other as Roman centurions were to Caesar. Balboa? What were his proud feelings as he looked for the first time at the Pacific? Just the same that ocean was as ordinary to a Central American Indian as the Mediterranean was to Balboa. But Leeuwenhoek? This janitor of Delft had stolen upon and peeped into a fantastic subvisible world of little things, creatures that had lived, had bred, had battled, had died, completely hidden from and unknown to all men from the beginning of time. Beasts these were of a kind that ravaged and annihilated whole races of men ten million times larger than they were themselves. Beings these were, more terrible than fire-spitting dragons or hydra-headed monsters. They were silent assassins that murdered babes in warm cradles and kings in sheltered places. It was this invisible—and sometimes friendly—world that Leeuwenhoek had looked into for the first time of all men of all countries.

This was Leeuwenhoek's day of days.

(Note the time; and check your speed of reading with the Reading Score Board, page 372.)

◆(◆

COMING TO CONCLUSIONS

1. How far had science progressed in those days?
2. What two qualities did Leeuwenhoek have which made him a great scientist?
3. Why was his discovery a great one?
4. How has his discovery influenced our lives?

EXAMINING PARAGRAPHS

Some paragraphs of the article you probably read rapidly. Others took slower reading. Paragraphs of narrative, those which tell a story, can usually be read faster. Paragraphs of exposition, those which explain something, usually go more slowly.

Here are key sentences of five paragraphs. How would you classify each paragraph, as a narrative or as exposition?

1. Today it is respectable to be a man of science. (page 368)
2. Antony Leeuwenhoek was born in 1632 amid the blue windmills and low streets and high canals of Delft, in Holland. (page 369)
3. Now this self-satisfied dry-goods dealer began to turn his lenses onto everything he could get hold of. (page 369)
4. There never was a less sure man than Leeuwenhoek. (page 370)
5. What he saw that day starts this history. (page 370)

PROOF OF THE PUDDING IN READING

List the details which De Kruif uses to prove topic sentences 1, 3, and 4 above.

Do you see why good readers always look for topic sentences? In the three paragraphs you have just analyzed you have seen the author's organization of his thinking. In each he stated what his main idea was going to be; that was his topic sentence. Then he gave a number of details to support his main idea. Good readers use topic sentences for two reasons: (1) they know that in them they will find the main ideas, and (2) they know that by using them they can speed up their reading.

Examine a few paragraphs in your history or science text. Notice the use of topic sentences and of supporting details.

IDEAS IN WORDS

Explain the meaning of each of these phrases:
1. had hardly begun to shake itself free from superstitions
2. shopped with a penny-pinching dreadful exhaustiveness
3. He visited alchemists and apothecaries
4. made better and better lenses with the fanatical persistence of a lunatic
5. peeped into a fantastic subvisible world of little things

PICTURES IN WORDS

What details in De Kruif's article make you see the kind of person Leeuwenhoek was? What adjectives and adverbs and picture-making verbs are used to build up the picture of the man?

READING SCORE BOARD

Number of Words in Story: 1550

Number of Minutes	15 1/2	7 3/4	6	5	4	3
Reading Rate	100 w.p.m.	200 w.p.m.	250 w.p.m.	300 w.p.m.	400 w.p.m.	500 w.p.m.

◀️ ELEANOR DOORLY

Mad Dogs and Others

Pasteur took up where Leeuwenhoek left off. Pasteur reasoned that there was a relationship between microbes and sickness. If the microbes could be counteracted, sickness might be overcome. Because of his work in this field, the pasteurization of milk and various kinds of inoculations have become common practices.

The following, published in 1938, tells the dramatic story of Pasteur's fight against the dreaded hydrophobia.

(Note the time when you begin reading.)

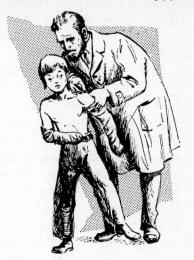

Pasteur went home to his mad dogs! And if you want to understand how really interesting this story is, you ought to be about sixty years old. For then you would remember the time when all the poor dogs wore muzzles in the hot weather and went about with their dry tongues hanging out, longing for water. You might remember, too, your own terror whenever you saw a dog, any dog, running towards you, because that dog might have been mad.

Everywhere, even in England, there were mad dogs; and to be bitten meant almost certain death and terrible, terrible pain.

Pasteur himself had a scene in his mind, which he could not forget. He was nine when it happened. A mad wolf had run through the countryside, biting everyone in its way; and with it had run terror through the hills of Jura. Eight people had died, and Pasteur had seen with his own

eyes the blacksmith burning the wounds of one man in an attempt to save his life.

Dogs had been mad from the beginning of time. Even Homer[1] talks of them. But for their bite there was no cure. People *talked* of cures: a hair of the dog that bit you; shrimps' eyes eaten whole; a well-beaten omelet of bottom oyster shells; sea baths, or, best of all: a pilgrimage to the shrine of St. Hubert. St. Hubert was a hunter of the forest of Ardenne. He had been dead a thousand years; but when the bitten man arrived at his shrine, the priest made a small slit in his forehead with a penknife and slipped into it the minutest thread of St. Hubert's thousand-year-old stole. Then he bound up the new wound and ordered the sufferer not to touch the bandage for nine days.

When all the magic cures failed, surgeons would cut off the bitten limb or bleed the sick man to death, or his

——From *The Microbe Man* by Eleanor Doorly, published by William Heinemann, Ltd.

[1] *Homer.* Greek poet of about the ninth century B. C.

friends would suffocate him in bed to save him from the awful agony of a death from hydrophobia.

Right up to Pasteur's time there was no remedy known for the most terrible of illnesses except the burning of the wound, and that was seldom done deep enough to save. No one knew anything about the illness except its terror; they did not even know that a mad dog would drink, though the man he had bitten would never touch water to quench his burning thirst. The dog's illness was called rabies, and the man's hydrophobia.

Four years before Pasteur talked on rabies with Virchow,[2] he had been given two mad dogs, the strangest of his gifts. One had bloodshot, miserable eyes and howled a weird, despairing howl as it snapped at everything within reach. The other was silent with sad eyes and a paralyzed mouth. For four years mad dogs had been constantly about him. Pasteur wanted the saliva of a mad bulldog for an experiment. His assistants held it down with their hands while he drew its deadly saliva into a glass tube held between his lips.

There have been few braver deeds than that told in any tale of adventure, but there was coming a day when Pasteur would do another deed that needed more courage.

Pasteur and many others were doing all kinds of experiments, but none seemed to give any certain information. They injected, for instance, the saliva of a child who had died of

hydrophobia, into a rabbit, and the rabbit died in forty-eight hours; whereas, if it had rabies or hydrophobia, it would have lived a month before getting ill. What disease had it died of? asked Pasteur. Why didn't bitten dogs and bitten people always get ill? He began to think that perhaps the rabies microbe could not always find its way to exactly the right part of the animal where it wanted to live. Where would that be? he asked. The brain, he answered, because the dog goes mad.

So, to make a long story short, Pasteur took to injecting the brain of a mad dog into the brain of a well dog. No one had ever thought of doing that before. And Pasteur was unhappy about it. He could not bear to hurt the dog, and this time he felt that it must be hurt. No one would hurt a dog merely to find out things, but surely it was right to hurt a few dogs in order to save thousands of other dogs from terrible pain? No one who had ever heard the horrible howling of a mad dog would think it right that all dogs, forever, should go on suffering from rabies, rather than that a few should suffer a scientist's experiment. But still Pasteur, who had a very soft heart, was worried about the dog who had had to have a hole in its head.

"Seing is believing," thought his assistant, Dr. Roux, and he brought the dog to see Pasteur. It ran about, sniffed round the room, wagged its tail, said: "At present I am comfortable, thank you." And Pasteur patted it and was grateful to it for being so happy.

[2] *Virchow.* A German scientist who specialized in the study of diseases.

That experiment showed Pasteur for certain that rabies lived in the brain, but even with the strongest microscope he could not see the microbe. If he could not see it, how could he grow it as he had grown microbes he had seen? You understand, don't you, that if you can't see a plant, you don't know if that wretched plant has grown since yesterday.

Naturally, many people said: "What can't be seen, isn't there; there is no rabies microbe."

Pasteur had an idea! Suppose he planted the microbe in something alive, not in soup! If he could not see it grow, he might be able to know whether it had grown or not by what it did. So he planted it in a live rabbit's brain. After a long time the rabbit died mad. Then Pasteur took some of its brain and planted that again. The second rabbit died quicker. Hullo! Had the thing grown? It was fiercer anyway. Pasteur took some of that rabbit's brain and planted it in a third; that was fiercer still. He went on till he had something so fierce that a rabbit developed the illness in seven days instead of twenty-eight. At seven days it remained fixed. He could make a rabbit develop rabies on any day he pleased. He could say, as if by magic: "Rabbit A will take twenty days to be ill, while Rabbit B will take only nine."

He had learned how to make that illness fiercer and fiercer. Could he make it less fierce and less fierce, till it was so gentle it wasn't there at all? He would try. He found that if he used monkeys instead of rabbits, the illness grew less fierce.

He hung a very little of an infected brain in a phial where the air was kept *very* dry. Each day it became drier; and as it dried, it became less poisonous till on the fourteenth day it was absolutely harmless.

Pasteur then injected a dog with fourteen-days' old brain. Next day with thirteen-days' old, and so on, till at last, master dog had the fiercest poison of all, the one-day old, from which he ought to have gone mad in seven days. But behold! he was well! And yes! all the mad dogs in the world could lay him in the dust and bite him whenever they liked, and he could never go mad.

Pasteur did dozens of experiments. Mad dogs bit inoculated dogs and non-inoculated dogs, and always the inoculated dogs lived and the non-inoculated died.

After that, if you loved your dog, you could have him patiently injected and he could never go mad.

But how many dogs were there in France? How many millions? How many vaccinators would there have to be? How long would the dog remain safe or would he have to be done each year? And all the puppies being born all the time? The problem was not solved.

The next thing that his dogs showed to Pasteur was that all dogs did not need to be inoculated. It was possible to wait till a dog was bitten and then inoculate him, and the inoculation was sure to stop rabies from developing. People began to ask if it were not possible to use Pasteur's vaccine for men. From England came a request to send some over for use.

But Pasteur wired "Impossible." Human beings are not dogs or even monkeys, and it is not safe to think that what helps an animal will help a man.

Pasteur was, nevertheless, longing to try his vaccine on human beings; but he dared not. He asked the Emperor of Brazil if he would allow a criminal condemned to death to be given the choice of "death or a rabies injection." But the law did not allow any such choice. Then Pasteur thought of trying it on himself but was dissuaded. When and how would he know if it was possible to save a human being from hydrophobia?

Then it happened, the great event! The event for which mankind had been waiting through all the long, long centuries.

Far away in Alsace, French Alsace, that had been made a foreign country for a time, nine-year-old Joseph Meister was going to school. He slipped out of his father's farm a little late and ran to make up for lost time. There he is, in the July morning, a little late schoolboy running over the field path on the way to the village of Meissengott, where his school is! His fair hair blowing in the wind, his blue eyes laughing at the world, he was expecting nothing but fun from the day, when suddenly, Grocer Vone's big dog, coming from nowhere across the fields, threw him down and bit him everywhere, except on his face, for he kept that covered with his poor small hands which were getting the worst of the bites. At last, for it seemed a long time though it was not, help came. Someone was

there with an iron bar to beat off the dog, someone who picked up Joseph and carried him home, while the dog ran off to bite his own master, who shot him. Mad? Yes! There was no doubt the dog was mad, because the vet found pieces of wood and straw in its stomach. So all the tales of mad dogs had come true in Meissengott. It was their turn. The poor parents and Joseph and Neighbor Vone went to Doctor Weber in the town of Villé; you can imagine how frightened they were. Joseph could scarcely walk because of his fourteen wounds; but they urged him on, for they were desperately afraid.

Dr. Weber cleaned the wounds with strong carbolic. "But," said he, "there is a man in Paris who will help you if any man can. You must go to him." They could not say no, even if it was a very long journey and they were only timid peasant folk.

So there, you see, he had come at last, the man whom Pasteur and all the world had been waiting for, the man for the experiment that could not be done, which was, even in Pasteur's words "impossible." But oh! how sorry Pasteur was for him and for himself. He had thought to try the experiment on some great hulking prisoner or perhaps on an old wise man, but never, never on a little boy.

Pasteur looked at him and looked. They say that if he had been a doctor, he would have known too much and so never dared to try the experiment. But Pasteur had a bold spirit; though he was old and wise, he loved taking risks like the brave young things. His penetrating eyes seemed to go right through Joseph Meister. He would have liked to be able to see whether he was going to have hydrophobia or not. It was two days since he had been bitten, and people did not all get ill. Suppose he gave this boy an illness in trying to save him? Suppose inoculations in boys and dogs turned out to have opposite effects?

Pasteur had to ask other people. He needed time. Would time itself spoil his chance of success? Anyway, he dared do nothing without advice. He arranged a comfortable room for Joseph and his mother and then went to see M. Vulpian and Dr. Grancher.

Vulpian asked *the* question: "Is there *any* way except your way of saving the boy from hydrophobia?"

"No!" said Pasteur.

"Then," said Vulpian, "it is not only right to try the inoculation, it is your bounden duty."

That same evening, little Joseph was brought crying to the laboratory. He thought they were going to give him a fifteenth wound, and he didn't want it. But when it turned out to be only a prick on his right side, he laughed and went back happily to play with all the white mice and guinea pigs and rabbits that were around in his lodging.

Every day Joseph went gaily to the laboratory to have his prick. It wasn't he who cared. They might give him as many pricks of that kind as they liked. But why did "dear Monsieur Pasteur" grow solemner and solemner? Joseph hadn't an idea! He didn't know that each day the prick was getting more dangerous, till at last there would be a day when the prick could produce hydrophobia in seven days, unless all the other pricks had made it impossible.

As that important day drew near, Pasteur was almost beside himself with anxiety. He knew, with one side of himself, that he would succeed; but with the other he could not believe it. He loved little Joseph. By that time he was feeling "if only it had been somebody else—not this little boy." He could not sleep, he couldn't work. When he dropped off to sleep, he awoke with the nightmare that he had failed, that Joseph was ill.

On July 16th he inoculated the fiercest vaccine. He knew that to be the bravest thing he had ever done. Joseph spent the day merrily playing and then kissed his "dear Monsieur Pasteur" good night and slept like a singing top. But Pasteur did not sleep at all.

After that, Joseph only needed watching to see what happened, but that would have been too much for Pasteur. He went for a holiday. He was at Arbois when at last the news came that all the time had gone by and that Joseph was indeed safe.

The great event had happened! Was it not perhaps the greatest event, save one, that ever did happen? For it was not only Joseph Meister who was cured then. A great door had been opened to science to find escapes for poor men from all kinds of illnesses.

(Note the time; and check your speed of reading with the Reading Score Board, page 378.)

ANOTHER MICROBE HUNTER

1. How did Pasteur continue the work begun by Leeuwenhoek?
2. What were some of the ways by which people tried to cure hydrophobia?
3. How did Pasteur inoculate against hydrophobia?
4. What was the greatest test of Pasteur's courage? Why was he fearful?

FOLLOWING CLUES TO CONCLUSIONS

Often the first sentence of a paragraph is a clue to what the paragraph is going to be about. Here are the topic sentences of five paragraphs. Without looking back at the paragraphs, what do you expect each to discuss? Later check with the paragraphs.

1. Pasteur himself had a scene in his mind, which he could not forget.
2. Dogs had been mad from the beginning of time.
3. Pasteur was, nevertheless, longing to try his vaccine on human beings; but he dared not.
4. As that important day drew near, Pasteur was almost beside himself with anxiety.
5. The great event had happened!

A VOCABULARY QUIZ

Choose the word or phrase that gives the meaning of the word in italics.

1. *hydrophobia*: (a) a form of hydroxide (b) an infectious disease (c) water
2. *rabies*: (a) a disease of dogs (b) rabble (c) a serum
3. *inject*: (a) to place under (b) to cover (c) to force into
4. *infected*: (a) contaminated (b) inferred (c) contained
5. *inoculate*: (a) to bring about immunity (b) to test (c) to make sick
6. *vaccine*: (a) substance free from germs (b) substance containing germs (c) antiseptic
7. *penetrating*: (a) penalizing (b) piercing (c) ringing
8. *anxiety*: (a) antipathy (b) frankness (c) uneasiness
9. *fierce*: (a) ferocious (b) precocious (c) fiesta
10. *depended*: (a) suspend (b) relied (c) defended
11. *minutest*: (a) time (b) smallest (c) degree of strength
12. *bounden*: (a) binding (b) boundless (c) bounty
13. *condemned*: (a) pronounced innocent (b) pronounced guilty (c) condensed
14. *dissuaded*: (a) persuaded against (b) persuaded to (c) persisted
15. *hulking*: (a) fearful (b) huge (c) clumsy

READING SCORE BOARD

Number of Words in Story: 2500

Number of Minutes	25	12 1/2	10	8 1/3	6 1/4	5
Reading Rate	100 w.p.m.	200 w.p.m.	250 w.p.m.	300 w.p.m.	400 w.p.m.	500 w.p.m.

A SELF-CHECK

In your reading, are you progressing in each of the following ways?

1. Are you forcing yourself always to read *forward*?
2. Do your eyes pick up several words at a time?
3. Do you almost unconsciously look for the key words in each line?
4. Are you reading more rapidly?
5. Does your comprehension show improvement?
6. Do you think through authors' ideas and come to your own conclusions?

YOUR OWN CONCLUSIONS

The selections in this chapter are harder to read than those in some of the other chapters. They require *thought*—and that is always hard. To get the greatest value from these articles requires: (1) thinking through the ideas, (2) seeing the relationship between one scientific discovery and another, (3) seeing the relationship with things near to us, and (4) coming to our own conclusions about the ideas presented. Hard work? Yes, indeed; but it's worth the struggle.

◀◀ HILAIRE BELLOC

The Microbe

The Microbe is so very small
You cannot make him out at all,
But many sanguine people hope
To see him through a microscope.
His jointed tongue that lies beneath
A hundred curious rows of teeth;
His seven tufted tails with lots
Of lovely pink and purple spots
On each of which a pattern stands,
  Composed of forty separate bands;
    His eyebrows of a tender green;
      All these have never yet been seen—
      But scientists, you ought to know,
      Assure us that they must be so . . .
      Oh! Let us never, never doubt
      What nobody is sure about!

◂◖ ROBERT LAWSON

That Kite

Electricity—like microbes—has grown from small beginnings to its present magic. The next three selections tell of the discovery and development of electricity.

According to Robert Lawson in *Ben and Me*, the great Benjamin Franklin had a good friend named Amos, who helped him in many of his experiments. In the following story Amos tells of the unwilling part he played in Ben's experiment with the kite and lightning. Oh, yes—Amos happens to be a *mouse*. This story, therefore, is a *mouse's-eye* view of the discovery of electricity.

(Jot down the time when you begin reading.)

THE QUESTION of the nature of lightning so preyed upon Ben's mind that he was finally driven to an act of deceit that caused the first and only rift in our long friendship.

I feel sure that brooding on this subject must have seriously affected his mind, for this is the only way in which I can excuse his treacherous conduct.

It came about in this fashion.

One of Ben's favorite forms of relaxation was kiteflying.

On his largest kite he had built for me a tiny platform. Made of light splinters of wood, this was securely lashed to the kite just where the sticks of the frame crossed. A stout railing surrounded it, and the floor was cushioned with milkweed down, so that a safer or more snug retreat could scarcely be imagined.

Sailing aloft in this was a delight-

ful sensation. The gentle motions of the kite, the warmth of the sun, and the broad view spread out below all combined to make it a thoroughly restful and enjoyable experience.

A new thrill was added when we contrived a tiny car slung to a pulley running on the kitestring. In this I could cast off from my little porch and go coasting in a long, glorious swoop to Ben and the earth far below.

To this car we later added a small sail, so that when the wind was sufficiently strong, I could sail up the string to the kite. Enabled thus to ascend and descend at will, I spent many happy hours at this thrilling sport.

That Deceit could raise its ugly head in such idyllic surroundings and bring to an end these innocent diversions seems particularly painful. I shall pass over as rapidly as possible the unfortunate happenings which almost brought our friendship to a close.

Ben had hinted that if I were willing to stay aloft during a thunder-

---From *Ben and Me* by Robert Lawson, by permission of Little, Brown & Co. Copyright 1939, by Robert Lawson.

storm, I could, being so close to the clouds, very easily determine the nature of lightning.

My reply to this proposal was prompt, decided, and in the negative—very strongly in the negative. So much so that Ben dropped the subject and had, I thought, given up the idea completely.

But alas for my trust in human honor! Little did I dream of the horrid plot that this electrical mania was causing to form in his disordered brain!

One hot July afternoon I had ridden aloft and, lulled by the gentle motion and the sun's warmth, had indulged in a long nap. From this I was awakened by a violent tossing of the kite. I at once realized from the black and threatening clouds that a sudden thunderstorm was rapidly approaching, its preliminary gusts already tossing the kite wildly about.

Hastily preparing to descend in my little car, I was horrified to discover that it was not there! Jerks on the string to signal Ben bringing no response, the ugly details of his plot began to dawn on me! I recalled his haste to launch the kite and his incessant talk while doing so, all designed to hide the fact that he had removed the car.

With or without my consent, he had resolved to keep me aloft during the storm!

I sought wildly for some method of descending the string, but the wind by now was so strong that all my efforts were required to cling to the frail platform.

The next half hour was the most awful experience of my life. The wild plunging of the kite, the driving sheets of rain, the incessant lightning flashes, and the crashing thunder all were so terrifying that I could only hang on and pray.

As shock after stiffening shock ran through my body, there was no further doubt in *my* mind as to the nature of lightning. It *was* electrical—decidedly so!

Blue sparks crackled from my whiskers, every hair stood on end, and my frame was convulsed by the never-ending shocks.

After what seemed hours of this torture, the storm passed; and I knew by the motions of the string that the kite was being lowered. Nearing the earth I saw that Ben had taken cover in a shed and was regarding my approach with the greatest eagerness.

Before I had reached the ground he was calling, "Was it, Amos? Was it electricity? WAS it?"

Even had rage not rendered me speechless, I should never have given him the satisfaction of an answer. As the kite touched earth, I descended and stalked past him in stony silence. Despite his questions and pleadings I pursued my angry way back to town, never pausing until I had reached the shelter of my home in the vestry.[1]

There, after my wondering family had dried me and dressed my burns, I fell into an exhausted sleep that lasted two days.

[1] *vestry*. A room in a church where the robes of the clergy are kept.

(Note the time; and check your reading rate with the **Reading Score Board**, page 382.)

A MOUSE'S-EYE VIEW

1. According to Amos, what is one of Benjamin Franklin's great contributions to science? How was it the beginning of a long chain of developments?
2. Can you name other contributions that Ben Franklin made?
3. In what ways does Amos add humor to the story?

A MOUSE'S VOCABULARY

Can you think of a synonym for each word in italics?

1. *preyed* upon Ben's mind
2. only *rift* in our long friendship
3. *treacherous* conduct
4. *Enabled* thus to *ascend* and *descend* at will
5. *idyllic* surroundings
6. electrical *mania*
7. *preliminary* gusts
8. *incessant* lightning flashes
9. *convulsed* by the nerve-ending shocks
10. my home in the *vestry*

READING SCORE BOARD

Number of Words in Story: 800

Number of Minutes	8	4	3 1/5	2 2/3	2	1 3/5
Reading Rate	100 w.p.m.	200 w.p.m.	250 w.p.m.	300 w.p.m.	400 w.p.m.	500 w.p.m.

◀ ROSEMARY AND STEPHEN VINCENT BENÉT

Benjamin Franklin

The Benéts do not seem to give Ben Franklin's pet mouse Amos any credit for the discovery of electricity.

Ben Franklin made a pretty kite and flew it in the air
To call upon a thunderstorm that happened to be there,
—And all our humming dynamos and our electric light
Go back to what Ben Franklin found, the day he flew his kite.

——From *A Book of Americans*, published by Rinehart & Company, Inc. Copyright, 1933, by Rosemary and Stephen Vincent Benét.

◄◄ EDWARD LONGSTRETH

The Speed of Words

Benjamin Franklin's discovery led to many other discoveries and inventions. Because of him, we can today, in a matter of seconds, talk to someone thousands of miles away. This play will show the steps by which we have now reached our amazing "speed of words." If you are going to act out this play, first list the members of the large cast.

NARRATOR: From the time the United States of America had been established as an independent nation, people became impatient for increasingly faster exchange of thought. As their commercial life grew more complicated and scattered, they became determined to reduce the time that elapsed between a question asked and the answer received. They wanted to bring about a meeting of minds with the least possible delay. To achieve more perfect service, many of them gave their lives. Great feats of daring were performed. By the middle of the century following the famous midnight ride of Paul Revere, the Thirteen Original Colonies had expanded westward to the Pacific Ocean—to California and gold. Suddenly, in the short space of a single year, that sparsely settled region became a rich and populous territory clamoring for admission to the Union. But in 1850 it was a long way for news to travel—between New York and the Golden Gate. One fine spring day, the Clipper Ship *Sea Witch* set sail for distant California.

Driving hard southward in all weather, past the equator into the Antarctic winter, the *Sea Witch* rounded Cape Horn, carrying every stitch of canvas possible day and night. Every mile of it, an ocean race against other great Clipper Ships somewhere at sea, racing for California, the land of gold and opportunity. . . .

VOICE: Land ho!

SAILOR: The Golden Gate, Captain Fraser! The Golden Gate!

CAPTAIN FRASER: Very good! . . . Well, Mr. Delano, I doubt if many of the ships that left port ahead of us are in before us. Ninety-seven days from Sandy Hook is fast time.

MR. DELANO: Ninety-seven days is a record, sir. It'll take good sailing and better luck to beat it, sir.

CAPTAIN FRASER: It's been a good crew, and you've got everything out of them. Pass the word forward the company'll give all hands a bonus.

MR. DELANO: Aye, aye, sir. Shall I make the longboat ready, sir?

CAPTAIN FRASER: Yes. Man it with the lustiest lads aboard. And have it in the water before the anchor. I've got a message for the Governor of the new State of California.

NARRATOR: Ten years later—California was a great commonwealth. But San Francisco and New York were still weeks apart. By fastest stagecoach route through the Southwest, it took almost a month for news to travel from coast to coast. Then, on March 26, 1860, the New York *Herald* carried the following announcement:

"To San Francisco in 8 days by the Central Overland California and Pike's Peak Express Company. The first courier of the Pony Express will leave the Missouri River on Tuesday, April 3d, at 5 o'clock P.M. and will run regularly weekly hereafter, carrying letter-mail only."

The first lap of this relay between the Atlantic Seaboard and St. Joseph, Missouri, was by telegraph. But the line ended at St. Joseph. There Johnny Frey impatiently waited for the signal that would start him on the first run of the Pony Express. A crowd of excited well-wishers was gathered around Frey and his restless horse. . . .

JOHNNY FREY: Whoa, boy. Take it easy. You'll soon have plenty of chance to run . . . This pony's a beauty, Al. And you've got him in great condition.

AL: He's got to be in top form, Johnny. Look at the crowd that's come to see you ride off on him. Listen! I just heard the train whistle. The mail's on time!

JOHNNY FREY: Good. . . . You ought to be riding today, Al, instead of staying here in St. Joseph looking after ponies.

AL: But I'm studying to be a telegraph operator, and you can't practice that on horseback. . . . Whoa, boy!

JOHNNY FREY: Who'd want to? This is better pay.

AL: Maybe my job'll last longer than yours. The telegraph's got as far as St. Joseph already.

JOHNNY FREY: The other end's 2000 miles away.

AL: They'll cut down that distance until you boys won't have any farther to ride than across the street there.

JOHNNY FREY: Well, right now us riders have got to get a lot of words to Carson City. . . . Hold his head, Al. I'm mounting up. . . . Whoa, boy! Let go, Al. The mail pouch must be waiting at the post office by now.

AL: Wait for the starting signal, Johnny.

JOHNNY FREY: Maybe the cannon won't go off. I don't want to lose a second.

MR. RUSSELL (*coming up*): Hey, there! Hold that courier. Wait.

JOHNNY FREY: Who's that?

AL: The big boss himself—Mr. Russell.

JOHNNY FREY: Gee.

MR. RUSSELL: Are you Johnny Frey?

JOHNNY FREY: Yes, sir.

MR. RUSSELL: Here's a message just came in by telegraph from Washington. It's from President Buchanan to the Governor of California. Guard it well.

JOHNNY FREY: With my life if necessary, sir.

MR. RUSSELL: Frey, as the first courier westward bound on the Pony Express, I and my partners, Majors and Waddell, wish you good luck and God-speed.

JOHNNY FREY: It's a real honor to ride for you, sir.

AL: There's the cannon, Johnny!

JOHNNY FREY: Let loose his head.

AL: Good luck!

MR. RUSSELL: Good luck, Frey!

JOHNNY FREY: Thanks—Good-by! I'm off! (*Horse gallops away.*)

NARRATOR: Johnny Frey galloped madly off on the first run—75 miles—on 3 horses. At the division point, the next rider would be ready and waiting. . . .

On through the wild Indian country by day and by night rode the daring riders on the fleetest horses America could breed—as far as Red Buttes Division Point, where another famous rider was waiting to carry the pouch to Three Crossings. His name was William F. Cody—better known to history as "Buffalo Bill."

AGENT: Here he comes, Bill—He's running late.

BUFFALO BILL: I'll make it up. . . . Steady, boy. . . . This horse is sure raring to go!

AGENT: Better take my rifle along. I saw a couple of Indians to the west this morning.

BUFFALO BILL: The rifle's too heavy. I won't have time to shoot it out with them, anyway. (*Hoofbeats come up.*)

AGENT: That rider looks all tuckered out.

BUFFALO BILL: Looks like he's been in trouble. Never mind me. Grab his horse.

RIDER: Here you are . . . the mail!

AGENT: I'll take the mail pouch, kid. What happened?

RIDER (*gasping*): Indians . . . raided last station . . . stole all the horses . . . killed the agent. . . .

AGENT: Easy, son. I'll help you out of the saddle.

RIDER: Never mind me . . . take the mail . . . this message from the President.

BUFFALO BILL: I got it, son. Run, Pony! We're late.

AGENT: Look sharp for Indians, Bill!

NARRATOR: Buffalo Bill galloped away, and just nine days and two hours after Johnny Frey had galloped westward out of St. Joseph, Missouri, a great crowd was gathered in the streets of Carson City, Nevada, near the post office and telegraph terminal. The crowd was waiting for the arrival of Buffalo Bill and the end of the first run of the Pony Express. A great cheer went up as Buffalo Bill galloped up to the post office. The message from the President to Governor Downey was safely delivered. Speed and endurance of man and beast . . . courage and devotion to duty . . . brought the Atlantic and Pacific shores within nine days of each other.

But in the fall of 1860, while the Pony Express was relaying messages across the lonely deserts of the west, this once marvelous speed began to seem an intolerable delay. Edward Creighton, an engineer, undertook to survey a telegraph route between California and the Missouri River. The Pacific Telegraph Company, incorporated by the legislature of the Territory of Nebraska, broke ground on July 4, 1861. Four working parties were sent out from central points with a thousand oxen hauling poles and wire. They had thirteen months to do the job, but they had completed the entire two thousand miles of line by November. And on the 15th of that month in the year 1861, little more than a year after Johnny Frey's first run on the Pony Express, the first telegraph message was sent across the country. And this message, sent to President Lincoln by Chief Justice Stephen J. Field of California, spelled the finish of the Pony Express. At this time Lieutenant Maury was making a survey of the ocean depths for the United States Navy. Cyrus W. Field, a man of vision, read the report. The report showed that between Newfoundland and Ireland, the ocean bottom was a plateau at no very great depth. The thought came to Field —"Why not carry a telegraph line across the ocean?" . . . But his desire to do this was stronger than any cable he could find, as his partner in the venture pointed out. . . .

Mr. Blockley: Field, your cable broke twice in 1857 and many times in 1858.

Cyrus W. Field: Nevertheless, Mr. Blockley, I propose we try again— and again—until we succeed.

Mr. Blockley: Now look here, Field. I've backed you a dozen times, but all these repeated failures . . . Well, I think we've dropped enough money to the bottom of the Atlantic.

Cyrus W. Field: We had it working for three weeks in 1858.

Mr. Blockley: It'll have to last longer than that to get our money back. And I won't throw more good money after bad.

Cyrus W. Field: But we've improved our cable and have better equipment to lay it. I'm convinced we can succeed. But if we quit now, we are sure to fail.

Mr. Blockley: The whole thing's nothing but a pipe dream. I won't even hear it discussed. You're a fool, Field. And a fool and his money are soon parted. That won't include me this time. Good day to you, sir!

Narrator: Blockley's withdrawal did not stop Field, though Field was forced to use English money and a ship from the English navy. Still, it was a difficult task. In 1865, after laying 1200 miles of new cable, the ship gave a lurch and the cable broke. But Field kept on, and in the summer of 1866, they were able to grapple the cable, splice it, and carry it the remaining 600 miles to Newfoundland. At last the transatlantic cable was successfully completed. One day a curious meeting between Cyrus Field and Mr. Blockley occurred in Field's office. . . .

CYRUS W. FIELD: Well, Blockley, this is unexpected. What can I do for *you?*

MR. BLOCKLEY: If you knew what it costs my pride to come here—but I'm in trouble. Desperate.

CYRUS W. FIELD: Compose yourself, man.

MR. BLOCKLEY: Compose myself! Field, unless I can reach my agent in London before the next packet arrives—I am a ruined man.

CYRUS W. FIELD: Well, the transatlantic cable is for everyone's use.

MR. BLOCKLEY: But at present rates, it would cost me nearly $7000 to send my instructions. I can't possibly put my hands on so much cash.

CYRUS W. FIELD: What do you want me to do?

MR. BLOCKLEY: Send that message for me. I'll pay you back twice over in a month.

CYRUS W. FIELD: You're sure it won't be sending good money after bad?

MR. BLOCKLEY: Please don't remind me of that. I've bitterly regretted my lack of faith in you and the cable.

CYRUS W. FIELD: Is your message ready?

MR. BLOCKLEY: Yes.

CYRUS W. FIELD: We'll send it at once.

MR. BLOCKLEY: You've saved my entire fortune! How can I ever repay you?

CYRUS W. FIELD: By subscribing to the cost of laying a new cable, American owned and operated.

MR. BLOCKLEY: Done! And gladly!

NARRATOR: But the telegraph was neither quick enough nor convenient enough. Not everyone knew the Morse Code. Business men had to use messenger service to the terminals, and replies were not always prompt. A conversation from office to office might take many hours, even days. Then, on March 10, 1876, on the top floor of a boardinghouse on Exeter Place in Boston, Alexander Graham Bell was working with his assistant, Thomas Watson. Bell had been making experiments, hoping to be able to transmit the human voice by wire. Watson had built a new transmitter according to Bell's instructions.

ALEXANDER BELL: Now, Mr. Watson, if you will take this receiver down the hall to my bedroom—and fasten it to the other end of the wire—

THOMAS WATSON: I will, Mr. Bell. Shall I move these batteries first? Are they in your way?

ALEXANDER BELL: No, they're all right—nothing but water and a little acid. And close all the doors between. I want a real test.

THOMAS WATSON: I won't be long. (*Door closes.*)

ALEXANDER BELL: Let me see—what shall I say—something that will be a real test—something unexpected—I'll—(*sound of batteries falling—glass breaking*) Those confounded batteries — Mr. Watson! — Come here!—I want you—Mr. Watson, come here, I want you—(*Door opens.*)

THOMAS WATSON (*astonished*): Mr. Bell, I heard every word you said!

ALEXANDER BELL: I wasn't testing the instrument! I knocked over the batteries and spilled the acid on my clothes! I was calling you—

THOMAS WATSON: But I heard— every word — distinctly — through the telephone!

NARRATOR: The telephone slowly but surely spread its wire over the country. Soon after 1880, hard-drawn copper wire was invented. By 1902, the first long-distance cable was in use between New York and Newark, ten miles away. But already ways and means were found to send words without the use of any wires whatever! . . . By wireless. On December 12, 1901, American newspapers carried the thrilling headline: "OCEAN SPANNED BY WIRELESS." . . . An enterprising reporter sought out Thomas A. Edison. . . .

REPORTER: Mr. Edison, my paper wants a statement from you.

THOMAS A. EDISON: What about?

REPORTER: Marconi's great achievement. . . . In St. John, Nova Scotia, he has received the call signal "S" sent from Cornwall in England.

THOMAS A. EDISON: I don't believe it. He's only experimenting to pick up calls from transatlantic liners on the Grand Banks, 300 miles out. . . . Cornwall is 1700 miles from Nova Scotia.

REPORTER: Here is a message we got from him. It says: "Confirm that signals were received here Thursday and Friday direct from Cornwall. Receiving wire suspended by a kite. Signed, Marconi."

THOMAS A. EDISON: Well, since Marconi has stated over his own signature that he has received the signals from England, I believe him, and I think he'll carry it to a commercial success. It's a great achievement, and he's a great experimenter... and that's signed, Edison!

NARRATOR: The very next year, 1902, in Fairmount Park, Philadelphia, an inventor named Nathan B. Stubblefield gave the first public demonstration of an instrument which sent the voice through the air without wires. His voice was heard a mile away. But, fearing to tell his secret to the world until his patent had been granted in 1908, he lost the fame that comes from acclaimed priority. Nevertheless, the wireless and radio developed side by side. In 1909 came the first famous rescue by wireless. Jack Irwin, a radio operator at Siasconset on Nantucket Island, picked up "C.Q.D.," which was then the distress signal, from the S. S. *Republic*, which was going down with 1500 people on board.

The United States Navy began to build the first high-powered radio station at Arlington near the National Capitol. Dr. Lee De Forest invented the "audion," or vacuum tube, and the modern age of speed and communication was on its way. Invention followed invention at a breathless pace. In 1915, a message was broadcast from Arlington and picked up in Paris, and in Honolulu, 5000 miles away.

On December 8, 1929, came the first historic conversation between a voice at sea and a voice on shore. In 1930, by short-wave radio, a voice encircled the entire globe. It traveled in relays from Station W2XAD in Schenectady, New York, via Honolulu, to Java and Australia, thence across the Pacific to North America, and back again to Schenectady . . . in just one eighth of a second!

Today, the human voice can be heard via the radio from the north and the south poles. Sports commentators can bring us play-by-play descriptions of games being played thousands of miles from our hearing. Police squads can be directed to the capture of fleeing criminals. Weather reports can be relayed instantly to all parts of the world; reports of disasters can be flashed without the waste of a second, to waiting rescue parties. Airplanes can be landed in the dark, in dense fog, and in blinding storms by directions given from landing fields. Surgeons on shore have actually directed operations at sea! The human voice has now found the ends of the earth!

❖❖❖

Tracing the Steps to Conclusions

1. By what steps has the "speed of words" been accomplished?
2. What has caused inventors to search for faster methods of communication?
3. How has each invention been part of a chain?
4. How has the world grown "smaller" with each invention?

Intelligent Guessing

Can you guess the meaning of each word in italics by the way it is used?
1. . . . this once marvelous speed began to seem an *intolerable* delay.
2. . . . the ocean bottom was a *plateau* at no very great depth.
3. . . . the ship gave a *lurch* and the cable broke.
4. Bell had been making experiments, hoping to be able to *transmit* the human voice by wire.
5. An *enterprising* reporter sought out Thomas A. Edison.

Atoms for Peace

As this article points out, the United States is leading the world in harnessing the atom for productive work. (Note the time when you begin reading.)

THE ATOM, symbol of man's fears today, is likewise the bright star of his highest hopes. A simple formula spells out the atom's awesome power for destruction. But the same formula may hold the key to man's eternal dream of peace and plenty.

Fulfillment of this dream of peace is perhaps closer than we realize. For the first great step toward making the dream real has been taken in the United States. There has been a shift of emphasis from the atom as destroyer to the atom as producer. Our best-informed atomic authorities have saluted this development. They hail it as potentially the best guarantee of peace on earth.

The harnessing of atomic energy for peaceful purposes has been the ultimate aim of U. S. policy ever since the secret of the atom was unlocked. When the atomic explosions over Japan wrote a thunderous finale to the tragedy of World War II, men of good will throughout the world hoped that a new age had dawned. They looked forward to the day when the miraculous power of the atom would be used for peace, not war.

What is the hope? What is the promise contained in the use of the atom as a source of power?

——Condensed from an article, "Atoms for Peace," in *Senior Scholastic*. Copyright, 1953, by permission of Scholastic Corporation.

The story begins one day about four years ago in a stone house at Arco, Idaho. In the house, a group of scientists clustered around a very commonplace object—an unlighted electric bulb. One of the men slowly turned a valve. The others kept their eyes glued to the bulb. Suddenly excited exclamations burst from their lips. The bulb glowed with light. For the first time in history, the atom had been used as a source of controlled electric power.

The glowing bulb at Arco marked the dawn of a new era as surely as did the first practical application of electricity, or the invention of the steam engine. It meant that a new, primary source of power had been harnessed and a vast, economic revolution was in prospect.

It took little imagination to recognize that if a few pounds of uranium could produce power comparable to hundreds of thousands of tons of coal or millions of gallons of oil, man's life on earth might be transformed. Deserts could be made to bloom. Factories could spring up where only primitive workshops had existed before. The relentless struggle for existence among millions of peoples of the earth—a struggle that is at the root of much international strife—might be eased beyond the fondest dreams of social visionaries.

The device used at Arco to take the power locked in the atom and convert it to electric current is known as an atomic reactor. A reactor is essentially the graphite honeycomb in which the famous controlled chain reaction takes place when uranium is introduced.

The chain reaction produces heat. From there on, the rest is comparatively easy. The heat is used to convert water into steam. The steam drives an ordinary turbine, The spinning turbine can be harnessed to do anything from producing electric current for a bulb to turning a ship's propeller. The atomic engine installed in the U. S. Navy's submarine *Nautilus*, in fact, is the same kind of mechanism as the one developed at Arco.

The nuclear plant will be a large-scale version of the Arco reactor. It will be capable of producing electric power for industrial use. The plant is to be built at one of the Government's three main atomic installations at Oak Ridge, Tenn., Paducah, Ky., or Portsmouth, Ohio. It will produce a minimum of 60,000 kilowatts of electricity—enough to supply a city of about 75,000 population.

The electricity will be used at the atomic installation itself. It may be put to work driving the hundreds of pumps used in the refinement of uranium, for example. Or it may be harnessed to light the homes and run the radios and TV sets of the thousands of workers at the atomic installations.

Atomic experts have little doubt that eventually the goal will be attained. They are far from discouraged by the present high cost of atomic electricity. They compare the current stage in the development of nuclear power to the early days of the steam engine and the automobile. Neither of these new inventions seemed economically feasible at first. Both were ridiculed by "practical" men.

Our atomic experts are confident that the Government's first nuclear power plant will show the way to new and better plants. It will bring ever closer the day when atomic electricity will make present-day fuels and sources of power seem as outmoded as the treadmill.

The prospect was eloquently expressed by Mr. Thomas E. Murray, a member of the U.S. Atomic Energy Commission, when he said:

"For years the splitting atom packaged in weapons has been our main shield against the barbarians—now, in addition, it is to become a God-given instrument to do the constructive work of mankind."

(Note the time. Check your reading rate with the Reading Score Board, page 392.)

COMPREHENSION CHECK

On your paper, write *True* or *False* for each of these statements:

1. The harnessing of atomic energy for peaceful purposes has been the aim of the United States.
2. One interesting experiment took place in Arco, Idaho.
3. In Arco, atomic energy gave the power for a television program.
4. Uranium instead of coal or oil can produce power.
5. Factories will not be able to use atomic energy.
6. The U.S. Navy's submarine *Nautilus* is atomic-powered.
7. A nuclear plant will be built in New York or Los Angeles.
8. The plant will produce enough electricity for a city of 75,000.
9. Experts are discouraged by the present high cost of atomic electricity.
10. Atomic experts believe that the Government's first nuclear power plant will show the way to new and better plants.

READING RATE

You probably noticed that you read the article much more slowly than you read a light piece of fiction. How do you account for this slower rate of reading? What other kinds of material require slower and more careful reading?

READING SCORE BOARD

Number of Words in Article: 820

Number of Minutes	8 1/5	4 1/10	3 1/3	2 3/4	2	1 3/5
Reading Rate	100 w.p.m.	200 w.p.m.	250 w.p.m.	300 w.p.m.	400 w.p.m.	500 w.p.m.

ORGANIZED THINKING

In reading articles such as "Atoms for Peace," you should train yourself to look for the blueprint of thinking. For example, can you state the main idea of each paragraph in "Atoms for Peace"? Find the topic sentences. Do the other sentences in each paragraph help to develop the topic sentence? Can you point out a paragraph that is made up of only one sentence?

Here are the first two paragraphs in outline form. Can you outline the rest of the article?

    I. The atom—fear and hope
        A. Power for destruction
        B. Power for peace and plenty
    II. Dream of peace closer
        A. First step taken in the United States
        B. Shift in emphasis from destroyer to producer
        C. Attitude of atomic experts
            1. New emphasis hailed
            2. New emphasis best guarantee of peace

Atomic Words

What does each of these words mean?

atom	uranium	nuclear
energy	reaction	splitting (of atom)

◀€ Candace Thurber Stevenson

Signatures

Even poets are concerned with the fearful problem of the atom. What is the point of view of this poet?

My fathers wrote their names in sweat
On forest and on farming land.
Each ax and plowshare, hard to get,
Spelled out a purpose in their hand.

My brothers wrote their names in steel.
Huge buildings rose at their desire;
They hitched explosion to a wheel
And harnessed lightning to a wire.

On air my children wrought their will.
Gaily they rode from cloud to cloud,
And if they dropped destruction, still
They liked their writing and were proud.

Their children sign their names in yet
More grimly catastrophic terms—
An elemental alphabet
Of splintered atom, stalking germs.

——Copyright, 1950, by American Mercury. From the book *First the Blade* by Candace Thurber Stevenson. Published by E. P. Dutton & Co., Inc.

◀€ David E. Lilienthal

This I Do Believe

As former Chairman of the United States Atomic Energy Commission, the author of this article speaks with insight concerning a world problem.

Back of the dramatic discovery of atomic energy is a long history of generation after generation of inquiring minds, restlessly questioning, testing, doubting, probing, seeking the truth about the nature of the physical world.

Was this release of the basic energy of matter an event over which we should rejoice, or should we tremble with apprehension that man had at

——From *This I Do Believe* by David E. Lilienthal, published by Harper & Brothers. Copyright, 1949, by David E. Lilienthal.

last let out of the bottle an evil jinni too powerful to be tamed? We are not yet in a position to judge of this question, for the time has been far too short. We would not say today that the discovery of fire is to be regretted. There is hardly a force more beneficent in the life of man. When fire is out of control, however, it can and does cause catastrophes of the most horrible kind. We have learned to live with fire. Indeed, we can hardly imagine our civilization in its best aspects without it. If, however, the only time we had ever seen fire was in battle, pouring out of a flame thrower, consuming human life, or dropped from airplanes to burn to a cinder a city of a million people, could we be sure that it had been a good discovery?

Whatever answer the future holds, this much I believe we must accept: There can be no putting the jinni back into the bottle. To try to bury or to suppress new knowledge because we do not know how to prevent its use for destructive or evil purposes is a pathetically futile gesture. It is, indeed, a symbolic return to the methods of the Middle Ages. It seeks to deny the innermost urge of the mind of man— the desire for knowledge.

Greater knowledge about the world will, I think, be the keynote of the immediate future. But greater knowledge alone will not be enough. There must also be greater love and understanding among men. And there must also be greater faith in humankind and in the purposes of the Creator of the Universe. Knowledge, love, faith— with these three the atomic age, the age in which we live, can become an age of mercy, of joy, and of hope, one of the blessed periods of all history.

There is open before us an unparalleled opportunity to build new and firmer foundations under our feet. We stand at the gateway of an age of expansion, of the flowering of modern imagination and the new skills and knowledge of mankind.

The task ahead may prove to be the boldest and most stirring adventure of the human spirit since the circumnavigation of the globe. That will be true if it can release a flood of pent-up genius, not alone in our works of hands and skills in management but in the development of the free spirit.

The necessary skills of organization and technology exist today, but this is not to say that it is automatic or inevitable that they will be used for an age of creation. We must have the will to set out boldly on the adventure, the resolution to begin from where we are. We need the will and the faith, we need a sense that *this* is the historic hour to turn the first shovel, to take the first steps.

◆◖◆

◆◖ TIME TO ANALYZE

The article you have just read is packed with thought from beginning to end. Consequently, you undoubtedly read it more slowly and carefully.

1. In one sentence can you state the main idea of the article?
2. Next analyze each of the paragraphs. What is the main idea of each?

3. Notice the length of some of Mr. Lilienthal's sentences. Do they cause you any reading difficulty?

4. Compare and contrast the article with "Atoms for Peace" on pages 390 and 391.

5. Next compare and contrast it with "Signatures" on page 393.

6. To what conclusions have you come?

MASTERING WORDS

Choose the word or phrase that most nearly defines each word in italics:

1. *probing:* (a) proving (b) answering (c) examining
2. *apprehension:* (a) dread (b) disgust (c) disdain
3. *jinni:* (a) supernatural being (b) master (c) ghost
4. *beneficent:* (a) harmful (b) helpful (c) terrifying
5. *catastrophes:* (a) casualties (b) occurrences (c) disasters
6. *aspects:* (a) appearances (b) aspirations (c) inspirations
7. *suppress:* (a) repress (b) encourage (c) surprise
8. *futile:* (a) useful (b) useless (c) used
9. *inevitable:* (a) indistinct (b) unpleasant (c) unavoidable
10. *resolution:* (a) revolution (b) determination (c) thought

◀ RICHARD E. BYRD

Alone

The last group of articles in this chapter deals with several aspects of the world of nature. The first tells the story of a man who was willing to risk his life to find out some of the secrets of *weather*.

Science sometimes takes people to strange and far-off places. In 1934 Richard E. Byrd settled himself at the very bottom of the world to spend five months alone. The rest of his Antarctic Expedition was 123 miles away, at Little America. The purpose of Byrd's experiment was to collect scientific information concerning the weather. The experiment almost cost him his life. (Note the time when you begin reading.)

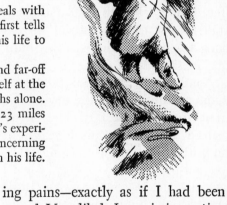

OUT of the deepening darkness came the cold. On May 19th, when I took the usual walk, the temperature was 65° below zero. For the first time the canvas boots failed to protect my feet. One heel was nipped, and I was forced to return to the hunt and change to reindeer mukluks.[1] That day I felt miserable; my body was racked by shoot-ing pains—exactly as if I had been gassed. Very likely I was; in inspecting the ventilator pipes next morning I discovered that the intake pipe was completely clogged with rime[2] and that the outlet pipe was two thirds full.

Next day—Sunday the 20th—was the coldest yet. The minimum thermometer dropped to 72° below zero; the inside thermograph,[3] which al-

[1] *mukluks.* Fur boots.

——From *Alone*, by Richard E. Byrd. Copyright, 1938, by Richard E. Byrd. Courtesy of G. P. Putnam's Sons.

[2] *rime.* White frost.

[3] *thermograph.* A thermometer that is self-registering.

ways read a bit lower than the instruments in the shelter, stood at —74°; and the thermograph in the shelter was stopped dead—the ink, though well laced with glycerin, and the lubricant were both frozen. So violently did the air in the fuel tank expand after the stove was lit that oil went shooting all over the place; to insulate the tank against similar temperature spreads I wrapped around it the rubber air cushion which by some lucky error had been included among my gear. In the glow of a flashlight the vapor rising from the stovepipe and the outlet ventilator looked like the discharge from two steam engines. My fingers agonized over the thermograph, and I was hours putting it to rights. The fuel wouldn't flow from the drums; I had to take one inside and heat it near the stove. All day long I kept two primus stoves burning in the tunnel.

Sunday the 20th also brought a radio schedule; I had the devil's own time trying to meet it. The engine balked for an hour; my fingers were so brittle and frostbitten from tinkering with the carburetor that, when I actually made contact with Little America, I could scarcely work the key. "Ask Haines come on," was my first request. While Hutcheson searched the tunnels of Little America for the Senior Meteorologist,[4] I chatted briefly with Charlie Murphy. Little America claimed only —60°. "But we're moving the brass monkeys below," Charlie advised.

"Seventy-one below here now," I said.

"You can have it," was the closing comment from the north.

Then Bill Haines's merry voice sounded in the earphones. I explained the difficulty with the thermograph. "Same trouble we've had," Bill said. "It's probably due to frozen oil. I'd suggest you bring the instrument inside, and try soaking it in gasoline, to cut whatever oil traces remain. Then rinse it in ether. As for the ink's freezing, you might try adding more glycerin." Bill was in a jovial mood. "Look at me, Admiral," he boomed. "I never have any trouble with the instruments. The trick is in having an ambitious and docile assistant." I really chuckled over that because I knew, from the first expedition, what Grimminger, the Junior Meteorologist, was going through: Bill, with his back to the fire and blandishment on his tongue, persuading the recruit that duty and the opportunity for self-improvement required him to go up into the blizzard to fix a balky trace; Bill humming to himself in the warmth of a shack while the assistant in an open pit kept a theodolite[5] trained on the sounding balloon soaring into the night, and stuttered into a telephone the different vernier[6] readings from which Bill was calculating the velocities and directions of the upper air currents.

That day I rather wished that I, too, had an assistant. He would have

---

[4] *Meteorologist.* A scientist specializing in weather, especially the variations of heat, moisture, winds.

[5] *theodolite.* An instrument used to measure horizontal and vertical angles.

[6] *vernier.* A small device used to make fine calculations.

taken his turn on the anemometer[7] pole, no mistake. The frost in the iron cleats went through the fur soles of the mukluks, and froze the balls of my feet. My breath made little explosive sounds on the wind; my lungs, already sore, seemed to shrivel when I breathed.

Seldom had the aurora[8] flamed more brilliantly. For hours the night danced to its frenetic excitement. And at times the sound of Barrier quakes was like that of heavy guns. My tongue was swollen and sore from drinking scalding hot tea, and the tip of my nose ached from frostbite. A big wind, I guessed, would come out of this still cold; it behooved me to look to my roof. I carried gallons of water topside, and poured it around the edges of the shack. It froze almost as soon as it hit. The ice was an armor plating over the packed drift.

At midnight, when I clambered topside for an auroral "ob,"[9] a wild sense of suffocation came over me the instant I pushed my shoulders through the trap door. My lungs gasped, but no air reached them. Bewildered and perhaps a little frightened, I slid down the ladder and lunged into the shack. In the warm air the feeling passed as quickly as it had come. Curious but cautious, I again made my way up the ladder. And again the same thing happened; I lost my breath, but I perceived why. A light air was moving down from eastward; and its bitter touch, when I faced into it, was constricting the

breathing passages. So I turned my face away from it, breathing into my glove; and in that attitude finished the "ob." Before going below, I made an interesting experiment. I put a thermometer on the snow, let it lie there awhile, and discovered that the temperature at the surface was actually 5° colder than at the level of the instrument shelter, four feet higher. Reading in the sleeping bag afterwards, I froze one finger, although I shifted the book steadily from one hand to the other, slipping the unoccupied hand into the warmth of the bag.

Out of the cold and out of the east came the wind. It came on gradually, as if the sheer weight of the cold were almost too much to be moved. On the night of the 21st the barometer started down. The night was black as a thunderhead when I made my first trip topside; and a tension in the wind, a bulking of shadows in the night, indicated that a new storm center was forming.

Next morning, glad of an excuse to stay underground, I worked a long time on the Escape Tunnel by the light of a red candle standing in a snow recess. That day I pushed the emergency exit to a distance of twenty-two feet, the farthest it was ever to go. My stint done, I sat down on a box, thinking how beautiful was the red of the candle, how white the rough-hewn snow.

Soon I became aware of an increasing clatter of the anemometer cups. Realizing that the wind was picking up, I went topside to make sure that everything was secured. It is a queer

---

[7] *anemometer.* A wind gauge.

[8] *aurora.* Aurora borealis, rays of light made by electricity in the air; northern lights.

[9] *"ob."* Observation.

experience to watch a blizzard rise. First there is the wind, rising out of nowhere. Then the Barrier unwrenches itself from quietude; and the surface, which just before had seemed as hard and polished as metal, begins to run like a making sea. Sometimes, if the wind strikes hard, the drift comes across the Barrier like a hurrying white cloud, tossed hundreds of feet in the air. Other times the growth is gradual. You become conscious of a general slithering movement on all sides. The air fills with tiny scraping and sliding and rustling sounds as the first loose crystals stir. In a little while they are moving as solidly as an incoming tide, which creams over the ankles, then surges to the waist, and finally is at the throat. I have walked in drift so thick as not to be able to see a foot ahead of me; yet, when I glanced up, I could see the stars shining through the thin layer just overhead.

Smoking tendrils were creeping up the anemometer pole when I finished my inspection. I hurriedly made the trap door fast, as a sailor might batten down a hatch; and knowing that my ship was well secured, I retired to the cabin to ride out the storm. It could not reach me, hidden deep in the Barrier crust; nevertheless the sounds came down. The gale sobbed in the ventilators, shook the stovepipe until I thought it would be jerked out by the roots, pounded the roof with sledge-hammer blows. I could actually feel the suction effect through the pervious snow. A breeze flickered in the room and the tunnels. The candles wavered and went out. My only light was the feeble storm lantern.

Even so, I didn't have any idea how really bad it was until I went aloft for an observation. As I pushed back the trap door, the drift met me like a moving wall. It was only a few steps from the ladder to the instrument shelter, but it seemed more like a mile. The air came at me in snowy rushes; I breasted it as I might a heavy surf. No night had ever seemed so dark. The beam from the flashlight was choked in its throat; I could not see my hand before my face.

My windproofs were caked with drift by the time I got below. I had a vague feeling that something had changed while I was gone, but what, I couldn't tell. Presently I noticed that the shack was appreciably colder. Raising the stove lid, I was surprised to find that the fire was out, though the tank was half full. I decided that I must have turned off the valve unconsciously before going aloft; but, when I put a match to the burner, the draught down the pipe blew out the flame. The wind, then, must have killed the fire. I got it going again and watched it carefully.

The blizzard vaulted to gale force. Above the roar the deep, taut thrumming note of the radio antenna and the anemometer guy wires reminded me of wind in a ship's rigging. The wind-direction trace turned scratchy on the sheet; no doubt drift had short-circuited the electric contacts, I decided. Realizing that it was hopeless to attempt to try to keep them clear, I let the instrument be.

There were other ways of getting

the wind direction. I tied a handkerchief to a bamboo pole and ran it through the outlet ventilator; with a flashlight I could tell which way the cloth was whipped. I did this at hourly intervals, noting any change of direction on the sheet. But by 2 o'clock in the morning I had had enough of this periscope sighting. If I expected to sleep and at the same time maintain the continuity of the records, I had no choice but to clean the contact points.

The wind was blowing hard then. The Barrier shook from the concussions overhead; and the noise was as if the entire physical world were tearing itself to pieces. I could scarcely heave the trap door open. The instant it came clear I was plunged into a blinding smother. I came out crawling, clinging to the handle of the door until I made sure of my bearings. Then I let the door fall shut, not wanting the tunnel filled with drift. To see was impossible. Millions of tiny pellets exploded in my eyes, stinging like BB shot. It was even hard to breathe, because snow instantly clogged the mouth and nostrils. I made my way toward the anemometer pole on hands and knees, scared that I might be bowled off my feet if I stood erect; one false step, and I should be lost forever.

I found the pole all right; but not until my head collided with a cleat. I managed to climb it, too, though ten million ghosts were tearing at me, ramming their thumbs into my eyes. But the errand was useless. Drift as thick as this would mess up the contact points as quickly as they were cleared; besides, the wind cups were spinning so fast that I stood a good chance of losing a couple of fingers in the process. Coming down the pole, I had a sense of being whirled violently through the air, with no control over my movements. The trap door was completely buried when I found it again, after scraping around for some time with my mittens. I pulled at the handle, first with one hand, then with both. It did not give. It's a tight fit, anyway, I mumbled to myself. The drift has probably wedged the corners. Standing astride the hatch, I braced myself and heaved with all my strength. I might just as well have tried hoisting the Barrier. Panic took me then, I must confess. Reason fled. I clawed at the three-foot square of timber like a madman. I beat on it with my fists, trying to shake the snow loose; and, when that did no good, I lay flat on my belly and pulled until my hands went weak from cold and weariness. Then I crooked my elbow, put my face down, and said over and over again, You fool, you fool. Here for weeks I had been defending myself against the danger of being penned inside the shack; instead, I was now locked out; and nothing could be worse, especially since I had only a wool parka and pants under my windproofs. Just two feet below was sanctuary—warmth, food, tools, all the means of survival. All these things were an arm's length away, but I was powerless to reach them.

There is something extravagantly insensate about an Antarctic blizzard at night. Its vindictiveness cannot be measured on an anemometer sheet. It is more than just wind: it is a solid wall of snow moving at gale force, pounding like surf. Because of this blinding, suffocating drift, in the Antarctic winds of only moderate velocity have the punishing force of full-fledged hurricanes elsewhere. The whole malevolent rush is concentrated upon you as upon a personal enemy. In the senseless explosion of sound you are reduced to a crawling thing on the margin of a disintegrating world; you can't see, you can't hear, you can hardly move. The lungs gasp after the air is sucked out of them, and the brain is shaken. Nothing in the world will so quickly isolate a man.

Half frozen, I stabbed toward one of the ventilators, a few feet away. My mittens touched something round and cold. Cupping it in my hands, I pulled myself up. This was the outlet ventilator. Just why, I don't know— but instinct made me kneel and press my face against the opening. Nothing in the room was visible, but a dim patch of light illuminated the floor, and warmth rose up to my face. That steadied me.

Still kneeling, I turned my back to the blizzard and considered what might be done. I thought of breaking in the windows in the roof, but they lay two feet down in hard crust and were reinforced with wire besides. If I only had something to dig with, I could break the crust and stamp the windows in with my feet. The pipe cupped between my hands supplied the first inspiration; maybe I could use that to dig with. It, too, was wedged tight; I pulled until my arms ached, without budging it; I had lost all track of time, and the despairing thought came to me that I was lost in a task without an end. Then I remembered the shovel. A week before, after leveling drift from the last light blow, I had stabbed a shovel handle up in the crust somewhere to leeward. That shovel would save me. But how to find it in the avalanche of the blizzard?

I lay down and stretched out full length. Still holding the pipe, I thrashed around with my feet, but pummeled only empty air. Then I worked back to the hatch. The hard edges at the opening provided another grip, and again I stretched out and kicked. Again no luck. I dared not let go until I had something else familiar to cling to. My foot came up against the other ventilator pipe. I edged back to that, and from the new anchorage repeated the maneuver. This time my ankle struck something hard. When I felt it and recognized the handle, I wanted to caress it.

Embracing this thrice-blessed tool, I inched back to the trap door. The handle of the shovel was just small enough to pass under the little wooden bridge which served as a grip. I got both hands on the shovel and tried to wrench the door up; my strength was not enough, however. So I lay down flat on my belly and worked my shoulders under the shovel. Then I heaved, the door sprang open, and I rolled down the shaft. When I tumbled into the light and warmth of the room, I kept thinking, How wonderful, how perfectly wonderful.

(Note the time, and check your speed of reading with the **Reading Score Board**.)

COLD FACTS

1. What facts about the weather was Byrd trying to discover?
2. What did he have to do to get these facts?
3. Of what value could knowledge of weather conditions at the South Pole be?
4. What hardships did Byrd suffer for the sake of science?

YOUR CONCLUSIONS

1. Is it right for a person to endanger his life as Byrd did?
2. Were his findings of sufficient value to justify the hardships?
3. Should America try to develop the Arctic and the Antarctic?
4. Could there be any danger in neglecting those parts of the world?

SEEING, HEARING, FEELING

Byrd has the ability to write the kind of sentences which make the reader see and hear and feel. Here are a few. Find a number of others which appeal to the senses.

1. Out of the deepening darkness came the cold.
2. My lungs gasped, but no air reached them.
3. The night was as black as a thunderhead.
4. Sometimes, if the wind strikes hard, the drift comes across the Barrier like a hurrying white cloud, tossed hundreds of feet in the air.
5. The gale sobbed in the ventilators.

UNDERSTANDING THROUGH CONTEXT

There were probably many words that you were not sure about, but from the general sense you guessed their meaning. What do you think the words in italics in these groups mean? They all appear in the first two paragraphs of the story.

1. One heel was nipped, and I was forced to return to the hut and change to reindeer *mukluks*.
2. the intake pipe was completely clogged with *rime*
3. the inside *thermograph*, which always read a bit lower than the instruments in the shelter,
4. the ink, though well *laced* with glycerin,
5. My fingers *agonized* over the thermograph,

Do the same thing with unfamiliar words in other paragraphs. Check your guesses with the dictionary.

READING SCORE BOARD

Number of Words in Story: 2730

Number of Minutes	27	13 1/2	11	9	6 3/4	5 1/2
Reading Rate	100 w.p.m.	200 w.p.m.	250 w.p.m.	300 w.p.m.	400 w.p.m.	500 w.p.m.

"Three Miles a Minute—Down!"

Six miles up, 46 degrees below zero—and a man steps out into the sky. Here is the story of another breathtaking experiment for the sake of science.

ONE CLOUDY DAY in October a daring parachutist, Arthur Starnes, bailed out of a transport plane six miles up in the Chicago sky, dropped like a rock for five and a half miles, pulled his rip cords, and floated to the ground. Starnes set a new world's record for the longest free fall ever survived by man. But more than that, his brief, clearheaded remarks gave literature its first account of how it feels to fall for miles through space.

Shortly after noon, Starnes boarded a Lockheed Lodestar, one of the few commercial planes in the country capable of flying above 25,000 feet. For an hour and 50 minutes the silvery monoplane spiraled into the sky —climbing, climbing. At 30,000 feet the plane leveled off. Starnes stepped to the door.

As the purpose of the jump was to provide data for the Army Air Corps, Starnes was burdened with 85 pounds of equipment. He wore a chute on his back, another on his chest. His coverall suit was electrically heated, with batteries in the hip pocket. There were headphones in his chamois helmet. His oxygen bottle was in a pocket on his right foreleg. A tiny radio transmitter strapped around his waist broadcast his heartbeats. On his chest, protected by an aluminum plate, were

——From Associated Press dispatch (Wide World Publications Division) in *The New York Times*, as reprinted in *The Reader's Digest*.

a cardiograph to register heart action, a pneumograph to record breathing, and a barograph to record air-pressure changes. An automatic motion-picture camera was strapped to his right hip, pointed downward.

At 30,000 feet the plane was barely distinguishable to watchers on the ground. Flying fast, it crossed the airport. Soon afterward listeners on a portable ground radio station heard a muffled "All clear" from Starnes's midget transmitter—the signal agreed upon that he had jumped out into the 46-below-zero cold.

"I had only two moments of fear," Starnes panted to the crowd in the cow pasture where he landed four and a quarter minutes later.

"The first was as I stood in the open door of the plane, trying to get enough oxygen inside my helmet and wondering if my equipment would clear the door frame. But the second, more frantic sensation was when my goggles frosted up in a cloud bank at 23,000 feet and my body went into a series of violent spins and somersaults.

"I threw my legs far apart and then crossed them alternately. That usually pulls me out of a body spin. But it had no effect this time. My head was clear, and I began counting to myself. I knew I was falling about 250 feet a second. When almost half a minute had elapsed, I felt I must raise my goggles and look at my altimeter."

The instrument was strapped to his wrist. He raised it to his cheek, lifted one lens in his helmet to see the long, slender needle. It pointed to 15,000 feet. After counting four or five he glanced at it again, pushing the goggles up so that he could see with both eyes. At about 5000 feet the frost evaporated, leaving the goggles clear.

"I knew the worst was over then," he said.

He finally righted his body by holding his right arm out sidewise, like a railroad signal. At 1500 feet he opened his back chute, and "blacked out" momentarily from the jolt. He now became visible for the first time to spectators on the ground. Three seconds later they saw his chest chute open. He alighted. By the time attendants reached him he was on his feet, helmet removed, grinning.

A stop watch attached to the parachute lines showed the free fall lasted one minute, 56 seconds. Starnes' top speed probably reached 180 m.p.h. A gloomy statistician calculated that if Starnes had not opened his chute at 1500 feet, he would have struck the earth in six more seconds.

❖❖❖

Getting Information Dangerously

1. What relationship is there between "Three Miles a Minute—Down!" and the story by Admiral Byrd?
2. What different kinds of information was Starnes getting?
3. What were his two moments of fear?
4. What might have happened to him? Cite the passage that gives that information.

A Right to Your Own Decision

If someone in authority asked you to take the jump that Starnes took, what would be your answer? What facts would bring you to the conclusion to jump or not to jump? Give your step-by-step reasoning pro or con.

✦← CHARLIE MAY SIMON

John James Audubon

John James Audubon is remembered for his beautiful pictures of the birds of America. Because his pictures are so exact and because he pictured not only the common but also the rare birds of this country, Audubon is also considered as a scientist. He is called an ornithologist, which is a big word meaning "one who specializes in birds."

(Jot down the time when you begin reading.)

A TALL, slender youth of eighteen stood at the prow of a sailing vessel and watched the gulls fly out from the west. It meant that land was near. For weeks, since he had left his home in France, he had seen nothing but the gray ocean and the clouds drifting overhead. Soon he would be in America! His dark eyes eagerly searched the horizon for the first sign of green; and he tried to remember, far back in his mind, what it had been like in that island home, here in the new world, where he was born. He had been so small when his father had taken him to France, that he could remember nothing of that remote past but the clear, sweet call of the mockingbird. That had stayed with him through all the years of his growing up. Would he find mockingbirds here, too? he wondered.

There was a notebook in his cabin on the ship, filled with drawings he had made of all the birds that came to nest in his village back home. But he must put such thoughts as that

——Taken from *Art in the New Land*, by Charlie May Simon, published and copyright 1945 by E. P. Dutton & Co., Inc., New York.

from his mind. Wasn't that the very reason he had been sent away, and not, as his father said, to look after some property in Pennsylvania? He had been a disappointment to his father, he knew, spending all his days watching the birds build their nests or feed their young or perch on a limb to sing, instead of attending to his lessons.

The boy's thoughts went back to those he left behind, his gay young sister, his stepmother, dearer to him than an own mother could be, and his father, kind in spite of his sternness, sending him here, no doubt, for his own good. Perhaps if he had tried a little harder, he might have been all that his father had wanted him to be. Here in this new world, he would begin again.

"Jean Jacques," the boy repeated his own name softly to himself. When he was very small he had been called *Fougere*, which means Fern in his own language. But that was no name for a boy, so it was changed to Jean Jacques. Now even that was not easy for American tongues to say. Jean would always be called John. "John James," he said. "John James Audubon."

Now they were approaching the harbor of New York. America! The land where a new life awaited all who came, and a man could make of it what he would! And when he gathered up his belongings, it was the notebook with the drawings of birds and his Cremona violin that he thought of first.

Whatever plans young Audubon might have had, to make himself into the man of business his father wanted him to be, he found his old love of birds and wild creatures returning, greater than ever, when he was settled at Mill Grove, his father's estate. There were birds he had never seen before, and new calls he must learn. He saw the peewees flying about the milldam, and he saw the first oriole come up from the South, and the scarlet flash of the cardinal's wing as it flew through the forest. Business could wait a little longer. Without a care in the world, he followed the call of the vireo or sat as still as a stone to watch the phoebes repair an old nest. He filled the rooms of his house with drawings and paintings of these birds, and with their tiny speckled eggs blown and strung on a thread. And on all the shelves and chimney pieces, there were stuffed squirrels and raccoons and opossums as well as fish and frogs and lizards.

He was a handsome young dandy in those days, gay and lighthearted, with all a Frenchman's gallantry. He wore the finest ruffled shirts, and he hunted in black satin breeches and leather pumps. There was not a ball or skating match or riding party that took place without him. It was then that he met Lucy. He called at the stately mansion of his neighbor William Bakewell; and he saw her for the first time, alone in the parlor. Even then he knew that she was the one he wanted to marry, and that as long as he lived, there would be no other woman in his life. How different she was, with her slender figure and her dainty manners, from the others he had met! She would understand his love of bird songs and the beauty of their flight. He saw her often after that. She taught him English, and he taught her how to draw. And he knew, without the words being spoken, that Lucy returned his love.

William Bakewell was fond of his new neighbor; but the lad was young yet, and his daughter was only seventeen. They must wait for a while before he would give his consent to the marriage.

"When you have established yourself in some kind of business, I shall give you my consent and my blessing," he said.

Audubon returned to France to visit his family, to tell his father about the affairs of his American estate, and to tell him, too, about Lucy. But old Captain Audubon was as stern as William Bakewell. How could a young man who did nothing all day but look at birds and make drawings of them think he could support a wife? Even here in France he was spending all his daylight hours wandering through the fields and woods to draw again the birds he had known in his childhood.

"You must go into business and earn your own money if you expect to marry," he said.

John James Audubon returned, after a year, to America. He had a friend his own age with him, and they spent their time on the boat making plans for the business they would start in the new world. Rozier, the young friend, thought of the fortune he would make; and Audubon thought of Lucy.

They worked for a while for others, for the experience it gave them, before they ventured into a business of their own. But they learned little by that experience. Rozier, too eager to get rich, lost all he had in indigo; and Audubon, working in New York, was paying more attention to the water birds on the harbor and in the marshes than he did to the work he had to do.

Daniel Boone had carved a way for the settlers in the wilderness that became Kentucky. He was an old man now. He had lost all his land and had moved across the river to Missouri. But the territory he had explored had become a state. Covered wagons and pack horses were following the blazed trail; and flatboats were floating down the river with a man's whole family and all his goods, to seek new land there.

"There's a fortune to be made there in the West," Ferdinand Rozier said. "We can buy our supplies here and take them to Kentucky to sell."

There are new birds in the unspoiled forests that I have never seen before, Audubon thought.

He returned to Mill Grove and sold his home there for money to buy goods to trade. And he said good-by to Lucy, promising to return for her as soon as the business prospered enough so that her father would consent to their marriage.

In Louisville, Kentucky, then a town of scarcely a thousand people, the two young men opened their store to sell calico and nankeen cloth and sugar and salt and tea. It was winter then. The bird calls were stilled, and there were only a few jays and woodpeckers and juncos to take young Audubon's mind off his work. By April he felt he had earned enough to return to Lucy and make her his bride.

It was an unknown future that awaited Lucy Audubon, setting off on horseback and coach, then down the river on a flatboat, to a wild new state where there were only strangers to welcome her. But she was not afraid. From now on her life was one with the life of John Audubon. She would go where he wanted her to go, and meet any hardships that came her way.

The hermit thrush called its clear, sweet note from the woods; and the young Audubon tried to keep his mind on the cloth he was measuring to sell. The wild pigeons flew in such numbers that they blackened the sky, as the young man wrote out his accounts on the paper before him. Now there was a new song, one that he had not heard before. He must see the bird that made this sound. Down went the quill pen, and off he went. Sometimes he was gone for as long as three days, swimming the river and wading through the marshes, to track down a sound in the forest. But Lucy understood. If only he did not have that business to think about! she sighed. If only he could roam the woods to his heart's content!

They went from Louisville to Henderson, then to Ste. Genevieve, in Missouri, and back to Henderson again. There were many new stores or mills started and given up, and many new partners who joined him for a while, then left him in despair. Rozier lost patience. How could he make a fortune with a partner who spent his days tracking down the sound of a bird instead of attending to his business? he argued. He, too, left and started a business of his own, so he could prosper alone.

Audubon lost money in every new venture that he tried. But now he was beginning to make the kind of drawing he wanted to do. He had tried with the birds on the wing, but they were so swift he could not get them on paper quickly enough. And he had tried shooting them and stuffing them, but they were so stiff and still that the drawings were as lifeless as the birds themselves. Now he had found a way of spreading the wings of these stuffed birds with thin wire, as if they were poised on the tip of a branch, ready to take off the next moment. He painted them on trees, eating the berries they loved, or building their nests or feeding their young among the colored blossoms and new leaves. It was like coming upon the birds themselves, to see life-size paintings of them in all their colors. One

could almost expect to hear them burst into song at any moment, or flutter away from their perches.

These drawings were destined to give pleasure to all the world for many generations to come, yet Audubon was a poor man at the time he made them, so deep in debt that there was no hope of ever getting out. They put him in jail for his debts, then let him go when his creditors took all that he owned except the clothes on his back and his precious drawings, which they did not want. They did not realize that these very drawings that they scarcely noticed were worth all the stores and mills in Kentucky at the time. Nor did Audubon realize it then. He had made them because it was the thing he wanted to do. But he felt he was a failure, until Lucy smiled and showed her faith in him. Then his own faith came back.

Suddenly he felt a sense of freedom, such as the birds of the forests had. Like a bird, he would go when and where he wanted from now on, and he would return always to his steadfast, loyal mate who stayed behind to look after their young. Now the plans for his *Birds of America*, put off too long, were beginning to take shape.

Lucy had but one thought, and that was that her husband must go on with the work he loved. She became a schoolteacher in Cincinnati to support herself and their two sons; and she waved good-by to John Audubon as he started out on a flatboat, floating down the Ohio toward the Mississippi. He had with him his gun and his dog and a boy of thirteen, who knew his way about the woods like a young Indian. They paid for their passage down to New Orleans by hunting game for the crew to eat. No bird flew past that escaped the keen eyes of Audubon. He saw and drew birds in this untamed forest that had never before been seen by white men, and birds, such as the ivory-billed woodpecker and the parakeet and the passenger pigeon, that will never be seen again. He was now as brown as the Indians with whom he sometimes camped when they tied up the boat for the night. In his yellow nankeen breeches, with his shirt unbuttoned at the throat and his hair hanging long over his shoulders, he was far from the dandy he had been in his youth.

In New Orleans and in the plantation towns of Mississippi, he painted portraits, and he taught drawing and music and dancing to earn his living. But more often he wandered through the woods in search of more birds to complete his collection of paintings and drawings. There were some who laughed at the sight of this man who painted pictures of birds when he might have been earning a good income by painting pictures of people instead. But only he and Lucy knew what it was that he wanted to do. He went on, and with each new painting that he made, he was brought that much nearer to his goal. Lucy came down to join him, and she provided a home for the little family by teaching in a plantation mansion.

At last the time came when Audubon gathered up the work of the past twenty years. Even now he did not call it finished. It would never be finished, for he would always be on the watch for some new bird he had never seen before. But he must find a publisher for what he had done.

America was still looking toward Europe, in those days, for her music and her art and literature. Every talented young man was going abroad to study, if he could possibly do so. But here was one who had come to America from Europe, and had become as American as Daniel Boone himself. This man had found a new art here in the New World. Such a thing had not been heard of before. No publisher in Philadelphia or New York wanted to take this huge portfolio of birds painted in life-size, from the wild turkey to the tiny hummingbird. But Audubon would not give up. He was determined to make these paintings into a book. With Lucy's savings added to his own, he set sail for England.

Though he had been a failure in the business of selling calico and salt and tea, John James Audubon managed to sell subscriptions to his book in Europe and later in America, to a thousand people at a price of a thousand dollars each. He worked with the publishers and engravers over it until each plate was as nearly like the original in line and color as it could be made.

Now the hard years of starvation and debts were over. The fame of this great work spread from England to America; and when Audubon returned, he found those who had once looked upon him as a failure were now proud to be called his friends.

But Lucy was not surprised at her husband's success. From the first she had had faith in his genius; and she knew there would come a time when the world would recognize it, too. There were no more months of waiting for his return while she worked to support the two boys. The family could be together now. They went to Europe and back again, and they wandered about America together in search of animals and birds they had not seen before.

The two sons, Victor and John, were old enough to take an interest in the birds and wild animals their father loved. There is no greater proof of the admiration of a son for his father than when he wants to do the same thing his father has done. The boys went out in the woods and brought home specimens of birds and animals, and of worms and snakes and frogs, as John James Audubon had done for the past twenty years; and they made drawings of them under their father's guidance.

The wanderings came to an end at last. Audubon was old and tired now; and he settled down in the home he had bought in upper New York City, where the loyal Lucy looked after him and took care of him until his death. And when the end had come, his sons carried on his work after him.

(Stop. What time is it? Check your speed of reading with the Reading Score Board, page 410.)

◆((◆

ANOTHER KIND OF SCIENTIST—THE ORNITHOLOGIST

1. Why can Audubon be classed as a scientist as well as an artist?
2. Why are his pictures of birds outstanding?
3. Why is his contribution to science important?
4. What different kinds of birds are mentioned in the story?
5. What hardships did Audubon have to suffer?

FOLLOWING THE AUTHOR'S PLAN

According to what plan did the author organize her story?

THE RIGHT WORDS

Can you match the words in Column I with the words and phrases in Column II?

I	II

Nouns

1. dandy
2. gallantry
3. indigo
4. venture
5. creditor

a. one to whom money is owed
b. fop
c. risky undertaking
d. courteous attention to ladies
e. a plant

Verbs

1.	established	a.	thrived
2.	proposed	b.	set up
3.	prospered	c.	balanced
4.	poised	d.	propounded
5.	destined	e.	decreed beforehand

Adjectives

1.	remote	a.	dignified
2.	stately	b.	faithful
3.	lifeless	c.	cherished
4.	precious	d.	without animation
5.	loyal	e.	distant

READING SCORE BOARD

Number of Words in Story: 2850

Number of Minutes	28 1/2	14 1/4	11 2/5	9 1/2	7	5 3/4
Reading Rate	100 w.p.m.	200 w.p.m.	250 w.p.m.	300 w.p.m.	400 w.p.m.	500 w.p.m.

◀◀ IVAN T. SANDERSON

The Mystery of Migration

Everyone knows something about the migration of birds: birds appear in northern sections in the spring and disappear in the fall. Their appearance and disappearance follow the strange laws of migration. The following article tells many interesting facts about migrations and emigrations.

(Note the time when you begin reading.)

WHY does one bird fly from the Arctic to the Antarctic and back again every year—a distance almost equal to that of the earth's circumference—while another spends its whole life

——Copyright 1944 by The Curtis Publishing Company. Used by permission of Ivan T. Sanderson and The Curtis Publishing Company.

around a small copse, never venturing more than a few yards beyond its confines? Why do birds set out from New Zealand across hundreds of miles of landless ocean and, after spending a few months in Australia, fly all the way back again? How do golden plover from Alaska find their way every year to the tiny islands of Hawaii in the limitless Pacific? What induces eels, after years of complacent puttering in European ponds and streams, to change their color, go down to the sea and swim thousands of miles across the Atlantic to lay their eggs; and, still more baffling, why should their tiny, fragile offspring spend three years struggling back along the same dangerous path while billions drop by the wayside?

The Romans started many fallacies[1] about migration—fallacies which persisted until recent times, and even still persist in out-of-the-way places. The ancients had a simple, peasant understanding of nature; but the Romans, and, after them, our own ancestors, with a growing interest in the complexities of existence, resorted to quite unnecessarily fantastic interpretations of what they saw. Before the rebirth of science two centuries ago, the western world still believed that swallows hibernated in the mud at the bottom of lakes.

After modern scientific investigation had shown that the birds which disappear from northern climes in the fall go to the tropics, and that migration is a natural habit common to a great part of the animal world, a confusion of quite another kind arose. All over the world, men had from time to time encountered vast armies of animals advancing across the face of the earth in countless millions, often without apparent cause. Many of these mass movements were of such

[1] *fallacies.* False ideas.

proportions as seriously to interfere with man's way of life.

The commonest example is probably the locust, a perennial scourge in many warmer lands, which has alarmed and mystified humanity since the dawn of history. One swarm which was scientifically investigated in the Red Sea covered an area of 2000 square miles, and the estimated weight of the insects that composed it—worked out at an average of one sixteenth of an ounce per insect—amounted to 42,850,000,000 tons. Yet another, even larger swarm passed over exactly the same route next day, the combined swarms said to have totaled more than the weight of Manhattan Island above sea level.

Other mass movements, though less frequent, are almost as well known. In the north of Canada and in Norway, vast hosts of little, almost tailless, ratlike animals known as lemmings pour down from the barren uplands from time to time and, after crossing the coastal plains, plunge into the sea and disappear. In South Africa, herds of delicate little antelopes known as springbok, pressed shoulder to shoulder and reaching in all directions as far as the eye can see, suddenly make their appearance and likewise plunge to their destruction in the sea. These unexpected eruptions of animal life occur in almost every country. I once walked for an hour through a continuous carpet of little hopping frogs in the grass fields of West Africa; and, while living in the jungles of South America, we became used to a never-ending succession of swarms of different insects, each lasting but a few hours or a few days. If you refer to back issues of the daily papers, you will see that hardly a summer season passes without some swarm of insects being reported from one part or another of greater New York. Last year, Brooklyn had two—first it was green flies, that appeared from nowhere; and then it was huge cockroaches with faces like Tojo, that appeared out of drains.

Such phenomenal appearances of animals should properly be described as emigrations. They arise from different causes, follow a different course, and end in a manner that is absolutely contrary to that of migration. The difference is between life and death, for migration is designed to make possible the continuation of the species, while emigration invariably ends in total extinction of the hordes. Emigration is, in fact, mass suicide.

Migration is an altogether different matter. It is an orderly and regular behavior pattern, and yet the very causes that induce it may be the same as those which prompt this mass suicide and exhaustion, as we shall see. The difference between emigration and migration is simple to comprehend. Whereas emigration always leads to the disappearance of the animals, in migration there is always a return to the point of origin of the journey, either by the very individuals that set out or at least by their offspring.

A great many different kinds of animals migrate, and every year more and more are added to the list of known migrants. The practice may be far more prevalent than we at present

believe, and may, in the end, be found to be almost universal. The degree of movement that it entails, however, varies greatly.

Troops of some kinds of South American monkeys migrate back and forth every few weeks between two areas of forest—a regular alternation that goes on throughout the years, but which never transgresses the boundaries of the two areas.

Perhaps the most extraordinary manner of migration is found among the lowly group of insects that includes the aphids, or green flies, so well known to fruitgrowers. There is a species that spends half the year on apple trees and the other half on the stems of grasses. These aphids happen to be used by certain ants as we use cows. They are herded and protected by the ants, and, in return, allow themselves to be squeezed periodically, so that a honeylike fluid which exudes from their bodies may be eaten by the ants. Now, the ants have discovered that the aphids have to migrate and, being solicitous of the welfare of their charges, they have the extraordinary intelligence actually to carry them down from the apple trees and to place them on the grass stems or to take them from the grass up to the apple trees, as the season of the year may demand.

It now appears that most frogs make seasonal migrations to breed. Many tree frogs not only descend to the ground but travel considerable distances to special ponds or rivers. We once had a forest camp in a narrow valley in Africa that led down to a large river. This turned out to be a highway of the frogs. At the beginning of the rainy season we were suddenly invaded one night by a host of rare frogs with green bones that live on the tops of the forest trees. They were traveling on the ground, and in a few moments the tent was covered with green-boned frogs; and when we went outside with a light, the whole world seemed filled with the same species, all traveling down to the river. A few nights later came a host of tiny yellow-and-brown fellows; a few days after, big brown frogs with spurs on their thumbs came hopping by. More than a dozen species went by in the space of as many days, each keeping to itself, and all going to the river. What is more, most of them returned within a month, headed back into the forests to spend the rest of the year.

In the circumpolar[2] regions, vast herds of reindeer move south every fall and north every spring. They travel in small parties, feeding as they go; but sometimes when the weather changes suddenly, they become jammed together in tremendous droves which travelers have described as covering the flat, barren ground as far as the eye can see. Solid masses of animals sometimes pass without cease for four or five days. Eventually, these vast aggregations break up into small parties again and spread out, for these are true seasonal migrations.

Almost every kind of animal migrates. Lawrence of Arabia speaks of meeting a mass of migrating poisonous snakes while advancing toward Mesopotamia with his Arabs during

the last war.[3] The snakes were so numerous and his army suffered so many more casualties from them than from the enemy that he was forced to retreat and make a long detour.

But the champion traveler of them all is probably the Arctic tern, a small, slender, white, gull-like bird with tapering wings and a forked tail. This species nests about the eastern and northern coasts of Canada as far north as Baffin Island and the north-western shores of Greenland. Small, numbered metal bands have been attached to the legs of nestlings in Labrador and the grown birds recaptured a few months later at the mouth of the Niger River in West Africa and in Natal on the Indian Ocean coast of South Africa. The latter place is a distance of nearly 9000 miles from Labrador; and as these birds follow an erratic course and as it is unlikely that a sea bird would cross the Kalahari Desert of South Africa, it appears that this individual, retaken in Natal, must have covered well over 10,000 miles. Nor is that the complete picture, for the Arctic tern is found in the Antarctic during our winter. Moreover, it is never met with on the eastern seaboard of either North or South America, while it is well known as a seasonal migrant up and down the western seaboard of both Europe and Africa. From this it has been inferred that this species migrates from Arctic America across the North Atlantic to Europe, thence down the coast past Africa to the Antarctic Ocean, and back up the same route the following spring—a distance, in all, of about

[2] *circumpolar.* Around the pole.

[3] *last war.* World War I.

24,000 miles, or almost equivalent to the total circumference of the earth.

The astonishing behavior of Atlantic eels, though also carried out for the purpose of breeding, falls into a class by itself, the causes of which are unknown, but for the origin of which there is a fascinating theoretical explanation. This is based on what is known as Wegener's theory of continental drift.

Eels spend many years of seemingly contented life in the ponds, ditches, and rivers of Europe and North America, where they are dark green in color and fairly active. Then all of a sudden their color changes to metallic silver and their shape to a more streamlined pattern, while a radical transformation takes place in their internal anatomy. Then, leaving their safe homes, they go down the rivers to the sea and head out into the Atlantic. Those from Europe head west, those from America head southeast, and both swim onward without pause until they meet over a great deep in the Atlantic Ocean south of Bermuda, where they sink down and disappear forever.

Later, an eruption of tiny, transparent, threadlike creatures with bulging black eyes comes welling up to the surface and, spreading out like an ever-expanding mushroom, streams off in two groups, one to the east and one to the northwest. Those going east keep swimming for three years while they change their shape, until they reach the shores of Europe. Those going west also change, but they arrive sooner at the American coast. Both shoals immediately start up the rivers and penetrate farther and farther, until they reach the abodes whence their parents started out. What is more, those that go to Europe are invariably the European species of eel, and those that go to America are just as invariably the American species.

Now, Wegener pointed out that the earth's crust is composed of two layers, the outer one being lighter and thinner, or less deep, than the oceans. Thus the continents are great concave rafts of this outer crust, resting on the second layer, like pieces of peel on a half-peeled orange. Wegener suggested that our earth originally had a complete skin of this outer layer, but that about half was lost by flying off into outer space and that the remainder then cracked up into big pieces and started to drift around to balance the earth, which was lopsided and wobbling. What is more, this scientist went on to show in a most ingenious manner that there is considerable evidence to support his theory.

He started by cutting out maps of the continents, and then, disregarding the oceans, he brought them together and showed that the east coast of North and South America fitted almost exactly into the west coast of Europe and Africa.

Now, should the eels have originated in the sea-filled crack between the Old and the New Worlds when they lay together, and have then developed the habit of spending their time between breeding season in the ponds and rivers of the near-by land on either side of the crack, they would have been called upon to make longer and longer journeys to their breeding grounds as the continents drifted apart, until it eventually became unfeasible for them to make the trip every year. Thus they would have to spend a longer rest period in fresh water and go less frequently to breed. It will be seen that they spend their whole lives resting and storing up energy for their great adventure and then, when fully mature, set out to the ancestral grounds, now thousands of miles away, where the eggs are laid.

Thus we see that the mystery of migration is a complex problem. It is a major life process of the whole animal world, and without it a great part of our earth's animal life would probably have long since become extinct.

(Note the time; and check your reading speed with the Reading Score Board, page 416.)

❖❮❖

Investigating the Mystery

1. Do you see the relationship between this article and the one about Audubon?
2. From the article, what do you find is the difference between migration and emigration?
3. Describe several examples of emigration.
4. Describe several examples of migration.
5. What is Wegener's theory on migration?
6. What, from your own experience, have you learned about the migration of birds and animals?

Investigating the Author's Plan

This article has as crystal-clear an organization of plan as any that you will find. Seeing that organization is a big step toward grasping Mr. Sanderson's ideas. Study the article in the light of the following questions:

1. What is the purpose of the first paragraph?
2. What does the last paragraph say?
3. What is the purpose of paragraphs 2 through 6?
4. What is the author doing in all the other paragraphs?

Now, on your paper, outline paragraphs 2 through 6. As you uncover the ideas in these paragraphs, notice the link between paragraphs 5 and 6.

Investigating Words

What does each of these words mean?

perennial	prevalent	transparent
scourge	exudes	ingenious
lemmings	solicitous	unfeasible
springbok	circumpolar	ancestral
eruptions	casualties	extinct

READING SCORE BOARD

Number of Words in Story: 2290

Number of Minutes	23	11 1/2	9	7 2/3	5 3/4	4 1/2
Reading Rate	100 w.p.m.	200 w.p.m.	250 w.p.m.	300 w.p.m.	400 w.p.m.	500 w.p.m.

◀◀ RODERICK L. HAIG-BROWN

Return to the River

In this story the author describes in accurate detail two salmon, Sachem and Chinook, as they travel up the Columbia River to the spawning areas. Leaping every obstacle, they strive to complete their life cycles in the upland shallows.

(Note the time when you begin reading.)

SACHEM and Chinook held on their way up the Columbia with a big school of spring-run fish all about them. It was still a conglomerate school, headed for several different spawning tributaries, and they were very much above the average size of the fish in it. Most of these were close to the May average of fifteen or twenty pounds; a few, early fish of the summer hog-run that comes to Rock Island on the tail of the spring run, were over thirty pounds. But, except only great Sachem, there was hardly a fish there weighing within ten pounds of Chinook's full fifty. Both Sachem and Chinook were exceptional fish. Chinook had left his nursery stream in the Snake water-

shed early in his first year and was returning after five vigorous years of feeding that had taken him to the north coast of the Queen Charlottes,[1] well beyond the limit of spring's long feeding range. Sachem was a year older and had traveled farther still, though he had spent part of his first year in a tributary stream above Grand Coulee; nearly six years of ocean life had carried him to a point off the southern coast of Alaska and built his body to its present huge size. Later in the year a few other fish like him would be running the big waters of the Columbia to seek spawning room far up the Snake or in streams that the insurmountable mass of Grand Coulee Dam now blocked from all salmon. There

----From *Return to the River* by Roderick L. Haig-Brown, copyright 1941 by Roderick L. Haig-Brown, by permission of William Morrow and Company, Inc.

[1] *Queen Charlottes.* Islands off the coast of British Columbia.

might be a few, very few, even larger, weighing perhaps ninety, perhaps a hundred pounds; but Sachem was a true giant of his species.

As the school passed through the middle reaches of the river towards Bonneville, they came upon nets. Above Portland the river reaches back into the beginning of the Cascade Range, flowing with impressive width between mountain-high banks of green timber and bald rock faces. From a distance it seems a smooth flow, serene and magnificent in sweeping breadth. Go down to the level of the water and there are waves lapping at the sandy beaches, white-flecked water whirled and murmuring over bars, smooth strong glides in deep channels, little upstream curving wavelets in the creased water behind the upthrust of big rocks. In the vastness, beyond river size, the power of each showing is deceptively reduced, but it is there, the power of a hundred rivers, a thousand streams, a hundred thousand creeks whose headwaters lie as far east as the summit of the Rockies, separated from the sources of the Mississippi and the Saskatchewan only by a few yards of granite.

Only a little above Reed Island the fish met another gill-net. It was a diver-net, drifting along a channel between the sandbars in a good flow of current. The school had started upstream from their shallow resting place of the night before less than an hour earlier and they were traveling steadily against the good current. A little below the net the passing of a tugboat disturbed a few fish near the outside of the school; they swung in, swimming fast; the movement spread to the other fish and reached Sachem almost as he came to the net. He started forward in a panicky rush, struck the eight-and-a-half-inch mesh at full speed and tore through the single curtain as though it were not there at all. Chinook, close behind him, burst the web again before it was well back of his head and several fish slipped through the holes the big fish had left. A few gilled but many more passed safely outside the net, for the school had struck only a few yards from the buoyed end.

They came to the tail of the strong race below Bonneville Dam less than a week after passing Vancouver. It was a clear day with a strong sun that lighted the little houses of the village and the great concrete structures of the dam to brilliant whiteness. Men still worked on the powerhouse to the south of Bradford Island, and only a single one of the twenty-three-foot runners turned in its draft tube, five revolutions in each four seconds, shedding a tiny part of the Columbia's flow into electricity. The rest of the mounting spring might of the river roared in increasing thunder through a dozen gates of the spillway dam north of the island. The water came under the steel gates, driven by a forty-foot head to shoot out and upward in solid, glassy, curving streams that broke over in savage crests of heavy tumbled whiteness ten feet higher than the foot of each gate. The crests broke again, fell back on themselves, fountained up in spires of water, gathered themselves, and crashed on in steep waves that made a white rapid of fierce water for more than a mile below the dam.

Sachem and Chinook came into this gladly. The growing strength of the broken current called to their own strength, its tossing thrust against them wakened every driving muscle of their great bodies, and they fought up steadily, almost swiftly, wide tails forcing the racing water behind them in swirling strokes of power. As the current grew stronger and wilder, the school broke up, each fish striving on its own. Sachem and Chinook remained together almost side by side. Little by little the solid strength of the water and the battering uncertainty of its flow began to slow them. Two or three hundred feet below the gates they swung over towards Bradford Island, seeking an easier flow. They found shelter behind a big rock near shore and rested briefly. Then Sachem drove out into the current again, and Chinook still followed him closely. They forced up strongly at first and Sachem leapt out once, his huge wide body dark and clear against the shattered whiteness. The full strength of the race caught them and slowed them again until they were moving foot by foot, then inch by inch. For a full minute they struggled side by side, near the surface, barely holding place, then sharply slacked the effort. The current carried them back and they turned down and found shelter to the side and near bottom. Again they rested only briefly; the rush of the current above them was a summons and they turned up into it. They quartered across, making headway, then swung back, still quartering. Brilliant light water was all about them, full of bubbles and foam, some of its strength lost in the breaking but giving only a light purchase for the thrust of their tails and the drive of their bodies. Sachem rolled his back out, so that it shone black in the sun and whiteness, then went down; Chinook followed him. Together they met the solid wall of water that forced under the gate, plunged into it, almost held; then it caught them up, hurled them over, tumbled them, battered them, threw them back down the race. They won out of it and slid suddenly into a quieter flow close against Bradford Island.

There were other fish in the smooth water and for a little while Sachem and Chinook rested there quietly. Sachem stirred at last, swam up to the surface and rolled once. He felt the current there, smooth and easy but strong enough to draw him. He slid forward into it, sought its changing direction between concrete walls, felt it suddenly strong, and had found his way into the Bradford Island ladder. Chinook followed a little behind him.

The ladder was a curving quarter-mile length of fast-flowing water that drew down across the island from the slough behind the powerhouse. It was cut into wide pools by six-foot walls of concrete over which the surface water flowed to join the race of the spillway and draw the salmon from it as their struggle in the heavy current wearied them. Sachem, holding near surface, came against the first wall and turned down from it to the concrete bottom of the ladder. A moment later he turned sharply upward and came out of the water in a curving leap that carried him over the wall and into the first pool of the ladder. Chinook was deeper in the water as he came up and felt a strong flow of current near one of the walls of the fishway; he held into it, swam easily through a wide opening in the cross wall of the first pool, turned to follow the draw of current, and was beside Sachem again.

The two fish worked up together from pool to pool in the bright water. The entrances were square gaps cut near bottom in the concrete cross walls of the ladder, alternating from left to right in each pool. A strong flow slid through the gaps against each solid wall opposite, then along well under the surface current to pass out through the lower gap to the next pool. The fish followed its turns easily, resting when they wanted in the eddying water of the pools, seldom near surface. Other fish passed up with them, chinooks, a few steelhead, lampreys, suckers, and some squawfish. The steelhead were restless and quick, their square tails forcing even more vigorously through the water than those of the chinooks; quite often they jumped instead of passing through the underwater gaps, and one of them, in panic or excess of energy, jumped wildly many times, striking the side wall of the ladder, smashing down into the rush of white water on the surface, sometimes falling back over the step he had gained. He grew calmer at last

and passed up with the others, silently and invisibly through the easy force of the gaps.

Sachem came at last to a steel grating across the ladder. He felt his way along it, pressing his nose to the narrow openings where the water came through, seeking a way to follow on into the current. He worked gently and persistently back and forth along the grating for several minutes; once or twice he pressed his nose tight against the bars and thrust with a tentative wriggle of tail and body as though trying their strength. At last he turned back and disappeared into the deep water of the pool. Other fish, Chinook among them, came up and searched for a way through the heavy grating. They turned away, came back, turned away again, swimming with calm, patient movements.

The grating was set across the ladder only a few steps below its entrance into Bradford Slough. In the center there was a heavy wooden hatch-door, tight closed. On the upstream side of this was a white plate set a few inches under the water and flanked by two little sentry boxes with forward-slanting glass windows that looked down on the plate. It seemed quiet there at the counting station, away from the roar of the spillway, and a little group of tourists stood watching the fish at the grating, seeing the green-roofed sentry boxes against the orange California poppies growing on the raw gravel bank thrown up behind them. A counter came down, passed among the tourists without a word and settled himself in one of the boxes. He opened the gate and almost at once a fish slipped through, then another, two out of perhaps half a million that would pass that way during the year.

Sachem and Chinook were resting deep in the pool when the gate was opened. The stir of other fish passing through moved them, and they came up to the grating again, worked along it, found the opening, turned away, came back. Sachem crept forward cautiously, wriggling his great body until his head was over the white plate. The tourists watched and called to each other and pointed. Even the man in the counting house moved forward a little on his stool to get a better sight of Sachem's great body, dim against the dark water of the pool. Sachem moved forward until his pectorals came over the plate; then the bright light reflecting from the white surface was too much for him, and he turned sharply and fled into the depths of the pool. Chinook obeyed the warning of his panic, but in a little while the two fish came back, still swimming slowly and cautiously. Sachem's head came over the plate again, then his pectorals, then his dorsal fin, breaking the surface. Chinook moved up almost in his shadow, his own wide head small beside the widest part of Sachem's huge body. Sachem's full length came over the plate and for a brief moment was sharply there against the white reflection; a dozen pairs of human eyes made the brief sight their own, for all time; the spread pectorals sensitive and almost deli-

cate, the huge width of the back, the full length of the mighty body, dorsal fin and tip of tail dark and gleaming above water in the sunlight, head tapered and graceful from bulky shoulder. Then it was gone. Sachem slid off the plate into the dark water of the next pool. Chinook followed him. The counter glanced quickly up at the tourists and smiled, accepting them for a brief moment as equals who would understand, then turned back to his watching.

The two fish passed quickly and easily up through the remaining steps and out into the slough. They searched and found the easy flow of current to the turbine under the south bank, followed against it a little way, then turned to rest in an eddy below the mouth of Eagle Creek.

Other fish were in the eddy and more came to it. In a little while a new school formed and went on.

Above Bonneville the river is narrow and deep right up to Cascade Locks, where the legendary span of the Bridge of the Gods is a mass of tumbled sunken rock clear across the bed of the river. In spite of the dam there is a fine current through the reach, and the school delayed only long enough to rest after climbing the ladder. One day later they were through the strong run of the cascades and well into the wide glassy curve where the banks of the river change from the moist green of the coast to the buff and gray rock-pierced sand of the interior. The gray cone of Wind Mountain, tremendous with rock on its upstream face, looked down on their passing; and the Washington streams, Wind River and the White Salmon Rivers, drew fish from the school until Hood River came down from Oregon, draining the snows from the ridge-veined face of tall Mount Hood. Even here, a hundred and fifty miles from salt water, there were nets, but Sachem and Chinook passed safely among them and came safely to the Dalles, where the river confines its breadth in depth as it slides brimming through a flume of lava two hundred feet high and a stone's throw wide.

They worked up the main channel, shouldering the water behind them in the slow crescendo of their upstream movement. At Bonneville they had left the last slight influence of ocean tide, and now they were free in the full fresh force of the river, fac-

ing strong clean flow or tumbled rapids for mile after mile as the river wound among the dry hills with their lava ramparts gaunt and black against burnt green.

Above the Dalles, almost a part of them still, is Celilo Falls. Sachem and Chinook came late to the falls; several weeks late in the year they ran. At Celilo Falls the Indians fish as they fished before any white men had seen the Columbia, raking the salmon with dip-nets from the eddies below the steep drop of the water.

Above Celilo there are no nets and little fishing of any sort. As they passed along the big island that splits the river above the falls and felt the swift flow of the Deschutes River's entrance, Sachem and Chinook seemed safe fish, within certain reach of their spawning.

(Check your rate of reading with the Reading Score Board, page 422.)

❖◖◗❖

Completing the Span

1. What obstacles did Sachem and Chinook have to pass?
2. What man-made device helped the salmon reach their spawning area?
3. What detail in the story shows people's interest in the number of salmon going up the river?
4. What did you learn concerning methods used for catching salmon?

Finding Out More

Use an encyclopedia or another reference book to find out more about the following:

1. Life cycle of a salmon
2. Grand Coulee Dam
3. Fish ladders
4. Kinds of salmon
5. The salmon industry

Number of Words in Story: 2680

Number of Minutes	26 4/5	13 2/5	10 3/4	8 9/10	6 7/10	5 1/3
Reading Rate	100 w.p.m.	200 w.p.m.	250 w.p.m.	300 w.p.m.	400 w.p.m.	500 w.p.m.

◄ J. Y. COUSTEAU

Shark Close-ups

In 1943 a new era began in undersea exploring. Two French naval officers, J. Y. Cousteau and Philippe Tailliez, and a civilian diver, Frédéric Dumas, began diving with the first aqualung, of which Cousteau was co-inventor.

The aqualung is an independent breathing apparatus. With it the men have dived into undersea pressures that have crushed submarines. They have explored sunken ships, have swum with sharks and whales, and have taken remarkable undersea pictures.

In this story, Cousteau tells of a hair-raising experience with sharks.

(Note the time when you begin reading.)

ONE sunny day in the open sea between the islands of Boavista and Maio, in the Cape Verde group, a long Atlantic swell beat on an exposed reef and sent walls of flume high into the air. We anchored by the dangerous reef to dive from the steeply rolling deck into the wild sea. Where there is a reef, there is abundant life.

Small sharks came when we dropped anchor. The crew broke out tuna hooks and took ten of them in as many minutes. When we went overside for a camera dive, there were only two sharks left in the water. Under the racing swell we watched them strike the hooks and thrash their way through the surface. Down in the reef we found the savage population of the open ocean, including some extremely large nurse sharks, a class that is not supposed to be harmful to man. We saw three sharks sleeping in rocky caverns. The camera demanded lively sharks. Dumas and Tailliez swam into the caves and pulled their tails to wake them. The sharks came out and vanished into the blue, playing their bit parts competently.

We saw a fifteen-foot nurse shark. I summoned Didi and conveyed to him in sign language that he would be permitted to relax our neutrality toward sharks and take a crack at this one with his super-harpoon gun. It had a six-foot spear with an explosive head and three hundred pounds of traction in its elastic bands. Dumas fired straight down at a distance of twelve feet. The four-pound harpoon struck the shark's head and, two seconds later, the harpoon tip exploded. We were severely shaken. There was some pain involved.

The shark continued to swim away, imperturbably, with the spear sticking from its head like a flagstaff.

One day I was on the bridge, watching the little spark jiggle up and down on the echo-sound tape, sketching the profile of the sea floor nine thousand feet below the open Atlantic off Africa. As I watched the enigmatic scrawls, the stylus began to enter three distinct spurs on the tape, three separate scattering layers, one above the other. I was lost in whirling ideas, watching the spark etch the lowest and heaviest layer, when I heard shouts from the deck, "Whales!" A herd of sluggish bottlenosed whales surrounded our ship, the Élie Monnier.

In the clear water we studied the big dark forms. One emerged twelve feet from Dumas. He threw the harpoon with all his might. The shaft struck near the pectoral fin and blood started. The animal sounded in an easy rhythm and we paid out a hundred yards of harpoon line, tied to a heavy gray buoy. The buoy was swept away in the water—the whale was well hooked. The other whales lay unperturbed around the Élie Monnier.

We saw Dumas's harpoon sticking out of the water; then it, the whale, and buoy disappeared. Dumas climbed the mast with binoculars. I kept the ship among the whales, thinking they would not abandon a wounded comrade. Time passed.

Libera, the keen-eyed radio man, spotted the buoy, and there was the whale, seemingly unhurt, with the harpoon protruding like a toothpick. Dumas hit the whale twice with dumdum bullets. Red water washed on the backs of the faithful herd, as it gathered around the stricken one. We struggled for an hour to pick up the buoy and tie the harpoon line to the Élie Monnier.

A relatively small bottlenosed whale, heavily wounded, was tethered to the ship. We were out of sight of land, with fifteen hundred fathoms of water under the keel, and the whale herd diving and spouting around the ship. Tailliez and I entered the water to follow the harpoon line to the agonized animal.

The water was an exceptional clear turquoise blue. We followed the line a few feet under the surface, and came upon the whale. Thin streams of blood jetted horizontally from the bullet holes. I swam toward three other bottlenoses. As I neared them, they turned up their flukes and sounded. It was the first time I had been under water to actually see them diving and I understood the old whaler's word, "sound." They did not dive obliquely as porpoises often do. They sped straight down, perfectly vertical. I followed them down a hundred feet. A fifteen-foot shark passed way below me, probably attracted by the whale's blood. Beyond sight was the deep scattering layer; down there a herd of leviathans grazed; more sharks roamed. Above in the sun's silvery light was Tailliez and a big whale dying. Reluctantly I returned to the ship.

Back on deck I changed into another lung and strapped a tablet of cupric acetate on an ankle and one on my belt. When this chemical dissolves in water, it is supposed to repulse sharks. Dumas was to pass a noose over the whale's tail, while I filmed. Just after we went under he saw a big shark, but it was gone before I answered his shout. We swam under the keel of the ship and located the harpoon line.

A few lengths down the line in a depth of fifteen feet we sighted an eight-foot shark of a species we had never before seen. He was impressively neat, light gray, sleek, a real collector's item. A ten-inch fish with vertical black-and-white stripes accompanied him a few inches above his back, one of the famous pilot fish. We boldly swam toward the shark, confident that he would run as all the others had. He did not retreat. We drew within ten feet of him, and saw all around the shark an escort of tiny striped pilots three or four inches long.

They were not following him; they seemed part of him. A thumbnail of a pilot fish wriggled just ahead of the shark's snout, miraculously staying in place as the beast advanced. He probably found there a compressibility wave that held him. If he tumbled out of it, he would be hopelessly left behind. It was some time before we realized that the shark and his courtiers were not scared of us.

The handsome gray was not apprehensive. I was happy to have such an opportunity to film a shark, although, as the first wonder passed, a sense of danger came to our hearts. Shark and company slowly circled us. I became the film director, making signs to Dumas, who was co-starred with the shark. Dumas obligingly swam in front of the beast and along behind it. He lingered at the tail and reached out his hand. He grasped the tip of the caudal fin, undecided about giving it a good pull. That would break the dreamy rhythm and make a good shot, but it might also bring the teeth snapping back at him. Dumas released the tail and pursued the shark round and round. I was whirling in the center of the game, busy framing Dumas. He was swimming as hard as he could to keep up with the almost motionless animal. The shark made no hostile move nor did he flee, but his hard little eyes were on us.

The shark had gradually led us down to sixty feet. Dumas pointed down. From the visibility limit of the abyss, two more sharks climbed toward us. They were fifteen-footers, slender, steel-blue animals with a more savage appearance. They leveled off below us. They carried no pilot fish.

Our old friend, the gray shark, was getting closer to us, tightening his slowly revolving cordon. But he still seemed manageable. He turned reliably in his clockwise prowl and the pilots held their stations. The blue pair from the abyss hung back, leaving the affair to the first comer. We revolved inside the ring, watching the gray, and tried to keep the blues located at the same time. We never found them in the same place twice.

Below the blue sharks there appeared great tunas with long fins. Perhaps they had been there since the beginning, but it was the first time we noticed them. Above us flying fish gamboled, adding a discordant touch of gaiety to what was becoming a tragedy for us. Dumas and I ransacked our memories for advices on how to frighten off sharks. *"Gesticulate wildly,"* said a lifeguard. We flailed our arms. The gray did not falter. *"Give 'em a flood of bubbles,"* said a helmet diver. Dumas waited until the shark had reached his nearest point and released a heavy exhalation. The shark did not react. *"Shout as loud as you can,"* said Hans Hass. We hooted until our voices cracked. The shark appeared deaf. *"Cupric acetate tablets fastened to leg and belt will keep sharks away if you go into the drink,"* said an Air Force briefing officer. Our friend swam through the copper-stained water without a wink. His cold, tranquil eye appraised us. He

seemed to know what he wanted, and he was in no hurry.

A small dreadful thing occurred. The tiny pilot fish on the shark's snout tumbled off his station and wriggled to Dumas. It was a long journey for the little fellow, quite long enough for us to speculate on his purpose. The mite butterflied in front of Dumas's mask. Dumas shook his head as if to dodge a mosquito. The little pilot fluttered happily, moving with the mask, inside which Dumas focused in cross-eyed agony.

Instinctively I felt my comrade move close to me, and I saw his hand held out clutching his belt knife. Beyond the camera and the knife, the gray shark retreated some distance, turned, and glided at us head-on.

We did not believe in knifing sharks, but the final moment had come, when knife and camera were all we had. I had my hand on the camera button and it was running, without my knowledge that I was filming the oncoming beast. The flat snout grew larger and there was only the head. I was flooded with anger. With all my strength I thrust the camera and banged his muzzle. I felt the wash of a heavy body flashing past and the shark was twelve feet away, circling us as slowly as before, unharmed and expressionless. I thought, *Why doesn't he go to the whale? The nice juicy whale. What did we ever do to him?*

The blue sharks now climbed up and joined us. Dumas and I decided to take a chance on the surface. We swam up and thrust our masks out of the water. The *Élie Monnier* was three hundred yards away, under the wind. We waved wildly and saw no reply from the ship. We believed that floating on the surface with one's head out of the water is the classic method of being eaten away. Hanging there, one's legs could be plucked like bananas. I looked down. The three sharks were rising toward us in a concerted attack.

We dived and faced them. The sharks resumed the circling maneuver. As long as we were a fathom or two down, they hesitated to approach. It would have been an excellent idea for us to navigate toward the ship. However, without landmarks, or a wrist compass, we could not follow course.

Dumas and I took a position with each man's head watching the other man's flippers, in the theory that the sharks preferred to strike at feet. Dumas made quick spurts to the surface to wave his arms for a few seconds. We evolved a system of taking turns for brief appeals on the surface, while the low man pulled his knees up against his chest and watched the sharks. A blue closed in on Dumas's feet while he was above. I yelled. Dumas turned over and resolutely faced the shark. The beast broke off and went back to the circle. When we went up to look we were dizzy and disoriented from spinning around under water, and had to revolve our heads like a lighthouse beacon to find the *Élie Monnier*. We saw no evidence that our shipmates had spied us.

We were nearing exhaustion, and cold was claiming the outer layers of our bodies. I reckoned we had been down over a half hour. Any moment we expected the constriction of air in our mouthpieces, a sign that the air supply nears exhaustion. When it came, we would reach behind our backs and turn the emergency supply valve. There was five minutes' worth of air in the emergency ration. When that was gone, we could abandon our mouthpieces and make mask dives, holding our breath. That would quicken the pace, redouble the drain on our strength, and leave us facing tireless, indestructible creatures that never needed breath. The movements of the sharks grew agitated. They ran around us, working all their strong propulsive fins, turned down, and disappeared. We could not believe it. Dumas and I stared at each other. A shadow fell across us. We looked up and saw the hull of the *Élie Monnier's* launch. Our mates had seen our signals and had located our bubbles. The sharks ran when they saw the launch.

We flopped into the boat, weak and shaken. The crew were as distraught as we were. The ship had lost sight of our bubbles and drifted away. We could not believe what they told us; we had been in the water only twenty minutes. The camera was jammed by contact with the shark's nose.

(Note the time. Check your reading rate with the Reading Score Board.)

BEING AWARE OF PARAGRAPH PATTERNS

Some paragraphs tell a story, others describe, and still others explain. A good reader is aware of the different kinds of paragraphs and reads in different ways. What kind of paragraph do you expect from the first sentence of each?

WHAT ARE YOUR CONCLUSIONS?

1. What value does such undersea diving have?
2. Would you do this kind of work? Why, or why not?

READING SCORE BOARD

Number of Words in Selection: 2230

Number of Minutes	22 1/3	11 1/6	8 9/10	7 1/2	5 1/2	4 1/2
Reading Rate	100 w.p.m.	200 w.p.m.	250 w.p.m.	300 w.p.m.	400 w.p.m.	500 w.p.m.

◄€ WILFRID S. BRONSON

Watching Ants

Did you know that ants live in cities and that all the inhabitants of a city have a single mother? Did you know that they keep "cows" and that they can do tap-talking? The following article is full of all sorts of amazing bits of information about the lowly ant.
(Note the time when you begin reading.)

WHEN I was a boy, I wanted to go to Africa and see wild animals as they live in nature. But of course I could not go. So I had to pretend that I was there. Since I could not go to Africa, I went out into the fields and lay staring for hours between the weeds and grass blades, with my eyes very close to the ground. I was not a boy watching ants but an explorer. The ants were naked savages in a vast and mighty jungle.

——Abridged from *The Wonder World of Ants* by Wilfrid S. Bronson, copyright, 1937, by Harcourt, Brace and Company, Inc.

Sometimes I saw them on safari,[1] marching in long, single files, each one carrying a precious burden as the tribe moved to some new camping ground. I visited their villages and went with them on their hunting trips. A June bug now became an elephant; a cutworm was a monstrous snake. A cricket was an antelope crashing through the underbrush, while grasshoppers climbing grass blades were gorillas in bamboo.

But watching ants is good fun

[1] *safari.* An expedition.

even without pretending anything. They are very interesting insects. Scientists have studied them for many years. They have found at least eight thousand different kinds of ants. For ants are common in almost every country. And just as the people of different countries have various ways of living and looking, so do the ants. Ants are divided into nations, too, and I'm sorry to say they sometimes make war upon each other as people do. Two ant nations may want to use the same ground in which to build their cities. One nation may want to enslave another. Or it may be that they fight just because they do not understand or like each other.

As among people, ants have many ways of getting their living. There are hunting ants who capture other insects, shepherd ants who care for little bugs from which they get sweet honeydew to live on as we get milk from cows and goats. There are farmer ants who grow all their own vegetables. There are thief ants who live entirely by stealing; and slave-making ants who kidnap the children of other ant nations to do all their work. And there are mighty wandering tribes of military ants who live by plunder and make war on every living creature in their path, driving even men and elephants before them.

Ants make their homes of earth, stones, wood, paper, or leaves. The very tiny Pharaoh ants may have their home right in your house. They have climbed aboard ships and traveled all over the world from Egypt. They find the weather warm enough to suit their tropical taste inside our heated houses, and help themselves in our pantries.

If you will go into the fields and turn over a few big stones, you are sure to uncover a city of ant people. You will see the workers who gather food for themselves and all the others, and the nurses who care for the baby ants. You will see some of the babies, too, though perhaps not all of them. Some may be in rooms deeper down in the earth. While ant babies grow, they change their form three times. First they are very small white eggs. When they hatch, they are like little, very fat, white worms.

The babies you are sure to see are the ones which are wrapped in silk cocoons. People call these "ant eggs." But they are not. They are cocoons in which the baby ants are changing from fat little worms to grown-up ants. When the time comes, the cocoons will be torn open by the ant nurses, and the new ants with their tender legs and bodies very gently helped out. You may see some of these new ants, still very pale in color. They will act quite helpless in the scramble that begins when you lift the stone. They won't be strong enough to work until the skin on their jointed bodies thickens and hardens into good stout armor. The workers and nurses carry them and all the cocoons down tunnels out of sight.

If you are lucky, you may see the queen. She is much larger than her people and the hind half of her is enormous. It is full of the eggs she is forever laying. Every ant, young or old, in that ant town is a child of hers. She lays all the eggs. It is her full-time job. The nurses keep her very clean, washing her with their tongues. They take the eggs as they are laid and tend them in rooms that are dry and warm. From outside in the great world, the workers bring in food to her, and all the people seem to love her very much. She may live for fifteen years; but when she dies, the whole city gradually dies out. There are no more babies being born. None of the workers can have children. And without their queen-mother they hardly care to live themselves.

If it is not too late in the summer, you may see princes and princesses in among the hustling workers. You can tell them because they have wings and bigger, better eyes than the workers. In spring and mid-summer it is their task to leave home and start new cities far and wide. On a certain day all of them must go forth. They fly high in the air where, with their fine eyes, they see the princes and princesses from other cities of their kind. With these they mate, still flying, then separate and descend to earth again. The princes are very stupid fellows. The workers always looked after them at home. But they may not go back there. And they don't know even how to feed themselves. So they die.

But the princesses, the new queens, they are splendid. Each one seeks a place to start her own new city. First she bites off her wings. She will never need them again. It is like taking off one's coat to go to work. With feet and jaws she digs under a log or stone, hollows out a room, and then stops up the door with earth. She must live alone in this room for months, perhaps almost a year, with no food. She has been well fed all her young life, but now she must live entirely on her stored-up fat. Soon she begins laying eggs. She washes them with her tongue. When the wormlike infants hatch, she feeds them with her oily spittle. She may lay more eggs and feed some to the babies. She may even eat a few to keep alive. She is getting thinner and thinner. After awhile the babies spin cocoons. In a few weeks their mother helps them out—new, weak, underfed, runty little ants. They must still be fed until their outsides toughen, a few weeks more. At last they break open the door and go out to look for food. They bring some back to their poor and hungry mother. She gets strong again. She grows fat and lays more and better eggs. The next ants to hatch will be bigger, healthier fellows. The city will soon be full of happy, strong, hard-working people who will tunnel out new streets and apartments and make things hum.

Not all the ant people go out for food. Some may have extra powerful jaws. These act as guards and soldiers in time of trouble. Some workers keep the tunnels and rooms clean. All rubbish is carried out and thrown on an ants' trash heap. Some attend the queen. And some care for the young, feeding them and moving them from room to room as they need more heat or air or moisture.

All live on liquid food. Even when they eat another insect, they chew it up, suck the blood, and spit out the rest. Many kinds of ants milk the little bugs called ant cows. They tend them with great care, placing them where they can suck plenty of sweet sap from the stems and leaves of plants. You can see them on the stems of many wild flowers and on rose-bushes. These cow bugs drink much more sap than they can use. It passes right through their bodies, only getting a little thicker and sweeter. The ants know how to make them give out delicious drops. They strike a cow bug's back with forelegs and feelers. The cow bug seems to enjoy this, and presently a glistening drop of honey-dew-milk appears. The ant laps it up and goes to the next cow bug.

The ant is not gathering this food for itself alone. It uses but a little of it. It has two stomachs in its body, one for itself and one for carrying food to "the folks back home," a stomach that belongs to all the people. Almost all its hinder body is used for this. When it returns, a nurse ant which has been busy indoors all day is sure to ask for honeydew. They place their mouths together. The one which has the honeydew brings up a drop from its public stomach and passes it into the nurse ant's mouth. This is how the whole city is fed. The nurse will give some of her drop to the babies, or to the queen.

When one ant wants food from another, it taps gently on the other's head with its feelers, using their telegraph code. They talk a great deal by this means. Much of the work is talked over. Perhaps one ant needs another's help in dragging home a heavy prize. If you watch long enough, you will see many problems settled by this tap-talking with the feelers.

Thus go the daily doings in one ant town, such as you may find under many a stone down in the deep jungle of the fields. If you will put the stone back just the way you found it, the ant townspeople will soon set things to rights again.

(How long did it take you to read the article? Check your reading speed with the Reading Score Board, page 431.)

❖❖❖

ANOTHER KIND OF SCIENTIFIC EXPLORATION

What interesting facts does Bronson tell us about each of the following? Cite the passage or passages which tell about each.

1. kinds of ants
2. ways of making a living
3. kinds of homes
4. ant cities
5. babies
6. queens
7. princes and princesses
8. ants' cows
9. ants' stomachs
10. tap-talking

AND STILL ANOTHER KIND OF EXPLORATION

You had no trouble in reading Mr. Bronson's article, did you? And when you had finished it, you probably had some very clear-cut ideas about it. One of the reasons the article was easy to read was the fact that Mr. Bronson told you paragraph by paragraph what his main idea was going to be. For proof of that statement, go back through the article now.

1. What is the purpose of the first two paragraphs?
2. What is the purpose of the last paragraph?
3. Can you point out the main idea of each paragraph throughout the rest of the article? How many topic sentences do you see?

Now put into outline form the five paragraphs indicated here:
Begin with: (page 428) As among people, ants have many ways of getting . . .
End with: (pages 428 and 429) If you are lucky, you may see the queen.

READING SCORE BOARD

Number of Words in Story: 1660

Number of Minutes	16 1/2	8 1/4	6 3/5	5 1/2	4	3 1/3
Reading Rate	100 w.p.m.	200 w.p.m.	250 w.p.m.	300 w.p.m.	400 w.p.m.	500 w.p.m.

❧ EDWIN WAY TEALE

An Adventure in Viewpoint

Did you ever try to put yourself into someone else's shoes and feel and think as you imagine that person must feel and think? That is one kind of adventure in viewpoint. The author of the following article suggests another kind of adventure. It is the adventure of putting ourselves, by means of our imagination, into the kind of world the animal, the bird, the fish, the insect know. There are so many worlds to enjoy it is a pity if we confine ourselves to only one.

ON THE thirtieth day of January, 1841, Henry Thoreau set down in his journal this record of a small adventure among the snow-covered fields of Concord.

"Looking down the river," he wrote, "I saw a fox some sixty rods

——From *Near Horizons,* by Edwin Way Teale. Copyright 1942 by Edwin Way Teale. Used by permission of Dodd, Mead & Co., Inc.

off, making across the fields to my left. As the snow lay five inches deep, he made but slow progress; but it was no impediment to me. So, yielding to the instinct of the chase, I tossed my head aloft and bounded away, snuffing the air like a foxhound and spurning the world and human society at each bound. It seems the woods rang with the hunter's horn, and Diana[1] and all the satyrs[2] joined in the chase and cheered me on."

Thus, for a few exhilarating moments, Henry Thoreau entered another world than his own. They are all about us—these other worlds—the world of the fox, the squirrel, the beetle, the fish, the bird. We need only the keys of curiosity and imagination to reach their infinite variety. Adventures in viewpoint are within the grasp of all.

When, like Thoreau, we imagine ourselves part of another realm—whether it is the weedy water-world of the perch, the grass jungles of the katydid, the mossy well of the frog,

the hot, conical sandpit of the ant-lion, the white foam-castle of the tiny froghopper, the fungus forests of the beetle, or the dark haunts of the earthworm and the mole—we are exploring as surely as though we were journeying across a tundra[3] or through the rain forest of some remote land.

To stop and wonder, to put ourselves for a passing moment in the place of the creatures around us—to visualize life from their standpoint—here, truly, is an adventure in exploring. Such journeys require neither ships nor trains nor rubber tires nor gasoline. They take only leisure moments from our time.

❖❰❖

YOUR VIEWPOINT—YOUR CONCLUSION

1. Why did Teale call this essay "An Adventure in Viewpoint"?
2. How does it remind you of the first paragraphs of "Watching Ants"?
3. How is this kind of adventure possible for everyone?

READING SLOWLY

Why did you read the essay slowly? What would you have missed had you read at your top speed?

LOOKING BACKWARD THROUGH THE CHAPTER

1. Can you point out the relationships between the following?
    a. "Leeuwenhoek" and "Mad Dogs and Others"
    b. "That Kite," "The Speed of Words," and "Atoms for Peace"
    c. "Alone" and "Three Miles a Minute—Down!"
    d. "John James Audubon," "The Mystery of Migration," "Shark Close-ups," and "Watching Ants"
2. What qualities must a scientist possess? How are those qualities exemplified in the selections in this chapter?
3. How can it be said that there are always inventors behind the inventor?
4. What is the value of Teale's "An Adventure in Viewpoint"?
5. Do you find any relationship between what you are studying in science class and the selections in this chapter?

[1] *Diana.* Goddess of the wood.
[2] *satyrs.* Creatures of the wood given to riotous fun.
[3] *tundra.* A treeless plain of cold regions.

SHARPENING YOUR WITS

Who Did What?

Can you name the person who did each of the following?
1. Who took undersea pictures?
2. Who painted beautiful pictures of birds?
3. Who first saw microbes?
4. Who studied hydrophobia?
5. Who experimented with lightning?

What Happened Where?

Write one sentence telling what scientific contribution was made in each place:
1. Philadelphia
2. Antarctic
3. Delft
4. France
5. Louisville, New Orleans, fields, and forests
6. An ant hill

Which Word Fits?

Choose a word or phrase to fit each definition.
1. ants' cows
   (a) relative's cattle   (b) aphids   (c) herds
2. elevated tract of land
   (a) desert   (b) plateau   (c) peak
3. periodical passing from one place to another
   (a) extension   (b) concentration   (c) migration
4. specialist in birds
   (a) ornithologist   (b) botanist   (c) biologist
5. self-registering thermometer
   (a) barometer   (b) thermograph   (c) anemometer
6. end of division or line
   (a) terminal   (b) termite   (c) terminology
7. infectious disease
   (a) rabble   (b) rabies   (c) rarebit
8. instrument consisting of lenses
   (a) microscope   (b) bifocals   (c) fluoroscope
9. huge water monster
   (a) mermaid   (b) siren   (c) leviathan
10. smallest particle of an element
    (a) amoeba   (b) atom   (c) microbe

MORE ABOUT SCIENCE AND SCIENTISTS

1. What other stories about scientists and their discoveries do you know? Consult the encyclopedia and other reference books, and report your findings in class.
2. What experiment or study have you conducted? Tell or write about it.
3. What conclusions have you come to concerning the place of science today?
4. On page 435, you will find a list of books on science which you will enjoy.

A Tricky Science Test[1]

If you can answer correctly nine questions in the following quiz, your ability to distinguish nature facts from superstitious beliefs is better than that of most persons; if 12 or more, your nature lore is exceptional. On your paper, write *True* or *False* for each of the statements. You will find the answers below, printed upside down; but don't peek now.

1. A wild animal is more likely to attack you if you are afraid of it.
2. Only the female mosquito ever bites you.
3. Moss grows thickest on the north side of trees.
4. Snow is merely frozen rain.
5. A chameleon takes on the color of the object on which it rests.
6. A person who cannot hear at all is deaf as an adder.
7. Summer is warmer than winter because the earth is then nearer the sun.
8. Beavers use their tails as trowels when building their dams.
9. Venomous snakes are immune to their own poison.
10. Horned toads squirt blood out of their eyes.
11. If you cut an earthworm in two, each half will become a new worm.
12. A shark must turn belly-up in order to bite.
13. Elephants live to be several hundred years old.
14. There is a bird that can fly backward.
15. Squirrels have an accurate memory for the places where they have buried nuts.

Answers to Questions or "A Tricky Science Test"

1. *True.* Most savage animals are peculiarly infuriated by human terror—possibly, as some naturalists believe, because a frightened person gives off a "scent of fear."
2. *True.* Only the female mosquito sucks blood; the male is content with nectar and other plant juices.
3. *False.* Moss-growth depends chiefly on the exposure of the land and the direction of the prevailing winds.
4. *False.* It is sleet which is frozen rain. Snow (flakes formed by the condensation of moisture at temperatures below freezing) falls directly as snow from snow clouds.
5. *False.* The chameleon's color-changes depend on temperature, emotion, health, and other factors unrelated to the chameleon's background.
6. *True.* An adder, like all other snakes, is deaf.
7. *False.* We're nearest the sun on January 2. We fail to get full benefit of its heat, however, because winter days are shorter, and the sun's rays are slanting.
8. *False.* The beaver employs its tail as a rudder in swimming or as a prop when standing on its hind feet.
9. *False.* This was universally believed among scientists until a few years ago, and is still taught in many textbooks; but recent experiments have shown that many venomous reptiles do perish from the poison of their own bite.
10. *True.* The horned toad's ejection of blood, which is intended to terrify enemies, is accompanied by a popping or clicking noise.

[1] "A Tricky Science Test" appeared as "Nature-Fact or Nature-Fiction?" by Alan Devoe in *The Reader's Digest*, April, 1943. Used by permission of the author and *The Reader's Digest*.

SCIENCE IN BOOKS

Beeler, N. F., and Branley, F. M., *Experiments in Science,* 1947 (Crowell).
  Entertaining, simple experiments and their processes.

Britton, Katherine, *What Makes It Tick?* 1943 (Houghton).
  The *how's* and *why's* of numerous inventions and mechanical devices.

Bronson, Wilfrid S., *Freedom and Plenty,* 1953 (Harcourt).
  Conservation in the U. S. A.

Burlingame, Roger, *Inventors behind the Inventor,* 1947 (Harcourt).
  Stories of individuals who inspired great inventors.

Candy, Robert, *Nature Notebook,* 1953 (Houghton).
  All the sides of the nature world.

Clark, G. Glenwood, *Thomas Alva Edison,* 1951 (Aladdin).
  Edison's early struggle for achievement and his great contributions.

Hogner, Dorothy Childs, *Earthworms,* 1953 (Crowell).
  Fascinating details about worms and plant life.

Judson, Clara I., *Soldier Doctor; the Story of William Gorgas,* 1942 (Scribner).
  The doctor who fought yellow fever at the Panama Canal.

Lane, Ferdinand, *All about the Sea,* 1953 (Random House).
  The sea and the life it contains.

Latham, Jean Lee, *Medals for Morse,* 1954 (Aladdin).
  A story of Samuel F. B. Morse as artist and inventor.

Morgan, Alfred P., *Boys' Book of Science and Construction,* 1948 (Lothrop).
  Clear descriptions of many phases of science, including experiments.

Reed, William M., *The Earth for Sam,* 1930 (Harcourt).
  The story of mountains, rivers, dinosaurs, and men.

Reed, William M., *Patterns in the Sky,* 1951 (Morrow).
  How to find the twenty-five most familiar constellations.

Selsam, Millicent, *Microbes at Work,* 1953 (Morrow).
  Their relation to food and plant growth.

Stevens, William Oliver, *Famous Men of Science,* 1952 (Dodd).
  Famous persons in various fields.

Playing
the Game

The Milk Pitcher

Certainly there are various kinds of pitchers, but the pitcher in this story is the home-run variety. However, there's also a cow in the story; and so there is much amusing confusion.
(Note the time when you begin reading.)

THE Fullers named their son "Philip" after his maternal grandfather. That was an error in judgment because the time came when the name Phil Fuller aroused chuckles and snickers among the pleasure-loving faces of the countryside. At the age of one Phil had practically settled upon red as the best color for hair. Sometime in his third year the truth was established that he was left-handed. When given something he did not want, he threw it away with violence.

This act seemed to set up pleasurable emotions in his young soul. His simple face widened into a grin, and before long he was heaving things around for the sheer love of heaving.

At four Phil sprouted a genuine freckle on his nose, the forerunner of a bumper crop; and even his prejudiced mother had to admit that his ears were large for their age.

The youth spent his fourth summer in the society of a Jersey calf named Lily, who was tethered in the orchard. Phil had nothing to do except to throw green apples at a tree with his left hand, and Lily's time was also her own. The child learned not to wince when she licked his pink nose with her rough tongue; and the calf put up with some pretty rowdy con-

——Copyright, 1929, by Howard Brubaker.

duct, too. Both infants cried when separated for the night. The tender attachment between Phil and Lil was the subject of neighborhood gossip as far away as the Doug Morton place at the bend of Squaw Creek.

When Phil was six, he threw a carriage bolt from the wagon shed into the water trough; and he laughed so boisterously over this feat that Mr. Harrington heard the noise while passing in a light spring wagon.

Phil had a misguided sense of humor. It seemed to him that throwing things was the world's funniest joke. As he picked up a stone and let it fly, the freckles on his face widened and he grinned expansively, showing vacant spots where he was changing teeth.

By this time his love for the cow stable had become a grand passion. Horses, dogs, cats, and pigs meant rather less in his young life than they do to most farm boys; but cows meant more.

Phil attended all the milkings with his father, dealt out bran, and threw down hay. He wandered in and out among bovine legs without fear; hoofs, horns, and teeth had no terrors for him. He was soon old enough to drive the cattle to pasture and bring them back.

At the age of eight he was probably the ablest red-headed cowboy and left-handed stone-thrower in Clinton Township. At this date in history he had drunk enough milk to float a battleship and thrown enough stones, sticks, bones, horseshoes, apples, corncobs, and baseballs to sink one. He was now the owner in fee simple of Lily's knock-kneed daughter, Dolly. This white-faced blonde flapper followed Phil around with adoration and bleated at the barnyard gate until her playmate came home from school.

That fount of knowledge was Clinton Township, District No. 5, known locally as Tamarack School. There he absorbed a reasonable quantity of booklore and learned to pitch a straight ball with speed and control. He is still remembered in educational circles as the southpaw[1] who hurled the Tamarackers to glorious victory over the Squaw Creek outfit, while unveiling the broadest grin ever seen on the lot and issuing many unnecessary noises. Although he had a lot of influence over a baseball, he could not make his face behave.

Baseball was the great joy of Phil's school years. Every spring when the frost came out of the ground, his flaming head sprang up on the soggy field like a tulip. He had never learned to bat well, but he was a thrower of great ability and a laugher and yeller of great audibility. In school when asked to give the boundaries of Baluchistan, he could scarcely make the teacher hear; but on the diamond his disorderly conduct was noted and

deplored as far away as Grandma Longenecker's cottage.

The game uncorked his inhibitions and released his ego. His habitual shyness vanished and gave place to vociferous glee. He did frolicsome things with his feet; his arms went round like a windmill wheel; sometimes he burst into what he wrongly believed to be song. Miss Willikans, the teacher, testified that Phil had easily the worst singing voice that had attended District No. 5 in her time—which would be nineteen years if she lived through this term, as seemed highly unlikely.

Inevitably there came an afternoon in late May when Phil's career as a Tamaracker had run its course. He twisted a button almost off his new coat, whispered a graduating piece about Daniel Webster, took his books and his well-worn right-hand glove, and went back to the cows.

At five o'clock the following morning the fourteen-year-old Phil became the vice president and general manager of the dairy department of the Fuller farm. His father was overworked, help was scarce and expensive, and the graduate of Tamarack was judged strong enough to handle the job. He milked all the cows that summer, cleaned the stalls, helped to get in the hay and fill the silo. He ran the separator; he churned; he carried skim milk to the pigs. The end of the summer found him a stocky lad of rather less than normal height, but with a rank growth of feet, arms, and ears. He had the complexion of a boiled beet, and his hair was exactly the shade of a two-cent stamp. His hands were large and fully equipped

---

[1] southpaw. A left-handed pitcher.

with freckles, calluses, bumps, cracks, warts, knuckles, and rough, red wrists.

Phil could lift with one hand Dolly's new calf, Molly, he could throw a ten-pound sledge hammer over the hay barn, he could sing like a creaky pump, and he shattered all known speed records from the stable to the dining room. He was an able performer with the table fork as well as with the pitchfork.

In September he took all these assets and liabilities and his first long pants, and went to Branford to live with Aunt Mary and Uncle Phineas, and attend high school. As he was winding up his affairs preparatory to this great adventure, it was clear that he had something on his mind. It came out one night at supper in the hiatus between the fifth and sixth ears of Golden Bantam.

"It's too bad they don't keep a cow," he said, apropos of nothing.

"Oh, sakes alive, child!" Mother exclaimed in surprise. "They wouldn't want to be bothered with a cow."

Phil's ears went red. He polished off his corncob and returned to the attack. "They wouldn't need to be bothered much. They have no horse any more, and there's room in the barn. I could feed her and milk her and everything. I bet Aunt Mary would be glad to have lots of nice milk and cream. We could tie her behind the buggy and take her in with us."

"Tie who—Aunt Mary?" asked father with ill-timed facetiousness.

"Dolly," said Phil.

A dozen objections were raised and disposed of. Aunt Mary and Uncle Phineas were consulted by telephone, and after the first shock they agreed to the outrageous plan. And thus it came about that Phil Fuller was the first case in recorded history of a boy who went to Branford High School accompanied by a private and personal cow.

During those first months of strangeness and homesickness, Dolly was his comfort and his joy, his link with the familiar. He brushed and polished that blonde cow until her upholstery was threadbare, pampered her with choice viands and clean bedding, scrubbed and whitewashed the interior of the old barn, put in window sashes to give Dolly more sunlight and a better view. Often when the day was fair, he led her around the block to take the air and see a little city life.

At six o'clock of a dark, bitter morning the neighbors could hear distressing noises issuing from Phineas Rucker's lantern-lit barn, and they knew from sad experiences of the past that another day was about to dawn and the redheaded Fuller boy was singing to his heart's true love.

Dolly was now in the full flush of her splendid young cowhood, and home was never like this. Phil plied her with experimental mixtures—beet pulp, ground oats, cottonseed meal— and carefully noted the results. The contented cow responded gratefully to this treatment. Before long she exceeded the needs of the Rucker family, and Phil was doing a pleasant little milk business with the neighbors. His immaculate barn, his new white overalls, his vocal excesses, and his free street parades, all helped trade. The milk inspector passed Dolly with high honors, and doctors recommended her for ailing babies. Presently she was one of Branford's leading citizens, a self-supporting twenty-quart cow, commanding a premium of three cents over the market price. Phil had discovered his lifework.

His second great discovery did not come until spring. On a blustery March day he was out on the diamond behind the high-school building warming up his left wing and chuckling over his favorite joke when Mr. Huckley, chemistry teacher and baseball coach, came along.

"Southpaw, eh!" he demanded. "Let's see what you've got, Fuller."

Phil gave a brief demonstration of his wares with Dinky Doolittle holding the catcher's glove.

"Plenty of steam and good control," the teacher said, "and your footwork is terrible. Now show us your curve."

"I haven't got any," Phil answered. "Nobody ever showed me how to pitch a curve."

"Somebody will now," Mr. Huckley said. "Whether you can do it or not is another question."

That was the beginning of a beautiful friendship and a new era in the life of Philip Fuller.

Mr. Huckley had pitched on the team of Athens University, of which he was a graduate. He liked Phil, admired his able hands, his abnormally developed forearms, his keen joy in the game. The coach saw great possibilities in this piece of raw material, and he spent a patient hour teaching Phil some of the rudiments of curve pitching; and in time they achieved a perceptible out curve. At the height of his exultation, the boy pulled out a nickel-plated watch and said:

"I ask you to excuse me now. It's time to milk my cow."

After a week of such instruction, Mr. Huckley handed down this decision: "You have the makings of a good pitcher, Phil, if you're willing to learn. You have a couple of fine qualities and not over twenty-five or thirty serious faults."

Phil's ears flushed with pleasure and embarrassment.

"Well, maybe I can get shut of some of them—I mean those—faults. I've got four years to do it in."

"Right-o. You have good control of your fast one, you have a nice little out, and you have the worst style of windup these eyes have ever seen."

Four years of study, dairying, and baseball, with summers of hard work on the farm, made Phil a different boy —different and yet curiously the same. His shoulders were broader, his arms longer and stronger, but he did not add many inches to his stature. He knew more mathematics, science, and history; but Latin was still Greek to him. Although he took on some of the manners and customs of his town contemporaries, he still had the gait of one walking over a plowed field. In time he learned to talk with girls without being distressed, but as a social light he was a flickering flame in a smoky chimney. He was a conspicuous success on the barn floor but a brilliant failure on the dance floor. His voice changed, but not for the better. His matin[2] song to Dolly now sounded like a bullfrog with a bad attack of static. He wrote a creditable little rural farce for the senior dramatic class and further distinguished himself as the worst actor on the American stage.

Though much ridiculed, he was universally liked and genuinely respected. On the ballfield he was a source of low comedy to friend and foe because of the eccentric behavior of his face and feet; but in his succeeding seasons on the mound he pitched the Branford High School out of the cellar position into respectable company, into select society, and finally, in his senior year, into the state championship of the small-town division.

At the joyfest in the assembly hall in celebration of this final triumph, Phil was forced to make a speech. He fixed his eyes upon his third vest button, and informed it in confidence that it was Mr. Huckley who had made him what he was today—which wasn't very much.

When his turn came, the chemist and coach arose and told the world a great secret about this Phil Fuller who had now pitched his last game for dear old B.H.S. Phil, he said, owed his success as a pitcher to his having been brought up in a cow barn. Constant milking had developed his forearm muscles to surprising strength, and the knots on his good left hand had enabled him to get a spin on the ball that produced his deadliest curves.

"I therefore propose," he said, "that Phil's girl friend, Dolly, be

[2] *matin.* Morning song.

elected an honorary member of the team."

This motion was seconded with a will and carried with a whoop, and Dolly became, as far as anyone could learn, the only cow that ever belonged to a ball club.

"Phil has told you," Mr. Huckley went on, "that he got some help from my coaching. If so, he has chosen a rotten way to pay his debt. Instead of going to a high-class and fancy culture factory like Athens, he has decided to enter Sparta Agricultural College. Athens and Sparta are deadly enemies in athletics, and some day Phil may use what I have taught him against my own alma mater. There is no use trying to keep Phil from running after the cows; but this is a sad blow to me. I didn't raise my boy to be a Spartan."

It was the county agricultural agent who had first put Sparta into Phil's head. The boy had naturally assumed that his education would cease with high school, but this Mr. Runkleman came into Dolly's palatial quarters one day and spoke an eloquent piece in favor of his own Sparta.

"A boy who intends to be an expert dairy farmer," he said in part, "ought to learn all there is on the subject. You have a natural gift for taking care of cows, but what you don't know about scientific dairying would fill a ten-foot shelf."

"That's so," Phil answered, "but I haven't got much money."

"You don't need much money. Lots of the boys are working their way through. I'll guarantee that you get a job in the college dairy barn. The work will pay your board, teach you the practical side, and you'll meet the nicest cows in the world."

This was a weighty inducement, and one crisp day in late September found Phil knocking at the door of higher education. He was a youth of five feet five with fiery hair and complexion, with ears that stuck out like red semaphores; a homely, awkward, likable boy, full of hope, inexperience, diffidence, and whole raw milk. His only regret was that he could not take Dolly with him to college.

Because of Mr. Runkleman's hearty recommendation, he got his job in the dairy barn; and he took a room in a house near by. His days sped by in a new kind of eternal triangle— boardinghouse, dairy, and classroom— and he was happy in all three places.

Every morning, at the ghastly hour of four, he trudged through windy blackness to the big concrete barn. Now followed several hours of milking, feeding, currying, and stable cleaning, in company with half a dozen other cow students, then home to breakfast and to class. In the late afternoon there was a repetition of these chores, followed by dinner, some study, and an early bed. Such was the wild college life of this flaming youth.

Football, the great autumn obsession, meant little to him. Basketball was more fun, but an habitual early riser makes a poor customer of night life. In fact, Phil made up his mind that, for the first year, he would waste no time on athletics.

Sibyl Barnett Samboy, the wife of Kenneth Samboy, director of Sparta athletics, said after Phil had been introduced to her at the freshman reception: "That's the first time I ever shook hands with a Stillson wrench."

Although he honestly intended to keep out of baseball, the first warm afternoon in March brought on an attack of the old spring fever. There was no harm, he thought, in getting out a ball and glove and tossing a few to "Spider" Coppery behind the barn while waiting for milking time. Before long it was a regular practice among the "cowboys" to beguile their idle moments with playing catch and knocking up flies; and presently there was talk of forming a team to play a game with the students of the horticulture department, otherwise the "greenhouse gang."

An insulting challenge was given and taken, and the game took place on a pleasant Saturday.

This contest was held upon the old ball grounds. The new stadium was built upon a better site, and the former athletic grounds with their little grandstand were given over to the general use of the students. Samboy was a firm believer in athletics for everybody. He loved to stir up little wars between classes, dormitories, fraternities, and departments. Often these little home-brew contests developed and uncovered talent for the college teams.

Along about the fifth inning of this ragged ball game, an uninvited guest appeared among the handful of spectators in the grandstand. Phil was on the mound at the time.

So Mr. Samboy's eyes were gladdened by the sight of a stocky, freckled, redheaded southpaw, who burned them over with power, who laughed from head to foot and uttered unfortunate noises.

Samboy talked with him after the game, poked his nose into his past, and urged him to try for the college team.

Phil protested that he was too busy with his classes and his cows. It was a long argument, but Samboy won.

"Report to Donnigan on Monday," said the director, "and tell him I suggested that he look you over. Every coach has a free hand with his own team, you know; but if he turns you down, let me know, and I'll give you a tryout on the freshman team. I'll speak to Professor Wetherby, if you like, and ask him to let you shift hours at the dairy while you're trying your luck on the diamond."

"You don't suppose"—Phil was visibly embarrassed—"there wouldn't be any danger of me losing that job—or anything? I wouldn't do that for all the baseball there is."

"Not a chance, Fuller. We don't give fellows positions here because they are good athletes, but we don't fire 'em either."

H. B. Donnigan — "Hardboiled Donnigan"—had learned his trade under the great Tim Crowley, of the Eagles. Donnigan's big-league days were over, and he was making a living coaching college teams. He used the Crowley method and the Crowley philosophy. All ball players were worms and should be treated as such.

He had spent his boyhood among the tin cans and bottles of a vacant lot in New York's gashouse district, and he never really believed that ball players could be grown in the country.

One trouble with his policy was that it did not work at all. It was rumored that when his contract expired at the end of the season, Samboy would let him go. A sense of his failure did not improve the coach's technique—or his temper. It was to this man-eating tiger that Samboy had cheerfully thrown the redheaded rookie from the cow barn.

"And now who let you in?" was Hardboiled Donnigan's address of welcome.

"Mr. Samboy said would you please look me over."

The phrase was perhaps an unfortunate one. The coach did exactly that.

"All right. Tell him I've done it; and if you're Lillian Gish, I'm Queen Marie."

"I'm a pitcher—southpaw." Phil's hard-earned grammar fled in this crisis. "I done good in high school."

"Oh, all right, stick around," said the testy coach. "When I get time, I'll see if you've got anything."

He seemed to forget all about Phil—who had not the slightest objection. The boy had a bad case of stage fright, partly from Donnigan's ill-nature, but more from the immensity of the empty stadium. He had almost made up his mind to sneak back to his beloved cows when he realized that he was being addressed.

"Hey, you—carrots—come out to the box and pitch to the batters." Donnigan took his place behind the plate. "Murder this guy," he muttered to Risler, a senior and the captain of the team.

Risler murdered, instead, the bright April sunshine in three brutal blows. The old miracle had happened again. The moment Phil took hold of the ball and faced the batter he forgot his fears; he remembered only that throwing a baseball was the greatest fun in the world.

"Hey, wipe that grin off your face," yelled the coach. "What do you think this is, a comic opery?"

Phil controlled his features with an effort while two more batters showed their futility. Donnigan handed his catcher's glove to "Swede" Olson.

"Gimme that stick," he growled. "You birds belong in a home for the blind!"

There were two serious mistakes that Phil could make in this crisis, and he made them both without delay. He struck out Hardboiled Donnigan, and he laughed. Of course, he knew better than to ridicule the coach; but there was something irresistible about the way Donnigan lunged for the last slow floater.

"All right, now you've done your stuff, get out!" yelled the offended professional. "And stay out. I can't monkey with a guy who won't take his work serious. Laugh that off."

A few snickers were thrown after the defeated candidate, but the players knew that Donnigan had committed a manager's unpardonable sin of turning down a promising recruit on account of a personal grudge—and he knew that they knew.

As for Phil, he left the stadium with genuine relief. The more he saw of Donnigan, the better he liked cows. He had kept his promise to Samboy;

now he would just sink out of sight and stick to business.

In reply to an inquiry, Samboy got a letter from Mr. Huckley stating that, in the opinion of an old Athens pitcher, Phil Fuller was the best that Branford High School had ever produced. The director showed this tribute to Donnigan.

"Oh, that's the sorrel top. He hasn't got anything but a giggle."

"Are you sure, Hank? We could use a good southpaw."

"I know, but he ain't the answer. The Athens bird is trying to frame us."

"I'll wish him on the freshmen then."

"Sure—give the kid a chanst, Ken," said Donnigan with affected good will. "He might show something if he ever gets over the idea it's all a big wheeze."

Phil was heartily welcomed into the freshman squad. In the presence of Samboy he performed ably in a practice game. His fast ball, well-controlled curve, and change of pace made the inexperienced batters helpless; and his strange conduct landed him in the public eye with a bang.

The college comic paper, *The Cut-up*, had a fine time over Phil. It discovered that the eccentric left-hander was a cow-barner, and it almost died of laughter at this joke.

"Phil Fuller, the Milk Pitcher," was the title of the piece. He was one of the wide-open faces from the wide-open spaces, the wit said, and sure winner of the standing broad grin. Also he proved the truth of the old saying, "Little pitchers have big ears."

But the result of the publicity was

that the crowd at the freshman-sopho-more game was the largest of the season. Among those present were old President Whitman, Professor Wetherby, and Mr. and Mrs. Kenneth Samboy.

The assembled underclassmen laughed until they ached at the grinning, gesticulating, noisy southpaw with the red-thatched roof. They greeted his queer, awkward windup with a yell invented by the sophomore cheer leader, a long, rhythmic "So-o-o, boss." But when he had won the game handily for the freshmen, the jeers turned to cheers.

Sibyl Samboy looked at her husband.

"And why," she asked, "is this infant phenomenon not on the varsity?"

"Hank can't see him somehow; and if I butt in, it upsets my whole system of government. Personally I'd pitch him in a game or two to season him and then try him on Athens. But it isn't worth a rumpus, Sib. After all, Fuller will be with us a long time yet, and Donnigan won't."

"Poor old Hank! I wonder what he's got against the boy."

"It's incompatibility of temperament, I guess. Hank thinks baseball is cosmic, and Phil thinks it comic."

"And you," said Sibyl, "think you're a wisecracker on *The Cutup*."

In the next issue of that little weekly there was a marked difference in tone. The fresh cowboy, it said, was showing ability as well as risibility. It was time Donnigan tried him out on the team.

There was something inevitable about the Phil Fuller movement.

Donnigan did not want him on the team, Samboy was committed to keep his hands off, and Phil himself had no craving to appear in that big stadium. But the team was limping through a disastrous season, and there were signs of disaffection among the players. The crowds dwindled; finances were suffering; and the all-important Athens game, the schedule's climax, was approaching like the day of doom.

Donnigan resisted as long as he could; but, schooled as he was in the professional game, he recognized one power greater than players, managers, or owners—the customer. And when white-haired Doctor Whitman called him into the president's office and intimated ever so gently that it might be just as well to give the public what it wanted, he gave in.

He did not surrender, but he retreated inch by inch. He gave Phil a uniform and let him practice with the team and learn the signals, then put him in at the end of a game to pitch a game that was already hopelessly lost. On the eve of the Athens contest he announced that he would pitch Hagenlaucher with Graybar and Fuller in reserve.

Any contest with the traditional foe always brought out the largest crowd of the season, but this year there was a novelty in the situation. The freshmen were out in full force, prepared to make an organized nuisance of themselves on behalf of their favorite character. When he appeared on the field for practice, they gave him a tremendous ovation.

Just before the game started, Phil realized that somebody was calling to him from the edge of the stand. To his great delight, this proved to be Mr. Huckley, who had traveled all the way from Branford to see the game.

"Phil," he said, "if you get a chance today, I want you to do your darnedest."

"I'd kinda hate to play against Athens after all you did for me."

"I know. That's why I spoke. Forget all that, Phil. If they put you in, pitch as you did last year against Milltown, Three Falls, Oderno, and Jefferson. Good luck!"

"Thank you, Mr. Huckley. I'll meet you right here after it's over. I've got something to tell you."

As he took his seat on the bench, his smile faded, and he lapsed into gloom. "He's scared stiff," thought Donnigan. "I won't dare to stick him in if Haggy blows."

But Hagenlaucher was not blowing up; he was pitching his best game of the season. The Athens moundsman was doing well, too; and there was promise of a tight pitchers' battle. But in time the game grew looser, the pitchers faltered, Haggy was getting wabbly.

The score stood 6 to 5 in favor of the visitors in the fifth when the umpire made the momentous announcement, "Greenwich batting for Hagenlaucher." At the same moment Graybar and Fuller left for the bull pen to warm up. The next inning would see a new face in the box.

Whose face? That was what all Sparta wanted to know; that was what Samboy wanted to know as he stepped out of the stand and walked up to Donnigan.

"Graybar," said the coach. "Fuller is scared to death. I guess he's got a yellow streak."

Samboy hesitated. The teams were changing sides now; and the embattled freshmen were booming in unison, like a bass drum: "Phil! Phil! Phil!"

"All right, you're the doctor, Hank. But I'll go and talk to the boy."

The new pitcher did his best, but he was a broken reed. A base on balls, a single, and a hit batter filled the bags, with nobody out; and the air was full of disaster. Captain Risler stepped to the box as if to steady the wabbly pitcher; Swede Olson, the catcher, joined this conference, which was further enriched by the presence of the lanky first baseman, Keeler.

Now Graybar handed the ball to Risler who made a sign toward the bench. There was an instant of suspense, and then out of the dugout appeared the gaudy head of Phil Fuller.

An avalanche of sound slid down upon the field. From the freshmen bloc came the long, rhythmic yell "So-o-o, boss." In the general confusion, Hardboiled Donnigan was scarcely seen emerging from the dugout. He seemed to shrink before the wave of noise; then he disappeared through an opening out of the field and out of the athletics department of Sparta.

Scarcely anyone in the audience knew that Donnigan had not ordered the change of pitchers, nor had Samboy. It was Risler, backed by Olson, Keeler, and the whole team. It was mutiny; it was rebellion.

But this was not the familiar Phil Fuller who had laughed and danced his way into the hearts of the fans. This was a serious Phil, a gloomy Phil. Life was now real; life was earnest. He took his long queer windup, and he threw the ball high, far too high. Olson made a jump for the ball, missed it, and landed in a heap. Before he could recover the ball, two runs had come over, and Athens rocked with laughter.

But so, to the amazement of the universe, did Phil Fuller. It suddenly seemed to the misguided youth that it was the funniest thing in the world that he should have thrown away the ball and let in two runs. The infield laughed in imitation. Philip was himself again.

Now the tension under which the team had been working suddenly relaxed as if a tight band had snapped and brought relief. The nervous, eager, do-or-die spirit suddenly disappeared, leaving the natural instinct of youth to have a good time. With the utmost ease the pitcher and the infield disposed of the next three batters, and in their half of the inning they began their climb toward victory.

It was a strange, exciting, hilarious game. Phil had never played in such fast company before or faced such a murderous array of bats. He was in hot water half a dozen times, but he never lost the healing gift of laughter.

And the team played as if baseball came under the head of pleasure.

Samboy said to Risler, who sat beside him on the bench in the eighth:

"Whether we win or lose, this is the answer. We're going to build a new idea and a new style of play around that southpaw. You watch our smoke for the next three years, Rissy."

"Just my luck, Ken. In about fifteen minutes I'm through with college baseball forever."

"Well, don't you ever regret what you did today. I can't officially approve it, but—there goes Phil fanning again."

Samboy now addressed the departing warriors.

"All right, boys—last frame and two to the good. All you have to do is hold 'em."

Now it appeared that Phil had been saving the finest joke of all for the end. The season was over, and he could take liberties with his arm. He dug his warts and bumps and calluses into the horsehide and proceeded to retire the side with three straight strike-outs, nine rowdy laughs, two informal dances, and an incredible noise that was a hideous parody on song.

But it was an altered and sobered Phil who found his old coach after the game and received his fervent congratulations.

"Were you worried, Phil?" Mr. Huckley asked.

"Yes, but I was glad they let me play. I had so much fun I forgot my trouble."

"What trouble, Phil?"

"Well, I got a letter from Father this morning, and my Dolly is terribly sick. Seems she got hold of an old paint can some place. Cows like to lick paint, you know; and it's deadly poison. They don't think Dolly will live. Maybe I left a can of paint somewhere myself. That's what bothers me."

"Listen, Phil. I was supposed to tell you, but you got away too quick. Your father telephoned me this morning. Dolly's out of danger. She's doing fine."

"Oh, boy!" cried Phil, and his eyes shone with tears.

Down in the field the Sparta students, led by the band, were circling the stadium in that parade of victory which must follow every triumph over Athens.

"There'll be plenty more ball games," said Phil, "but there'll never be another cow like Dolly."

(How long did it take you to read the story? Check your reading rate with the Reading Score Board.)

❧❧❧

PITCHING IDEAS

1. What were some of Phil's peculiarities?
2. Which of his peculiarities bothered Coach Hardboiled Donnigan?
3. What was worrying Phil on the day of the big game with Athens?
4. What was the most important thing in Phil's life?
5. How is this story different from most of the sports stories you have read?

SURPRISING WORD COMBINATIONS

The story is full of surprising and amusing ways of saying things. Here are two examples. Can you find at least ten more?

1. At the age of one Phil had practically settled upon red as the best color for hair.

2. . . . even his prejudiced mother had to admit his ears were large for their age.

COLORFUL FIGURES OF SPEECH

Here are two examples of the clever use of similes and metaphors. How many other examples can you find?

1. his arms went round *like a windmill wheel*
2. as a social light he was a *flickering flame in a smoky chimney*

INTELLIGENT GUESSING

Can you guess intelligently at the meanings of these?

1. The game uncorked his *inhibitions* and released his *ego*.
2. the students of the *horticultural* department, otherwise the "greenhouse gang"
3. Hank thinks baseball is *cosmic*, and Phil thinks it's comic.

READING SCORE BOARD

Number of Words in Story: 5690

Number of Minutes	57	28 1/2	22 3/4	19	14 1/4	11 3/8
Reading Rate	100 w.p.m.	200 w.p.m.	250 w.p.m.	300 w.p.m.	400 w.p.m.	500 w.p.m.

DIFFERENT WAYS OF READING

Do you realize that you read in a number of different ways? Sometimes you sit down to read for the sheer fun of it (very much as you read "The Milk Pitcher"). You are not looking for any facts; you are not in a hurry; you are simply reading and having a good time doing it. Then sometimes you read in another way. You want a few bits of information, and those few bits have to be gleaned from a whole mass of material. So you glance quickly through the material, looking only for the few facts you want. In other words, you are skimming. Then there is still another way that you read. Let us say that you have a reading assignment in history or science—a tough one—and you must know step by step and fact by fact everything that is in that assignment. Certainly you do not read such material casually as you would "The Milk Pitcher," and you surely would not dare to do any skimming. You read carefully and conscientiously for information.

◂◖ ERNEST LAWRENCE THAYER

Casey at the Bat

You have probably heard people talk about "Casey at the Bat" without realizing that there is a poem by that name. Here is the famous poem about the famous Casey.

The outlook wasn't brilliant for the Mudville nine that day;
The score stood four to two, with but one inning more to play;
And so, when Cooney died at first, and Barrows did the same,
A sickly silence fell upon the patrons of the game.

A straggling few got up to go in deep despair. The rest
Clung to the hope which springs eternal in the human breast;
They thought, if only Casey could but get a whack, at that,
They'd put up even money now, with Casey at the bat.

But Flynn preceded Casey, as did also Jimmy Blake;
And the former was a pudding, and the latter was a fake.
So upon that stricken multitude grim melancholy sat,
For there seemed but little chance of Casey's getting to the bat.

But Flynn let drive a single, to the wonderment of all,
And Blake, the much despisèd, tore the cover off the ball.
And when the dust had lifted, and they saw what had occurred,
There was Jimmy safe on second, and Flynn a-hugging third.

Then from the gladdened multitude went up a joyous yell,
It bounded from the mountaintop and rattled in the dell;
It struck upon the hillside and recoiled upon the flat,
For Casey, mighty Casey, was advancing to the bat.

There was ease in Casey's manner as he stepped into his place,
There was pride in Casey's bearing and a smile on Casey's face;
And when, responding to the cheers, he lightly doffed his hat,
No stranger in the crowd could doubt 'twas Casey at the bat.

Ten thousand eyes were on him as he rubbed his hands with dirt;
Five thousand tongues applauded when he wiped them on his shirt;
Then, while the writhing pitcher ground the ball into his hip,
Defiance gleamed in Casey's eye, a sneer curled Casey's lip.

And now the leather-covered sphere came hurtling through the air,
And Casey stood a-watching it in haughty grandeur there:
Close by the sturdy batsman the ball unheeded sped.
"That ain't my style," said Casey. "Strike one," the umpire said.

From the benches, black with people, there went up a muffled roar,
Like the beating of the storm waves on a stern and distant shore;
"Kill him! Kill the umpire!" shouted someone in the stand.
And it's likely they'd have killed him had not Casey raised his hand.

With a smile of Christian charity great Casey's visage shone;
He stilled the rising tumult; he bade the game go on;
He signaled to the pitcher, and once more the spheroid flew,
But Casey still ignored it; and the umpire said, "Strike two."

"Fraud!" cried the maddened thousands, and the echo answered, "Fraud!"
But one scornful look from Casey, and the audience was awed;
They saw his face grow stern and cold; they saw his muscles strain;
And they knew that Casey wouldn't let that ball go by again.

The sneer is gone from Casey's lips; his teeth are clenched in hate;
He pounds with cruel violence his bat upon the plate;
And now the pitcher holds the ball, and now he lets it go,
And now the air is shattered by the force of Casey's blow.

Oh, somewhere in this favored land the sun is shining bright;
The band is playing somewhere, and somewhere hearts are light,
And somewhere men are laughing, and somewhere children shout;
But there is no joy in Mudville—mighty Casey has struck out.

1. What line of the poem gives you the biggest surprise?
2. Why did Casey deserve what came to him?
3. Are people whom you know ever like Casey?
4. What details in the poem show that Thayer must have known baseball?

⋆⋆ JOHN GARTNER

Peewee Half

Here is a great story about a boy who was too light to play football—but who did, and won glory for himself and for his team.
(Jot down the time when you begin reading.)

THE first time I saw Don Meek I shook my head. Even with the relatively poor football material we had at Western State College, his 125 pounds and slight build seemed like too great a handicap.

"Meek, you're not big enough for this business," I told him frankly. "Carrington's Cadets and Marshall University's gang will break you in two. Better forget it."

Don swallowed a couple of times, and his lips quivered. Finally he got hold of his voice.

"But, Coach, I've *got* to play football. I'm tougher than you think."

I surveyed the small ankles and wrists and imagined that slight figure in scrimmage with my motley crew, let alone against conference opposition. I had started to speak when I got a good look at his eyes. Something about them seemed strangely

—————Reprinted from *The Open Road for Boys*. Used by permission of author and magazine.

familiar, as if I had seen him before, and known him.

"Okay, Don," I said and crossed my fingers. "You can try it for a few days."

At the end of the first two weeks I knew that if my gang hoped to win any games, they would have to play an original brand of football. I spent three or four hectic evenings figuring out an offense and came up with some wild forward-lateral stuff and flea-flickers that would either go all the way or backfire completely. And through it all Meek was the last sub on the bench. I was simply afraid to use him.

On the day of the opener with Davis College I felt as jittery as any of the players. I held my breath as quarterback Tom Jensen took the high kick and came back upfield. If we got any quick injuries, it would be curtains.

Jensen went down on our 30. He

jumped up quickly, however; and the team went into the "T." Jerry Sparks, left half, started in motion, Jensen faked neatly to the full, then rifled one out to Sparks on the dead run. The surprise caught the Davis flank off guard, and Jerry went 25 yards. Almost got away, too.

The bleacherites sat dumfounded. I'd taken pains to see that all the publicity about our gang played up the small number on the squad and its lack of weight and experience. When they saw Sparks shoot around the end for a real gain, they didn't believe it. But when Jensen pulled a forward lateral that ended up in Sparks's hands over the goal, they really let out a yell. I kinda' grinned, too, because whatever happened, at least we'd scored.

I tried to resign myself when the Davis safety took the next kickoff and dodged his way to the 40. They punched once for two and came back with an in-and-out off-tackle for three. A pass fell incomplete, and they had to kick. Jensen took the boot on our 15 and came back to the 20. I listened to his high voice call out the numbers and watched Sparks start in motion. The strong side line-backer followed him out. Jensen handled the oval cleanly and slipped it to fullback Ray Jones, who ducked over the vacated position for six. I edged forward on the bench.

Jensen kept it up. Using about six plays, he mixed it so well that the Davis defense was chasing all over the field. Just before the half gun he sneaked over center himself for our second counter.

During intermission I was on the spot. I didn't know what to say to the gang. Jensen was a natural tactician, doing a swell job at calling plays. Sparks's open field work and speed, coupled with Jones's average plunging, had put us ahead. The rest were playing at their top, and I knew it. So I just pulled the old stock half-time stuff.

"Gang, the game's not over yet. You've got to go out there and play the next half even harder than the first. You're ahead, but not enough to be sure of victory. That Davis crew will wake up and come back hard. You've got to stop them."

But the second half was a repetition of the first. Davis's men waked up enough to hold us to one six-pointer but they were never a threat themselves. In the last three minutes I put in the subs, and shivered when Meek took the pigskin and whipped around the end. He ran like a scared rabbit and changed direction at full speed. He shifted once, slapped straight into a tackler he hadn't seen, and went down like a sack of flour. I was off the bench and on the field immediately; but he bounced up, shook himself, and went to position. I stopped, turned, and sat down. Meek had made 20 yards! The gun stopped the play after the full crashed once for no gain.

The gang in the stands went wild. In the locker room the boys were laughing and horsing. I still couldn't believe it. Those green kids winning a game! Probably Davis was not better off for material than we were. I began to worry about the next one.

We squeaked over Lombard by one point, 7 to 6. A little overconfidence crept in during the week, and the boys didn't look too good. Meek didn't get into the game.

In the third contest, with Janesville, I had two regulars on the bench, Center Bob Timmons suffering from a wrenched knee and right tackle Tass Sosnowski from a couple of bruised ribs. Yards of tape held the rest of the team together, and I began to see my dreams of a miracle fade. But Lady Luck sat on our bench, and we won by two touchdowns.

During the next two weeks our razzle-dazzle fooled Hardford and Colston enough to give us victory. But it was a battered line-up that did the trick. The team clicked because Jensen, strategy-master, and Sparks, speed-merchant, were still in there. Meek played a minute or two in each game, and I began to wonder if I was a fool for not playing him more. The kid was greased lightning.

Marshall University's squad had met Carrington and eked out a one-touchdown victory. We had Carrington next and were to top the season with Marshall on Thanksgiving Day. I looked at that taped-up squad of mine, and my heart jumped into my throat. It hadn't been too bad against the rest of the schools, but squads like these next two were out of our class. I was walking slowly back to the dressing rooms when Meek tapped my shoulder.

"Coach, I've got to play against Carrington and Marshall. I won't get hurt. I can't explain why, but it means more than ever to me now." Here his voice broke, and he lowered his face for an instant. I tried to hedge.

"It would be suicide, boy. Those fellows are big and tough."

There was stark drama in his face. And in that instant a 25-year-old memory came out of the past and hit me right between the eyes. I had seen that same look on a big tackle playing with my first team at Western a long time ago. I didn't remember why he had looked like that, but I did recall that his name was Meek!

"Don," I said, "what's your father's name?"

"James, sir," he replied, and his lips firmed even more.

"I should have known," I almost whispered. "Your dad played every minute of every game in 1920. Where is he now?"

"He'll be at the Carrington game. He didn't want you to know who I am."

"Maybe you can play a little, Don. I'll sleep on it."

A big crowd thronged the bleachers around Western's field. Even after long years at the game, my stomach was turning flips. I took special care to pad up all the bruises and fix all ankle and knee wraps perfectly. It took four cartons of adhesive. Meek got his share.

All luck can't be good, and the Carrington outfit was tough. Jensen and Sparks shot the works for one touchdown while Carrington picked up two. It was still 14 to 7 just before the end of the game; and as we took a punt on our own 15, I cleaned the bench. I felt that the jig was up and knew very well how badly the subs wanted to play. Meek's deep blue eyes bored through me.

"Okay, Don. In for Sparks." The youngster went about his warm-up in a businesslike way. Two plays, three at most, and the game would be over. A loss, but a creditable game anyway. I called the sub quarter aside.

"Let Meek carry one play, no more. Take your time so you won't have to kick."

Part of the crowd got up and started to leave. We were in a bad place for a right-side offense, about 16 yards in from the side line. The quarter bounced with the count, and the ball was passed. The fake was sloppy, and the whole defense saw the lateral to Meek. The kid took it on the run and stopped short just a yard from the side line.

Meek hesitated while the big Carrington line came through. I averted my eyes to keep from seeing the pounding Don was about to take, all the while berating myself for sending him in. Then I heard the crowd roar. I looked up and saw Don in full speed coming directly across the field toward our bench.

I jumped up along with the regulars as he eluded the end and cut to the corner of the field. The defensive right half launched himself into the air, but his fingers only flicked Don's flying heels. The safety was more cagey, coming up gradually to corner the runner on the side line. The defensive man threw a block to try to force Don outside. The kid stopped dead and cut back. But the whipping heel of the blocker caught him on the knee and spun him around. I could feel the pain myself as Don hobbled the last 20 yards to the goal and fell over the line.

I got there in time to pick him up almost as soon as he hit. As I cut the elastic and examined the injury, I heard the yell which indicated a successful kick. We were tied with Carrington. Don's face was as impassive as ever. "The knee's okay, Coach. Sorry we didn't win." Then with a great effort he got up, walked to the bench and sat down. I scarcely heard the final gun after our opponents had been stopped on their 35.

In the locker room there seemed to be more than usual well-wishing and glad-handing, but I didn't get the drift right away as I was baking out Don's knee. It seemed a miracle that the joint still held together. I made him flex it several times and fingered it thoroughly, but everything seemed in one piece. I kept looking for Jim Meek, but he didn't show up.

It wasn't until the morning paper came out that I realized everyone was giving me credit for the strategy in tying the great Carrington team! What a laugh! That's the way it goes in the coaching game, however; so I just let myself soak in the honeyed phrases set forth in print before my eyes:

"Old Mike Thomas, master coach, outfoxed mighty Carrington yesterday when he sent in Rabbit Don Meek for the last two minutes of the game. The play that enabled the underdog Western team to tie the game 14 to 14 was a most perfect piece of football strategy."

I chuckled at that lead. What

would have been said if our opponents' line had broken Meek in two?

The piece went on to say: "When the locals take on the powerful Marshall University Blues on Thanksgiving Day and win the undisputed championship of the conference, it will mark the close of 25 years of outstanding coaching by the gridiron genius, Mike Thomas."

But I knew that miracles don't happen on successive week ends.

Meek was as chipper as ever on Monday. At least, his play and ball handling were snappy enough. But that look in his eyes was still there. I watched him flash through the formations and was seized by a great temptation. Use him at right half along with Jensen and Sparks! Then we'd have a wide threat both ways; almost any plugger could pick up a few yards through the middle if the defense was spread to cover both sides. It might be enough to beat Marshall!

But my better judgment snapped off that idea, quick. He might go for a few plays. After that it would be an ambulance and the hospital. When a man has coached for 25 years, he finds it a whole lot easier to sleep nights if his conscience is clear.

On Wednesday, during the last light practice before the game the next day, a stranger came on the field. When he was about ten feet away, I knew it was Jim Meek.

I smiled and extended my hand. Jim reached for mine, but his face was unsmiling.

"Hello, Mike. Remember me?"

"Sure, Jim! Right tackle on the '20

team. All-Conference, and played every minute without substitution. How's everything?"

Jim Meek's face remained impassive. I knew from the look in those deep-set eyes that whatever was bothering Don was also bothering his father.

"Mike, I want to talk to you—about Don. I didn't want you to know he was my boy, but. . . ." Here his voice trailed off. His eyes glistened as he looked at Don moving like a flash of light.

"Mike, tell me. Is he any good?"

"Good? Give him several pounds more, and he'd be an All-American. He's got everything but size. As it is, if I played him a full quarter, he'd probably be crippled the rest of his life."

Jim Meek's face hardened even more. "Mike, he's got to play tomorrow!"

My eyes widened as I looked at the big man. If only the boy had some of that heft! Then I shook my head. "I thought you knew me better than that, Jim. I still run the team. The kid's too light."

"But he's *my* boy, Mike. You said he was good. I'd rather have him hurt physically than carry that promise on his mind the rest of his life."

I pricked up my ears. "What promise?"

"My two other boys were football players, Mike. When they left for the service, Don promised them that he would take their places on the football field."

I still couldn't see why the boy had to butcher himself because of a promise like that. But the tears welled into Jim Meek's eyes as he continued.

"Ten days ago we received word that both boys were lost. Now Don feels that promise was sacred. I've tried to talk him out of it, but he's firm. I'd rather have him hurt physically, Mike, than mentally."

I turned away and my mind was spinning. The picture seemed different now. In this case it was a question whether the cure or the affliction would be worse. And there are still people who think football doesn't build character! I could hardly believe my own words.

"All right, Jim, I'll use him part of the time. But better knock on wood."

The Thanksgiving crowd overflowed onto the temporary bleachers set up at the ends of the field. Don smiled just a little when I told him I'd talked with his dad and that I would use him part of the time. But it wasn't a smile of pleasure or satisfaction. The lines on his face indicated more of a prayer than anything else.

I didn't have much information on Marshall's strong and weak points. But I did know they had a powerhouse back named Zuber who was rated as a cinch for the little All-America. He was a 220-pound bruiser who could run, kick, pass, and block. When the blue-clad outfit came on the field, I recognized him instantly. Boy, what a piece of football flesh! I looked over at Meek warming up with the rest of my boys and breathed a silent prayer. David and Goliath. Only this time David didn't have a slingshot.

I didn't start Don. He looked at me sharply but took his seat on the bench without a word. Jensen won the toss and chose to receive. The boot went over the goal, and it was our ball on the 20. Jensen bounced, and Sparks started in motion. Jensen's fingers flicked, and the full hit right into the arms of Zuber. No gain. Jensen counted again; and Jerry Black, right half, started in motion. The backer followed him out and left Zuber to cover the center. Jensen's lateral was handled cleanly, and Black made one yard.

Sparks's kick was short and high, and Marshall's safety returned to midfield. Zuber began his deadly punching. My boys tried, but even a good big line would have had its hands full stopping the drives of that human tank. Just before the quarter he scored. When he went on to kick the conversion, I got to my feet and scanned the subs.

My eyes stopped on Meek. The kid's face was an accusation—accusing me of breaking my word. I called him.

"Don, go in at right half. Break wide; and when you're about to be tackled, step outside. Tell Jensen to try that new stuff. Protect yourself, or you don't stay in."

I sat on the bench and silently prayed. David was going out to meet Goliath. Sparks returned the kick to the 30. Jensen bounced, and Don started in motion. Then he stopped, and Sparks went laterally. Zuber hesitated, then followed Sparks. Jones hit center for seven yards.

Three more times the double man-in-motion stuff sucked the first line of the secondary out, and we had two first downs. The bleacherites were yelling. So far Meek hadn't handled the ball and hadn't been touched. Marshall called time and a sub went in.

Play resumed, and we started again. This time Zuber stayed in the middle, and the half came up on the second man-in-motion. But Jensen had uncannily figured the thing out; he slipped a fast lateral to Meek.

The kid lashed out for the side line. The covering back lacked the speed to stay with him, and Don came sprinting down just inside the line. The safety made a try, missed, and Don crossed the goal without a hand having been on him! Sparks kicked the goal. I uncrossed my fingers.

Marshall came back hard. When Zuber started banging his way again, I was forced to make two changes in the line. The boys just couldn't stand up under that beating. The half ended with Marshall on our five.

During the rest period I spent the time taping and bandaging. There wasn't any particular pep talk necessary, as I knew the boys were in there pitching with everything they had. Meek's face was as impassive as ever.

Marshall chose to receive the second half, and I left Don on the bench. Zuber started slamming away again. But even a Goliath tires eventually. Twice the Blue team barely made the firsts. On our ten Zuber faked a plunge, slipped the oval to the inside back, who in turn lateraled to a half who went around the end unmolested for the counter. The giant's toe slipped on the conversion, and the ball sailed inches wide. Then I put Meek back in.

I'll never forget that last quarter. Zuber's high kick settled into Don's arms, and he was off. Interference formed as he angled for the side line. I watched those slender legs flash like a deer's, and crossed my fingers again. Suddenly he was cornered. He lowered his head and drove.

I needn't have jumped from the bench. Meek bounced up and took formation immediately. As I sat down Jensen began counting. When I looked, Sparks was whirling over to the right end, Jensen fading with the ball. Jensen kept his eyes on Sparks till the last second, turned, and whipped a long pass down to the left side line. Fifty yards downfield, all alone, Meek took the pass and jogged over the goal! When Sparks kicked the point, even my eyes got blurred.

Zuber started driving again, and his power was terrible to witness. The minutes slowly ticked off as the giant beat his way down the field. Meek, at defensive half, kept edging closer and closer until I sensed that it was time for them to throw one. As I called for the sub, the pass was completed behind my peewee half.

Sparks made an heroic attempt but missed, and the Marshall ball carrier went over for another touchdown. I waved the sub back to his seat and dropped dejectedly to the bench. We were sunk this time, 19 to 14.

The ref's whistle and the thud of the kick brought my chin from my hands. One minute to go. The boot was good, and Sparks took it deep in our territory. He bowled straight down the field, and the Marshall linemen converged.

Just before they hit him, Sparks's right arm whipped up and rifled the ball laterally toward the left side. Right into the hands of Meek! But Marshall's right end came charging for the kid. Don jabbed a savage stiff arm on the tackler's helmet and spun to the infield.

He dodged two men, then seemed to be swarmed under. Suddenly the ball squirted out from the mass of players back into the hands of Sparks! Sparks flashed to the opposite side line and then cut back.

Only one man was left between the runner and the goal. Zuber, the giant, stood poised, ready to make the tackle. Sparks eased up momentarily, and a shadow seemed to shoot ahead and take Goliath right across the thighs. It was Meek. Although he threw his 125 pounds into the man with all the power he could muster, he failed to knock him from his feet. But the delay was all Sparks needed. The gun sounded as he crossed the goal.

I felt limp as a rag when I tried to walk on the field. The gang formed a circle and gave a yell for Marshall. Then I saw Meek's face. The boy was whole both mentally and physically. The kid who was too light to play college football!

(Stop. Check your reading time with the Reading Score Board, page 460.)

✦⟨⟨✦

THINKING IT OVER

1. In what ways is the plot of this story a very ordinary one?
2. In what ways is the story new and fresh?
3. What made Don Meek a good football player?
4. What sort of persons were Mike Thomas and Jim Meek? Point out details in the story that tell.
5. What elements of good sportsmanship are seen in the story?
6. Why is this a good story for all of us to read?
7. Why is the name of the story good?

MEANING BEYOND THE WORDS

Many times there is a meaning in sentences that goes beyond the mere words. What do these sentences mean to you?

1. If we got any quick injuries, it would be curtains.
2. There was stark drama in his face.
3. Even after long years at the game, my stomach was turning flips.
4. I cleaned the bench.
5. The lines on his face indicated more of a prayer than anything else.
6. Only this time David didn't have a slingshot.
7. When Sparks kicked the point, even my eyes got blurred.
8. The boy was whole both mentally and physically.

COLORFUL LANGUAGE OF FOOTBALL

Can you match the words and phrases in these lists?

Nouns

1. scrimmage
2. oval
3. strategy
4. formation
5. interference

a. blocking of opposing players
b. play that follows after the center has put the ball in play
c. plan of procedure
d. football
e. arrangement of players

Verbs

1. faked
2. eluded
3. converged
4. launched
5. rifled

a. feigned
b. met at one point
c. stole
d. escaped
e. set in action

Adjectives

1. motley
2. incomplete
3. impassive
4. limp
5. defensive

a. not finished
b. mixed
c. resisting attack
d. indifferent
e. flexible

Adverbs

1. laterally
2. uncannily
3. barely
4. dejectedly
5. momentarily

a. mysteriously
b. temporarily
c. in a line almost parallel with the goal line
d. unhappily
e. scarcely

READING SCORE BOARD

Number of Words in Story: 3770

Number of Minutes	38	19	15	12 1/2	9 1/2	7 1/2
Reading Rate	100 w.p.m.	200 w.p.m.	250 w.p.m.	300 w.p.m.	400 w.p.m.	500 w.p.m.

"Peewee Half" is sufficiently exciting to make you want to read rapidly. Suppose you were reading a newspaper account of the game. If you are a serious football fan, how do you think you would read the article? If you are only a lukewarm fan, you would probably *skim* the article to get the main points.

Bring some newspapers to class, and practice skimming. Make your eyes run down the columns to pick out the major points of interest.

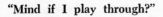

"Mind if I play through?"

"When he's proved to himself about twenty more times that it's safe, he'll let ME take a ride."

"He was all right until he looked back, and then he fainted."

"Slippery, isn't it?"

"I'm on stilts."

Bill King

"That makes three! If you can't play with your mouth shut, we'll have to replace you!"

"That would have been a homer if his mother hadn't made him promise to stick with the baby."

"Relax, Frank. You know a full-grown bear can't climb a tree."

"If you hadn't broken your paddle at the last minute, we might have made it!"

◀ FRANKLIN M. RECK

The Diving Fool

"Fancy diving," says the author, "is the tensest, most nerve-racking kind of competitive sport." That is what this story is about. As you read, try to decide who "the diving fool" really is.
(Note the time when you begin reading.)

I STUMBLED on to "Sunny" Ray one afternoon in the pool at the State College gym. I had just taken a dive— a front jackknife—and was hoisting myself over the edge of the tank when I caught a glimpse of a flashing white body bouncing off the end of the springboard and scooting up into the air. That was Sunny Ray, although I didn't know it then.

What caught my eye was the surprising height of his dive. I craned my neck around to see the finish of it, meanwhile supporting myself foolishly half in and half out of water. What I saw gave me a warm thrill. At the very top of his dive, he bent easily at the hips and gracefully touched his

extended toes with his fingers. He opened out effortlessly and was perfectly straight before he entered the water. The same dive I had just completed—only much better done.

A pleased glow crawled up the back of my neck as I climbed out of the pool and turned around to watch for the unknown diver to appear. I was puzzled. I know most of the divers in school. I'm the varsity diver myself. And nobody in school could do a front jackknife like the one I had just seen.

When the head finally bobbed up, over near the polished nickel ladder, I saw a mouth framed for a laugh, and a pair of alert, chuckling eyes. A fun-loving face if there ever was one. Not mischievous—but radiating fun.

I stepped on the board, feeling elated, somehow, and without a moment's hesitation performed a fairly difficult dive—a forward one and a half. That's the one where you make a complete somersault and a half and enter the water headfirst. The moment I completed it, I thrashed quickly to the ladder, climbed out dripping, and looked around at the board. Fun-loving was just stepping forward, and in another instant he was flying like a bird for the ceiling. High up, he tucked, turned one and a half times and slanted for the water like an arrow.

Golly, but it was beautiful! There was a rollicking challenge in it, too. Grinning all over, I strode out to the end of the board and rose up on my toes with my back to the water. Let Fun-loving try this one! Gathering all my strength, I leaped backward and upward, at the same time pulling my knees to start my body on its whirl. When the old sense of gravity gave me the order, I thrust out my hands backward and felt myself sliding into the water with a satisfying *suff!* A pretty good backward one and a half, I thought, as I scudded for the edge of the pool. And a blasted difficult dive!

I glanced quickly at the board. Sure enough, there was Fun-loving, poised with his back to the water and his arms extended for the jump—just as I had been, a moment before. Up into the air he went. His smooth, white body doubled into a knot, whirled too fast for the eye, and opened out into a perfect arch. In another instant his pointed toes had disappeared softly into the water.

The perfection of it choked me. Why in the dickens wasn't he out for the varsity? I walked over to him, as he vaulted, catlike, out of the pool.

"My name's Weed," I said, sticking out my hand. "Art Weed."

He gave me a firm grip and grinned at me. "Mine's Donald Ray—for no good reason."

"I just wanted to say," I told him, "that I know about three more hard dives, but something tells me they wouldn't stump you. Who'd you dive for last?"

"Nobody."

I was surprised. "You mean to say you've never done any diving in competition?"

Ray shook his head.

"Where in blazes did you learn?"

His face flushed at my abrupt question. "Oh, just—I don't know. At resorts and places."

"Freshman?"

"No. Second year. I came here from Simpson this fall."

"Why aren't you out for the varsity?"

"Why—I guess I never thought about it. Diving always seemed—well —fun. I've never taken it seriously."

"I think you ought to," I told him earnestly. "Why not be here tomorrow afternoon at three o'clock? That's when the varsity practices."

Ray's eyes lit up with pleasure. "Gosh—d'you think there's any use?"

I caught my chortle before it reached my lips, and shoved it back into its chortle-box. If he didn't know how good he was, I didn't intend to enlighten him. He'd find out soon enough.

"It won't hurt to try out, anyhow," I answered casually. "Will you be there?"

"Sure!" he came back eagerly.

"Don't forget," I smiled back at him as I started for the showers. He was looking at me, open-mouthed, face all alight. He didn't take his eyes off me until a group of fellows yelling "Sunny!" drew his attention.

"Sunny," I grinned. "Sunny Ray. . . . Just fits him. Gosh, I like him."

Thrills chased each other up and down my spine as I hurried through my dressing and hustled up to Coach Allen's office. Scotty Allen and I are good friends. I'd do a back jackknife off the Eiffel Tower into a bathtub if he asked me to. He's a good, hard driver with a well-concealed sense of sympathy and an unfailing sense of humor.

I opened the door to his office all keyed up; and as I always do when I'm keyed up, I tried to calm myself—stifle my feelings.

"Hello, Coach," I said, very casually, as though I had just dropped in to pass the time of day.

"Hello yourself," answered Scotty, barely glancing up from the trial cards he was studying. "What are you so excited about? Has the United States declared war or something?"

"No," I replied, slightly disappointed. "Not since morning, anyway. I hate to disturb you, but I just dropped in to ask if you really wanted to win first at the Conference meet."

"I do have peculiar leanings that way," he smiled, still gazing at his trial cards. "But some of the other teams have the same silly idea—particularly Lawrence."

"Would first place in the dives help out any?"

"It would give us five points," he answered. "Why? Have you finally mastered that gainer one and a half? I always said you had it in you—"

"Not me, Coach!" I blurted joyously. "I know my limit. I know that Kramer, of Lawrence, for one, can beat the tar out of me. But I've just discovered a kid who can spot Kramer ten points and then wallop him! Coach, he's—he's—"

Words failed me.

"He is, is he?" commented Scotty indifferently. "Where'd you stumble on to him?"

Pent-up words rushed out of my mouth. "In the pool, just a half hour ago. Saw him do a front jack, a forward one and a half, and—gosh—Coach, his front jack would take him over a bar twelve feet above the pool. No kidding! And—"

"Does he keep his feet together?"

"Yes, sir! And his toes pointed. And he arches with his stomach instead of his chest—"

The coach began to look interested and respectful. I ran on.

"He's taller than I am, and slender, and graceful as a cat! He's a diving fool!"

I was just beaming, I guess, because Scotty smiled at me appreciatively. "When do I get a look at this phenom?"

"At practice tomorrow. He's eligible for the varsity, too, because he's had a year at Simpson! Wait until you see him!"

"I hope he's as good as you say he is," said Scotty, looking at me quizzically. Then he leaned my way confidently. "I've just come from a meeting of the athletic council. We went over the plans for the new field house, and the council wants to build the pool with only five hundred seats."

"Holy smokes!" I ejaculated. "Is that all?"

"There ought to be two thousand seats!" exploded Scotty. His lips closed in a thin line, and his eyes burned so hotly at me that I thought my shirt would catch fire. "I'd give my right eye to win that Conference —show 'em! And a first in the dives would be a godsend. The athletic council ought to wake up!"

"Sunny Ray's your man," I yelped gleefully. "Unless I'm blind as well as cockeyed, there's no diver in this Conference can beat him."

"How about second place, too?" Scotty asked, looking at me intently.

I blushed. I'm only an ordinary diver, and the coach knows it. I just haven't the brilliance—the flash— that Kramer of Lawrence has—or Sunny Ray.

"I'll knock off my usual fourth place."

"Somebody ought to knock off your block!" he snorted.

I laughed. Scotty is always prodding me to be better than I can be, and I'm always trying. But it's like trying to make a silk ear out of a sow's purse—or whatever it is. It can't be did. I'll always be fairly good, but I'll never be sensational.

The next afternoon, at three, I undressed in record time and fairly flew down the steps leading to the pool. Frank Richardson and Jack Crandall, our two dash men, were already in the water, thrashing out their twenty laps. Several others of the squad were chatting and laughing near the springboard. These hailed me when I slid through the door on the wet tile. The coach wasn't down yet.

Over in the corner, sitting on a canvas chair and studying his curled-up toes, was Sunny Ray. I walked over to him.

"'Smatter, Ray," I grinned, "is your lunch doing handsprings?"

"No, I just—" he turned a slightly pale face upward, "I never did anything like this before."

"Don't worry," I reassured him. "It's just practice."

I knew what Sunny's feelings were. Fancy diving is the tensest, most nerve-racking kind of competitive sport. When you want to vent your energy strenuously, you've got to poise delicately—to make every move just so. And hovering over you, every minute, is the specter of a flop. Sunny, for the first time, was beginning to realize all this. I looked down and noticed him shivering almost imperceptibly.

"Better take a practice dive," I suggested. "Start the old circulation."

"I—I guess I'll wait a while," he replied.

Just then, Scotty came into the pool. I trotted over to him, brought him to the corner, and introduced Sunny.

"Just a minute," the coach smiled, "until I put this gang to work."

A few minutes later, after he had

started the distance men on their long grind, Scotty turned to us.

"All right, Art," he called, "go through your dives. You follow him, Ray."

I slapped Sunny on the back. "Give it all you've got," I whispered, and then started for the board.

I completed my swan dive—it felt like a good one—and clambered out of the water to watch Sunny. He was standing halfway up the board, nervously rubbing his hands together. He dropped his hands to his side, clenched them involuntarily, and started. Three steps up the board, a short final leap, and Sunny was traveling skyward. His head was back, his arms outspread, and his body perfectly arched. But just at the top of his dive, he broke—bent at the hips—and dropped headfirst into the pool.

"Gosh, Coach," I murmured, "that'll happen to anybody. He tried to go too high and had to bend to get down."

Scotty nodded. I went nervously to the board for my second dive while Sunny was climbing out of the pool. I was terrifically anxious for him to make good—to dive as beautifully as he had yesterday.

But he didn't. I don't mean that he flopped completely. He just didn't go quite so high, didn't turn so swiftly, didn't enter the water so cleanly. He was intent, serious, and just a bit uncertain. His last dive was the back one and a half, and he splashed quite a bit of water on it. I turned to the coach. He looked entirely unconvinced.

"You wait," I said earnestly. "You haven't seen anything."

"He'll make a pretty fair diver," Scotty said gently. "He's a bit green."

I felt like shouting: "Fair diver! You take my word for it, he's a natural-born champion!" But I knew there had been no evidence of it today.

In the next two practices—the last two before the dual meet at Lawrence—Sunny improved only slightly. He was trying desperately hard, but the realization that he was diving before critical eyes seemed to upset him. He couldn't call out the bounding, carefree brilliance that was somewhere inside of him. On Friday the team left for Lawrence, and Sunny Ray stayed behind.

We lost the Lawrence meet by a heartbreaking score—35 to 33. I placed second in the dives to Kramer. Kramer is a marvelously flashing performer—just like Sunny was the first time I saw him.

"Golly," I confided in the coach on the train going home, "I wish I could dive like Kramer! Isn't he beautiful? But—he's no better than Sunny. Not so good."

I said it challengingly, but I didn't get a rise out of Scotty. He just looked at me queerly. Made me want to duck my head, sort of.

During the next week, Scotty began driving the squad. The Conference meet was only three weeks away, and there was one more hard dual—with Tech. So far, we had lost only the one meet, and we had a fair chance for the big title. We worked like blazes and were happy. I had double duty—practicing dives and working out for the relay.

On the Thursday before the Tech meet I got down to practice early. Sunny was already in the pool.

" 'Lo, early bird!" I yelped. "Found any worms?"

"Fat, woolly ones," retorted Ray. "They're all gone. You might as well trot back to your nest."

"You don't trot to a nest," I reproved him. "You fly. And here goes!"

I stepped on the board and did my swan dive.

"That wasn't high enough," chided Sunny. "You should fly like an iggle. This way."

High up into the air he soared, like a zooming sea gull. I whistled. *That* was something like!

"When an iggle has corns on his feet," grinned Sunny, vaulting out of the water, "he flies above a mounting and scratches 'em—like this."

Three slow steps, that predatory pounce on the end of the board, and he was again shooting for the ceiling. Away up there, he quickly jacked, touched his toes with his hands, and dropped. Straight as a plumb line. No splash.

I chuckled joyfully.

"What happens," I asked him with mock seriousness, "when an iggle has a cramp?"

"He makes for a cloud," Sunny replied lightly, "and doubles up. Poor iggle."

Again he sailed skyward. Unbelievably high up, he tucked, turned one and a half times and zipped for the water. I was seeing the real Sunny now!

"Don't mind me," I told him weakly. "I'm just a groundhog."

He made a couple of mysterious passes at me with his hands.

"Now," he anounced in a deep, formal tone, "you're a naviator. A naviator hunting iggles. Chase me."

For a quarter of an hour we played our game. Sunny's face was all alight. He wasn't on inspection now—he was disporting himself naturally and joyously.

"What do you two think you are," grunted Frank Richardson, who had just come in, "a couple of bounding porpoises?"

"Porpoises!" I bellowed. "He called us porpoises! Tell him what we are, Sunny!"

"We're iggles," grinned Sunny.

"We live in igloos," I added.

"And spend all our time iggling."

Frank Richardson backed away from us slightly in awe.

I turned to Sunny. "He doesn't understand," I murmured. "He's an eel."

"And eels," finished Sunny, "can't speak igglish."

Chortling foolishly, he ran to the board and did another perfect one and a half.

There was a lump in my throat, but it tasted sweet. I sensed that somebody was standing close to me, and I turned around to see Scotty looking keenly at the circular ripples that marked the end of Sunny's uncannily beautiful dive.

"I've been watching from the balcony," the coach said in my ear. "I'm beginning to understand."

"Wasn't that wonderful?" I

gulped. "He's a diving fool, isn't he?"

Scotty didn't answer, but his eyes were shining.

I didn't sleep a lot that night. For about a half hour I lay in bed and thrilled over Sunny's performance. Then it occurred to me that he was the man to go to Tech with the team tomorrow night. I wasn't particularly needed on the relay. Either Wilson or Harwood could take my place. And the coach couldn't take more than ten men.

"The ax," I grunted, half aloud, "will fall tomorrow."

"Shut up," growled a sleepy voice in the next bed. You just don't have any chance to be sorry for yourself in a fraternity house; so I turned over and shut my eyes.

The next morning, at breakfast, I decided not to wait for the ax to fall. At nine-fifty—between classes—I went up to Scotty's office. I knew he'd be in because he has swimming classes in the morning.

He was studying those blasted time cards of his. "If you're trying to figure out why you should take two divers to Tech, you can quit," I told him. "I've got two exams next Monday, and I'd be just as well satisfied if you'd let me stay home."

The coach looked at me thoughtfully. "Don't you think you could win first at Tech?"

I had a good laugh. The same story. "I *know* Sunny can win first. That boy—gosh—" Thinking of those dives he made yesterday left me speechless.

Scotty looked straight at the wall in front of him. I began to get fidgety

—to feel that I had spoken out of turn. Tried to help him out with his job, and all that.

"I don't mean," I explained hastily, "that I don't want to go! I do—but—"

"Might as well break Sunny in," Scotty interrupted. "You'd better take a workout while we're gone."

I had a sudden glimpse of that rollicking squad of mermen cutting up on the train and me sitting around a fraternity house.

"I will," I replied, getting to my feet and walking unsteadily to the door. "I—I'll take a workout tomorrow afternoon."

That night, when I saw the gang off at the train, Sunny drew me aside.

"Gee whiz, Art," he blurted out, "this isn't right."

I grinned. "The best man wins, Sunny." I roughed him up a bit, to steer him away from anything sentimental.

"B-but," he said, holding me off, "I'm not sure I'm the best man."

"You've never seen yourself dive!" I chuckled.

That night, at the fraternity house, several of the brothers wanted to know why I wasn't out of town with the team.

"Trying out a new diver," I explained. "Sunny Ray."

"Is he good?"

"He's the coming champion," I asserted with conviction.

"Heck," mourned one of the fellows. "I thought we had the coming champ right here in the house!"

"Don't be funny," I grunted.

Saturday morning I had a couple of classes. In the afternoon I went down to the pool and punished the springboard savagely. In the evening I went to the movie and saw nothing on the screen except my mind's picture of the team battling Tech—of Sunny soaring upward. After the show I hurried to the *Campus Daily* office to get the results.

"We won, 40 to 28," Spike Hanlon, the sporting editor, informed me as he handed me the summary.

I scanned it eagerly to see how Sunny had come out in the dives. Halfway down was this paragraph:

"Fancy dives: First, Marlowe, Tech, 108.6; second, Floyd, Tech, 102; *third, Ray, State College, 96.*"

Sunny had flopped! I knew what had happened just as though I'd been there. I could almost feel the coldness that possessed Sunny's knees the first time he walked out to the board before a thousand rooters and three judges. Just like walking up to a blasted electric chair!

"Just the same," I murmured, "he's the greatest natural diver I've ever seen. And he's going to win first at the Conference!"

Monday afternoon, just as I went into the locker room to undress, the coach called me. He led me to his office, where he drew up a second chair and motioned me to sit down in it.

For a couple of minutes he scribbled busily on a sheet of paper, and then he shoved it over to me.

"Barring upsets," he said, briefly, "that's how things will stack up at the Conference meet."

This is what he'd written on the sheet:

	State Lawrence	Col.	Others
200 yd. relay	5	3	3
50 yd. dash	3	5	3
100 yd. dash	3	5	3
150 yd. backstroke	3	2	6
200 yd. breast stroke	3	2	6
440 yd. swim	2	8	1
300 yd. medley relay	5	1	5
	24	26	27

Dives

"We'll take first in the fifty and hundred, and we'll sweep the four-forty," he said. "Lawrence will take the relay and push us in the dashes. We haven't got a chance in the medley—we may take a fourth. Which means that the dives will tell the story. You and Sunny—" he paused.

I knew how badly the coach wanted to win the Conference. The athletic council was disposed to regard swimming lightly. And now, with the plans for the new field house under consideration, swimming at State College was at the crossroads. I had two visions—one of a spacious pool, built to accommodate thousands of rooters; another of an ordinary pool, around which a narrow bank of spectators sat hemmed in by walls.

"I haven't said much to the athletic council," Scotty said, reading my thoughts, "because I wouldn't have been listened to. But if we win the Conference, I will talk—and I'll get a respectful hearing."

I cleared my throat huskily. "Looks like it's up to Sunny and me, doesn't it?"

My face must have been kind of pale and long because the coach grinned. "It is—but don't take it too seriously. Just give me the best you've got. And see if you can't work that self-conscious fear out of Sunny. He was utterly lost at Tech. It was a new and terrible experience for him."

Sunny and I did hard labor the first week. We bounced and bounced off the end of the springboard until the bottoms of our feet were sore. On two occasions Sunny was his own buoyantly unconcerned self, and his glorious diving made us jubilant. But during the second week, when every practice brought the crisis closer, he seemed to lose his grip. He became uncertain — hesitant — fatal traits in diving! I plugged along at my usual mediocre level.

The coach looked on, urgently cheerful. But when I caught him off guard, his face was drawn and his eyes a bit worried. The day before we were due to leave for Lawrence, he called me aside.

"You and Sunny," he grinned, "have about wrecked my composure. At times Sunny is a marvel—at other times he flops unaccountably. And you—well, if I didn't know you, I'd say you weren't trying as hard as you might."

He paused a moment and then went on: "We've *got* to have that first in the dives. I've decided to take both of you liabilities to the meet, and I want you to talk Sunny into the title."

He waited a moment, while I looked at him in blank amazement.

Was the coach going nutty? His eyes didn't look a bit wild—just blazing with purpose. He went on—

"Talk him into it! Take his mind off the ordeal. Get that joyous look into his face."

"I—I'll try," I stammered.

The coach drew a long breath. "That's all I can ask. And if you *really try—*" he looked at me long and searchingly—"you'll win the Conference title for me."

I'd never seen three thousand rooters at a swimming meet before, and the sight almost unnerved me. We'd come through the preliminaries safely—Sunny and I—along with the dreaded Kramer of Lawrence, Marlowe of Tech, and three others, and we felt good—until we saw that crowd. Lawrence has an immense new field house and a tremendous pool, 150 feet long and 60 wide. Around it rise banks of seats almost to the high steel girders. They were jammed solid with spectators.

We sat down on a bench at the diving end of the pool, feeling awed and shriveled in our bathrobes.

"Thank the lord," chattered Sunny, "the d-divers don't come until next to the last."

I was too busy wondering how I could talk Sunny into his natural self to answer. At the moment, the job seemed utterly beyond me.

We had stayed in the locker room until the last minute, and the meet got under way almost immediately after we entered the pool. Before I knew it, the relay swimmers had thrown off their bathrobes and stepped up to the edge. They were lifting their feet gingerly and rubbing their arms.

I'll never forget that relay. One hoarse, unpunctuated roar accompanied the swimmers from the first lap to the last.

Lawrence led all the way. Frank Richardson, our last man—he's the fastest dash man in the Conference—made a heroic effort to overtake the purple swimmer and lost by inches. Lawrence 5, State 3. The other schools weren't going to count in this meet. It was a battle royal between Lawrence and State!

We took only a fourth in the next event—we haven't a good breast-stroke man—and Lawrence took first. That made it 10 to 4. I shivered and blamed the cold. Attendants had opened most of the high windows, much to the comfort of the rooters and the discomfort of the swimmers.

Good old Frank Richardson took his expected first in the fifty, and Crandall took an unexpected fourth. Six points in one splash! Lawrence got only three. State 10, Lawrence 13.

The long 440 grind was all ours because we have the best distance men in the Conference. First and second place put us ahead 18 to 15. I noticed that the tense lines around Scotty's mouth had relaxed a bit.

We were shut out of the 150-yard backstroke, while Lawrence pulled a second. That evened the score at 18-all. I felt almost exhausted with the tension. The crowd was hoarsely mad. I looked around at Sunny. His face was utterly blank, but his eyes told me he was having bad dreams. My throat was sticky, and I didn't dare talk—but I had to. Only the hundred, now, and then the fancy dives. State College needed that big pool! Time for me to start talking Sunny into the championship!

I felt like saying to him: "Snap out of it, you lily-livered, palsied pup!" But I felt that way, too—lily-livered and palsied. I clenched my trembling fingers and squared my shoulders.

"Gotta be light-hearted—gay!" I gritted between my closed teeth.

"Wh-what?" queried Sunny.

I laughed aloud. I hadn't meant that remark to be heard.

"I was just saying," I grinned to Sunny, "that you and I are letting this thing get our goats. And that isn't right."

I laid a calm hand on his bare knee and felt the tremor of it. I was stronger, cooler, now; and some of my new-found composure must have passed to Sunny, because he smiled faintly. I nodded reassuringly to the coach, who was looking my way tensely.

The hundred was called. The squad leaped up and patted Frank Richardson on the back.

"Go to it!" we all muttered to him. I was tickled to see Sunny on his feet, too.

Frank won the hundred in 55.2, with the Lawrence man a body length behind, and the rest trailing. State 23, Lawrence 21! Lawrence would most certainly win first in the medley relay, and we wouldn't take more than one point. That would leave it 26 to 24, in favor of Lawrence—not counting the dives. We needed at least six points in the dives—Sunny's first and my fourth—to win!

"All out for the fancy dives!" bawled the announcer.

Sunny's face paled.

"Come on, Sunny," I said calmly. "You need a bath—and it's Saturday night."

The squad milled around us, helping us off with our bathrobes and slapping us on the back. I hoped fervently that Sunny wasn't taking to heart their tense, eager expression. Every face said: "It's up to you!"

Diving is a terrific test of a man's nerves! When your muscles are crying out for vigorous action, you've got to restrain them. Thousands of eyes are glued on you, and you alone. You're the star performer, in a spotlight. And the slightest misstep, the least error in timing, may cause your downfall!

Sunny's voice called me out of my nerve-racking thoughts.

"Are we going to t-take a practice dive?" he asked.

I squared my shoulders. I had a job to perform. *This meet was up to me!*

"No," I replied seriously. "I'm an iggle."

"Wh-what?"

"I'm an iggle," I repeated, "and an iggle never dives. He swoops. Swatch me."

Without looking back at Sunny, I walked up to the board and took my first practice dive — a swan. As I climbed out of the water, I noticed the coach looking at me with a confident smile. I walked back to where Sunny was standing, rubbing his thighs.

"I tried to swash that beam up there with my tail feathers," I told him, "but I missed it. Heck."

Sunny grinned at me for the first time that night. "No wonder," he said, starting for the board. "Your tail feathers have moulted."

My heart bounded. Sunny at least had a comeback! I watched him eagerly as he poised and started forward. He sailed up—not quite so high as I could have wished, but still, better than I had expected.

I racked my brains for my next line. As he came up to me, dripping, I smiled.

"You swished it," I said, "with a swooping swish. I'm going after it with a swiping swoop."

A little weak on that remark, I thought dolefully, as I strode up and took my second practice—a running half gainer. Streaming wet, I clambered out and walked back to Sunny, putting on an expression of mock disgust.

"I swiped too hard," I grunted, "and got all dusty."

"I swish I could swoop like that," he said, grinning.

I chuckled joyously. Kramer, the Lawrence diver, walking past us to the board, looked at us in dumb amazement. After Kramer, Sunny started up.

"If you get dusty, swoop down and swash," I cautioned him.

"All right," he chuckled. "Here goes for a swishing swoop."

"A swiping, soaring swoosh!" I encouraged him.

I could have wept out of pure joy. His one and a half was a thing of beauty, and I knew then that everything was all right. There'd be just one more crisis—when the clerk called Sunny for his first official dive. The nonsense chatter—silly as it seemed —was working on Sunny's naturally buoyant spirit.

"You fellows had enough practice?" an official near us inquired.

We nodded. I felt a tightening in my throat.

A man with a megaphone walked to the edge of the pool.

"The next event," he sang out to the crowd, "is the fancy dive. Each man is required to do four dives— the plain front, the plain back, the front jackknife and the back jackknife. After that, he does four difficult dives of his own choosing! First man up, Kramer of Lawrence. The plain front!"

Kramer did a good dive—too good for our comfort—and won a storm of applause.

"Ray! State College!" bellowed the announcer.

This, for me, was the critical point. Sunny's first dive!

"That beam, iggle," I whispered to him solicitously, "is still dusty."

" 'Sawful," he whispered back, "I'll swish it."

Sunny went so high on that dive that I was afraid he'd have to break. But he didn't. At the very top of his dive, his feet rose gracefully toward the ceiling, his back perfectly arched every moment. And that smooth entry into the water! Golly!

He walked back to me with a lighthearted grin glistening through the water streaming from his hair.

"Did I get it?" he asked.

"Every speck," I gurgled. "I'll go up and polish it." I felt supremely confident now. Sunny, I felt sure, was going to come through!

And I was right. Every time he stepped on the board, he grew better. Not an uncertain step. No sudden hesitancy. And, all through it, we played our game. The crowd, the sober-faced judges with their pads, the loud applause meant nothing to us. We were too intent upon sweeping that skyward beam immaculately clean. Weren't we iggles? Iggles can not be bothered with mundane things. They dust the mountaintops!

I looked over to where our squad was sitting, noticed the look of awe on Frank Richardson's face and the happy smile on Scotty's lean countenance. My heart leaped fiercely.

Sunny's last dive—that marvelously sinuous thing of flashing turns called the gainer one and a half—brought forth an unrestrained outburst from the crowd. Not another diver had done so well—I felt sure of it.

Dripping and content, our play of iggles ended, we walked back to the bench. The coach bounded forward to meet us.

"Fine work, Sunny," he said warmly. Then he turned to me.

"Art," he grinned, "I didn't think you had it in you."

"It worked," I bubbled happily. "Didn't it?"

The coach just looked at me, his face all alight. The rest of the squad pulled us to the bench, wrapped our bathrobes about us, and rubbed our legs and arms with towels, meanwhile babbling joyfully in our ears.

I didn't respond to their outburst because I was trying to dope the status of the meet. The results of the dives would not be announced until after the medley relay was finished—that was the last event. Sunny's first and my fourth—if I was that lucky—would give us six points. Kramer of Lawrence had most certainly won second. That would make the score 29 to 24 in our favor. Lawrence would win first in the medley. 29 to 29! We had to have a fourth in the medley!

But we didn't get it. We were shut out completely. I felt sick at heart. That glorious diving—for nothing . . .

"While we're waiting for the results of the fancy dives," called an announcer, "I'll read you the status of the meet so far. Lawrence 26, State College 23—" As the announcer read off the other scores, a clerk walked up to him with a sheet of paper. I gripped Sunny's leg, hard.

"Results of the fancy dives!" bawled the megaphone. "Ah-ha! You'd never guess!"

I felt exultant. That was Sunny!

"First——" came from the megaphone " — Weed, State College, 108.4."

I almost fell off the bench. Me—me? A wave of hand clapping pelted the walls.

"—Second, Donald Ray, State College, 103.2—"

Another wave of hand clapping.

Unaware of what I was doing, I got to my feet.

"He's—he's cockeyed!" I yelled. Unfortunately, I had picked a dead calm in which to give utterance to my thoughts. The crowd tittered.

"I'm cockeyed!" the announcer singsonged. "I'll have to have my eyes examined. Third, Kramer, Lawrence, 99.8. Fourth, Marlowe, Tech, 94. Fifth, Hendricks, Cole, 91.5. Final results of the meet: State College 31, Lawrence, 28—"

I didn't hear the rest of it because about eight husky swimmers were trying to pull me apart. Still dazed, I jerked myself free and walked to the coach. It wasn't right, because I'm just not good enough to beat Sunny and Kramer!

"Sunny won those dives, Coach," I protested. But he just grinned at me. I felt the need of explaining myself.

"It worked out just as we planned," I elaborated painfully. "I did what you said—talked him into it—"

"*You talked yourself into it*, you diving fool, you," laughed Scotty. "Haven't I been telling you all season you had it in you?"

I just stared at him; and if I looked as dumb as I felt, I must have been a sight. *Me* Conference champion?

"Nope," I said positively. "There's something wrong."

Sunny had his arm around my shoulder; and he tightened it, grinning.

"You've never seen yourself dive, iggle," he chuckled.

(Note the time, and check your reading speed with the Reading Score Board.)

Answer in "Igglish"

1. Who was the diving fool?
2. The only two well-rounded characters are Sunny Ray and "I." What fine qualities does each show? Cite passages in the story for proof.
3. What does *psychology* mean? Was any psychology used in the story?
4. Why is the last sentence exactly right?

Diving for Words

Can you match the words and phrases in these colums?

Nouns

1. front jacknife
2. chortle
3. composure
4. hesitancy
5. status

a. calmness
b. kind of dive
c. laugh
d. condition of affairs
e. indecision

Verbs

1. thrashed
2. ejaculated
3. restrained
4. uttered
5. elaborated

a. worked out in detail
b. exclaimed
c. spoke
d. beat
e. suppressed

Adjectives

1. eligible
2. sensational
3. rollicking
4. buoyant
5. mock

a. unusual
b. lighthearted
c. sham
d. qualified to be chosen
e. very jolly

Adverbs

1. indifferently
2. quizzically
3. strenuously
4. involuntarily
5. solicitously

a. vigorously
b. anxiously
c. teasingly
d. unconcernedly
e. without control

Reading Score Board

Number of Words in Story: 6040

Number of Minutes	60	30	24	20	15	12
Reading Rate	100 w.p.m.	200 w.p.m.	250 w.p.m.	300 w.p.m.	400 w.p.m.	500 w.p.m.

Can you analyze the way that you read "The Diving Fool"? Did your method of reading change in any way when the scores were given near the end of the story?

◆◀ ROBERT BENCHLEY

The New Strokes

You can relax now. The name Benchley is warning enough that what you are about to read is the height of foolishness.

IT WILL be interesting to see what the new season will bring out in the way of novel swimming strokes. I'll bet it involves the use of an auxiliary motor strapped on the shoulders.

When I was learning to swim, people just swam. The idea was to keep afloat and, in an orderly fashion, to get somewhere if possible. If there was nowhere you wanted to get to, you just swam quietly round and round until your lips got blue. Then you went in.

The stroke that I was first taught was known as the "breast, or gondola, stroke." High out of the water by the bows. It was dignified and stately and went something like this: "One-two-three-sink! One-two-three-sink!" The legs were shot out straight behind, like a frog's, except that they were not good to eat.

Then the more sporting among the swimming crowd took to swimming tipped over on one side, with one ear dragging in the water. This was considered very athletic, especially if one arm was lifted out of the water at each stroke. But even then the procedure was easy going, pleas-

ant, and more of a pastime than a chore. It was considered very bad form to churn.

But with the advent of the various "crawls," swimming took on more the nature of a battle with the elements. You had to lash at the water, tear at the waves with your teeth, snort and spit, kick your feet like a child with tantrums, and, in general, behave as if you had set out deliberately to drown yourself in an epilepsy. It became tiring just to watch.

I never learned the names of the new strokes as they came along, but I gather that the instructions for some of them must read:

The Australian Wrench: Place the head under water up to the shoulder blades. Bring the left arm up, over and around the neck until the fingers of the left hand touch the right cheek (still under water). Shove the right arm sideways and to the left until the right shoulder touches the chin. Then shift arm positions suddenly and, with great splashing, propel the body through the water by lashing upward and downward with the feet and legs. The head is kept under water during the entire race, thereby eliminating both wind resistance and breathing. It is bully fun.

The Navaho Twist: Rotate the entire body like a bobbin on the surface of the water, with elbows and knees bent. Spit while the mouth is on the up side. Inhale when it is under. This doesn't get you much of anywhere, but it irritates the other swimmers and makes it difficult for them to swim.

The Lighthouse Churn: Just stand still, in water about up to your waist, and beat at the surface with your fists, snorting and spitting at the same time. This does nothing but make you conspicuous; but, after all, what is modern swimming for?

◄€ EDWARD J. NEIL

A Ride with the Red Devils

Edward J. Neil went to Lake Placid in February, 1932, to report for the Associated Press the winter sports of the Olympics. While he was there, the American team took him down the dangerous mile-and-a-half run. This is the story he wrote of that seventy-mile-an-hour ride. It is so good, by the way, that it won a Pulitzer citation.

THEY took me down the most dangerous mile and a half in the entire sports world today, gave me thrills enough to last a lifetime, and then before my eyes laid the picture of sudden death and destruction.

Seven o'clock in the morning, deadly cold on top of Mount Van Hoevenberg,[1] and the bobsledders of eight nations, men who can't have nerves, laughed and chatted. At their feet lay the Frankenstein contraptions known as bobsleds, 500 pounds of steel and oak.

We were at the start of the Olympic bob-slide, mile and a half of ice

[1] *Mount Van Hoevenberg.* Near Lake Placid, New York.
——From an Associated Press dispatch. Used by permission of Wide World Publications Division.

twisting through twenty-five awesome bends and hairpin curves down the mountain, the racing strip that in two days has sent eight Germans to the hospital. Today it all but killed two.

The starter gets word from a telephone strung along the side that all is clear.

"Get ready," he yells. "To the mark. Harry Homberger's Red Devils."

"You asked for it, let's go," Harry shouts.

He's a pleasant kid of 26, a civil engineer from Saranac Lake, who built the slide. He is a pilot, four lives and a steering wheel in his grasp.

They say he's the greatest bobsled

driver ever—the Albie Booth of bob-sleds; 158 pounds, but his shoulders widest in the crew. His world record is 1:52 for one and a half miles.

We pull on brilliant red jackets, leather helmets that cover the face entirely, leaving slits for eyes and mouth. We settle on the sled, bracing feet, gripping straps with hands shielded in padded gloves. I was No. 3, between huge Percy Bryant and the brakeman, Ed Horton, who yanks the steel jaws that clutch at the ice when we need to slow down.

Solemnly men of other nations shake our hands. They do that before each run; act as though they never expected to see you again. Particularly does Fritz Grau, German captain, slap our backs. So did Albert Brehme, Hellmuth Hoppman, and Rudolph Krotkin. An hour later they were all in a hospital. Grau and Brehme may die. "It's not so fast today," Homberger says, "but I'll do my best to give you a thrill."

One heave and we're off. The foreigners dash for the telephone; each station calls off our progress. I've watched them stand there tense, silent, seeming to be praying there'll be no shout. "They've jumped a bank."

We pick up speed on the first drop. The steel runners sing; the wind tears at your hunched head — 40. . . . 50 . . . . 60 miles an hour. "Lean," screamed Horton.

Up came a dazzling wall of ice. I leaned hard. We sweep to the top.

The runners slide, catch. That was the turn called The Eyrie.

It's 60 again, and going up. One after another come the blinding banks, 10, 20, 30 feet high. Desperately I leaned this way, that way, gasping for breath, helpless, straining. Tears stream from your eyes. You think you can't hold on another second. You fight, surge, and then you're out of the curve and flying on a straightway, 70 miles an hour; you get a breath.

The curves are getting steeper. You're taking them eagerly. Exultation sweeps from your toes, reaches your throat. Back goes your head, and you howl with the joy of it.

You're ready for par. "White-face," a vertical semicircle of ice 35 feet thick, at 70 miles an hour. "Shady corner," again at 70. You fly into the wall, smash off again, and just when you think you're gone, another straightway.

The final test, a surge of every drop of blood through your veins, the apex of sporting thrills and the end of many a bobsled career—"zig-zag"— a whip to the left, a leap of 5 feet, all four runners off the ground, to straighten out, a whip to the right, one last burst, and you are at the finish line, limp, exhausted.

A minute later we were drinking coffee, and my nerves shimmered the liquid in the cup.

"Slow," said Hank; "about two minutes."

We started back. Almost to Shady we heard another bob screaming down the course at 70 miles an hour. It swerved; runners shrieked; the sled swept up the incline, smashed through the top, four bodies hurled through the air into a deep ravine below. It was our friends, the Germans.

We raced up the slide, helped carry the battered, blood-soaked, unconscious forms to the ambulance.

"That's the way it goes," Homberger sighed.

Twenty minutes later they're racing down again.

❖❄❖

FOLLOWING THE COURSE

1. From the article, what picture do you have of a bob-slide? Read aloud the sentences which give you these pictures.

2. How is a bobsled race conducted?

3. How do you feel when you read about the handshaking that goes on before each race?

4. Why is the last sentence necessary to the story?

SEEING THE RACE

Mr. Neil has used colorful words to make his readers feel the thrill of the bob-sled ride. What does each mean?

1. *Frankenstein* contraptions
2. *awesome* bends
3. *hairpin* curves
4. *yanks* the steel jaws
5. steel runners *sing*
6. *dazzling* wall of ice
7. *vertical* semicircle
8. *fly* into the wall
9. *whip* to the left
10. nerves *shimmered* the liquid

No doubt you read "A Ride with the Red Devils" at breakneck speed because of the excitement of the subject matter. Here is another brief article on the same subject. Do you read it with the same speed? What is the cause for the difference in the rate of reading? What specific information do you find? Can you explain now why material packed with information slows down reading speed?

The coasting sled came into use after 1870 in the United States. The original coasting sled was the "clipper" type, which was built low, with long, pointed sides, and runners of round steel rods. The "girl's sled" was a light, short box, with high, cut-out or skeleton sides, and wide, flat runners. The double-runner or bob-sled was formed of two clipper sleds joined end to end by a board and steered by ropes, a wheel, or a crossbar. Four to ten persons rode in the bobsled.

——From *The World Book Encyclopedia*, published by Field Enterprises, Inc. Used by special permission.

◄ᴄ HERBERT ASQUITH

Skating

If you are just now learning to ice skate, you can sym-
pathize with the "I" in this poem. What fun Mary—
and the other experts—must have gliding and skimming and curving! Come on; let's try again.

When I try to skate,
My feet are so wary
They grit and they grate:
And then I watch Mary
Easily gliding,
Like an ice-fairy;
Skimming and curving,
Out and in,
With a turn of her head,
And a lift of her chin,
And a gleam of her eye,
And a twirl and a spin;
Sailing under
The breathless hush
Of the willows, and back
To the frozen rush;
Out to the island
And round the edge,

Skirting the rim
Of the crackling sedge,
Swerving close
To the poplar root,
And round the lake
On a single foot,
With a three, and an eight,
And a loop and a ring;
Where Mary glides,
The lake will sing!
Out in the mist
I hear her now
Under the frost
Of the willow-bough
Easily sailing,
Light and fleet,
With the song of the lake
Beneath her feet.

——"Skating" from Herbert Asquith: *Pillicock Hill*. Used with the permission of The Macmillan Company and William Heinemann, Ltd.

LOOKING BACKWARD THROUGH THE CHAPTER

1. What different sports are covered in the selections in this chapter?
2. How were the chief characters alike, and how were they unlike?
3. What elements of good sportsmanship did you find in the selections?
4. What other sports stories and sports writers do you know and like?
5. What makes a good sports story?

CHECKING UP

Who Wrote What?

Can you match the titles and authors of the following?

1. The New Strokes   a. Franklin M. Reck
2. The Diving Fool   b. Ernest L. Thayer
3. The Milk Pitcher   c. Robert Benchley
4. Peewee Half   d. Howard Brubaker
5. Casey at the Bat   e. John Gartner

Who Did What?

To what character does each of these lines refer:

1. Mr. Samboy's eyes were gladdened by the sight of a stocky, freckled, red-headed southpaw.
2. He went so high on that dive that I was afraid he'd have to break.
3. Ten thousand eyes were on him as he rubbed his hands with dirt;
   Five thousand tongues applauded when he wiped them on his shirt.
4. They took me down the most dangerous mile and a half in the entire sports world today.
5. The stroke that I was first taught was known as the "breast, or gondola, stroke."

WHAT DO THESE MEAN?

Choose the word or phrase in each line that most nearly gives the meaning of the word in italics:

1. *traditional:* (a) tractable (b) outlandish (c) customary
2. *cosmic:* (a) vast (b) cosmopolitan (c) amazing
3. *strategy:* (a) coaching (b) plotting (c) victory
4. *eluded:* (a) escaped (b) eloped (c) ended
5. *dejectedly:* (a) harmoniously (b) sadly (c) villainously
6. *chortle:* (a) choral (b) chug (c) chuckle
7. *solicitous:* (a) worried (b) solitude (c) solemn
8. *buoyant:* (a) floating (b) cork (c) lively
9. *impassive:* (a) impassioned (b) calm (c) nervous
10. *inhibition:* (a) restraint (b) inhumanity (c) ingenuity

MORE ABOUT SPORTS

1. What story can you tell or write about sports? It may be about some exciting event that you saw or took part in. It may be about your struggle in learning

some sport. Sad or funny, everyone likes to hear or read a good sports story. This is your chance to score!

2. Read the sports column in the newspaper. What interesting facts do you find out about some of your favorite players?

3. If you enjoy sports stories, the list below will be helpful.

Sports Stories

Anderson, C. W., *Tomorrow's Champion*, 1946 (Macmillan).
The handling and training of colts for racing.

Beim, Jerrold, *Rocky's Road*, 1953 (Harcourt).
A boy's choice between the school newspaper and basketball.

Bishop, Curtis, *Hero at Halfback*, 1953 (Steck).
Human interest and football tactics.

Bonner, M. G., *The Dugout Mystery*, 1953 (Knopf).
The Young Yankees and Young Dodgers—and a mysterious theft.

Colby, C. B., *First Fish*, 1953 (Coward-McCann).
How to catch him.

Davis, Mac, *The Lore and Legends of Baseball*, 1953 (Lantern).
Short pieces, briskly compiled.

Felsen, Gregor, *Bertie Comes Through*, 1947 (Dutton).
The "fat boy" who tries every sport and finally wins.

Lochlons, Colin, *Stretch Smith Makes a Basket*, 1949 (Crowell).
Junior-high-school basketball with exciting games and classroom fun.

Meader, Stephen, *Sparkplug of the Hornets*, 1953 (Harcourt).
How Peewee won his place on the basketball team.

O'Rourke, Frank, *Flashing Spikes*, 1948 (A. S. Barnes).
Top-notch baseball story—one of the best in the "field."

Scholz, Jackson V., *Gridiron Challenge*, 1947 (Morrow).
Character growth through football.

Tunis, John R., *All-American*, 1942 (Harcourt).
Football—with a background of racial prejudice in high school.

Tunis, John R., *Go, Team, Go!* 1954 (Morrow).
Boys and basketball, and trouble with betting.

Tunis, John R., *The Iron Duke*, 1938 (Harcourt).
The breaking of the two-mile track record at Harvard.

Verral, Charles S., *Captain of the Ice*, 1953 (Crowell).
From Canada to New England with ice hockey.

B.C.   1200–1300 A.D.

Aesop   Saadi
Old Testament
of The Bible
(Psalm 23)

Across

the Ages

1600–1700	1800–1900	1900–
Jean de La Fontaine	W. H. Hudson	Jesse Stuart
	Joel C. Harris	Laura I. Wilder
	Washington Irving	Eric Knight
	Charles Dickens	Howard Pease
	Henry W. Longfellow	Armstrong Sperry
	Abraham Lincoln	A. E. Housman
	Walt Whitman	Arthur Guiterman
	Ralph W. Emerson	Osa Johnson
	Oliver W. Holmes	Raymond L. Ditmars
	Christina G. Rossetti	Alfred Noyes
	John G. Whittier	J. Frank Dobie
	Eugene Field	Carl Sandburg
	Emily Dickinson	Stephen V. Benét
	Robert Browning	Donald C. Peattie
	O. Henry	Joyce Kilmer
	Edward Lear	Robert Frost
	Paul L. Dunbar	Rachel Field
		John McCrae
		Robert McCloskey
		William Saroyan
		Clarence Day
		T. A. Daly
		Ogden Nash
		Paul de Kruif
		Hilaire Belloc
		Robert Lawson
		Richard E. Byrd
		Ivan T. Sanderson
		Robert Benchley

In this book you have been adventuring in good stories and poems. You have read for the sheer fun of reading. At the same time you have been urged to try to improve your reading skills. Very obviously, the better you can read, the more you will enjoy what you read.

Are you satisfied with the progress you have made this year in mastering the skills of reading? Check yourself by this inventory test.

◄◄ COMPREHENSION

1. After reading a page, do you know what you have read?
2. When you check yourself, is your understanding correct?

◄◄ RATE OF READING

3. Has your speed of reading improved this year?
4. Have you formed the habit of forcing your eyes to pick up several words at a time?
5. In a line of print, do your eyes now automatically seek the key words and slip over the unimportant ones?
6. Have you broken yourself of the habit of looking back to pick up words which you think you may have missed?
7. If you had the habit of lip reading, have you broken yourself of it?

◄◄ VOCABULARY DEVELOPMENT

8. Has your store of words grown considerably?
9. Have you learned to do "intelligent guessing" of the meaning of words when you read them in context?

◄◄ READING FOR SPECIFIC DETAILS

10. Do your eyes pick up specific details that are important?
11. Are you able to locate specific details quickly?

◄◄ READING WITH CORRECT ENUNCIATION AND PRONUNCIATION

12. Have you broken yourself of lazy habits of saying words?
13. Do you consult a dictionary when you are not sure of a pronunciation?

◄ RECOGNIZING THE AUTHOR'S ORGANIZATION OF SUBJECT MATTER

14. Do you follow the sequence of events in a story?
15. Can you reduce to an outline an author's explanation of ideas?
16. Can you glance over a long encyclopedia article and find quickly what you want?

◄ READING TO INTERPRET

17. Have you learned to read and enjoy poetry?
18. Can you interpret satisfactorily what poets say?

◄ READING TO GET A POINT

19. Do you quickly get the point of a story that you read?
20. Do you catch hidden meanings by reading between the lines?

◄ READING TO DRAW CONCLUSIONS

21. Do you think through what you read?
22. In the light of what you read, do you come to your own conclusions?

◄ READING IN DIFFERENT WAYS

23. Do you gauge your speed according to the type of material you are reading?
24. Can you skim successfully?
25. Can you read with ease such materials as charts, graphs, directories, indexes, and timetables?

Akeley, Carl Ethan (1864–1926), the American explorer, taxidermist, inventor, and sculptor, was born in Orleans County, New York, and became interested in taxidermy as a boy. From 1895 to 1909, he was with the Field Museum, Chicago, and after that, with the American Museum of Natural History in New York. He revolutionized the practice of taxidermy by being the first to show animals in their native haunts. Dr. Akeley made many trips into darkest Africa, and died in the Belgian Congo.

Benchley, Robert Charles (1889–1945), was born in Worcester, Massachusetts, and received his education at Harvard. Translator, advertising agent, personnel worker, editor, humorist, and actor—all give a picture of his career. During his lifetime, he appeared in more than twenty-five one-reel motion pictures, the first being *Treasurer's Report*, which was the very first all-talking picture ever made. His *How to Sleep* received the Academy Award in 1936. He also acted as master of ceremonies on numerous radio broadcasts. It has been said that "as a writer of nonsense for nonsense's sake, he was unsurpassed." He made fun of himself in order to be funny. Among his collections of humorous sketches are *My Ten Years in a Quandary*, *Inside Benchley*, and *Benchley—Or Else*.

Benét, Stephen Vincent (1898–1943), was born in Bethlehem, Pennsylvania, into a family of writers. Rosemary Carr Benét, whom he married in France, is also a writer. He was graduated from Yale and later attended the Sorbonne in France. Having been awarded a Guggenheim Fellowship in 1926, he took his family to Paris, where he wrote *John Brown's Body*. It won the Pulitzer Prize for poetry in 1929. *The Devil and Daniel Webster*, a prose story, was his next success; and he and his wife, together, wrote *A Book of Americans*.

Byrd, Richard Evelyn (1888–1957), born in Winchester, Virginia, is one of three brothers known as Tom, Dick, and Harry. Throughout his life he has won renown as a traveler and an explorer. At the age of twelve he sailed around the world alone. He was the youngest boy in Virginia Military Academy, and after graduation from the University of Virginia, was appointed a midshipman at Annapolis. On May 9, 1926, accompanied by Floyd Bennett, he made the first airplane flight over the North Pole. Although retired from the Navy because of a broken foot, he has been made a Rear Admiral in recognition of his polar exploits. Among his stories of these trips to both the North Pole and the South Pole are *Skyward*, *Little America*, *Discovery*, and *Alone*. The last is a thoughtful study of his lone vigil at the advance base of the Little America expedition.

Day, Clarence Shepard, Jr. (1874–1935), known for his humorous sketches of *Life with Father* and *Life with Mother*, was an invalid for the greater part of his life. Born in the city of New York, he was educated at St. Paul's School and Yale. After naval service in the Spanish-American War, he was stricken with arthritis, which crippled him for the rest of his life. A very human and understanding person, he has revealed himself through his many humorous essays.

De Kruif, Paul (1890–   ), was born in Zeeland, Michigan, of Dutch forebears. Educated at the University of Michigan, he later became professor of bacteriology there. He has become best known for his popular scientific articles in current magazines and for several interesting and readable books on science, including *Microbe Hunters* and *Hunger Fighters*.

Dickens, Charles (1812–1870), was born in London of very poor parents. As a boy, he worked in a warehouse pasting labels on bottles. He attended school for two years and then went to work in a lawyer's office. In 1836 his *Pickwick Papers* began to appear in monthly issues, and Dickens's success as a writer was assured. He became famous through such books as *David Copperfield, Oliver Twist,* and *Nicholas Nickleby* as an exposer of social wrongs. His *A Tale of Two Cities* is one of the most dramatic stories ever written about the French Revolution, and *A Christmas Carol* has become a classic among Christmas stories.

Dickinson, Emily Elizabeth (1830–1886), America's chief woman poet, was born in Amherst, Massachusetts, and spent her whole life there. She withdrew from life and lived as a hermit, not going beyond her own garden gate for twenty years, because of an unfortunate love affair. During her lifetime, only two of her poems were published; the remainder were printed after her death, though she had asked that they be burned.

Ditmars, Raymond Lee (1876–1942), the man who knew more about reptiles than anyone alive, was born in Newark, New Jersey. After being graduated from the Barnard Military School, he took a position at the American Museum of Natural History, mounting and labeling insects. Later he became curator of reptiles at the Bronx Zoo, then caretaker of mammals, and finally director, a position which he held until his death. Two of his most popular books are *The Book of Living Reptiles* and *Strange Animals I Have Known.*

Dunbar, Paul Laurence (1872–1906), the son of two escaped slaves, was born in Dayton, Ohio. His first job was that of elevator boy. Later he became an assistant in the Library of Congress. His early poems were printed in local papers; and some later ones were published in a small volume, at his own expense. Simplicity, tenderness, and sweetness mark his verse in dialect; and much of it has been set to music.

Emerson, Ralph Waldo (1803–1882), is considered one of the great thinkers and scholars of New England. He was born in Boston, Massachusetts, was educated at Harvard University, and later studied at the Divinity School. After several years, he left the ministry and devoted his time to writing. He was a noted lecturer, essayist, and poet.

Field, Eugene (1850–1895), born in St. Louis, Missouri, became known as a poet of the West. Most of his life was devoted to journalism, and all his verse and stories were first printed in newspapers. He had a remarkable sense of humor as well as a fond love for children, as shown in much of his writing. Among his best-loved poems are "Little Boy Blue" and "Wynken, Blynken, and Nod."

Field, Rachel Lyman (1894–1942), although born in the city of New York, spent most of her childhood in Massachusetts and Maine, later the background for many of her stories. She studied playwriting at Radcliffe, and after several editorial jobs in New York, undertook writing books for children. As the author of *Hitty* (1929) she became the first woman to receive the Newbery Medal awarded annually for distinguished children's literature. Among her adult novels are *Time Out of Mind* and *All This, and Heaven Too,* both with New England settings. She is also the author of much fine poetry.

Frost, Robert (1874–   ), although born in San Francisco, has become famous as the true New England poet. He studied at Dartmouth and Harvard. His poetry shows his love for country life. He has received the Pulitzer Prize for poetry four times, in 1924, 1931, 1937, and 1943. Three of his best-known books are *North of Boston, A Boy's Will,* and *Come In.*

Garland, Hamlin (1860–1940), born in a log cabin in Wisconsin, became famous for his stories of Middle Western life. His *A Son of the Middle Border* has been cited as perhaps the finest regional American novel; and its sequel, *A Daughter of the Middle Border,* won the Pulitzer Prize in 1922.

Guiterman, Arthur (1871–1943), was born in Vienna, Austria, of American parents, and was brought to New York at the age of three. He attended the public schools and was graduated from the College of the City of New York in 1891. Throughout his life he excelled in sports, but earned his living as a reporter, editor, and later freelance writer, devoting his time, for the most part, to light verse.

Harris, Joel Chandler (1848–1908), the creator of "Uncle Remus," was born near Eatonton, Georgia. Rabbit hunts proved more attractive than education. His first job was typesetter on a Southern plantation newspaper, *Countryman.* Here he learned the legends and animal lore of the Negro, which he put into a column for the *Atlanta Constitution.* He featured the character "Uncle Si," the forerunner of "Uncle Remus." The famous "Tar Baby" story has been translated into many languages. He is noted for his unfailing humor and his ability for writing in dialect form.

Holmes, Oliver Wendell (1809–1894). Born in Cambridge, Massachusetts, this New England essayist, poet, teacher, and physician was brought up in cultured family surroundings. After graduation from Harvard, he studied to become a doctor. His first literary venture was a poem, "Old Ironsides," published in the *Boston Daily Advertiser* in 1830, over the initial H. Many of his poems, such as "The Deacon's Masterpiece," are marked by wit and humor.

Housman, Alfred Edward (1859–1936), English classical scholar and poet, was born in Fockbury, Worcestershire, and received his education at Oxford. From 1892 to 1911, he was Professor of Latin at University College, London; and from 1911 to 1936, at Cambridge. As a poet, he is known for his lyrical, melodious style with its rather pessimistic undertones. His best-known poetry collection is *A Shropshire Lad.*

Hudson, W. H. (1841–1922), one of the greatest masters of English prose, was born in Argentina. A lover of nature in all its forms, from serpents to birds, he knew the life of the pampas and the cities. He spoke Spanish as well as English, from his earliest childhood. Among his best-known and best-loved books are *A Little Boy Lost,* a story founded on his own childish adventures; *Far Away and Long Ago,* with more memories of his youth; and *Green Mansions.*

Irving, Washington (1783–1859), often called the "Father of American Literature," was born in the city of New York and was named for the "Father of His Country." He was the youngest of eleven children. Traveling abroad in Italy, France, and England, he became, through his writings, a sort of literary ambassador. He won fame with his humorous *Knickerbocker's History of New York* and *Sketch Book.* In the latter appear his two immortal stories, "The Legend of Sleepy Hollow" and "Rip Van Winkle." Many consider Irving's sketches to be the beginning of the American short story.

Johnson, Osa (1894–1953), born in Chanute, Kansas, and educated in the high school there, early left the scenes of her youth to travel the world over with her husband, Martin Johnson. They took motion pictures of cannibals and head hunters of the South Seas and made five trips into the African jungles. The excitement of these travels is reflected in her books, especially *I Married Adventure* and *Four Years in Paradise.*

Kilmer, Joyce (1886–1918), was born in New Brunswick, New Jersey. He attended Rutgers University and was graduated from Columbia in 1908. After teaching Latin at Morristown High School, he turned to writing. During World War I, he was a member of the Rainbow Division and was killed while scouting a machine-gun nest. Aline Kilmer, author of "I Shall Not Be Afraid," was his wife.

Knight, Eric (1897–1943), born in Menston, Yorkshire, came to America in 1912 after working in numerous mills and factories. He started as copy boy in Philadelphia, and was soon writing feature articles. Although he studied art, he was forced to give it up after becoming colorblind during the first World War. He resumed newspaper work and went to Hollywood to write for films. Mr. Knight served as a major in the United States Army in World War II and died in an airplane crash. *Lassie Come-Home*, an immortal dog story, and *The Flying Yorkshireman*, amusing fantastic tales, are among his best-known books.

Lawson, Robert (1892–1957), one of our greatest illustrators, makes no claim to any special aptitude for drawing or writing in his youth. Born in the city of New York, he experienced the "usual childhood in a usual suburban town"—Montclair, New Jersey. After studying at the New York School of Fine and Applied Art, he set up a studio in Greenwich Village. During World War I, he served with a camouflage division in France. He has won the two highest honors of juvenile literature: the Caldecott Award for the best picture book of 1940, *They Were Strong and Good*; and the Newbery Medal for the most distinguished children's storybook in 1945, *Rabbit Hill*.

Longfellow, Henry Wadsworth (1807–1882), was born in Portland, Maine, and received his college education at Bowdoin. He traveled extensively in France, Spain, Italy, and Germany, in preparation for a teaching career. This he began at Bowdoin and continued at Harvard. In spite of a number of personal tragedies, Longfellow never lost his cheerful outlook. His poetry is marked by its easy rhythms and simplicity of expression. He is the only American poet whose marble bust stands in the Poets' Corner at Westminster Abbey. Walt Whitman called him the "universal poet of . . . young people," and probably more persons have learned to love poetry because of him than because of any other poet.

McCloskey, Robert (1914–   ), as a child in Hamilton, Ohio, "drew, painted, and made things." He won a scholarship to the Vesper Grove School in Boston and later studied at the National Academy of Design. Inducted into the army during World War II, he worked on diagrams and maps at Fort McClellan, Alabama. He was honored with the Caldecott Award in 1942 for his distinguished picture book *Make Way for Ducklings*. Although his home is at Cornwall Bridge, Connecticut, he spends much of his time on an island he bought in Maine, where he wrote his most recent juvenile, *Blueberries for Sal*. It seems probable that his "Homer Price" will join the gallery of immortal boy heroes.

Nash, Ogden (1902–   ), was born in Rye, New York, and educated at St. George's School, Newport, Rhode Island, and at Harvard. After several years with various publishing firms, he withdrew to devote his time to writing and has contributed numerous humorous poems to several periodicals. Among his books of poetry are *Hard Lines*, *I'm a Stranger Here Myself*, and *Versus*. All his verse is marked by surprising ideas and fearless rhyme schemes.

Noyes, Alfred (1880–1958), an English poet, was born at Wolverhampton, Staffordshire; and the effect of his youth by the sea is reflected in his poetry. After being graduated from Exeter College, Oxford, Noyes went to London, where he soon made a literary name. He has visited the United States on several lecture tours but makes his home in London and on the Isle of Wight. Many of his poems are characterized by a glow of romance and adventure.

Pease, Howard (1894–   ), born in Stockton, California, early took to the sea as a wiper on a freighter. After graduation from Stanford University, he became a teacher. However, he claims to have been interested mainly in writing since his early youth, and many of his adventure tales reflect his love of the sea. Among them are *The Jinx Ship*; *The Black Tanker*; *Night Boat, and Other Tod Moran Mysteries*; and *Bound for "Singapore."*

Peattie, Donald Culross (1898–   ), was born in Chicago, Illinois, and was graduated from the University of Chicago.

After working as a reader in a publishing firm, he decided to become a nature writer and studied scientific subjects at Harvard. He now lives in Santa Barbara, California, where he is acquainting himself with Western natural history. Known as "America's most lyrical naturalist," he is also a poet in prose. In addition to his nature works, he has written a number of portraits of great Americans. Among his best-known books are *An Almanac for Moderns, Green Laurels, The Road of a Naturalist,* and *Journey into America.*

Porter, William Sydney (1862–1910), known to most readers as O. Henry, was born in Greensboro, North Carolina. His life seems to have been full of mishaps. After working as a bank teller in Texas, he was tried for embezzlement. In 1898 he was sentenced to prison in the Ohio State Penitentiary, having been involved in a robbery. The origin of his pen name O. Henry is unknown; but it has been suggested that it might refer to Orrin Henry, a prison guard. Leaving prison in 1901, O. Henry went to Pittsburgh and then to New York. After his death, readers began to appreciate his short stories, which depict all phases of human nature, and feature, in many, a surprise "twist at the end."

Rossetti, Christina Georgina (1830–1894), English poet, wrote only a few volumes of verse; but because of their beauty and simplicity, she is world-famous. She was a deeply religious woman, as may be seen in much of her poetry. Throughout a large part of her lifetime she was ill, but her poetry shows only her cheerful spirit.

Sandburg, Carl (1878–   ), American poet and biographer, was born in Galesburg, Illinois, of Swedish descent. He left school when he was thirteen years of age and worked at many unskilled jobs. After enlisting in the Spanish-American War, he worked his way through Lombard College, then became a journalist in Chicago. While working on his monumental life of Lincoln, which won the Pulitzer History

Award for 1940, he toured the country with his guitar, singing folk songs. *Rootabaga Stories* is one of his most popular books for young people.

Saroyan, William (1908–   ), born in Fresno, California, of Armenian parents, has become famous for his plays and stories. He left school at an early age to become a telegraph messenger. Although he is thought by some to be conceited and a little odd, he is gifted in writing things that "breathe," as he describes them. He was awarded but refused the Pulitzer Prize of 1940 for drama for the play *The Time of Your Life. The Human Comedy* and *My Name Is Aram* are typical examples of his best work.

Schauffler, Robert Haven (1879–   ), is famous as a poet, an essayist, and a biographer. He was born of missionary parents in Bruenn, Austria, but was brought to this country at the age of two. Schauffler was graduated from Princeton University. He became a musician and wrote on a number of musical topics. He is probably chiefly remembered for his collections of poetry and prose dealing with our various national holidays.

Seton, Ernest Thompson (1860–1946), was born in South Shields, Durham, England, but spent his childhood in the backwoods of Canada, where he learned to hunt, trap, camp, and farm. He helped found the Boy Scouts of America and was Chief Scout for five years. Always interested in natural history, Seton wrote about wild-animal life. Some of his best books are *Wild Animals I Have Known, The Biography of a Grizzly,* and *Two Little Savages.*

Sperry, Armstrong (1897–   ), was born in New Haven, Connecticut, educated at Stamford Preparatory School, Yale University Art School, and the Art Student League in New York. He showed an early enthusiasm for drawing and painting, as well as a gift for writing expressively. After serving in the navy during World War I, he spent two years roaming the islands of the South Pacific. Many of his stories for boys depict his experiences during that period. *Call It Courage, Storm Canvas, Hull Down for Action,* and *Danger to Windward* are popular favorites.

Stuart, Jesse (1907–   ), author and poet, was born in Kentucky, lives in Kentucky, and writes about Kentucky. As soon as he could hold a pen, he decided to be a writer, and to portray W-Hollow to the world at large. He received his education in a one-room schoolhouse and at Lincoln Memorial University and Vanderbilt University, where his term paper six years later (1938) became his first book, *Beyond Dark Hills.* After a year in Europe (1937) on a Guggenheim Fellowship, he returned to his Kentucky farm. Among his works are *Man with a Bull-tongue Plow* (poems), *Trees of Heaven,* and many short stories.

Van Dyke, Henry (1852–1933), was born, the son of a clergyman, in Germantown, Pennsylvania, and became a minister himself after being graduated from Princeton. He later taught English literature there. After serving three years as ambassador to the Netherlands and Luxembourg, he became a chaplain during World War I. He returned to Princeton but retired from teaching and devoted his time to lecturing and the writing of essays, short stories, and poetry.

Waldeck, Theodore J. (1894–   ), although only eighteen years of age when he made his first trip to Africa, later led his own expeditions to the Belgian Congo, Abyssinia, East Africa, the Sudan, and British Guiana. He has described the numerous exciting adventures of these trips in several books, including *On Safari, Treks across the Veldt, Lions on the Hunt, The White Panther,* and others.

Whitman, Walt (1819–1892), the "Father of Free Verse," was born of Quaker parents in Huntington, Long Island, New York. After little formal schooling in Brooklyn, he tried several different jobs— printer, politician, and later, editor. His love for his native land is seen in all his poetry. He is remembered as the "good gray poet."

Whittier, John Greenleaf (1807–1892), the poet who became the "voice of the middle-nineteenth-century New England farmer," was born in Haverhill, Massachusetts, of Quaker parents. His childhood was that of his own "barefoot boy" on the farm described in *Snow-bound,* and he attended the district school. After being a newspaper editor, he worked for the antislavery cause and was a founder of the Republican party. Chiefly, however, for his love of nature, shown in his poetry, he is remembered as a kind of American Burns.

Wilder, Laura Ingalls (1867–1957), was born in the Little House in the Big Woods in Wisconsin. After journeying by prairie schooner into Indiana, she lived in the Little House on the Prairie. Then she went back to western Minnesota, and later to Dakota Territory on the shores of Silver Lake. In 1894, she and her husband settled in a little white farmhouse in the Ozarks. She has lived the life she so vividly depicts in the "Little House" series.

Young, Ella (1865–1956), was born in Ireland and lived there until 1926, when she came to America. During her childhood she heard the stories of ghosts and banshees which are a part of Irish folklore. Those weird stories and her life in Ireland influenced her when she began to write. She is famous for such books of fantasy as *The Tangle-coated Horse, The Unicorn with Silver Shoes,* and *Celtic Wonder Tales.*

acclamation (ăk'·lȧ·mā'shŭn). Loud applause.

admonish (ăd·mŏn'ĭsh). Warn.

adroitly (ȧ·droit'lĭ). Skillfully; cleverly.

advent (ăd'věnt). Coming; arrival.

Aesop (ē'sŏp).

aggregations (ăg'rē·gā'shŭnz). Gatherings.

agility (ȧ·jĭl'ĭ·tĭ). Alertness; quickness in moving.

Akeley (āk'lĭ), **Carl.**

Akeley, Mary L. Jobe (jōb).

alabaster (ăl'ȧ·bȧs'tẽr). Nearly white, of or like a gypsum stone of fine texture.

alacrity (ȧ·lăk'rĭ·tĭ). Briskness; cheerful readiness.

amain (ȧ·mān'). At full speed; with full force.

anguish (ăng'gwĭsh). Distress; extreme pain of mind or body; torment.

annihilated (ȧ·nī'ĭ·lāt'ěd; -ĭd). Destroyed; wiped out entirely.

antiquated (ăn'tĭ·kwāt'ěd; -ĭd). Old-fashioned; bygone.

antiquity (ăn·tĭk'wĭ·tĭ). Great age.

archipelago (är'kĭ·pěl'ȧ·gō). Group of islands closely located.

artisans (är'tĭ·zănz; är'tĭ·zănz'). Skilled workmen.

Asquith (ăs'kwĭth), **Herbert.**

audacious (ô·dā'shŭs). Daring; bold; insolent.

audible (ô'dĭ·b'l). Capable of being heard; actually heard.

auxiliary (ôg·zĭl'yȧ·rĭ). Helping; assistant.

avarice (ăv'ȧ·rĭs). Greediness for wealth.

Bakeless (bāk'lěs), **John.**

Bates (bāts), **Katharine Lee.**

Belloc (běl'ŏk), **Hilaire** (hĭ·lâr').

Benchley (běnch'lĭ), **Robert.**

Benét (bě·nā'), **Rosemary; Stephen Vincent.**

benevolence (bē·něv'ô·lěns). Generosity.

Bennett (běn'ět), **Henry Holcomb** (hōl'kŭm).

bog (bŏg). Swamp; marsh.

brandish (brăn'dĭsh). Shake or wave threateningly.

Bronson (brŏn'sŭn), **Wilfrid S.**

Browning (broun'ĭng), **Robert.**

Brubaker (broō'bāk·ẽr), **Howard.**

Byrd (bûrd), **Richard E.**

Carey (kâr'ĭ), **Ernestine Gilbreth** (gĭl'brěth).

Carryl (kăr'ĭl), **Charles Edward.**

casually (kăzh'ŭ·ȧl·ĭ). Offhandedly; unconcernedly.

centurions (sěn·tū'rĭ·ŭnz). Captains of a century in the Roman army.

circumvent (sûr'kŭm·věnt'). To entrap; overcome by trickery.

complex (kŏm·plěks'; kŏm'plěks). Complicated; intricate; hard to follow.

complicity (kŏm·plĭs'ĭ·tĭ). Sharing in guilt; being an accomplice.

composure (kŏm·pō'zhẽr). Calmness; repose.

concede (kŏn·sēd'). Allow; grant.

confiscated (kŏn'fĭs·kāt'ěd; kŏn·fĭs'kāt·ĭd). Seized for public use.

conspicuous (kŏn·spĭk'ŭ·ŭs). Prominent; obvious; attracting attention.

contemporary (kŏn·těm'pô·rěr'ĭ). Of the same age; existing at the same period.

copse (kŏps). A grove of small trees.

courier (koōr'ĭ·ẽr). A messenger.

Cousteau (koōz·tō'), **J. Y.**

Crane (krān), **Nathalia** (nȧ·thäl'yȧ).

cryptic (krĭp'tĭk). Mysterious.

cunning (kŭn'ĭng). Sly; crafty; clever.

Curtis (kûr'tĭs), **Natalie** (năt'ȧ·lĭ).

cutlass (kŭt'lȧs). Short, heavy, curved sword.

Daly (dā'lĭ), **T. A.**

Davis (dā'vĭs), **Bob.**

Day (dā), **Clarence.**

decry (dē·krī'). To find fault with; to belittle publicly.

De Kruif (dě krīf'), **Paul.**

demigod (děm'ĭ·gŏd'). A divine or semi-divine being.

depredation (děp'rē·dā'shŭn). Plunder; ravaging.

descried (dē·skrīd'). Caught sight of, at distance.

despotism (děs'pŏt·ĭz'm). Tyranny; severity.

Dickens (dĭk'ěnz), **Charles.**

Dickinson (dĭk'ĭn·s'n), **Emily.**

dirge (dûrj). Musical composition expressing mourning.

disintegrating (dĭs·ĭn'tē·grāt'ĭng). Decomposing; decaying; falling apart.

dismayed (dĭs·mād'). Depressed in spirit.

disoriented (dĭs·ō'rĭ·ěn·těd';-tĭd'). Confused (lost bearings).

Ditmars (dĭt'märz), **Raymond L.**

diversion (dĭ·vûr'shŭn; -zhŭn; dī-). Amusement.

Dobie (dō'bĭ), **J. Frank.**

cāke, vȧcation, dâre, băd, husbȧnd, färm, mȧsk, ȧgo; bē, mẹre, dẹpend, běnd, oftĕn, bakẽr; bīte, bĭll, famĭly; bōld, ô'clock, fôrm, fŏg, ŏff, fŏrget; toō, docile (dŏs'ĭl). Easily taught or managed; gentle.

domains (dô·mānz'). Landed properties.

Doorly (dôr'lĭ), **Eleanor.**

dubious (dū'bĭ·ŭs). Uncertain; doubtful.

Dunbar (dŭn'bär), **Paul Laurence.**

dynamos (dī'na·mōz). Machines converting mechanical energy into electrical energy.

Eisenberg (ī'z'n·bûrg), **Frances.**

ells (ĕlz). English measure (45 inches).

elocution (ĕl'ô·kū'shŭn). Art of reading or speaking effectively in public.

Emerson (ĕm'ẽr·s'n), **Ralph Waldo** (wôl'dō).

enigmatic (ē'nĭg·măt'ĭk; ĕn'ĭg-). Puzzling; hard to explain.

erroneously (ĕ·rō'nē·ŭs·lĭ). Incorrectly; mistakenly.

evinced (ē·vĭnst'). Clearly showed; displayed.

expansively (ĕks·păn'sĭv·lĭ; ĭks-). Widely; extensively.

exultation (ĕk'sŭl·tā'shŭn). Rejoicing; glory in victory.

facetiousness (fa·sē'shŭs·nĕs). Wit; humor.

Fauset (fô'sĕt), **Arthur Huff.**

feasible (fē'zĭ·b'l). Practicable; possible.

fervently (fûr'vĕnt·lĭ). Ardently; warmly.

fervor (fûr'vẽr). Ardor; intensity of feeling.

Field (fēld), **Eugene; Rachel.**

flaw (flô). Squall; wind.

flourish (flûr'ĭsh). Brandish; waving threateningly.

flume (flōom). Streaming water.

flustered (flŭs'tẽrd). Confused.

frantic (frăn'tĭk). Wild; violent.

Freeman (frē'mǎn), **Douglas Southall.**

frenetic (frē·nĕt'ĭk). Frenzied; frantic.

Frost (frŏst), **Robert.**

Gardner (gärd'nẽr), **Mona.**

Garland (gär'lǎnd), **Hamlin.**

Gartner (gärt'nẽr), **John.**

Gilbreth (gĭl'brĕth), **Frank B., Jr.**

Grey Owl (grā oul).

grimly (grĭm'lĭ). Unyieldingly; sternly.

Guiterman (gĭt'ẽr·mǎn), **Arthur.**

guttural (gŭt'ẽr·ǎl). Harsh; rasping; sounded in the throat.

habitude (hăb'ĭ·tūd). Native character or attitude.

Hackett (hăk'ĕt), **Walter.**

Haig-Brown (hāg-broun), **Roderick L.**

halidom (hăl'ĭ·dǔm). Holiness.

Harris (hăr'ĭs), **Joel Chandler.**

Henry (hĕn'rĭ), **O.; Robert D.**

hibernated (hī'bẽr·nāt'ĕd; -ĭd). Passed the winter.

Holmes (hōmz), **Oliver Wendell.**

Hosford (hŏs'fẽrd), **Dorothy.**

Housman (hous'mǎn), **A. E.**

Hovey (hŭv'ĭ), **Richard.**

Hudson (hŭd's'n), **W. H.**

hydra-headed (hī'dra·hĕd'ĕd; -ĭd). Serpentheaded (nine-headed serpent slain by Hercules).

ignominious (ĭg'nô·mĭn'ĭ·ŭs). Dishonorable; disgraceful.

imperceptibly (ĭm'pẽr·sĕp'tĭ·blĭ). Very slightly.

impetuous (ĭm·pĕt'û·ŭs). Impulsive; violent; hasty.

inadvertently (ĭn'ǎd·vûr'tĕnt·lĭ). Thoughtlessly; heedlessly.

incompatibility (ĭn'kǒm·păt'ĭ·bĭl'ĭ·tĭ). Contrariness.

indiscriminate (ĭn'dĭs·krĭm'ĭ·nĭt). Haphazard; promiscuous; random.

indulgently (ĭn·dŭl'jĕnt·lĭ). Compliantly.

inevitable (ĭn·ĕv'ĭ·ta·b'l). That which cannot be avoided; bound to happen.

infinite (ĭn'fĭ·nĭt). Boundless; vast; without limit.

instantaneous (ĭn'stǎn·tā'nē·ŭs). Occurring instantly.

instinctively (ĭn·stĭngk'tĭv·lĭ). Prompted naturally; involuntarily.

interposed (ĭn'tẽr·pōzd'). Injected; interrupted.

invocation (ĭn'vô·kā'shŭn). A prayer invoking a blessing.

Irving (ûr'vĭng), **Washington.**

Johnson (jǒn's'n), **Osa.**

jovial (jō'vĭ·ǎl). Merry; gay.

Kilmer (kĭl'mẽr), **Joyce.**

kilometer (kĭl'ô·mē'tẽr; sometimes kĭ·lǒm'ē·tẽr). Metric measure of length 0.62137 mi.

Knight (nīt), **Eric.**

lacerate (lăs'ẽr·āt). To cut; to mangle.

lackadaisical (lăk'a·dā'zĭ·kǎl). Affectedly listless or languid.

La Fontaine (là fôɴ'tĕn'), **Jean de** (zhäɴ dẽ).

lŏŏk; doubt, boil; ūse, ûtensil, bûrn, cŭp, circŭs, menü; chase; get; song; that, thick; cult**u**re, verd**u**re; K = ch in German ich, ach; boɴ; yes; zh = z in azure.

Lawson (lô′s'n), **Robert.**

Le Gallienne (lĕ găl·yĕn′), **Richard.**

Lear (lēr), **Edward.**

leviathan (lê·vī′á·thăn). Huge (whale) aquatic monster.

Lilienthal (lĭl′ĭ·ĕn·thôl′), **David E.**

Lincoln (lĭng′kŭn), **Abraham.**

logical (lŏj′ĭ·kăl). Relating to logic; reasonable.

Longfellow (lŏng′fĕl′ō), **Henry W.**

Longstreth (lŏng′strĕth, **Edward.**

luminous (lū′mĭ·nŭs). Shining; bright.

Lynch (lĭnch), **James M., Jr.**

McCloskey (má·klŏs′kĭ), **Robert.**

McCord (má·kôrd′), **David.**

McCrae (má·krā′), **John.**

MacLeod (măk·loud′), **Mary.**

McSpadden (măk·spăd′dĕn), **J. Walker.**

malevolent (má·lĕv′ô·lĕnt). Desiring evil; arising from ill will; malicious.

mammoth (măm′ŭth). Huge; very large.

manifest (măn′ĭ·fĕst). Plain; clear; understandable.

Meigs (mĕgz), **Mildred Plew.**

melancholy (mĕl′ăn·kŏl′ĭ). Depressing; dismal.

menace (mĕn′ĭs). Threat.

metamorphosed (mĕt′á·môr′fōzd; -fōst). Transformed; changed.

Miller (mĭl′ēr), **Helen Louise.**

Montgomery (mŏn(t)·gŭm′ēr·ĭ), **Rutherford** (rŭth′ēr·fērd) **G.**

morbidly (môr′bĭd·lĭ). Unhealthfully; gloomily.

motives (mō′tĭvz). Impulses; causes.

mundane (mŭn′dān). Earthly; worldly.

muster (mŭs′tēr). Assembling of men for roll call; gathering.

Nash (năsh), **Ogden.**

Neil (nēl), **Edward J.**

Noyes (noiz), **Alfred.**

pandemonium (păn′dê·mō′nĭ·ŭm). A wild tumult.

pantomime (păn′tô·mīm). Dumb show.

patrimonial (păt′rĭ·mō′nĭ·ăl). Inherited.

patronizingly (pā′trŭn·īz′ĭng·lĭ). Condescendingly; with an air of superiority.

Pease (pēz), **Howard.**

Peattie (pĕt′ĭ), **Donald Culross** (kŭl′rŏs′).

perfunctory (pēr·fŭngk′tô·rĭ). Automatic; done unthinkingly.

perversely (pēr·vûrs′lĭ). Obstinately; contrarily.

pestilent (pĕs′tĭ·lĕnt). Troublesome.

phenomenal (fê·nŏm′ê·năl; -n'l). Rare; unique.

phial (fī′ăl). Shallow bowl or bottle.

pillage (pĭl′ĭj). A plundering.

placidly (plăs′ĭd·lĭ). Calmly; peacefully.

Porter (pōr′tēr), **William Sydney.**

prodigy (prŏd′ĭ·jĭ). Highly gifted individual.

protozoa (prō′tô·zō′á). Single-celled animals, mostly aquatic—living in water.

Proudfit (proud′fĭt), **Isabel.**

prudent (prōō′dĕnt). Cautious; careful.

Purdy (pûr′dĭ), **Claire Lee.**

Pyle (pīl), **Katharine.**

Quiller-Couch (kwĭl′ēr·kōōch′), **Sir Arthur.**

ravaged (răv′ĭjd). Plundered; pillaged; looted.

recipient (rê·sĭp′ĭ·ĕnt). One who receives.

Reck (rĕk), **Franklin M.**

reiterated (rê·ĭt′ēr·āt′ĕd; -ĭd). Repeated.

relentless (rê·lĕnt′lĕs; -lĭs). Immovably persistent.

relinquished (rê·lĭng′kwĭsht). Gave up.

remonstrated (rê·mŏn′strāt·ĕd). Protested; objected.

retorted (rê·tôr′tĕd; -tĭd). Answered; angrily replied.

Richards (rĭch′ērdz), **Laura E.**

Rossetti (rô·sĕt′ĭ), **Christina Georgina** (krĭs·tē′ná jôr·jē′ná).

Rosvall (rôs′vôl), **Toivo** (doi′vô).

rubicund (rōō′bĭ·kŭnd). Ruddy; flushed.

rudiments (rōō′dĭ·mĕnts). Elementary or first principles.

Saadi (sä·dē′).

sagacity (sá·găs′ĭ·tĭ). Shrewdness; keenness of judgment.

Sandburg (săn(d)′bûrg), **Carl.**

Sanderson (săn′dēr·s'n), **Ivan T.**

sanguine (săng′gwĭn). Cheerful; hopeful.

Saroyan (sä·rō′yän), **William.**

Schauffler (shôf′lēr), **Robert Haven.**

secluded (sê·klōōd′ĕd; -ĭd). Isolated; shut off from others; hidden from sight.

sedge (sĕj). Marshy, grasslike herb.

Seton (sē′t'n), **Ernest Thompson.**

Sewell (sū′ĕl), **Helen.**

shrewd (shrōōd). Keen; sharp.

siesta (sĭ·ĕs′tá). Short rest especially at midday.

cāke, văcation, dâre, băd, husbănd, färm, màsk, ágo; bē, mẹre, dẹpend, bĕnd, oftĕn, bakēr; bīte, bĭll, famĭly; bōld, ô′clock, fôrm, fŏg, ŏff, fŏrget; tōō,

silhouetted (sĭl'ŏŏ·ĕt'ĕd; -ĭd). Solidly outlined (in profile).

Simon (sī'mŭn), **Charlie May.**

simultaneously (sī'mŭl·tā'nē·ŭs·lĭ; sĭm'ŭl-). At the same time; at once.

sinuous (sĭn'ū·ŭs). Winding; bending.

Smith (smĭth), **Samuel Francis.**

somnolent (sŏm'nō·lĕnt). Drowsy; sleepy.

sparsely (spärs'lĭ). Thinly; scantily.

spectral (spĕk'trăl). Like a specter or ghost.

Sperry (spĕr'ĭ), **Armstrong.**

stanch (stänch; stånch). Loyal; true; steadfast.

statistician (stăt'ĭs·tĭsh'ăn). A person engaged in compiling statistics.

Stevenson (stē'vĕn·s'n), **Candace** (kăn'dá·sē) **Thurber** (thûr'bĕr).

Stuart (stū'ērt), **Jesse** (jĕs'ē).

substantially (sŭb·stăn'shăl·lĭ). Really; actually.

subtlety (sŭt''l·tĭ). Delicacy; crafty shrewdness.

succulent (sŭk'ū·lĕnt). Juicy.

superb (sū·pûrb'). Rich; grand; supremely good.

Teale (tēl), **Edwin Way.**

terminal (tûr'mĭ·năl). The end of the line.

Thayer (thâr), **Ernest Lawrence.**

theoretical (thē'ō·rĕt'ĭ·kăl). Depending on a theory or guess; speculative.

tory (tō'rĭ). An extreme conservative; opposed to change.

traction (trăk'shŭn). Motive power.

tranquil (trăng'kwĭl; trăn'-). Quiet; calm.

ultimate (ŭl'tĭ·mĭt). Final; last.

undeleterious (ŭn'dĕl·ē·tēr'ĭ·ŭs). Unharmful.

Van Dyke (văn dīk'), **Henry.**

varmint (vär'mĭnt). Objectionable person or animal.

velocity (vē·lŏs'ĭ·tĭ). Speed; quickness of motion.

vindictiveness (vĭn·dĭk'tĭv·nĕs). Revengefulness.

vintage (vĭn'tĭj). Wine.

virago (vĭ·rā'gō; vī-). Brawling; quarrelsome woman.

visionaries (vĭzh'ŭn·ĕr'ĭz; -ēr·ĭz). Persons who see visions; those whose projects may be impractical.

vociferous (vō·sĭf'ēr·ŭs). Clamorous; noisy.

void (void). An unfilled or empty space.

Waldeck (wäl'dĕk), **Theodore J.**

wanton (wŏn'tŭn). Unruly; having no real cause; without regard for justice.

Wells (wĕlz), **Carolyn** (kăr'ō·lĭn).

Whitman (hwĭt'măn), **Walt.**

Whittier (hwĭt'ĭ·ēr), **John Greenleaf.**

Wilder (wīl'dēr), **Laura** (lô'rá) **Ingalls** (ĭng'gălz)

Williams (wĭl'yămz), **J. H.**

withe (wĭth; wĭth; wīth). A slim flexible twig.

Young (yŭng), **Ella.**

lŏŏk; doubt, boil; ūse, ûtensil, bûrn, cŭp, circŭs, menü; chase; get; song; that, thick; cultŭre, verdŭre; K = ch in German ich, ach; bоN; yes; zh = z in azure.

Sketches, Essays, and Speeches

Plays

Poems

* The poems marked with an asterisk are suitable for use as speaking-choir selections.